The Guidebook for Linemen and Cablemen

The Guidebook for Linemen and Cablemen

Wayne Van Soelen

DELMAR
CENGAGE Learning™

Australia • Brazil • Japan • Korea • Mexico • Singapore • Spain • United Kingdom • United States

DELMAR
CENGAGE Learning™

The Guidebook for Linemen and Cablemen
Wayne Van Soelen

Vice President, Technology and Trades SBU:
    Alar Elken

Editorial Director: Sandy Clark

Acquisitions Editor: Ed Francis

Development Editor: Kim Blakey

Marketing Director: Dave Garza

Channel Manager: Erin Coffin

Marketing Specialist: Penelope Crosby

Production Director: Mary Ellen Black

Senior Production Manager: Larry Main

Production Editor: Benj Gleeksman

Project Editor: Christopher Chien

Editorial Assistant: Sarah Boone

Art/Design Coordinator: Francis Hogan

For product information and technology assistance, contact us at
Cengage Learning Customer & Sales Support, 1-800-354-9706
For permission to use material from this text or product,
submit all requests online at **www.cengage.com/permissions**
Further permissions questions can be emailed to
permissionrequest@cengage.com

ISBN-13: 978-1-4180-3842-7

ISBN-10: 1-4180-3842-3

Delmar
Executive Woods
5 Maxwell Drive
Clifton Park, NY 12065
USA

Cengage Learning is a leading provider of customized learning solutions with office locations around the globe, including Singapore, the United Kingdom, Australia, Mexico, Brazil, and Japan. Locate your local office at **international.cengage.com/region**

Cengage Learning products are represented in Canada by Nelson Education, Ltd.

For your lifelong learning solutions, visit **www.cengage.com/delmar**

Visit our corporate website at **www.cengage.com**

Notice to the Reader

Publisher does not warrant or guarantee any of the products described herein or perform any independent analysis in connection with any of the product information contained herein. Publisher does not assume, and expressly disclaims, any obligation to obtain and include information other than that provided to it by the manufacturer. The reader is expressly warned to consider and adopt all safety precautions that might be indicated by the activities described herein and to avoid all potential hazards. By following the instructions contained herein, the reader willingly assumes all risks in connection with such instructions. The publisher makes no representations or warranties of any kind, including but not limited to, the warranties of fitness for particular purpose or merchantability, nor are any such representations implied with respect to the material set forth herein, and the publisher takes no responsibility with respect to such material. The publisher shall not be liable for any special, consequential, or exemplary damages resulting, in whole or part, from the readers' use of, or reliance upon, this material.

Printed in Canada
    3 4 5 6 7 11 10 09 08

Contents

CHAPTER 1   Essentials for Powerline Workers 1
1.0 Introduction to Safe Work on Powerlines 1
1.1 So You Want to Be a Powerline Worker 1
1.2 Managing Personal Safety Risk 8
1.3 Managing Risk in the Working Environment 14
1.4 Reduce Risk when Climbing and Working Aloft 29
1.5 Managing Emergencies 40
Review Questions 50

CHAPTER 2   Electrical Power System Overview 51
2.1 Introduction 51
2.2 Electrical Energy 51
2.3 Generation of Electrical Energy 52
2.4 Transmission of Electrical Energy 57
2.5 Electrical Distribution 62
Review Questions 68

CHAPTER 3   Electrical Units 69
3.1 Introduction 69
3.2 Electrical Potential 70
3.3 Electrical Current 72
3.4 Electrical Resistance 75
3.5 Electrical Power 80
Review Questions 83

CHAPTER 4   Alternating Current (AC) 85
4.1 Introduction 85
4.2 Characteristics of AC 85
4.3 Reactance in AC Circuits 90
4.4 AC Power 97
4.5 AC or DC Transmission 99
Review Questions 102

CHAPTER 5   Three-Phase Circuits 103
5.1 Introduction 103
5.2 Characteristics of Three-Phase Circuits 103
5.3 Delta-Connected Systems 107

5.4 Wye-Connected Systems 109
5.5 Three-Phase Power 111
Review Questions 114

CHAPTER 6   Awareness when in an Electrical Environment 115
6.1 Introduction 115
6.2 Connecting a Load in Series with a Circuit 116
6.3 Connecting a Load in Parallel with a Circuit 118
6.4 Electrical and Magnetic Induction 123
6.5 Voltage Gradients 127
6.6 Working with Neutrals 132
6.7 Vehicle Grounding and Bonding 133
6.8 Electromagnetic Fields 139
6.9 Minimum Approach Distance 146
Review Questions 148

CHAPTER 7   Constructing Powerlines 151
7.1 Before a Work Order Is Issued 151
7.2 Constructing a Pole Line 159
7.3 Constructing an Overhead Transmission Line 190
7.4 Constructing an Underground Distribution Line 202
7.5 Underground Transmission Lines 212
Review Questions 217

CHAPTER 8   Working with Conductor and Cable 219
8.1 Electrical Properties of a Conductor 219
8.2 Overhead Conductors 226
8.3 Working with Overhead Conductors 233
8.4 Underground Cable 241
8.5 Working with Underground Cable 251
8.6 Working with Fiber-Optic Cable 260
Review Questions 264

CHAPTER 9   Operating Switchgear 265
9.1 Switching Characteristics and Switching Hazards 265
9.2 Switching to Provide an Isolation Guarantee (Lockout/Tagout) 274
9.3 Using Maps to Locate Switchgears 276
9.4 Operating Isolating Switchgears 281
9.5 Operating Protective Switchgears 284
9.6 Underground Distribution Switchgears 294
Review Questions 301

CHAPTER 10   Circuit Protection 303
10.1 Introduction 303
10.2 Transmission System Protection 304

10.3 Distribution Protection 307
10.4 Specifying Protection for a Distribution Feeder 313
10.5. Over-Voltage Protection 323
10.6 System Grounding for Protection 337
10.7 Protection from Corrosion 342
Review Questions 345

CHAPTER 11   Installing Personal Protective Grounds 347
11.1 Reasons to Install Personal Protective Grounds 347
11.2 Applying the Grounding Principle to Control Current 348
11.3 Applying the Bonding Principle to Control Voltage 353
11.4 Controlling Induced Voltage and Current from Electromagnetic
Induction 358
11.5 Procedures for Applying Protective Grounds 361
11.6 Specific Grounding Hazards 365
11.7 Protective Grounding of Underground Cable 370
Review Questions 374

CHAPTER 12   Connecting and Troubleshooting Transformers 375
12.1 Introduction 375
12.2 Transformer Basics 376
12.3 Transformation Effect on Current 383
12.4 Transformer Losses and Impedance 386
12.5 Transformer Protection 388
12.6 Single-Phase Transformer Connections 391
12.7 Three-Phase Transformer Connections 397
12.8 Three-Phase, Secondary-Voltage Arrangements 409
12.9 Troubleshooting Transformers 415
12.10 Working on a Voltage Conversion 416
12.11 Specific Hazards Working with Transformers 420
Review Questions 421

CHAPTER 13   Supplying Quality Power 423
13.1 Introduction 423
13.2 What Is Power Quality? 424
13.3 Factors Affecting Voltage in a Circuit 426
13.4 Voltage on the Transmission-Lines System 428
13.5 Distribution Substation Voltage 429
13.6 Distribution Feeder Voltage 430
13.7 Feeder Voltage Regulators 431
13.8 Capacitors 440
13.9 Troubleshooting No Power, High Voltage, or Low Voltage 444
13.10 Harmonic Interference 449
13.11 Voltage Flicker 453

13.12 Ferroresonance 454
13.13 Tingle Voltage 458
13.14 Investigating a Radio and Television Interference (TVI) Complaint . . 463
Review Questions 465

CHAPTER 14   Working with Aerial Devices and Digger Derricks 467
14.1 Checking Out the Truck 467
14.2 Monitoring a Hydraulic System 471
14.3 Stabilizing a Boom-Equipped Vehicle 475
14.4 Electrical Protection for Working with Noninsulated Booms 478
14.5 Electrical Protection for Working with Insulated Booms 482
14.6 Operating a Digger Derrick 485
14.7 Operating an Aerial Device 489
Review Questions 493

CHAPTER 15   Rigging in Powerline Work 495
15.1 Introduction 495
15.2 Using Rigging Hardware 496
15.3 Lifting a Load 514
15.4 Working with Tensioned Conductors 520
Review Questions 528

CHAPTER 16   Working It Hot 531
16.1 Safety Strategy for Hot-Line Work 531
16.2 Working on a Hot Secondary 537
16.3 Rubber-Glove Work 538
16.4 Hot-Line Tool Work 544
16.5 Barehand Work 550
Review Questions 554

CHAPTER 17   Tree Work in an Electrical Utility Environment 555
17.1 Vegetation Management in Electrical Utilities 555
17.2 The Hazards of Tree Work 562
17.3 Tree Work Near Electrical Circuits 563
17.4 Essential Skills for Tree Work 569
Review Questions 586

CHAPTER 18   Working in Substations 587
18.1 What Is a Substation? 587
18.2 Maintaining and Operating a Substation 594
18.3 Constructing a Substation 598
Review Questions 603

CHAPTER 19   Outdoor Lighting Systems 605
19.1 Types of Outdoor Lighting 605

19.2 Luminaires, Lamps, and Structures 608
19.3 Lighting Ballasts 614
19.4 Lighting Circuits and Controls 616
19.5 Maintenance and Troubleshooting Outdoor Lighting Systems 624
19.6 Safety and Environmental Hazards Working with Outdoor Lights 625
Review Questions 629

CHAPTER 20   Revenue Metering 631
20.1 Introduction 631
20.2 Determining Cost to the Customer 631
20.3 Types of Revenue Metering 634
20.4 The Workings of a Meter 637
20.5 Single-Phase Metering 641
20.6 Polyphase Metering 645
20.7 Transformer-Rated Metering 651
Review Questions 657

Preface

The National Joint Apprenticeship and Training Committee (NJATC) is the training arm of the International Brotherhood of Electrical Workers and National Electrical Contractors Association. Established in 1941, the NJATC has developed uniform standards that are used nationwide to train thousands of qualified men and women for demanding and rewarding careers in the electrical and telecommunications industries. To enhance the effectiveness of this mission, the NJATC has partnered with Delmar Cengage Learning to deliver the very finest in training materials for the electrical profession.

Knowledge of fundamentals is critical to the success of a modern electrical technologist. Every project, every piece of knowledge, and every new task will be based on all of the experience and information that you get as you progress through your career. This book contains much of the material that will form the foundation for your electrical knowledge.

The Guidebook for Linemen and Cablemen is a comprehensive resource dealing with managing risk in powerline work, work methods, and the details of working in an electrical environment. This book can be used as both a training manual and a reference book. Used as a training manual it is important that the content is studied chronologically, in order to fully understand the concepts presented in later chapters. The essential "must know" topics that linemen and cablemen are required to understand in order to work effectively and safely in an electrical environment are addressed in this book.

The manuscript and proofs were reviewed by the NJATC Outside Line Construction Advisory Committee and the material meets all guidelines and requirements established by the Committee.

Prerequisites

This book is for a person working or training to work on electrical utility circuits. Reference is made to equipment and material with the assumption that the reader knows or will be shown what they look like. The early chapters are intended for a person entering electrical-utility work. Later chapters assume some experience as a powerline worker.

Objective of Material

Electrical utilities have an abundance of manuals and reference material for the people who work on powerlines. However, most of the information supplied by the utility or employer involves work procedures, rules, and regulations and widely scattered electrical reference material.

This book fills the need for a convenient single-volume reference source on the operation of an electrical-utility system. Existing sources of information tend to be very basic electricity and magnetism theory or complex theory at an engineering level. This book deals with equipment and situations that powerline workers are exposed to in their daily work. There is a rapid growth in the technology affecting the operation of electrical utilities. Many customers have concerns about the quality of their power supply. To some degree, the powerline worker has exposure to all aspects of an electrical-utility system.

This book also provides a foundation that will aid in understanding procedures, rules, and regulations. This foundation includes the mechanical aspects of the job, such as working with rigging, trucks, stringing wire, and tree felling.

This book is intended to help the powerline worker meet the expectation that he or she will have the knowledge and skills to construct, operate, and maintain the lines and cables in an electrical utility system.

Publisher Acknowledgements:

Steve Anderson, Consulting Reviewer

The publisher would like to thank Steve Anderson, principle reviewer in the development process of The Guidebook for Linemen and Cablemen. *He graciously shared his expertise in the development of this book and for that, the publisher would like to extend its appreciation. His expertise coupled by his extensive experience in the electrical power industry makes Mr. Anderson a highly respected consultant in the industry.*

Additional Acknowledgements:

This material is continually reviewed and evaluated by Training Directors who are also members of the NJATC Education Committee. The invaluable input provided by these individuals allows for the development of instructional material that is of the absolute highest quality. At the time of this printing, the Educational Committee was comprised of the following members:

Bill Stone
JATC of the Northwest Line
Construction Industry

Charles Young
Southwestern Line Constructors

Craig Healy
Missouri Valley Line Constructors

Dan Dade
American Line Builders Joint
Apprenticeship and Training Program

Don Jamison
Missouri Valley Line Constructors

Stephen Uhl
Northeastern Joint Apprenticeship
Training Committee

Armando Mendez
JATC Power Linemen Apprenticeship

Doug Peters
Tennessee Valley Public Power
Associates

Lloyd Roberts
Southeastern Linemen Constructors
Apprenticeship Training

Mike Neighbors
Alabama Power Authority

SK Pelch
Mountain States Line Constructors

Virgil Melton
Southeastern Linemen Constructors
Apprenticeship Training

Stephen Uhl, Northeastern Joint Apprenticeship Training Committee, deserves special acknowledgement and thanks for his untiring dedication and work on behalf of the electrical line industry and his uncompromising commitment to seeing this project to its conclusion.

CHAPTER 1

Essentials for Powerline Workers

Topics to Be Covered	Section
Introduction to Safe Work on Powerlines	1.0
So You Want to Be a Powerline Worker	1.1
Managing Personal Safety Risk	1.2
Managing Risk in the Working Environment	1.3
Reduce Risk when Climbing and Working Aloft	1.4
Managing Emergencies	1.5

1.0 Introduction to Safe Work on Powerlines

1.1 So You Want to Be a Powerline Worker

Orientation to Powerline Work

1.1.1 The powerlines work environment is one of a kind. Even when first starting out, you will be exposed to high-risk hazards on a daily basis. You will be introduced to tools not found in a typical hardware store. The knowledge needed to understand the work and to carry it out safely is not taught in any high school. Many of the tools and equipment are unique to the "lines" working environment, and an orientation to each new setting is essential.

The contents of this chapter, along with explanations from a mentor, can serve as part of an initial orientation. *This text supports training but does not take the place of classroom or field training.* Training and confirmation of training (testing) are mandatory before doing the tasks described in this book.

The Nature of Line Work

1.1.2 A huge variety of work is available for powerline workers.

Outdoor Environment

People coming into line work recognize that the work is outdoors. On larger construction-type jobs, the work requires being outdoors all day. Some powerline workers will find themselves standing on top of a tower, at 20 degrees below zero, waiting for a helicopter to pick them off the top. Some will be working in high heat and humidity while wearing flame-retardant clothing and rubber gloves and rubber sleeves. Others will work on trouble and service work and will spend much of their days—or nights—driving in all kinds of weather and traffic.

Rugged Work

This work requires upper-body strength for climbing, as well as for lifting heavy crossarms and coils of wire, for lifting a conductor on an insulator, and for closing a mechanical press. While back-saving devices are available, many lifting tasks straddle the boundary between lifting manually or using a mechanical aid—and you probably can guess which course of action many powerline workers take.

Independent Work

The nature of this work is such that lineworkers are frequently part of a small crew or are working alone and without supervision. Each job is different and requires planning and decision making that can have major consequences on safety or on a community's power supply.

From Shovel to Computer

A powerline worker can spend an hour or two trying to get boulders out of the bottom of a wet hole, then an hour or two retrieving complex switching information or importing data on a mobile field computer. Lines work ranges from very ordinary labor to complex high-tech work.

Safety Responsibilities and Expectations

1.1.3 Under the law, both the employer and the employee have safety responsibilities and rights. The laws may be worded differently in each jurisdiction, but the basics are the same everywhere.

Employer's Responsibilities

An employer has a general duty to provide work and a workplace free from recognized hazards and must also provide standards, rules, and regulations that apply to the work being done. An employer must also ensure that employees have, maintain, and use safe tools and equipment. An employer that sets up a safety management system will find it effective for managing the many safety responsibilities required.

An employer must inform employees of their rights and duties under the employer's safety and health program and, of course, must not discriminate against employees who exercise their rights under a labor law.

Employers have other duties, such as informing employees of the existence of their medical and exposure records. Employers also must provide these records to employees upon request.

Employee Safety Responsibilities and Rights

Labor laws are written to protect employees. An employee should become very familiar with Occupational Safety and Health Administration (OSHA) regulations so that there is little doubt as to their responsibilities and rights. In summary, employees are responsible for performing their jobs safely, complying with all occupational safety and health standards and rules, following their employer's safety and health program, following their supervisors' instructions, participating in required training classes, reporting any potential hazardous conditions to their supervisors, and wearing personal protective equipment when instructed. Employees also must report any job-related injury or illness to the employer and seek treatment promptly.

An employee has legal rights and is entitled to protection for safety on the job. One such right is that an employee is not allowed to be punished or discriminated against by an employer for such acts as complaining to the employer, union, or any government agency about job safety or health hazards.

Safety Committee

A safety committee is a great vehicle for promoting workplace safety. It gets employees, supervisors, and management together to solve safety problems. Typically, a safety committee encourages employee involvement in improving workplace safety and gives employees input into making recommendations to the top of an organization.

An ideal safety committee would have its function and role within the organization well defined. Committee members should have had training on safety and health legislation, how to prepare a safety strategy, how safety can be managed, how to conduct a risk assessment, and how to investigate an accident.

The committee should meet at least every three months, and a prepared agenda and the minutes should be recorded, distributed, and posted on bulletin boards. The committee's role should include assisting management with developing and monitoring safety programs by

- having committee members involved in accident investigations,
- reviewing accident investigation reports,
- monitoring the status of any action plans from safety meetings and accident investigations,
- initiating problem-solving teams to address priority safety issues,
- participating in regular physical condition inspections of the workplace, and
- participating in regular internal assessments of the effectiveness of safety programs.

Managing Safety

1.1.4 Ideally, an employer will have set up a complete safety management system. Figure 1–1 shows a focus on safe work model that illustrates the types of safety

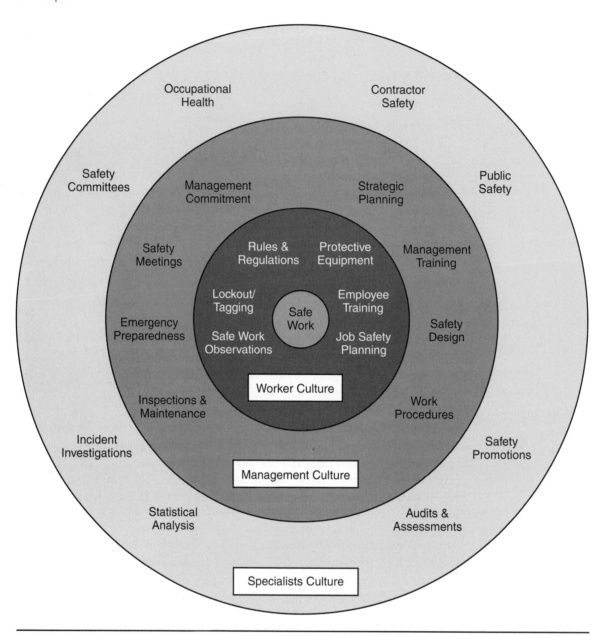

Figure 1–1   Focus on safe work model.

functions or elements that must be managed. It also shows the relative influence of each element on supporting safe work.

Safety Elements that Impact the Worker Culture

The elements shown within the inner band of the model have a direct impact on worker safety. Because people in utilities often work without direct supervision, having the elements of the inner circle in place supports the worker when decisions are being made that impact safety. The elements and actions that most impact the worker culture are these:

Rules and regulations are developed, introduced, easily retrievable, and enforced.

Lockout/tagging procedure is developed, workers are trained, responsibilities assigned, operating diagrams available, all switchgear assigned nomenclature, and application of the procedure monitored.

Employee training is well coordinated, new employees are given a thorough orientation, and employees receive skills proficiency training and safety-related training.

Job safety planning policy is in place, and people are trained to do project safety planning, daily job safety planning, and process monitoring.

Work observations policy is in place, and supervisors and managers are trained in conducting effective work observations.

Protective equipment is provided, and people are trained in their use and inspection and are monitored.

Safety Elements that Establish the Management Culture

The elements within the middle band have a direct impact on the management culture but are one step removed from influencing the worker culture. Consequently, deficiencies identified within these elements should be given second priority.

Management commitment is demonstrated by having a health and safety policy and by showing visible participation, responsibility, and accountability.

Strategic planning is demonstrated by setting performance objectives and a strategy for achieving them. A safety program manual, available to all, outlines coordination of the complete safety program.

Management and supervisors receive safety management training along with supervisory skills training. A programmed orientation for new managers and supervisors is in place.

Safety meetings are scheduled, an agenda set, and minutes kept, and a company document with guidelines for safety meetings is in place.

Written work procedures for critical technical and maintenance tasks are developed, documented in a procedure format, and introduced.

Safety design analyses—such as job safety analysis, hazard analysis, ergonomic analysis, and a hazard registry (risk assessment)—are tools used regularly to reduce risk in the workplace.

Inspections and maintenance of critical tools and equipment, mobile equipment, and system equipment are scheduled and carried out.

Emergency preparedness plans are prepared for fire prevention, first aid response, spills response, and evacuation.

Safety Elements that Impact the Specialists Culture

The elements within the outer band are generally administered and carried out by specialists such as safety professionals. Deficiencies identified within these elements should be given third priority.

Occupational health is administered to ensure air and water quality, noise is controlled, hazardous materials are managed, and biological and physical agents are identified and controlled.

Health and safety promotion is administered for programs such as the employee assistance program (EAP); health, safety, and wellness communication; and off-the-job safety and safety performance recognition. These programs should be introduced to all new employees during orientation.

Joint health and safety committees' role and function are defined, committee members receive training, meetings are scheduled, and committee activities are monitored.

Contractor safety policy is in place with a requirement for contract administrators to be trained in contract administration, contract monitoring, and conducting a contractor orientation.

Public safety is administered so that public access is controlled at worksites, public hazards involving utility plants are identified and controlled, any accidents involving the public with a utility plant are investigated, and public electrical safety awareness is promoted.

Incident investigations are carried out based on an established policy requiring an initial reporting and investigation, a detailed investigation for defined serious incidents or incidents with a high potential for harm, follow-up activities, and injury management.

Statistical analysis is carried out and incident summary reports, incident statistical reports, and proactive measures statistical reports are prepared.

Audits and assessments such as employee surveys, internal assessments, and external audits are carried out.

Orientation for the New Employee

1.1.5 An employer should have a programmed orientation for new employees, temporary employees, and employees going into a new position within the organization.

The orientation should include an overview of applicable safety policies, health and safety programs, and rules. Some training cannot wait for a time for when there are enough employees to make a class. Depending on the work given, there may be an immediate need for safety training such as first aid, CPR, hazardous materials management, defensive driving, fire response, confined space entry, electrical safety awareness, forklift operation, traffic flagging, trenching/shoring, and chainsaw operation.

Participate in Safety Meetings and Job Briefings

1.1.6 Powerline workers can and should provide feedback, suggestions, and questions at safety meetings and at job briefings.

Characteristics of a Good Safety Meeting

A good safety meeting must be planned ahead and scheduled. An agenda should be set, minutes kept, attendance recorded, and follow-up actions recorded and posted on bulletin boards. A safety meeting schedule should include critical safety topics.

Safety meetings are good vehicles for updating staff on current safety issues, technical issues, new policies, new tools, and equipment and for jointly solving technical and safety problems.

Characteristics of a Good Job Briefing

Federal labor laws in the United States require that, at a minimum, a job briefing must cover the hazards associated with the job, the work procedures involved, special precautions, energy source controls, and personal protective equipment.

The foundation of a good job briefing is a discussion, on the job site, structured around a daily job briefing checklist or written job plan. (See the Tailboard Conference Plan in section 1.3.1 for a sample job briefing form that focuses on high-risk hazards and the barriers needed to control the hazards.)

Conduct

1.1.7 Powerline workers are very visible because they work in public. They travel in vehicles that are like traveling billboards. Driving inconsiderately or acting out, such as road rage, in a company truck would, of course, be reflected back to the company.

The work can include sensitive communications with customers, such as work that impacts on private property, notification of a power outage, or a disconnect for nonpayment.

To the public, you are the power company. Behave responsibly.

Reporting Incidents and Accidents

1.1.8 Utility employers require that all accidents and close calls be reported. If a minor injury is not reported and later results in blood poisoning or a need for knee surgery, for example, you may have to prove that it resulted from an on-the-job accident. Even if the injury seems so minor that it does not need to be reported to insurance or for compensation, having it recorded in a supervisor's log or diary offers you financial protection from a future flare-up.

Any incident with a high potential for harm, even without injuries, should be reported and investigated as though it were a severe accident. The lessons learned may prevent a fatality in the future.

The Line Work Culture

1.1.9 A powerline worker who has braved the elements, worked at heights in the wind and snow, worked on live circuits, stepped out of a helicopter onto a structure, operated large equipment, and perhaps experienced a potentially fatal near-miss accident tends to become overly self-confident, and the line work culture tends to have a macho aura. The risk of the job becomes one of its attractions. This culture has traditionally resisted change, especially to new safety equipment. Over time, line workers have less and less willingness to accept risk or to take the extra steps needed to use additional safety equipment.

When Charlie White, a first baseman for the Boston Red Sox, came onto the field wearing a thin protective glove after baseball had been a bare-handed game for about 25 years, with broken hands and split thumbs he was laughed off the field. Even in today's National Hockey League, only sissies wear face visors.

Similarly, there has been major resistance to wearing or using hard hats or traffic vests, or potential testers; to consistently applying grounds; and, currently, to using fall arrest equipment. Such elements of this culture will probably always be present, but an old slogan from aviation should be part of your work code: "There are old pilots and there are bold pilots, but there are no old bold pilots."

Risk in Line Work

1.1.10 Line work is a potentially high-risk job. Powerline workers suffer a high rate of fatal and permanently disabling injuries. This working environment is very unforgiving. High exposure leads to potentially fatal hazards such as burns from an electrical contact, falling from a height, asphyxiation in a vault, or wayward vehicular traffic bursting into a work zone.

The definition of risk shows why powerline work is considered a high-risk occupation:

$$Risk = Consequence \times Exposure \times Probability$$

Where:

Consequence = *the damage or injuries caused when an accident occurs.*

Exposure = *the amount of time a person is within a hazardous area.*

Probability = *the likelihood of making contact with a hazard.*

Powerline work is considered high-risk because the *consequences* of accidents are often severe. Risk is more than merely the odds of having an accident. Not much can be done about *consequences* or *exposure.* Risk is reduced by using *controls (barriers),* such as safety equipment that will lower the *probability* of contact with a hazard.

1.2 Managing Personal Safety Risk

Reduce Risk by Using Only Approved Equipment

1.2.1 An employer is responsible for providing approved personal protective equipment, tools, and hardware that meet regulatory requirements.

An employee is responsible for inspecting and using the equipment provided as required by regulatory jurisdictions and the employer. An employee is responsible for reporting equipment defects and for taking defective equipment out of service.

This text assumes that only trained, qualified people carry out powerline work, using only approved equipment, and that the equipment is inspected as required. Therefore, these requirements will not be repeated in this text for each situation.

Rubber Gloves as Personal Protective Equipment

1.2.2 Rubber gloves (sleeves) are used as personal protective equipment when working in the vicinity of live circuits. They also can be used as a tool in hot-line work.

The following are some typical rules for use of rubber gloves as personal protective equipment in distribution work:

1. *Ground to Ground Rule:* Rubber gloves shall be worn continuously while working on any structure carrying live conductors.

2. *Cradle to Cradle Rule:* Rubber gloves shall be worn from the time a bucket truck boom leaves its cradle until it is back in the cradle.

3. *Extended Reach Rule:* Rubber gloves shall be worn any time a worker is able to reach out and touch a live conductor, which is generally 5 feet (1.5 m).

4. *Lock to Lock Rule:* Rubber gloves shall be worn when a vault or cabinet with a live cable is opened and shall be worn continuously until the vault or cabinet is locked.

Examples of Rubber Gloves Used as Personal Protective Equipment

1. When opening and closing air-break switches, circuit breakers, or electronic reclosers at an equipment site.

2. While using hot-line tools, though this varies among utilities, from requiring them for all hot-line tool work, to prohibiting them for all hot-line tool work, to requiring them on distribution voltages only, to requiring them when using switch sticks in wet weather.

3. When moving or handling energized underground primary cables.

4. When removing sheaths and sleeves from cables and joints and when opening or cutting cables unless proven deenergized.

5. When working on energized secondaries and services.

6. When removing vines, weeds, and such that have grown into energized pad-mounted equipment.

7. When handling ropes and conductors while stringing in the vicinity of live circuits.

How to Use Rubber Gloves as Personal Protective Equipment

The class or voltage rating of rubber gloves should be close to the voltage of the equipment or lines being worked on, but it is also appropriate to use rubber gloves as personal protective equipment when setting poles or on switchgear handles of voltages higher than the glove ratings. In these instances, rubber gloves are not to be used as the primary protection but only as a backup that might make a difference when things go wrong.

Types of Rubber Gloves

Rubber gloves (and in many places rubber sleeves) are used every day in distribution line work. Rubber gloves come in four different classes or voltage ratings, as shown in Table 1–1. The voltage ratings of the gloves are expressed as nominal voltages from one hot wire to another, expressed as phase-to-phase (Ø to Ø). Rubber gloves are more likely to be exposed to phase-to-ground voltages, which can be calculated by dividing the phase-to-phase voltage by $\sqrt{3}$, or 1.732.

TABLE 1–1   Rubber Glove Voltage Rating

Class 0	Class 1	Class 2	Class 3	Class 4
< 1,000 kV	< 7.5 kV	< 17 kV	< 26.5 kV	< 36 kV
Volts	Ø to Ø	Ø to Ø	Ø to Ø	Ø to Ø
Red Label	White Label	Yellow Label	Green Label	Orange Label
Minimum Distance between Tops of Protectors and Rubber Gloves				
1/2 in. (13mm)	1 in. (25mm)	2 in. (50mm)	3 in. (75mm)	4 in. (100mm)

Rubber gloves come in different lengths, can be straight or have a bell cuff, can have five fingers or one finger (mitten style), can have two contrasting colors or one color, and come in various sizes. They are always used with a protective leather glove. Because the cover does not have any insulating value and can easily provide a path for electricity to flow, check that the rubber glove extends past the leather protector glove. The minimum distance between the top of the protector glove and the rolled top of the rubber glove is shown in Table 1–1.

Inspecting Rubber Gloves

Rubber gloves are not very rugged and can be punctured easily. Therefore, you must inspect them before use. The most effective way to have a close look at a glove is to inflate it and examine it for damage. When the glove is inflated, a second color coming through the black color, as well as any other cuts, cracks, or splinters, are more visible.

The most effective way to inflate the glove is with a portable mechanical inflator. This inflator allows a much closer inspection of a glove. Listening for air leaks is another method of inspection but may not be effective around noisy streets and highways. Inflating a rubber glove by rolling the cuff toward the palm to trap air (roll-up

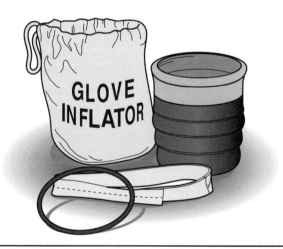

Figure 1–2   Rubber glove inflator.

method) is used very commonly but is a hurried method because preventing the air from escaping while inspecting the glove and listening for air leaks requires skill and perseverance. The roll-up method must be taught in the field by demonstration.

Wear Head Protection

1.2.3 Hard hats are part of a powerline worker's uniform. Line work involves work around overhead structures, hoisting operations, and many other opportunities for severe bumps.

Powerline workers wear Class E (Electrical) hard hats. When new and clean, they would have passed a 20,000-volt electrical test. The electrical rating is, of course, not to be depended on for any circumstance; it is only an indication of backup protection that might make a difference if things go wrong. Class G (General) and Class C (Conductive) hard hats are *not* to be worn by powerline workers.

Both Type 1 and Type 2 hard hats meet the same top-impact standards, but Type 2 also has protection in the sides, front, and rear. Some utilities are now requiring Type 2 hard hats.

Wear Eye Protection

1.2.4 Eye injuries are relatively easy to avoid by wearing appropriate eye protection. Most employers require that eye protection be worn at all times on the job.

Fortunately, safety glasses are relatively comfortable and stylish. Prescription safety glasses, or eye protection that is worn over prescription lenses, is available. Filter lenses that have a shade number are needed for protection from light radiation, such as electric arcs.

Always do the following:

1. Wear eye protection during switching, installing, and removing protective grounds, working on a hot primary or secondary circuit for protection from the ultraviolet light of an electrical arc or flash and from flying copper or aluminium particles. (The latter are nonmagnetic and are difficult for a doctor to remove.)

2. Wear eye protection when there is a risk of flying particles, such as striking steel with steel or working with toughened glass insulators.

3. Wear eye protection when exposed to strong alkalies or acids during battery boosting, when cleaning rubber hose, when refurbishing hot-line tools, or when cleaning an aluminum conductor with lye in hot water.

4. Wear eye protection when firing on wedge connectors.

5. Wear eye protection when working with high-pressure hydraulic hoses and other hydraulic tools.

6. Wear eye protection when working with power tools, such as a chain saw or drill.

Wear Safety Footwear

1.2.5 A variety of safety footwear is used in utility work, such as footwear that provides mechanical protection, electrical resistance, electrical conductivity, and chain-saw resistance.

Mechanical Protective Footwear

Reduce the risk of foot injuries by wearing footwear; a steel toecap and puncture-resistant sole for mechanical protection. "PR" is the designation for "puncture-resistant."

Electrical Shock Resistance Footwear

Like a hard hat with an electric rating, electric shock-resistant (ESR) boots might provide backup protection from step potentials. The initial electric test of up to 18 kV for a new clean boot would be much less or nonexistent in long, wet grass or in mud, but there have been incidents where they have made a difference. There are deep-heel dielectric boots available that can be worn with climbing spurs.

There are employers that require dielectric overshoe footwear (Electrical Hazard (EH) Footwear) that does provide protection farther up the leg. Usually these boots are specified for use on a particular job, such as working around a truck with an uninsulated boom.

Work boots with nailed soles or stitching that goes all the way through the sole are very conductive and should *not* be used for work around powerlines.

Electrical Conductive Footwear

Electrical conductive footwear is used for two purposes:

1. For bare-handed work from a bucket. The boots help to bond a worker to the metal grid in the bucket and avoid painful electric shocks.
2. To prevent the buildup of static electricity on a person's body and painful electric shocks each time a grounded object is touched when working with hot-line tools from steel transmission-line structures and in high-voltage substations.

Chain Saw Resistant Footwear

For regular chain saw users, wear the boots that are designed specifically for minimizing foot injuries caused by accidental contact with a running chain saw.

Slip-Resistant Footwear

While there is slip-resistant footwear available for certain conditions, for utility workers the most extreme situation is the need to walk on ice. The most common aids to traction on ice are devices that can be attached to regular footwear.

Wear Flame-Retardant Clothing

1.2.6 A powerline worker is exposed to electrical arcs and flashes from work such as switching operations, energizing equipment (transformers), accidental short circuits, working on hot secondary lines, and installing meters. Wearing materials such as nylon, polyester, or rayon during an electric arc or flash can increase the severity of the injuries because the clothing keeps burning and the melted "plastic" material burns into the skin. For severe burns, preventing infection is a large part of medical care and melted clothing in the skin is a major complicating factor. The

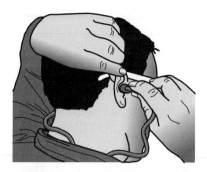

Figure 1–3   How to insert earplugs.

U.S. Occupational Safety and Health Act adopted a rule prohibiting employees exposed to electric arcs or flames from wearing clothing that could increase the extent of an employee's injuries should an arc occur.

The burns from a flash or arc are bad enough. Avoid the risk of having clothing catch fire and burn from the body like a torch by wearing flame-retardant (FR) clothing.

Wear Hearing Protection

1.2.7 Typical situations in which a powerline worker requires hearing protection are work with or near a portable two-cycle engine, a small four-cycle engine, a chipper, a compressor, a rock drill, a jack hammer, or a helicopter.

The most common hearing protection for powerline work is disposable earplugs. They must be inserted properly with clean hands. Hold the earplug between the thumb and forefinger, then roll and compress the ear plug into a small cylinder. To make a snug fit, straighten the ear canal by using one hand to reach over your head and pull up and back on your ear and use the other hand to insert the earplug. The earplug will now expand and fill the ear canal.

Remove an earplug slowly by twisting it to break the seal, thereby reducing the risk of hurting your ear drum.

Identify and Protect from Chemical Hazards

1.2.8 Programs to manage chemicals are in place everywhere, probably because it is a regulatory requirement. Employers are required to establish a written hazard communications program that includes ensuring that containers are labeled, material safety data sheets (MSDS) are available, and employees trained. Employers are required to maintain a list of the hazardous chemicals in the workplace. Chemicals are everywhere, and any used in the workplace require a hazard evaluation, material safety data sheets, labeling, and training.

As a powerline worker, identify any high-risk chemicals used in your work and ensure that you have the training, know the relevant work procedures, and use the required personal protective equipment to work with these chemicals.

- *Polychlorinated biphenyls (PCBs)* are not an immediate hazard to a person but breathing in the by-products of a fire involving PCBs is a major health hazard. Stay upwind from any fire involving equipment with insulating oil, which may be contaminated with PCBs (e.g., pyranol, askarel, inerteen).

Report all incidents involving PCBs. Utilities have stringent procedures and training involving spills, cleanup, transportation, and disposal.

- *Methyl hydrate (methanol)* is used as a drying agent for insulated booms and hot sticks. It is a Class I flammable liquid, so it must be handled as though it is gasoline. Drinking it is fatal.

- Work with *lead cables or cables wrapped with asbestos* requires training and, under certain conditions, respiratory protection.

1.3 Managing Risk in the Working Environment

Job Planning and Job Briefing

1.3.1 A good job planning format allows documentation of a job sequence, identification of high-risk hazards and effective barriers for each step, and a minimum amount of writing. The job plan shown in Figure 1–4 is an example of one such format. To be effective, a job plan must be written down.

Job:	Tree Fallen on Circuit, Cutouts Open on Two Phases, One Conductor Broken	
Job Steps	**Major Hazards**	**Required Barriers**
1. Take a clearance on the circuit and place grounds.		
2. Remove tree.	Tree leaning heavily on line, uncertain of how it will drop if cut.	Rope the tree and pull it off the line with the truck. Keep everyone clear.
3. Repair broken conductor.	Potential between ends of broken conductor.	Install grounds on each side of break and use the intact conductors as a jumper.
4. Remove grounds and surrender clearance.		

Figure 1–4   A sample format for planning smaller jobs.

A good job plan includes the following:

- *Upstream documentation:* Job planning must include a study of existing conditions, especially in relation to identifying hazards. A line crew should have been issued an applicable instruction order, engineering drawings and layout, and a materials list.

- *Written job sequence:* Everyone on a line crew must know how a job is to proceed. A plan laying out the job steps should be kept in a simple format and scaled to the complexity of the job.

- *Identification of major hazards:* Each job step should be checked for potential high-risk hazards. Effective barriers should be chosen to control each identified hazard.

- *Pre-job briefing:* A pre-job briefing is much more focused and effective when there is a written job sequence with high-risk hazards and appropriate barriers for each step identified and discussed. See Figure 1–5: Tailboard Conference Plan.

Minimum Approach Distance as a Barrier

1.3.2 Maintaining a minimum approach distance to exposed live conductors is the most common barrier a powerline worker uses to avoid electrical contact.

In most jurisdictions, occupational safety regulations do not allow an unqualified person to come within 10 feet (3 m) of a distribution electrical circuit and an additional 4 inches (10 cm) for every 10 kV over that which works out to 14 feet (4.3 m) for 169 kV, 16 feet (4.9 m) for 230 kV, and 25 feet (7.6 m) for 500 kV.

To work closer, a person either must be trained and declared qualified by an employer or must be undergoing on-the-job training under the direct supervision of a qualified person. A powerline apprentice becomes qualified by electrical awareness orientation training and over the course of time by demonstrating the ability to perform work safely in the vicinity of live circuits. A qualified person would know and understand the contents of "Awareness when in an Electrical Environment" (Chapter 6).

Orientation to electrical awareness should include learning to identify power conductors, neutral, open-wire bare secondary, wrapped secondary, tree wire, telephone cable, streetlight circuit, and the voltage on each. Some structures will have three or four circuits, each with a different voltage. While the length of insulation or the voltage reading on a transformer might determine the voltage of a circuit, it is best to ask the owner of the lines. It is the voltage level that determines the allowable minimum working distance. A powerline worker also must be able to recognize hazards such as a broken crossarm, a broken insulator, or a fallen conductor that could cause contact even when working outside of the qualified minimum approach limit.

Government regulators and utilities have developed tables listing the minimum approach distance from various voltages for different levels of qualified people and equipment. The minimum approach distances in Table 1–2 apply to work in the vicinity of a live circuit and to live-line work. The flashover voltage for a live-line

Tailboard Conference Plan

Prepare, discuss, and review the job plan with the crew. Use this form daily and whenever a change is introduced to the job.

Job Being Performed:

Date	Crew Members Present

Hazard Identification List

Gravity	Electricity	Mechanical	Kinetic/Vehicular
Falling from a height Falling objects Falling structures Climbing obstructions	Electrical contact Induction/backfeed Static charge Ground gradients Flash potential Boom contact	Equipment failure Lifting with the boom Max. working loads on rigging Conductor/guy tensions Vehicle stability	Traffic control Driving conditions Moving loads

Have We Considered?

People	Procedures	Hardware/Equipment	Environment

Person in charge
Qualification of personnel
Job coordination with other
  work groups
Communication
Worker fatigue
Pedestrian control
General public
	Isolation of apparatus
	Adequate grounding
	Work protection/Hold off
	Vehicle grounds
	Distribution standards
	Confined space entry
	Emergency rescue
	  procedures
		Work equipment
		Tools and Personal
		  Protective Equipment
		  (PPE)
		Vehicles
		Structures
		Safe loads for rigging
		Warning devices
		Physical barriers
			Other utilities
			Weather conditions
			Soil conditions
			Lighting conditions
			Work schedules

Major Hazards	Barriers to Eliminate or Control

How will we execute a rescue? _____

Exact location for emergency aid: _____

Figure 1–5 Tailboard Conference Plan.

TABLE 1–2   **Typical Minimum Approach Distances**

Maximum Phase-to-Phase Voltage (Maximum Phase-to-Ground Voltage)	Minimum Approach Distance Phase-to-Ground Exposure	Minimum Approach Distance Phase-to-Phase Exposure
.05 to 1.0 kV	Avoid contact	Avoid contact
Up to 15 kV (8.7 kV)	2 ft., 1 in. (64 cm)	2 ft., 2 in. (66 cm)
Up to 36.0 kV (20.8 kV)	2 ft., 4 in. (72 cm)	2 ft., 7 in. (77 cm)
Up to 46.0 kV (26.6 kV)	2 ft., 7 in. (77 cm)	2 ft., 10 in. (85 cm)
Up to 72.5 kV	3 ft. (90 cm)	3 ft., 6 in. (1.05 m)
Up to 121 kV	3 ft., 2 in. (95 cm)	4 ft., 3 in. (1.29 m)
Up to 145 kV	3 ft., 7 in. (1.09 m)	4 ft., 11 in. (1.50 m)
Up to 169 kV	4 ft. (1.22 m)	5 ft., 8 in. (1.71 m)
Up to 242 kV	5 ft., 3 in. (1.59 m)	7 ft., 6 in. (2.27 m)
Up to 362 kV	8 ft., 6 in. (2.59 m)	12 ft., 6 in. (3.8 m)
Up to 550 kV	11 ft., 3 in. (3.42 m)	18 ft., 1 in. (5.50 m)
Up to 800 kV	14 ft., 11 in. (4.53 m)	26 ft. (7.91 m)

tool is the same as it is for air. A fiberglass live-line tool may be better insulation than air, but the distance needed on a tool is an air gap between the hands on a live-line tool and the live conductor.

Taking out an Isolation Guarantee Using a Lockout/Tagout Procedure

1.3.3 Do not approach a hot circuit closer than the minimum approach distance unless you are insulated, the circuit is insulated, or the circuit has an *isolation guarantee* (commonly called a "clearance" in many places) in place based on a formal lockout/tagout procedure, and protective line grounds are installed. An isolation guarantee is a document prepared by a responsible person that states that (1) a particular line or piece of electrical equipment has been disconnected from all known sources, (2) all feed points have been opened, tagged, and/or locked, and (3) the isolation will remain in effect until formally surrendered.

Be aware that when you cross utility boundaries on storm trouble, the lockout/tagout procedure in other utilities may not have the same terms and meaning. For example, a "hold off" tag can be used to tag an isolating device for a work isolation guarantee while it may be used in another utility to block the automatic re-close on a breaker. "Deenergize" can mean isolating a circuit while in another utility it can mean applying protective grounds on a circuit.

Typical Failures Involving Improper Application of a Lockout/Tagout Procedure

- Incorrect identification of the required circuit.
- Incorrect identification of switchgear being operated.
- Failure to test for potential before installing protective grounds.
- Failure to install protective grounds to prove isolation.
- Working outside the scope of the isolated and grounded circuit or equipment.

- Neighboring hot circuits or equipment encroaching into the isolated and grounded work zone.

- Taking a circuit off-potential, as an extra safety barrier, with no intention to place protective grounds. Even if the intent is to treat the ungrounded circuit as energized, the hot-line work methods get compromised. If a circuit is deenergized to provide a safe (or safer) working condition, you must apply the full lockout/tagout procedure, including the installation of protective grounds.

Protection from Traffic

1.3.4 Exposure is high-risk when working along a roadway because the consequences of a wayward vehicle entering a worksite can be severe.

Local jurisdictions dictate the type of traffic control needed when utility work will affect the free flow of traffic. Many jurisdictions provide pocket-size field manuals showing minimum requirements for various types of work. In the United States, the Federal Highway Administration issues the National Manual on Uniform Traffic Control Devices (MUTCD). This document is used as a reference for most of the utility rules governing traffic control.

Being very visible with signs, flags, cones, warning lights, highly visible clothing, flaggers, and police presence is usually effective for channeling traffic around a work area. However, motorists are often distracted by rerouted lanes, signs, workers, and equipment and will not see any reason to stop for work operations such as low-hanging wires being strung across a roadway.

The selection, placement, and spacing of traffic control devices will depend on the proximity of work to traffic, the roadway type (number of lanes and traffic speed), and the length of time workers will be exposed to traffic. A physical barrier such as a large truck (crash truck) parked in a closed traffic lane should be considered for very vulnerable locations.

Manuals and standards for temporary traffic control covers rules for flaggers, high visibility clothing and the placement of devices that regulate, warn, and guide road users. Table 1–3 covers some utility work specific hazards that are not found in regulatory standards.

Working in a Confined/ Enclosed Space

1.3.5 Depending on the jurisdiction, underground utility vaults (man holes), tubs, and open top spaces more than 4 feet deep such as trenches (one interpretation) are considered to be an enclosed space. Because most electrical utility confined spaces are designed for entry under normal operating conditions, the Occupational Safety and Health Regulations in the U.S. has declared them to be an enclosed space versus a Permit Required Confined Space. An enclosed space still needs to be tested for oxygen deficiency, flammable gases, and vapors. It is not necessary to prepare a confined space entry permit for an enclosed space as compared to confined spaces that are entered infrequently, such as tanks, vessels, silos, or hoppers.

1. For workers who enter an enclosed space infrequently, preparing a permit (Figure 1–7) before entering will reduce the risk of overlooking an important step in the procedure.

2. Testing is done by a qualified person using equipment that has been calibrated.

TABLE 1–3   Utility-Specific Traffic Hazards and Barriers

Hazard	Barrier
Traffic makes contact with a conductor or rope being strung across a roadway during a *slack stringing operation.*	Stop traffic *before* running wire or rope across a roadway. Waiting for a break in traffic and then stopping vehicles entering the work zone increases the risk. Drivers often do not see any obstruction when only a wire is suspended across the road.
Traffic makes contact with a conductor or rope being strung across a roadway during a *tension stringing operation.*	*Caution:* If a road crossing is a much longer span than others in a pull, it is vulnerable to extra conductor sagging into that span.
The *elbow of an aerial bucket* stretches over an open lane of traffic, and a contact is avoided only if an approaching truck is alerted to the hazard (Figure 1–6).	Rider poles and/or truck booms can be set up to reduce the risk of a conductor coming down into traffic. Block off enough lanes to cover the potential of the boom elbow over the roadway or use a dedicated observer.
Letting traffic run over a wire being strung across a road can be picked up by the tires of a fast-moving vehicle.	Stop traffic, then direct drivers to proceed slowly over wires on the roadway.

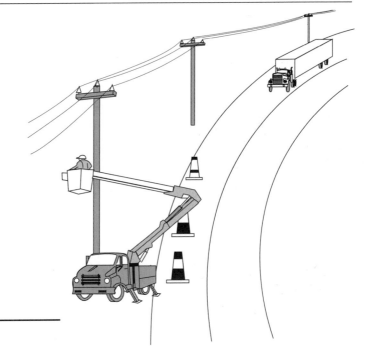

Figure 1–6   Traffic hazard alert.

3. Testing is done for oxygen deficiency, flammable gases, and vapors before removing a cover so that a spark created by the opening of a cover or hatch will not cause an explosion. Remote probes are used to check for explosive gases. *Caution:* Flammable gases or vapors may not show up on a test until oxygen is introduced into the space.

4. After opening, test again for oxygen deficiency, flammable gases, and vapors, as well as for common hazardous chemicals.

Electrical Utility Enclosed Space Entry Permit

Site Location and Description: _____

Supervisor: _____

Date and Time Issued: _____

Date and Time of Expiration: _____

Authorized Entrants: _____ _____

_____ _____

Attendants: _____ _____

Identify Potential Hazards	Control Measures	Additional Control Measures
Inadequate Electrical Clearances	Lockout/Tagout/Ground	_____
Limited Exits	Set Up Rescue Capability	_____
Traffic and Pedestrian Control	Set Up Barriers	_____
Lack of Natural Ventilation	Ventilate	_____
Airborne Combustible Dust	Ventilate	_____
CO from Vehicle Exhaust	Ventilate	_____
CO_2 from Rotting Vegetation	Ventilate	_____
Nitrogen from Pressurized Cable	Ventilate	_____
H_2S	Ventilate	_____
The vault is over 15 ft. (4.5 m) deep	Ventilate	_____
Hot Work (i.e., soldering, pouring compound, cutting, or heating)	Ventilate	_____
Other: _____	Purge—Flush and Vent	_____

Test and Monitor Atmosphere (record monitoring every 2 hours)

Test to Be Taken	Limit	Completed	Time	Time	Time
% oxygen	19.5–23.5%	_____	_____	_____	_____
% LEL (LFL)	10% Max.	_____	_____	_____	_____
Carbon monoxide	35 ppm	_____	_____	_____	_____
Hydrogen sulfide	10–15 ppm	_____	_____	_____	_____
Other toxics	PEL	_____	_____	_____	_____

Rescue Readiness

Communications Setup	_____	Lifelines, Hoisting Equipment	_____
Full-body Harness	_____	Explosion-proof Lighting	_____
Protective Clothing	_____	Respiratory Protection	_____
Fire Extinguishers	_____	Special Tools	_____

Other Information/Specific Requirements _____

This information and the work covered by this permit have been reviewed with all entrants and attendants. Safety procedures have been received and are understood. All appropriate items have been completed.

Entry Authorized _____

Title _____

Date/Time _____ / _____

THIS PERMIT SHOULD BE KEPT POSTED AT THE JOB SITE.

Figure 1–7 Electrical utility enclosed space entry permit.

Ventilate to Reduce Risk

The risk of a contaminated atmosphere is greatly reduced through continuous ventilation. Ventilate all areas of the enclosed space continuously so that the ventilation provides clean air at a rate of at least 200 cubic feet per minute per occupant, or in an enclosed space larger than 2,000 cubic feet, six air changes of the confined space volume per hour.

Typically, use a blower with a capacity of 1,000 cfm or greater. The blower should be located to ensure that engine exhaust gases are not blown into the confined space (see Figure 1–8). Ventilate the confined space by blowing air into the space for at least 5 minutes before entering.

Historically, about 60 percent of fatalities involving confined spaces occur when attendants perform a rescue.

Ideally, all entrants wear a full-body harness, which is kept attached to a hoist (Figure 1–9) to allow a rescue without the need to enter the confined space.

Reduce Your Risks Working in Vaults

1. Do not climb into or out of a vault by stepping on cables or hangers.

2. Before tools or material are lowered into the opening of a vault, ensure that everyone below is clear of the area directly under the opening.

3. Reliable communications, through two-way radios or equivalent means, shall be maintained among all employees involved in the job.

4. If duct rods are used, they are installed in the direction presenting the least hazard to employees. A worker should be stationed at the far end of the duct line being rodded to ensure that the required minimum approach distances are maintained.

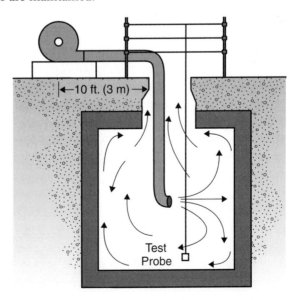

Figure 1–8 Ventilating a vault ventilator.

Flame-Retardant
Rope

Figure 1–9 A typical rescue rig.

5. When multiple cables are present, the cable to be worked on shall be identified by testing or spiking.

6. An impending fault is indicated when a cable in a vault has one or more abnormalities, such as oil or compound leaking from cables or joints, broken cable sheaths, hot localized surface temperatures of cables or joints, or joints that are swollen beyond normal tolerance. The defective cable should be deenergized before anyone works in the vault.

7. When work is performed on cables in vaults, ensure that the metallic sheath continuity is maintained. A lethal voltage may be present between the ends of a break in the sheath.

Working in Excavations and Trenches

1.3.6 At an excavation site, protect yourself from the following hazards.

Underground Utilities

- Get locations for gas, water, sewer, telephone, TV, and power lines.
- Before working on or moving energized cables, inspect them for damage.

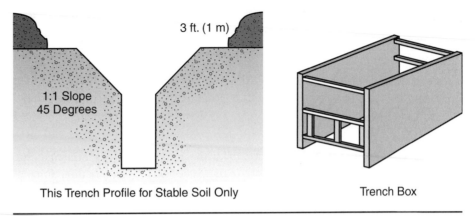

This Trench Profile for Stable Soil Only

Trench Box

Figure 1–10 Protective barriers for trenching.

Confined/Enclosed Space Hazards

- Carry out air sampling in trenches more than 4 feet deep where oxygen deficiency or other hazardous atmospheres could reasonably be expected to exist.

- Reduce the risk of cave-ins from material that could fall or roll from an excavation face or from material piled next to an excavation.

- Place a protective system, such as sloping, benching, shoring, or a trench box when exposed to the hazard of falling or sliding material from an excavated bank or side more than 4 ft. (1.2 m) high above a worker's feet (Figure 1–10).

- Figure 1–11 shows an example of the slope angles needed for certain types of soils. Refer to applicable regulations regarding the minimum slope, bracing, and piling needed for the various types of soil in your work area.

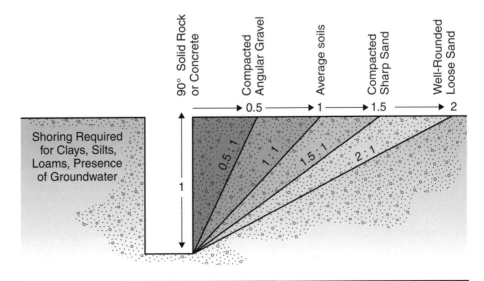

Figure 1–11 Slope angles of a trench.

- Keep excavated material and work equipment at least 3 ft. (1 m) from the trench to prevent overloading and stress cracks.

- When caught in a cave-in, run or jump *up* the bank, not down.

- Do not work within reach of an excavating machine. Work so you face it.

- A sudden downpour can fill a trench and cause rain-soaked soil to give way. Leave a trench during a sudden downpour because the rain can fill a trench and cause rain-soaked soil to give way.

- Provide a stairway, ladder, or ramp for a hurried escape route at a distance of no more than 25 feet (7.5 m) in any direction.

Shot Stones

- When working in a trench, it is not unusual to be on the receiving end of a stone "shot" from between a truck tire and pavement. Have loose stones swept from your work area.

Working in Heat and Cold

1.3.7 Powerline workers work outdoors, in all kinds of weather. Transformers tend to burn out on overload on the hottest or coldest days of the year.

A human body is most efficient within a temperature range of $+/-3°F$ $(+/-2°C)$ of the body's normal temperature of 98.6°F (37°C). The internal human thermostat works very well but will be stressed or overwhelmed when working outdoors on very hot days or very cold nights.

Working in the Heat

Symptoms of heat stress are headaches, dizziness, lightheadedness, irritability, confusion, upset stomach, fainting, and/or pale, clammy skin. Heat stress left untreated could lead to a fatal heat stroke.

To avoid heat stress, do the following:

- Before you get thirsty, drink a lot of water.

- Wear light, loose-fitting, breathable clothing, such as cotton.

- In extreme heat, take short breaks in air-conditioned vehicles or buildings or in the shade.

- Eat smaller meals and avoid caffeine and sugar.

- Flame-retardant clothing may increase the risk of heat stress; therefore, these precautions become more critical.

Working in the Cold

Symptoms of cold stress that could lead to dangerous hypothermia are severe shivering, slurred speech, clumsiness, poor judgment, confusion, apathy, slow pulse or slow breathing, excessive fatigue, drowsiness, reduced sense of touch, less grip strength, and less ability to sense heat, cold, and pain.

To avoid cold stress, do the following:

- Have regular warm-up breaks in a heated truck cab or indoors with an opportunity to remove clothing to prevent sweating. A person who has become damp or sweaty will chill quickly and be susceptible to hypothermia.
- Hot drinks will provide energy and warmth and will prevent dehydration.
- Use a buddy to check each other's face for frostbite.
- Dress for the cold by wearing layers, including an outer shell to protect from the wind and inner insulated layers. Layers can be added and removed to stay comfortable and to avoid getting damp.
- Wear a good winter hard hat liner covered with a parka hood; half a person's heat loss can be through the head.

First Aid for Frostbite and Hypothermia

Superficial frostbite will show up as white skin areas, typically on the face. The buddy system is needed because victims will not feel or know that they have frostbite. Frostbite is treated by placing a warm hand over the white spots. Do not rub the skin because it will break the small frozen capillaries and make a face quite ugly.

More severe frostbite can occur, first in the toes, fingers, or face. When an area becomes cold, white, and numb, it must be heated. When heated, first-degree frostbite will cause the area to become red and is not unlike a first-degree burn; second-degree frostbite will form blisters, not unlike a second-degree burn. Keep the body warm and supply hot drinks to treat any accompanying hypothermia.

If frostbite shows up as dark skin or cold and lifeless extremities, keep the body warm to treat hypothermia and *seek medical aid*. Do not warm the body part yourself. The outer surface will thaw first, and the artery that normally supplies the needed oxygenated blood to keep the thawed area alive will still be frozen.

Protection from Drowning

1.3.8 Reduce the Risk of Drowning while Working on or Near Water

- Wear a personal flotation device. If the work involves very cold water or traveling across ice, wear a personal floatation device (survival suit), which protects against hypothermia.
- Any boat used for powerline work should be of a size that meets or exceeds regulations and is equipped with safety gear such as paddles, a fire extinguisher, an anchor, and a first aid kit.
- Tie up when working from boats, barges, or on dams.

Reduce the Risk of Drowning when Traveling on Ice

No ice crossing is without some risk! Ice conditions vary and can change from day to day and hour to hour. Watch for changing water levels on the headwater for a power dam. Avoid slushy ice, ice near rivers or currents, ice that has thawed and

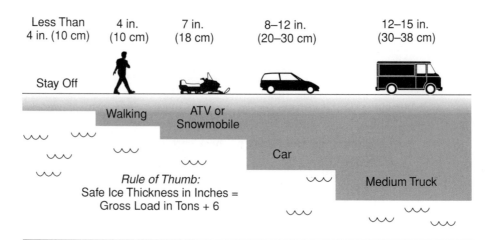

Figure 1–12 Minimum clear, hard ice thickness.

refrozen, layered or rotten ice caused by sudden temperature change, ice covered by a heavy blanket of snow, and pressure ridges due to wind or current pressure.

Talk to people with local knowledge about ice conditions and routes to take, and test for the thickness of clear ice (Figure 1–12). Wear a survival suit to protect against hypothermia.

When walking on ice, walk tied together in pairs 10 feet (3 m) apart. Carry a long pole and ice picks. In an emergency with poor ice conditions, the lead person should wear a body harness with a rescue rope tied to it.

> *Snowmobile or all-terrain-vehicle (ATV) travel on ice should be done with at least two machines spaced 100 feet (30 m) apart.*

Ice travel with large trucks or large off-road equipment requires preparation and testing to reduce risk.

- Prepare an ice road by scraping away snow and flooding it to build up the ice thickness.
- The rule of thumb "Safe ice conditions in inches = Gross load in tons + 6" applies to clear ice. A crack in the ice reduces the load-bearing capacity to one-half; intersecting cracks reduce the load-bearing capacity to one-quarter.
- Travel slowly. The wave created under the ice by a moving vehicle can break the ice. The heavier the vehicle, the slower it should travel.

Working around Helicopters

1.3.9 Helicopters can provide the sky hook that powerline workers often want. Helicopters are used to carry out patrols, string conductors (pilot lines), set line workers on top of structures, hover to support a line worker carrying out bare-handed work on a conductor, set poles, hang crossarms, build towers, and carry loads into difficult terrain.

If flying as an observer, a powerline worker should help identify flying hazards in a wire environment, such as crossing circuits, shield wire, lateral taps, and such. Warning signs on structures should be in place to point out many of these hazards.

Before a job involving a helicopter begins, a discussion between the ground crew, signal person, and pilot will help all workers understand the safety barriers, work methods, and signals to be used.

Wear Personal Protective Equipment

- Wear eye protection to prevent substances caught in the downwash from contacting the eyes.

- Wear a hard hat, secured by a chin strap or other device.

- Wear tight-fitting clothing to prevent clothes flapping in the downwash from being caught in the hoist line or from interfering with other work.

- Wear hearing protection.

Approaching a Helicopter

- When approaching a helicopter, stay in a position visible to the pilot.

- Keep away from the tail rotor (Figure 1–13).

- Stay in a crouched position when in range of the main rotor.

- Carry all tools and equipment below waist level.

- Secure or move loose gear outside of the downwash area, at least 100 feet (30 m) from the helicopter to reduce the likelihood of flying materials.

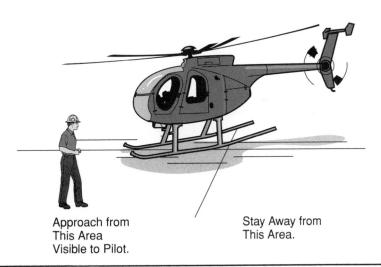

Approach from
This Area
Visible to Pilot.

Stay Away from
This Area.

Figure 1–13 Approaching a helicopter.

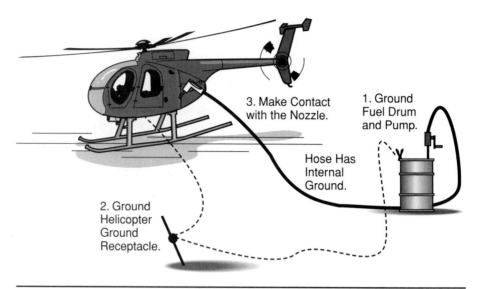

Figure 1–14 Fueling a helicopter.

Working Under a Helicopter

- Only trained workers may hook or unhook loads under a helicopter.
- A signal person must be designated to direct, signal, and communicate with the pilot.
- Ground the static charge that builds up on a helicopter before touching a suspended load.
- Use an insulated tool to attach and remove a pull-away-type ground.

Fueling a Helicopter

If involved in refuelling a helicopter in the field, ensure that all metal parts are bonded together to prevent a static discharge (spark). Follow the sequence described in Figure 1–14.

Working Alone **1.3.10** A general principle for powerline work should be that rescue capability is available when working on circuits over 750 V, when working at heights of more than 10 feet (3 m), or when working in a confined space.

When a second person is needed, the second person must be trained and equipped to perform applicable rescues: pole-top rescue, emergency bucket rescue, bucket lowering, tower rescue, tree rescue, and/or confined space rescue. First aid, artificial resuscitation, and/or cardiopulmonary resuscitation (CPR) are part of the qualifications needed by a second person.

Typical One-Person Tasks in Some Utilities

- Operating switches by means of an operating handle or switch sticks.
- Re-fusing circuits or equipment with a hot stick or extension stick.

Working Near Gas Pipelines and Communications Cables

1.3.11 While underground electric utilities are hazardous when contact is made with an auger or backhoe, hitting a gas line can be very explosive and hitting communications cables, sewers, water lines, or underground tanks can be very disruptive, embarrassing, and expensive.

Below-ground utilities are usually located when planning a job, but contact with an underground plant is not unusual. When there is any doubt, dig by hand or use a heavy duty industrial vacuum loader (sucker) truck that pneumatically sucks up solids, sludges, and slurries.

Identify and Protect from Biological Hazards

1.3.12 Almost every location has biological hazards that must be controlled. Most people are familiar with biological hazards in their own locations, but biological hazards may be unique to other regions of the country. While contact with these hazards is quite rare, it is prudent to inquire.

Poisonous snakes, killer bees, swarming wasps, ticks that cause Lyme disease, mouse/rat droppings that cause the Hanta virus, poison ivy and poison oak, mosquitoes that carry West Nile virus, and various diseases from bird/bat droppings may be present. All these hazards result in unique symptoms that can vary from mild irritation to death.

Reduce the Risk of Public Electrical Contact

1.3.13 Overhead and underground powerlines are constructed to be out of reach of the general public. While utility work is carried out, the public is further protected by barricades around stringing equipment, covers over dug holes, traffic and pedestrian controls, grounded conductors that are tied down temporarily, covers placed over hot meter bases, and so on.

Powerline workers are the most qualified people to identify potential public electrical contact hazards with utility circuits and should report any of the following:

- Flagpoles, antennas, and ladders within striking distance of an electrical circuit.
- Cranes, boom trucks, and ladders within 10 feet (3 m) of a hot distribution circuit.
- Construction and buildings being erected within established safe limits.
- Trees near powerlines, such as those in suburban streets, school yards, and parks, that are liable to be climbed by young people.
- Farm equipment, such as grain augers and high loads, being moved under lines.
- Irrigation systems with large solid streams of water near transmission lines.
- House movers traveling under powerlines.
- Digging activity or posts or bars being driven into the ground near transmission or distribution cables.

1.4 Reduce Risk when Climbing and Working Aloft

Working at Heights

1.4.1 Climbing and working at heights is one of the skills that separates line work from most other work. Falling from heights has traditionally been the second-highest cause of fatalities in line work. Powerline workers work at heights from buckets, poles, substation structures, transmission towers, and helicopters. Risk is reduced through training, using proper equipment, maintaining equipment, and using a fall arrest system where applicable.

Some Fall Protection System Facts

1.4.2 More employers are implementing the use of fall arrest for pole and tower climbing as time goes on. The justification is based on the fact that there are good fall arrest systems available and nonuse might be seen as a failure to exercise due diligence.

Specific Hazards when Working from a Ladder Climbing Poles

1.4.3 Climbing an extension ladder does not require fall protection probably because there is no practical way to provide it. Working from a ladder requires extra steps to protect from the hazards listed in Table 1–8.

1.4.4 Equipment is available to climb all poles, concrete, steel, wood, and so on. There are step bolts and ladders, especially on transmission line poles. There are detachable steps. There are nut fasteners embedded into steel poles that allow step bolts to be screwed in as needed. There are various designs of climbers, including a style more popular in Europe that looks like a cant hook coming out from the front of the foot, as shown in Figure 1–17. Cutting out would be rare, but they are not as maneuverable as the spurs worn in North America.

In North America, climbing wood poles with spurs is the norm. Climbing a pole safely is an essential skill for powerline workers, and the discussion that follows must be accompanied by field demonstrations and training. Fall arrest is mandatory in some jurisdictions during training and is required for all climbing in other jurisdictions and utilities.

Climbing with Spurs

If possible, climb up the back or high side of the pole, as shown in Figure 1–18. Climb with short steps approximately 8 to 10 inches (20 to 25 cm) apart, keeping the knees about 8 inches (20 cm) from the pole. Long steps will automatically bring the knees into the pole, increasing the risk of the spur cutting out. The hands on the backside of the pole should be at shoulder level. If the hands are higher, the arms will be under more strain.

Aim the gaffs at the heart (center) of the pole, with the toes pointed outward. Raise the left foot and left arm together, and then the right foot and right arm together, a movement that is opposite to walking.

Look up to see where you are going and to avoid climbing hazards on the pole such as knots, bolts, cracks, and climbing too high into electrical hazards. If your knees are away from the pole and the spurs are properly sharpened, there is no need to look at your feet.

When descending, lock, aim, and drop. Lock the knee so that the leg is straight, aim the gaff to the center of the pole, and then drop your full weight and spur into the pole. Long steps can be taken descending, and the steps will get longer with increased confidence. The upper gaff will break out easily when taking longer steps

TABLE 1–7   An Introduction to Fall Arrest Systems

Fact	Details
Falling from a height is a common cause of fatal accidents to powerline workers.	After electrical accidents, the most common cause of fatal accidents to powerline workers has been falling from a height. Falls can be initiated by many factors over which a powerline worker has little or no control, such as wind, ice, knots, rot, loose hardware, leaning structures, and rigging failure.
	While a bucket is sometimes a safer alternative, climbing is often necessary. A fall protection system is the most effective means of reducing the risk of falling to the ground.
There are four types of fall protection.	**1.** A **work positioning system** is a personal positioning system to allow a worker to be held in place while keeping hands free for work. A body belt and pole strap constitute a work positioning system. To have fall protection while changing position on a structure, a fall arrest system is used along with a work positioning system.
	2. A **fall arrest system** is used to prevent a fall to the ground after a fall has been initiated from a structure. A fall arrest system is passive and activated only after a fall occurs. The harness worn in a bucket is a fall arrest.
	3. A **suspension system** is used to suspend a worker who is being transported up or down vertically. It is used to do tree work, work at transmission suspension insulators, and bare-handed work while suspended by a link stick/live line rope, as well as to lower a worker suspended from a winch from a helicopter. To have complete fall protection, a fall arrest system or a secondary backup must be used. For helicopter work, a backup fall protection system relies on the extensive engineering and maintenance involved in the work method.
	4. A **travel restraint system** is a system in which a worker is tied to an anchoring point to prevent reaching an area where free fall could occur. Utility workers on dams or on top of large station transformers use this system.
Without a fall arrest system, there is no backup *physical* barrier to prevent a fall to the ground.	About 60% of falling accidents to powerline workers occur while climbing and 30% while relocating. After a fall is initiated, only a fall arrest system will prevent a fall to the ground; a quick reactive grab or hug of a pole often is not enough.
	Practical pole climbing and tower climbing fall protection systemsare available. After initial resistance to learning a different climbing method, powerline workers can become very comfortable using fall protection equipment when climbing poles and towers. The Jelco Pole Choker in Figure 1–15 shows one example of a successful pole-climbing fall arrest system. A retractable lanyard is used to climb past obstructions.
A full-body harness is the only acceptable attachment of a body in a fall arrest system.	Safety belts that are worn aroundthe waist are acceptable for a travel restraint system or to stop a fall less than 2 ft. (0.6 m) but not as part of a fall arrest system. In a fall, all of the falling force would be concentrated in the abdominal region, if the belt is worn properly, with the D-ring in the middle of the back at the waist line, probably causing internal damage to the body. A full-body harness distributes falling forces throughout the torso, dispersing the forces through the shoulders and down through the thighs.

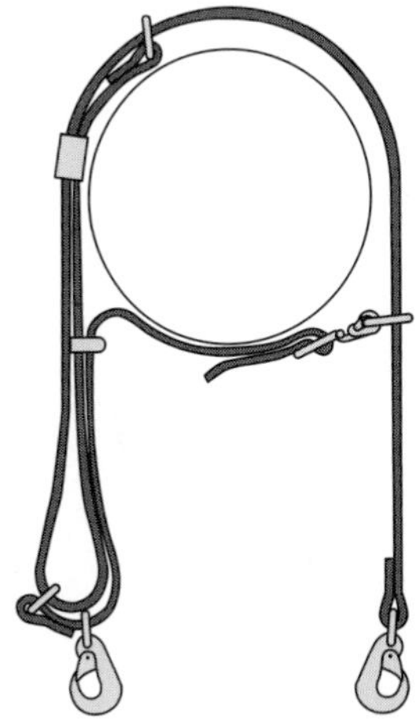

Figure 1–15   A Jelco pole choker.

TABLE 1–8   **Ladder Hazards**

Hazards	Barriers
Electrical contact	• All ladders used by utility workers should be nonconductive, preferably fiberglass. • A nonconductive ladder reduces the risk of injury in case of contact with a live conductor and can provide an insulated platform when working on secondary voltage.
Falling from a ladder	• Face the ladder while climbing. • Maintain at least three points of contact—for example, two feet and one hand or, preferably, belt in to the ladder with pole strap. • Avoid overreaching. Keep hips within the ladder uprights. • Never stand above the fourth rung from the top. • Climb the ladder with both hands free. Use a tool belt or pull up material after climbing. • Belt into the ladder with the pole strap around both rails and one wrap around a rung.
Falling with a ladder	• Stabilize the bottom of the ladder. On grass or gravel, use the ladder feet in the spike position. On hard, stable surfaces, use the feet in the flat-foot position. • Tie the top of the ladder, especially if on an aerial cable. Throw a rope over the aerial cable and use it to help set up and tie the ladder into position. • The minimum length of overlap between two sections of an extension ladder should be 3 ft. (1 m) for ladders up to 36 ft. (11 m) high and 4 ft. (1.2 m) for ladders over 36 ft. (11 m) high. • Set the ladder at a proper angle; about 75 degrees. The ladder angle is correct when a person standing at the foot of the ladder can reach the ladder with outstretched arms as shown in Figure 1–16. Another rule of thumb, set the horizontal distance of the foot of the ladder out 1/4 of the working length of the ladder.
Transferring from the ladder to a roof and vice versa	• Extend the ladder above the roof by at least three rungs to provide a handhold. • Transfer to the roof from the side of the ladder, not over the top rung.

and rolling the knee outward. Look at your feet to avoid obstructions and hazards when descending.

If climbing without a fall arrest system, "hitchhiking" up and down the pole using the pole strap is a good option. Using the pole strap when climbing automatically keeps the knees away from the pole and doesn't require as much strain on the arms, especially on large poles. The old-fashioned idea that a pole should be climbed without the pole strap is no longer valid. Hitchhiking up or down a pole can be done smoothly by learning to raise or lower the pole strap by keeping both hands on the strap near the dees and flipping the pole strap up or down, coordinated each time with the hips moved slightly toward the pole. There are extensions for pole straps in cases of large-diameter wood transmission poles.

Sneaking up the pole by lightly setting the gaffs into the pole looks good but will cause an increased risk of the gaffs cutting out.

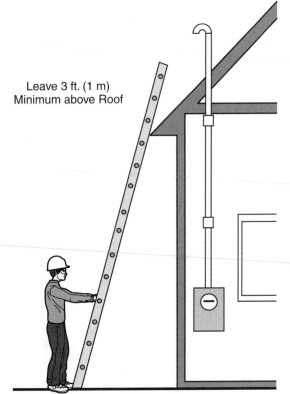

Leave 3 ft. (1 m)
Minimum above Roof

Stand Erect and Touch Ladder
with Arms Straight Out.
The Base Distance Will Be a
Minimum 1/4 H
Maximum 1/3 H

Figure 1–16 Set ladder at proper angle.

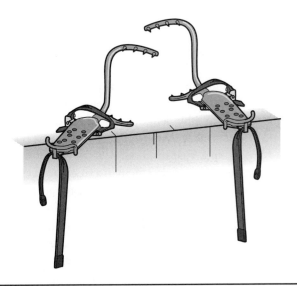

Figure 1–17 European-style climbers.

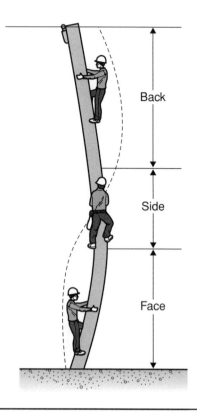

Back

Side

Face

Figure 1–18   Climb the back of the pole.

Sizing and Maintaining Spurs

The top of the spur shank must be in the hollow between the knee and the calf, as high as possible without it touching the bottom of the kneecap. If too short, the shank will dig into the calf of the leg, and if too long, it will touch the bottom of the kneecap and will be cripplingly painful. Instructions will say to measure the leg from the instep to 1/2 inch (13 mm) below the kneecap for the shank length, but the length is very critical for comfort. Some trial and error may be best if that can be arranged. Adjustable spurs would allow trial and error for determining the final comfortable length, and then you can install rivets to get rid of the rattle and movement that are common with the pins or bolts.

Spur guards should be used when walking with spurs, especially through ditches and when storing them in a truck. A puncture wound from a spur gaff is very painful.

The gaffs need to be kept sharp while maintaining their proper shape. Sharpening is a precise task that initially requires an instructor, a gaff gauge, and probably the manufacturer's instructions. There seem to be two differing opinions about sharpening a gaff. One suggests filing the gaff on the two outer surfaces to make a point while never sharpening a gaff on the underside because it changes the angle of the gaff. The other is to file the underside only, filing it flat and straight except for the end tip. Figure 1–19 illustrates the proper shape of the gaff.

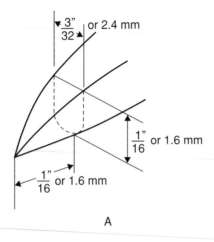

$\frac{3"}{32}$ or 2.4 mm

$\frac{1"}{16}$ or 1.6 mm

$\frac{1"}{16}$ or 1.6 mm

A

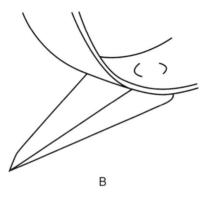

B

Figure 1–19   Proper shape of a spur gaff.

The gaff length is 15/8 inches (4 cm) for new *pole* climbing spurs and 2 3/4 inches (7 cm) for new *tree* climbing spurs. A gaff is measured on the underside and should not be less than 11/4 inches (3 cm) for *pole* climbing spurs or less than 2 3/8 inches (6 cm) for *tree* climbing spurs. Some utilities do not allow replaceable gaffs. The instructions that come with a gaff gauge must be consulted because the procedure is not self-explanatory, as shown in Figure 1–20.

In addition to the use of a gauge, a pole cut-out test will show whether the gaffs are sharpened properly. As shown in Figure 1–21, fasten the foot strap of the spur without fastening the leg strap. While standing on the ground and supporting the top of the spur with one hand, insert the gaff lightly into the pole (about 1/4 inch or 1/2 cm) at the normal climbing angle. Maintain enough pressure to keep the gaff in the pole, and with your hand, push the top of the climber against the pole and then push down. A gaff that is sharpened properly will cut into the pole and hold at a distance of 2 inches (5 cm) or less. A gaff that is shaped properly but is dull will cut into the pole and hold, but usually at a distance greater than 2 inches (5 cm). A gaff that is very dull or not shaped properly will cut out or plow through the wood for a distance greater than 2 inches (5 cm).

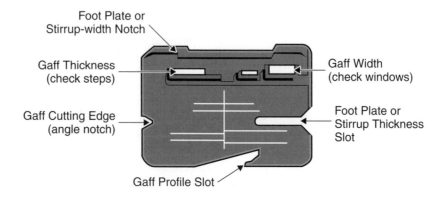

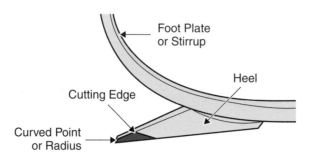

Figure 1–20 Gaff gauge.

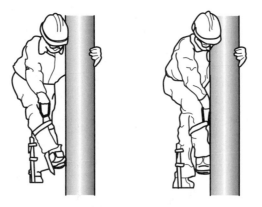

Figure 1–21 Pole cut-out test.

Sizing the Body Belt

Body belts come with gut straps, suspenders, and as part of a full-body harness, floating dees. Body belt size is based on the distance between the two "dees" around a person's back from one hip bone to the other hip bone (Figure 1–22). Too short and a body belt will pinch the hip bones and will be instantly uncomfortable. Too long and it will be like a choker and the belt will feel uncomfortable after about 5 minutes, or longer depending on the length. The dees should be just forward of the hip bones, not on them. A rule of thumb says "Measure from seam of pant, around buttocks to other seam, and add 2." The only way to ensure that a person has the proper-size belt is to try some different sizes and various work positions on a pole, ideally over a month or so.

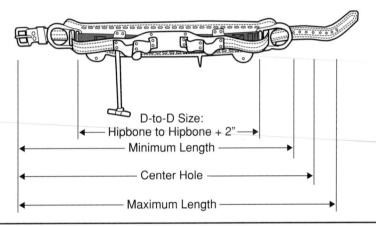

Figure 1–22 Measuring a body belt.

The Pole Strap

Pole straps (safety straps, positioning straps) are generally made with nylon impregnated with neoprene to provide good wear resistance. Pole straps have an internal layer with a contrasting color that shows through when the belt is considered worn and needs replacement. The colored layer may become discolored because of abrasion and, therefore, requires regular and thorough visual inspections for wear. Pole straps wear out much quicker when used on lattice tower steel. The pole strap shown in Figure 1–23 is typical but is not used with some of the pole climbing fall arrest systems. It is used along with the fall arrest systems on transmission line towers. Some pole straps have slide buckles that allow for easier length adjustments.

The pole strap snap hook openings should face away from the body to prevent accidental opening. This was much more important before the introduction of locking snap hooks, as shown in Figure 1–24.

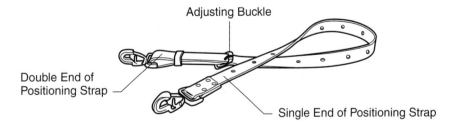

Figure 1–23 A pole strap.

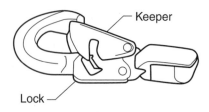

Figure 1–24   A locking snap hook.

Work Positioning

The pole strap should be adjusted so that a person is not too far away from the work. A rule of thumb, while seated in the belt, is to place an elbow against the stomach so the fingers can easily contact the pole.

Pole workers often have to reach out a long way, such as when dead-ending a conductor. The pole strap is lengthened, as long as is practical, and with one leg low, locked, twisting around slightly *with* the body belt, one can face the work to be done. The other leg does nothing.

When lifting a conductor from a stringing block onto an insulator, ideally a gin or other lifting device is used. However, if the weight is within range of being lifted safely, this cannot be done with an outstretched arm. Lengthen the pole strap so that the shoulder is under the final position of the conductor, belt in as high as possible above the conductor, put the conductor on your shoulder, and lift.

Reduce the Risk of Falling from a Pole

1.4.5 Falling from a pole is one of the high risks to which a powerline worker is exposed. Ensure that you have protection from the hazards listed in Table 1–9.

Reduce the Risk of Falling with a Pole

1.4.6 Poles have an average service life of 30 to 40 years. One safety code requires pole replacement when one-third of the load-carrying capacity of the pole is lost. Unless there is confidence in a pole testing instrument, use the guidelines that follow before climbing a pole. A hammer test, rocking test (sway test), or bore test may not be enough of a safety barrier when the consequence of being wrong can be fatal.

Working Aloft in a Bucket

1.4.7 When working from a bucket of an aerial device, a fall arrest system must be worn. An approved fall arrest consists of a full-body harness with a lanyard in series with a shock absorber attached to a dee ring on the back of the harness. The other end of the lanyard is attached to a specifically designed anchor point on the boom.

Falling from a bucket truck has not been an uncommon occurrence. Causes have included overreaching or being ejected from the bucket by a leveling cable failure; the bucket truck being struck by another vehicle; the bucket catching on a structure or hardware and suddenly releasing; an object, such as a pole, crossarm, or tree, striking the bucket; and lifting by using the bucket instead of a jib.

TABLE 1–9   **Reduce the Risk of Falling from a Pole**

Hazards	Barriers
A handline securely fastened to the body belt is snagged by a passing vehicle or by a work vehicle on the job site.	Carry the handline on a breakaway hook or similar device. Although the probability of a vehicle catching on a handline may seem rare, it has caused at least one fatality while a lineman was belted into a tower.
A hot conductor is in contact with the pole.	Eliminate possible "pole shock" hazard. Do not climb until the conductor is lifted clear from the pole or the circuit is isolated and grounded.
The pole to be climbed has workers at the bottom of the pole driving ground rods or using a tamper.	Eliminate a possible serious consequence of falling. Do not climb a pole while this work is in progress.
One climber is interfering with another climber.	Wait until the other climber is belted into position before starting to climb.
The pole has knots, weather cracks, rot, or loose hardware.	These climbing hazards can be controlled best by using a fall arrest system.
A powerline worker is climbing while not looking up, increasing the hazard of making contact with a hot conductor.	Confidence in climbing ability allows a line hand to look up while climbing. Use a dedicated observer for novice climbers.
A pole strap can slip over the top of a pole. Exposure to this hazard is increased when climbing a new pole with no hardware on it.	Install at least one bolt near the pole top when setting a pole. This can act as both a physical and a visual barrier. Always belt in below a physical barrier when working near the top of a pole.
The integrity of the hardware supporting a live conductor is suspect and could cause a live phase to fall.	Recognize known hazards such as aluminum-capped dead-end insulators, wood pins, potentially weak conductors such as #4 ACSR or #6 copper, damaged guy wires, and porcelain insulation on switch gear.
Weather-related conditions, such as high wind or ice-coated poles, increase the risk of climbing a pole.	Fall arrest systems are the most effective barriers for these climbing hazards.

Trained and experienced climbers do fall from poles when action is not taken. Protection for the hazards is listed in Table 1–9.

Falling/Dropping Hazards Specific to Tower Work

1.4.8 Working on steel transmission line structures have hazards that are distinct from working on wood poles. Ensure you are protected from the hazards listed in Table 1–11.

Reducing Risks in the Future

1.4.9 There has been quite a lot of research conducted and working robotic units manufactured to do line work. Part of the motivation is to find a safer way to work on lines.

TABLE 1–10   **Reducing the Risk of Falling with a Pole**

If	Then
The pole is older than 20 years or is obviously unsafe.	Support the pole with a line truck boom, ropes or guys, or by lashing a new pole alongside it.
The pole species has a history of early failure.	
There are burn marks, woodpecker holes, a large knot, and/or several smaller knots at the same height on the pole.	
The anchor rods and down guys have lost their galvanized coating or are corroded (e.g., near pipeline).	
The pole is beside a trench and/or is in soft, wet, or loose soil.	
There are indications of a shallow setting (e.g., a former ground line above the existing ground level may be seen).	
The strain will be altered while working aloft.	
The pole will be stripped of all conductors and guys. (The pole holds up wires, but the wires also hold up the pole.)	
The pole leans more than 5 degrees.	

1.5 Managing Emergencies

Managing and Communicating Emergencies

1.5.1 A utility/employer must have in place plans, procedures, and training for such emergencies as an electrical system failure, fire, injuries on the job, and the need for rescue from aloft or from a confined space.

Communication can make the difference between life and death during an emergency. Emergency code words should be designated that will open up a radio and that will give a control center the authority to isolate a circuit without question.

First Aid Summary

1.5.2 The purpose of first aid is to preserve life and apply measures to stabilize the effects of an injury. Take first aid and CPR training. Ensure that you know the emergency radio procedures for your utility.

In summary, look for and apply aid for the three B's in the following order of priority:

1. Breathing.

2. Bleeding.

3. Bones.

TABLE 1–11   Falling/Dropping Hazards Specific to Tower Work

Hazards	Barriers
Tower climbing hazards include slippery soles, slippery steel, long reaches to the next handhold, frost, ice, wind, or missing a step bolt. A fall from a tower is usually fatal.	Fatal falls have happened to the best climber on a crew. Training and experience are not the best barriers. Fall protection is the only *physical* barrier available to prevent a fall while climbing. Climb up and down towers with a three-extremity contact on the tower at all times. Do not hold onto the step bolts, but slide the hands on either side of the main member at the corner so that you always have hands on the steel.
Objects falling from a tower and striking a worker below can be lethal.	Ensure that no one is under a tower while work is in progress. Workers involved in running a hand line or tag line should work from a position that is clear of any potential falling material.
Material being sent up strikes the tower or spins uncontrolled on the load line.	Tag lines should be used to maintain control of material being raised or positioned. During tower erection, the load line must not be detached from a member or section until the load is secured.
High winds, snowstorms, and ice- or frost-covered steel increase the risk of falling from a tower.	Unless specific training or barriers have been put in place for the hazard encountered, work aloft should not be started during these conditions.
Tripping or loss of balance occurs while carrying tools or material across a tower.	Fall protection is the only *physical* barrier against falling while walking across a tower bridge.
The jolt from a static electric shock while climbing from an insulated ladder onto steel or when contacting a ground wire while climbing a wood structure can result in inadvertent movements.	Being prepared and making a fast slap with the hand to bond onto the grounded object will reduce the shock and the risk of an inadvertent movement. Fall protection is the only *physical* barrier to prevent inadvertent movement.
Climbing or crawling over an insulator string is an unstable platform for climbing, as well as a potential source for a serious gash from a broken insulator.	Use a ladder, platform, or scaffold to work at or beyond an insulator string. Fall protection is the only *physical* barrier available to prevent a fall from an unstable platform.

Take the following actions as first aid:

1. If no oxygenated blood is getting to the brain, brain cells start to die. Therefore, first check the airway for breathing, apply artificial respiration, or apply cardiopulminary resuscitation (CPR) if you observe no breathing or heartbeat.

2. If the person is breathing, check for bleeding. Apply direct pressure on any bleeding wounds to prevent excessive blood loss.

3. If the person is breathing and not bleeding, check for fractures. Take care and time to prevent movement of broken bones. Unless the broken bone has ruptured a major artery, broken bones do not require speed.

CPR Summary

1.5.3 One result of an electric shock can be that the heart goes into fibrillation. When that happens, the individual heart muscle fibers do not work together and the blood no longer circulates efficiently. Cardiopulmonary resuscitation (CPR) can be used to manually circulate oxygenated blood to the brain until medical aid is available. The summary below is for people who have been trained in CPR.

1. *Check for response.*
   - Does the casualty respond to voice or painful stimulus?
   - If *yes,* check the casualty for other conditions and call for help if necessary.
   - If *no,* shout for help and continue.

2. *Check for breathing.*
   - Open the airway, tilt back the head, and lift the chin. Is the casualty breathing?
   - If *yes,* place the casualty in the "recovery position" and call for help.
   - If *no:*

3. *Give two effective rescue breaths.*
   - Are you alone?
   - If *no,* ask a helper to call an ambulance.
   - If *yes,* carry out resuscitation for 1 minute, then call for an ambulance.

4. *Look for signs of circulation.*
   - Are there signs of circulation?
   - If *yes,* continue rescue breaths: 10 breaths a minute for an adult or 20 breaths a minute for a child. Repeat step 2 after every set of breaths.
   - If *no:*

5. *Start CPR.*
   - For an adult, alternate 15 chest compressions with 2 breaths.
   - For a child or infant, give 5 compressions to 1 breath.
   - Continue CPR until emergency help takes over, the casualty moves or takes a breath, or you are too exhausted to continue.

CPR is intended to artificially pump oxygenated blood to the brain until a defibrillator can be used on the heart. Some utilities/contractors keep an automated external defibrilator (AED) on designated trucks to be used by trained personnel.

Seek Medical Attention for Electric Shock

1.5.4 The extent of damage from electric shock is not always visible. After initial first aid treatment, it is prudent to seek medical attention if any of the following is observed:

1. There is or was any loss of consciousness.
2. There is any burn mark. A burn mark indicates that electric current has entered and exited the body and has done unknown damage to internal tissue and organs.

3. The victim exhibits an irregular heartbeat or there is an irregular heartbeat.

4. The victim experiences persistent pain and/or anxiety about the nature of the injury.

Bucket Rescue

1.5.5 There are four different situations in which some form of rescue involving a bucket truck could be needed.

1. Although rare, there have been occasions when a boom and bucket had to be lowered but the truck engine had broken down and there was no power to the unit. Some units can be lowered using battery power. Rotating and/or lowering a bucket with no power are best left to a mechanic. Even a mechanic has been known to lose control of a boom while trying to bleed off the holding valves. No one should be in the bucket during a no-power lowering of a bucket.

2. Evacuating (self-rescue) from a bucket of a disabled unit can be done by waiting for another bucket or by lowering oneself using a rope and descent device designed for this purpose (Figure 1–25). A good rope and a taut line hitch will also do the job, but may be slower to get prepared. Bucket escape should be practiced from a safe height or with a fall arrest backup on a scheduled basis.

3. If the person aloft becomes incapacitated, the lower controls can be used to bring down the bucket. This should be practiced so that it becomes second nature to lower the bucket to a flat surface or another bucket rest where the casualty can be pulled out.

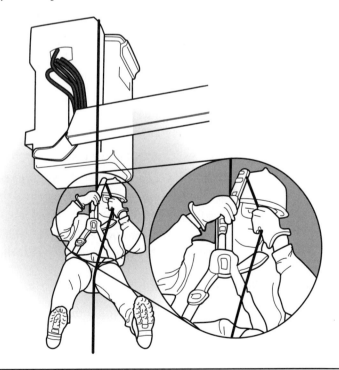

Figure 1–25 Self rescue from a bucket.

4. History has shown that when a victim slumps in a bucket, one strong person is often not enough to pull him or her out. Various devices are used to pull a victim from a bucket. Using the device chosen by the utility/employer requires practice. Some buckets tilt, however, so it is critical to be able to lower it to a position where the tilt function will work. Pulling people out of a bucket using the device chosen by the utility/employer needs a scheduled practice. Even for buckets that allow tilting to remove a casualty needs practice, especially to learn the quickest way to get a bucket to ground level. Devices to remove a casualty from a bucket includes a bracket that can be mounted on the lip of the bucket which has a small hand-cranked winch to pull out the casualty. Rope blocks (done up in a bag) anchored on top of the upper boom where the blocks would be above the casualty when the lower boom is up and the upper boom slants down.

Rescue from Pole Top, Tower Top, or Substation Structure

1.5.6 The primary goal for a rescue from aloft is to lower an injured person to the ground as quickly as is safe to do so and to start first aid or CPR while waiting for medical assistance.

A tower top or substation structure rescue will be very similar to a pole top rescue but with different rigging to lower the victim. In all cases, the rescue procedure involves lowering a casualty as quickly as possible.

Some lessons learned that have evolved into specific rules include the following:

- Some utilities/employers insist that a job briefing include emergency measures, including having a copy of emergency telephone numbers and the type of rescue that personnel should be ready to perform.

- Some utilities/employers require a hand line to be hung anytime a person is working aloft. The rope and hardware must have a 10-to-1 working load factor and undergo scheduled inspections.

- To remove a casualty from an electrical contact quickly, some utilities/employers require a live line cutter to be readily accessible on the pole during any hot work.

- Code words are set up with system control to allow quick isolation of a circuit.

- Some utilities/employers require rescue packs on every aerial lift regardless of whether or not the baskets tilt since they assume it may not always be possible to lower the baskets all the way to the ground.

- Some utilities/employers place a priority on keeping the deck of a bucket truck free of hardware, especially near the lower hydraulic controls.

A Pole Top Rescue Procedure

The pole top rescue procedure that follows is a generic one-person climbing rescue. If an aerial basket or more people are available, the steps needed for the rescue are the same in principle but easier to manage. The number of steps and the details may appear lengthy and a lot to remember in an emergency, but a rescue becomes instinctive with regularly scheduled practice sessions.

TABLE 1–12 A Pole Top Rescue Procedure

Step	Action	Details
1	Call loudly to the injured employee.	At the first indication of a problem, call "Are you OK?" loudly to the worker aloft. If the casualty responds but seems stunned or dazed, a rescue is probably needed, but the timing will not be as critical because the victim is breathing. Conscious victims of an electrical contact will often say they can descend on their own. Try to convince them to at least wait for a pole top rescue rope arrangement as a backup for fall protection.
		If there is no response, timing is critical.
2	Call for help.	At the first indication of the need to perform a rescue, call for help using a prearranged call or code words on the company radio or get help from nearby observers. The utility/employer should have prearranged code words that immediately take priority over all other radio traffic.
3	Evaluate the situation.	If the casualty is still in contact, call for system control or dispatch to drop the circuit, preferably using prearranged code words to avoid a lot of discussion. If that doesn't work, the situation is that the casualty is energized and the pole may be energized. There is a risk to any rescuer who climbs the pole. Unfortunately, it may be obvious from the ground that it is too late for a rescue.
		By climbing with rubber gloves on and taking short steps, a rescuer may be able to get high enough to push the casualty with a hot-line tool, cut the conductor with hot-line cutters, install a ground or toss a rope around the casualty, and pull clear. *Note:* This procedure assumes a worst-case scenario of a one-person climbing rescue. Removing a casualty from a hot line using a bucket truck would certainly be much safer for a rescuer.
		If the casualty is in a precarious position, well within the minimum approach limit, decisions about the need for rubber gloves, a shotgun stick, live line cutter, and/or grounds will be needed to clear the victim. Sometimes sliding an existing hose to cover the contact spot will work.
		If the casualty is clearly not in contact, proceed with the rescue.
4	Plan the rescue.	Prepare to use the rigging that the utility/employer has specified and used during training and practice.
		• If a hand line is to be used, either get it from the truck or use the one already up the pole. (A utility/employer who specifies a hand line would ensure that the hand line design and hardware are suitable and inspected on a regularly scheduled basis.)
		• If a special rescue rope is to be used, it is usually 1/2-inch nylon, double the length of the highest pole climbed. Some have a fork spliced in with a snap at each end that can be snapped into the body belt of the casualty.
		• A sharp knife should (already) be a regular tool in the tool belt.
		• Decide where the hand line/rope will be hung before going aloft. Putting the rope over a crossarm about 1 foot away from the casualty is ideal, however there are many poles without crossarms. When all else fails, a screwdriver may need to be driven into the pole and the rope wrapped around the pole.

(continued)

TABLE 1–12   *Continued*

Step	Action	Details
		• If the casualty is still in contact, or a live circuit complicates the rescue, a decision will be needed as to which tools will have to be carried or pulled up the pole. Choices will be rubber gloves, protective line grounds, hot-line cutter, and shotgun stick. Ideally, you will have dispatch/system control isolate the circuit.
5A	Climb up and belt in below the casualty, if the casualty is in contact or another precarious position.	If the casualty is still in contact, there is a high probability that there are voltage gradients along the pole. Wear rubber gloves, take short steps, and plan to stop below the casualty. Climb up and belt in just below the casualty so that a hot-line tool (cutter) or rubber gloves can be used to move the hot conductor or the casualty.
5B	Climb to the rescue position.	Climb to a position slightly above and to one side of the casualty, keeping in mind that this position may be very close to the hot circuit.
6	Assess the casualty's condition.	If the casualty is breathing and/or conscious, the speed of the rescue is less urgent. Reassure the casualty while preparing to lower him or her to the ground. If a casualty insists that he or she is able to climb down, the rescuer should insist on rigging the pole top rescue rope as a backup.
		If the casualty is not breathing, it is urgent to get oxygenated blood to the brain as soon as possible. The best place to do that is on the ground. Before lowering, some utility/employers specify four quick mouth-to-mouth breaths to fill the lungs; some specify lower only and others specify starting CPR aloft.
7	Rig the rescue rope or hand line.	Different methods are used. It is important to use and practice the method specified by your utility/employer.
		One method: Place the rescue line over an object that will allow an obstruction-free descent (idealy a crossarm) 2 to 3 ft. (5 m) from the pole, and wrap the short end twice around the fall line. Pull the slack from the short end and pass it around the casualty under the arms, then tie it with two half hitches (some specify three). The knot should be in front of the casualty, near one armpit and high on the chest. Take up the slack in the rope, grip firmly, and cut or unsnap the casualty's safety strap (see Figure 1–26).

Figure 1–26   The keilling knot.

1. Pass Line through Both "D" Rings.   2. Then Behind and Twist Lines.   3. Return to Front and Tie Bowline.

Step	Action	Details
		Some use a hand line where the short side rope is used, and they drop the hand line pulley to the ground.
		Some have a hand line that is designed with a snap below the hook, and they split the hand line there. The pulley is left in place and the hook is woven through one of the casualty's dees and hooked into the other dee. The fall line is wrapped anywhere to get friction.
		Warning: When the rope is wrapped twice around an object (crossarm) to get friction, the rope end bearing the casualty's weight must stay under the slack rope used to let the casualty down or the casualty will get hung up.
8	Lower the casualty to the ground.	Take the slack out of the line, then cut the safety strap. Cut the strap on the side opposite the desired swing. Lower the victim, and control the descent with one hand on the rope fall line and the other hand guiding the casualty through any lower obstructions.
		If a lot of obstructions are present, a rescuer may need to follow the casualty down to push and pull around obstructions.
9	Administer first aid and/or CPR.	When the casualty reaches the ground, apply first aid and, if needed, CPR (look, listen and feel, 2 breaths, 15 compressions, check pulse).

Fighting Fire in the Electrical Environment

1.5.7 It is not unusual for a line crew to be called out to a pole or transformer fire. They are also called by fire departments that cut off the power to buildings that are on fire. *Isolating a circuit in or near a fire creates the safest environment for line crews and firefighters.* Safe methods exist for fighting a fire in an electrical environment, but they should be carried out only by trained personnel in an emergency.

Cutting conductors down will change the stress on the pole, so secure the pole as necessary. Check for hot conductors lying on the ground. Water flowing near hot conductors will be conductive and hazardous to anyone walking on the wet ground.

Figure 1–27 shows the three ratings important to a powerline worker when fighting a fire around powerlines. Any extinguisher used in an electrical environment must have a C rating in combination with another rating. The extinguishers normally carried on electrical utility trucks are rated as ABC which can be used for transformer fires, pole fires, or vehicle fires.

A transformer fire is actually a flammable liquid fire with the added hazard of it being in an electrical environment. However, if a transformer is on fire, the transformer is not salvageable. Stay upwind—if the transformer oil is contaminated with PCBs, the smoke has some very dangerous chemicals in it.

A pole fire is a wood fire in an electrical environment. Be aware, however, that any spent dry powder lying on a crossarm or on other hardware can become contaminated and conductive, especially in damp conditions. Wet powder could become a path to ground and cause an explosive arc near any worker trying to put out a fire.

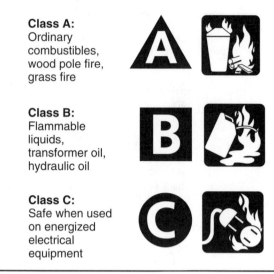

Class A:
Ordinary combustibles, wood pole fire, grass fire

Class B:
Flammable liquids, transformer oil, hydraulic oil

Class C:
Safe when used on energized electrical equipment

Figure 1–27   Types of fire extinguishers.

What Is an Electrical Fire?

The only real electrical fire would be an electric arc, but that is not the type of fire put out with fire-fighting equipment. An electrical fire refers to a fire in an electrical environment. Any extinguisher used in an electrical environment must have a C rating in combination with another rating. Figure 1–27 shows the three ratings important to fighting fires in which a powerline worker may be involved.

For example, a transformer fire is actually a flammable-liquid fire with the added hazard of it being in an electrical environment. A fire extinguisher rated as BC is needed for a flammable-liquid fire in an electrical environment. However, if a transformer is on fire, the transformer is not salvageable. Workers should stay upwind because if the transformer oil is contaminated with polychlorinated biphenyls (PCBs), the smoke has some very dangerous chemicals in it.

A pole fire is a wood fire in an electrical environment and would require an AC extinguisher, or the more common ABC extinguisher. Be aware, however, that any spent dry powder lying on a crossarm or on other hardware can become contaminated and conductive, especially in damp conditions. Wet powder could become a path to ground and cause an explosive arc near any worker trying to put out a fire.

Stay back when using a fire extinguisher. Even a small extinguisher can have pressure equal to a large extinguisher; it only contains less powder.

Water and Electricity

Everyone has been made aware that water and electricity do not mix. However, exposed electrical apparatuses and water do mix every time it rains. When insulators are clean, the rain does not cause the circuits to trip out. It is the combination of water and some kind of contaminant that causes electrical current to flow. Water becomes a conductor when it dissolves salts from contaminants.

When a line crew washes insulators on live circuits, the water does not normally short out the circuit. A high-pressure pump (600 to 850 psi) is used to blast the dirt off the insulators. Instead of a solid stream of water, a special nozzle is used to break up the stream into fine particles. This allows a closer limit of approach for the powerline worker. The nozzle must be grounded for the following reasons:

1. A grounded nozzle drains the static charge that can be generated by the water flowing through the nozzle.

2. A grounded nozzle drains any current flowing from the live circuit through the stream of water to ground.

Firefighters can be trained to use water for fighting fires near powerlines. Some fire crews have been trained to use water with a spray or fog stream on 230 kV from 15 feet away or up to 50 kV from 10 feet away. A solid stream using a 5/8-inch nozzle can be used on circuits up to 230 kV from 30 feet. Before firefighters are trained, the water in their jurisdiction is tested for unusually high salt or mineral content. Live conductors lying on the ground are very dangerous when water is applied to them. Water flowing on the ground is conductive and is a hazard to anyone touching the wet soil. There will, however, be less voltage between the ground gradients when spread over a longer distance.

Electrical System Emergencies

1.5.8 When storms hit and an electrical system goes down, powerline workers go to work.

Some Notes for Powerline Workers

- A major storm with many utility customers out of power is a crisis but not an emergency. Any institution or person that has a life-and-death need for uninterruptible power has the responsibility to have backup generation. Line work must be planned, job briefings carried out, and complete lockout/tagout procedures used for an isolation guarantee.

- Many utilities insist that any outside crews work to the host utility standards. Some utilities provide an orientation and a booklet for outside crews with a brief description of the voltages, the type of system control, the hours of work, fusing requirements, and much more.

- Ideally, the host utility will give an outside crew work that is confined to a circuit or specific geographic area where the work is independent of other crews. Line work requires everyone on a job site to know the same job plan, take part in the same job briefing, use procedures that will not conflict with others, and stay within the confines of one isolation guarantee covered by a lockout/tagout.

- Fatigue, namely lack of sleep, will be an issue. Rest during the delays that frequently occur in the administration of outside crews. Ideally, work will be scheduled to take advantage of all the daylight hours available.

Review Questions

1. Based on the safe work model shown in Figure 1–1, name three elements that have the most direct influence on safe work.

2. Why is it important to report all accidents or near misses?

3. Based on the risk formula, if the probability of tipping over while working from a bucket truck is low, but the consequence could be very high, why is the work considered high-risk?

4. What is the rubber glove rule for your employer?

5. What is the purpose for inflating a rubber glove when doing a pre-use inspection?

6. What is the difference between a job briefing and a job plan?

7. Name three high-risk eye hazards in line work.

8. Name two ways to positively identify a neutral wire.

9. How can an isolated line be proven to be deenergized?

10. What tests are performed before entering a confined space?

11. Name four hazards when working in excavations or trenches.

12. What are two signs that a coworker may be suffering from heat stress?

13. How can a powerline worker help protect the public from making contact with powerlines?

14. How can a powerline worker reduce the risk of a pole falling to the ground while working aloft?

15. Name four safety courses that are a necessity for line work.

CHAPTER 2

Electrical Power System Overview

Topics to Be Covered	Section
Introduction	2.1
Electrical Energy	2.2
Generation of Electrical Energy	2.3
Transmission of Electrical Energy	2.4
Electrical Distribution	2.5

2.1 Introduction

Three Systems within the Power System

2.1.1 This chapter gives an overview of an electrical power system. There are three main systems within an electrical utility power system:

- The *generation system* converts other forms of energy into electrical energy.

- The *transmission system* transmits energy over long distances. It includes the rights-of-way, transmission lines, switching stations, and substations.

- The *distribution system* distributes the energy to industry, commercial customers, farms, and residences. It includes subtransmission lines, distribution substations, distribution feeders, transformers, and services.

2.2 Electrical Energy

Energy

2.2.1 To do any kind of work requires energy. Energy has the ability to produce change or exert a force on something. There are many forms of energy, some of which are chemical, solar, potential, thermal, and electrical. Energy cannot be created or destroyed, but it can be converted from one form to another.

Many forms of energy can be converted to electrical energy. The generation of electricity is a process of converting other energy forms to electrical energy. Electrical energy is utilized when it is converted back to other forms of energy.

Utilization of Electrical Energy

2.2.2 Electrical energy is known as an energy source that is easily converted into power and light. The utilization of electrical energy comes from its four main effects:

- *Thermal effect:* The heat produced by electrical current is desirable for toasters, heaters, and ovens during the utilization stage, but it is wasted energy in the generation, transmission, and distribution stages.

- *Luminous effect:* Light is emitted when a filament is heated or an arc is generated. The design of incandescent, fluorescent, and sodium vapor lights takes advantage of this effect.

- *Chemical effect:* Electrical current can break down certain chemical molecules into their component atoms. For example, water (H_2O) can be broken down into hydrogen and oxygen through a process called *electrolysis*. Electrolysis is used in industry for electroplating and the manufacture of aluminum.

- *Magnetic effect:* The magnetic field around a wire can be increased by winding the wire into a coil around a core of magnetic material. This effect is used by a utility for generators, transformers, and reactors. At the utilization stage, the magnetic effect is used for motors, solenoid switches, circuit breakers, telephones, and stereo speakers.

2.3 Generation of Electrical Energy

Generation Basics

2.3.1 When a wire is moved within a magnetic field, an electrical charge is induced into the wire. Almost all commercially generated electricity involves the movement of wire coils in a magnetic field. In practice, this normally means that many electromagnets are installed on a wheel or armature, which is turned inside a *stator* mounted with many wire coils.

The armature is connected to a turbine (Figure 2–1). The turbine is a wheel with blades mounted on it. The water, steam, or wind pushes against the blades and causes the turbine to turn.

Turning the Turbine

2.3.2 A surprising number of prime movers or sources of energy can be used to spin a turbine. The earliest energy forms used for this purpose were falling water and wind. Almost all of the suitable falling water or *hydraulic* sites in the world have been harnessed, are spinning turbines economically, and are relatively pollution free. Harnessing the tides and winds to spin large turbines for commercial generation is a more recent development.

Most of the electrical energy produced in the world comes from the use of steam as a force to spin the turbines. The steam is converted from the heat energy of burning coal, oil, natural gas, wood chips, and garbage; or steam can come from

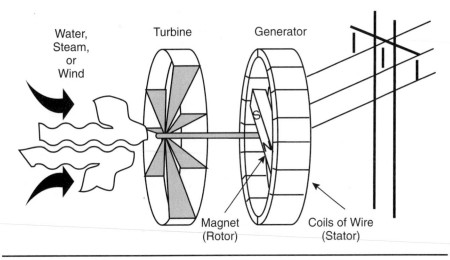

Figure 2–1 Simple generator.

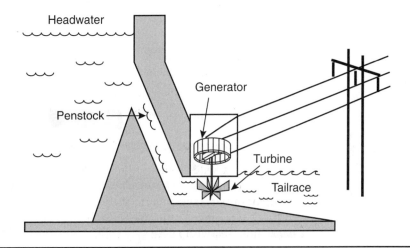

Figure 2–2 Hydraulic generator.

the heat energy generated by a nuclear reactor or from geothermal (underground heat) sources.

Hydraulic Generation

2.3.3 Hydraulic stations are built where advantage can be taken of water at a higher level dropping to a lower level (Figure 2–2). This is normally accomplished by building a dam on a river with a suitable water flow and where a substantial difference in water level is created. The headwater formed by the dam is the potential energy that will be converted to electrical energy.

The headwater is funneled through a pipe called a *penstock*. The water rushes down the penstock and hits the turbine blades with a force that comes from the

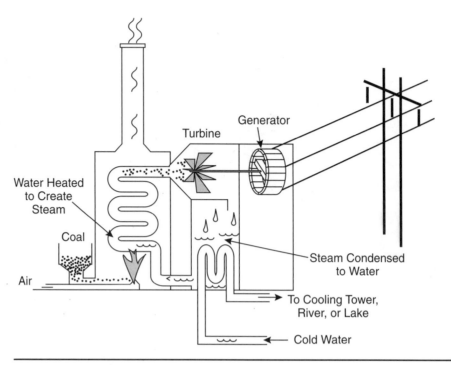

Figure 2–3 Steam turbine.

water's speed and weight. The turbine spins, which in turn spins the generator. The water continues out through the tailrace and back into the river.

Generation from Steam

2.3.4 Generating heat from the burning of fossil fuels such as coal, oil, and natural gas, or from a nuclear reactor, is the most common commercial method of creating steam. The steam expands and pushes against the turbine blades, causing the turbine to turn.

Like a hot-water heating system in a house, the water in a steam plant is in a closed loop that is heated and cooled again and again (Figure 2–3). A heat exchanger in the boiler heats the water in the closed loop, and another heat exchanger uses water from an ocean, lake, or river to cool the steam and condense it back into water. The water is then pumped back to the boiler to be reheated.

Nuclear Generation

2.3.5 A nuclear generating station is similar to a conventional steam plant except it uses a nuclear reactor to create heat for making steam. The heat comes from uranium atoms splitting in a controlled reaction.

Uranium is a dense, unstable element. Neutrons, which are particles within the nucleus of an atom, are easily knocked free from a uranium atom nucleus. A uranium atom splits if it is struck by a free neutron given up by another atom. When an atom splits, more neutrons are released that in turn hit other atoms, splitting them, and thereby causing a chain reaction. A nuclear *fission* (splitting) of atoms generates a huge amount of heat.

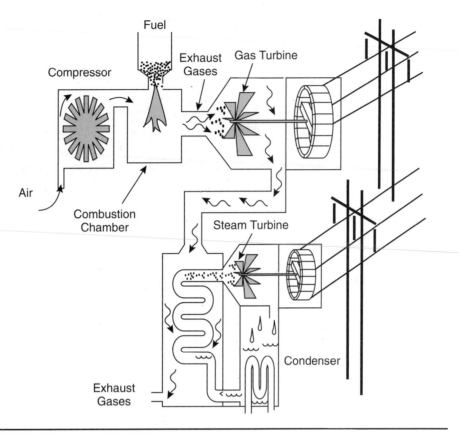

Figure 2–4 Combined-cycle generation.

Gas Turbines

2.3.6 The hot exhaust gases from the burning of oil or natural gas in a high-pressure combustion chamber can spin a turbine when the exhaust gases expand through the turbine blades, much like the way a jet engine operates. High-pressure air is added to the combustion chamber to add more force to the escaping gases.

The most efficient way to use the gas turbine is in a *combined-cycle* system (Figure 2–4). After the hot exhaust gases spin a gas turbine, the still hot gases heat water to make steam and spin a steam turbine. Usually, several gas turbines feed hot exhaust to one steam turbine.

Cogeneration

2.3.7 Cogeneration plants are generating stations used to generate electric power and heat. The electric power can be sold to the grid, and the heat, which would otherwise be waste heat, is sold to a central heating plant or manufacturer. Because it is impractical to transport heat over any distance, cogeneration stations are built close to their heat users.

Cogeneration stations (Figure 2–5) are fired by fuels such as natural gas, wood, agricultural waste, or peat moss. Steam pressure generated by burning the fuel turns the turbines and generates power. Normally, about one-third of the energy

Figure 2–5 Cogeneration plant.

in the original fuel can be converted to steam pressure to generate electricity. The excess heat supplied to the customer is usually in the form of relatively low-temperature steam exhausted from the turbines.

Alternative Electrical Energy Sources

2.3.8 A small percentage of the total electrical supply is generated from alternative sources. Some of these alternative sources provide the most economical way to supply electrical energy to remote locations where it is not practical to build a line to the customer.

- Some commercial generation stations use the *ocean tides* to spin turbines. These are hydraulic stations that take advantage of unusual high tides in some locations in the world. For example, the high tides in the Bay of Fundy in New Brunswick, Canada, are used to generate power.

- In some locations, especially in California, hundreds of *windmills* (wind turbines) form large-scale "wind farms." Wind energy varies with the cube of the wind speed: When the wind speed doubles, eight times more energy is generated.

- *Geothermal* generating stations generate steam from the heat below the surface of the earth.

- *Engines* (diesel, gasoline, gas) are used to run generators in remote communities and as standby units.

- *Solar energy* is responsible for many alternative energy sources. Solar energy is more than just sunlight. It is the heat from the sun that indirectly gives us the winds to drive a wind turbine and the rain that gives us the water to turn the hydraulic turbines. A *photovoltaic cell* (solar cell) can generate electricity directly from sunlight without the need for turbines. When sunlight strikes a photovoltaic cell made from material such as silicon, electrons are dislodged and caused to move. Free electrons collect on one surface of the cell, causing an imbalance between the front and back surfaces. An electron flow (electrical current) is produced when the front and back of the cell are put into a circuit.

Figure 2–6 Transmission line corridor.

- The burning of *biomass* can produce steam to spin steam turbines. Products such as sawdust and bark from the lumber industry, wood from fast-growing tree plantations, ethanol from corn, or methane from the decomposition of vegetation and garbage are burned in relatively small generating stations in many areas.

- *Fuel cells* generate electricity through an electrochemical process. The system converts the chemical energy of hydrogen or hydrocarbons and oxygen into electrical energy. In a fuel cell, hydrogen and oxygen are combined to form water and electricity (the opposite of the old experiment in which hydrogen and oxygen are produced when electricity is passed through water). The hydrogen needed for a fuel cell can be found in natural gas, coal-derived gas, ethanol, gasoline, and other fuels.

2.4 Transmission of Electrical Energy

Transmission of Electricity

2.4.1 Electrical energy can be transported economically over long distances. Electricity is transmitted from the generating station to the customer load centers on high-voltage transmission lines. A transmission line can be compared to a water pipe: The higher the pressure and the larger the pipe, the more water will flow through the pipe. Similarly, the higher the voltage and the bigger the wire, the more electrical energy will be able to flow through the transmission line.

Typical Transmission Line Construction

2.4.2 The vast majority of transmission lines are overhead because underground lines are prohibitively expensive for long-distance transmission. Overhead conductors are suspended on structures such as lattice steel towers (Figure 2–6), wood poles, concrete poles, or steel poles. The purpose of a structure is to keep high-voltage conductors insulated from ground in all kinds of weather and out of reach of accidental contact. Tall structures allow long spans and, therefore, fewer structures.

The insulator length or size is dependent on the voltage: The higher the voltage, the longer the string of insulators. Conductors are usually stranded aluminum with a steel core. Aluminum is a good conductor of electricity, and the steel core gives the conductor tensile strength. A strong, lightweight conductor can be strung with less sag over long spans.

Transmission Line Voltage

2.4.3 Commercial stations generate power at a voltage ranging from 13,800 volts to 24,000 volts. A step-up transformer station next to a generation station boosts the voltage (pressure) so that it can be transmitted efficiently. Generation voltages are boosted up to common transmission line voltages such as 115,000 volts; 230,000 volts; 345,000 volts; 500,000 volts; and 765,000 volts. The high voltages are normally expressed in kilovolts (kV) so that a 500,000-volt line becomes a 500-kilovolt line. As a rule of thumb, if the voltage is doubled, the energy that can be transmitted is quadrupled without an increase in line losses.

Extra high voltage (EHV) lines, such as 500-kilovolt circuits, use bundled conductors, which are two, three, or four conductors tied together with spacer dampers. Conductors are bundled to counter certain problems caused by extra high voltage; however, the increased conductor capacity plus the high voltage allows a single 500-kilovolt circuit to carry the equivalent of eight 230-kilovolt circuits.

Transmission System Substations

2.4.4 The terminals of transmission lines are at substations and switchyards. Substations (Figure 2–7) are voltage-changing stations. Transformers can step up the voltage to allow for the efficient high-voltage transmission of power or can step down the voltage to allow for a more manageable voltage to distribute the power down roadways and streets.

Figure 2–8 shows a typical layout of a small transmission substation. Note that the layout is designed so that the station can continue to feed out on each subtransmission line when any one component is out of service.

Switchyards

2.4.5 Switchyards are found at the terminals of transmission lines. A switchyard has disconnect switches, circuit breakers, relays, and communications systems to provide circuit protection. Switchyards allow the routing of power through various circuits to ensure that customers continue to receive service even when some parts of a power system fail.

A switchyard ties the many circuits coming into the yard to a common circuit called a *bus*. The term *bus* comes from the word *omnibus,* which means a collection of numerous objects or, in this case, a collection of numerous circuits. A bus must be able to carry very high current and, therefore, usually consists of large, rigid aluminum or copper pipe or very large conductors. Switchyards are usually within the same fenced area as the transformer and form part of the substation.

Figure 2–7 Transmission substation.

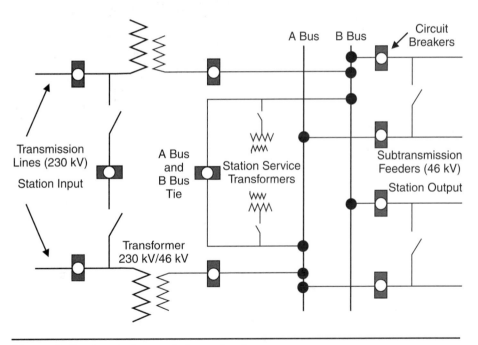

Figure 2–8 A typical transmission station layout.

Communications between Stations

2.4.6 Operators in a control room monitor meters and alarms that indicate the condition of the substations and lines within their zone of control. An operator can open and close switchgear in remote generating stations and substations. This "supervisory control" of the system depends on communications systems between stations.

Figure 2–9 Wave trap.

To transmit information and signals from station to station, utilities use telephone lines, utility-owned fiber-optic cable, powerline carrier systems, microwave systems, or satellites. Because continuous communication is critical, usually more than one system is in place in case one of the systems fails.

Telephone lines are a common link between stations. The use of fiber-optic cable strung in the shield-wire position on transmission lines is becoming a popular mode of communication.

A powerline carrier system uses the powerline conductors to transmit information. The communication signals are sent on to and received from the power conductors by a device that looks like a potential transformer but is a coupling capacitive voltage transformer (CCVT). To keep the transmitted signals within the desired sections of the powerline, wave traps (Figure 2–9) are installed. The wave trap, which looks like a large cylindrical coil, stops the signals from continuing farther down the line.

Microwave communication between substations requires towers (Figure 2–10) with microwave antennas in each station. Microwave-sending and -receiving

Figure 2–10 Microwave tower in substation.

antennas need a direct line of sight with no obstacles between them. Microwave towers are located on hills, where possible, and are about 60 to 100 kilometers (35 to 60 miles) apart to relay the signals between towers.

Electrical Power Pools

2.4.7 Generating stations are interconnected by transmission lines into giant regional pools or grids that cross utility boundaries. The flow of electric power in these grids goes where it is needed. The flow could go south during a heat wave to feed peak air-conditioning loads or north during a cold snap to feed the peak heating loads.

Metering at line terminals or substations determines the amount of energy that crosses utility boundaries and what payment needs to be exchanged. Sometimes a utility's transmission line only transfers or *wheels* power from one neighboring utility to another. The utility receives payment for supplying this wheeling service.

Blackouts and Brownouts

2.4.8 There was a huge *blackout* in the central and northeastern United States and Canada on August 14, 2003. The failure in one element of the power pool started a chain reaction that led to a loss of most of the transmission grid. A fault on one transmission line caused another transmission line to overload and fail, which caused the generation that fed the line to be isolated from the grid, which overloaded neighboring lines and generation. Protection schemes are in place to isolate failures to the offending location. However, these protection schemes can be overwhelmed and fail.

Along with improved protection schemes, utilities have procedures that intentionally lower the voltage on or shed load from the system when the customer demand is greater than the system can supply.

When customer demand on the power pool is higher than available generation or transmission lines can provide, shedding or dropping load is a last resort. Before any load is shed, the voltage is lowered on the grid, which reduces the total energy supplied to the customers. Customers may notice that their lights become a little dimmer and their motors run hotter. About twice a year some utilities conduct tests by reducing the voltage on the system. These *brownouts* are generally only noticed by customers who are already receiving below-normal voltage in ordinary times.

After intentionally reducing the voltage on the system, and if there is still not enough to meet customer demand, some large industries have their loads dropped from the system first. These industries have a contract with the utility that allows the dropping of their loads in exchange for better rates.

In the unusually cold winter of 1993–1994, there was difficulty meeting the demand in Washington, D.C. Instead of implementing rotating blackouts, demand was reduced by closing federal buildings on the coldest days.

When all else fails, electrical load is shed on a rotational basis to the general population for a preset time. The deliberate dropping of load on a rotational basis results in *rolling blackouts* to specific geographical areas for specified periods of time, usually 30 or 60 minutes.

2.5 Electrical Distribution

Distribution Basics

2.5.1 The *transmission system* brings electrical energy close to the load center and transforms the voltage down to a subtransmission voltage or directly to a distribution voltage.

The *distribution system* (Figure 2–11 and Table 2–1) consists of subtransmission lines feeding distribution substations, which transform the voltage down to distribution feeder voltage. Distribution feeders deliver the energy to a transformer at the customer's premises and transform the voltage to a utilization level. By far, the biggest volume of line work involves the distribution system.

Distribution System Designs

2.5.2 A distribution system can be laid out to give varying degrees of service continuity. A system with a high degree of service continuity is more expensive and is found where the customer density is high, namely, in cities.

Radial System

2.5.3 The layout of a radial system (Figure 2–12) is much like the design of a tree. The main trunk is one of the three-phase feeders going out from a substation.

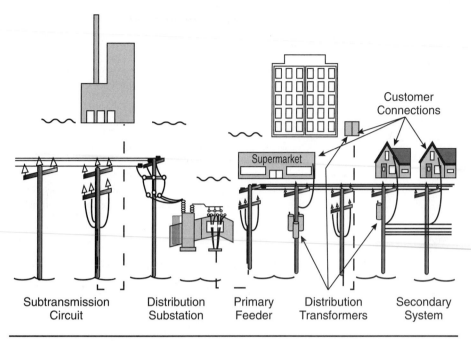

Figure 2–11 A distribution system.

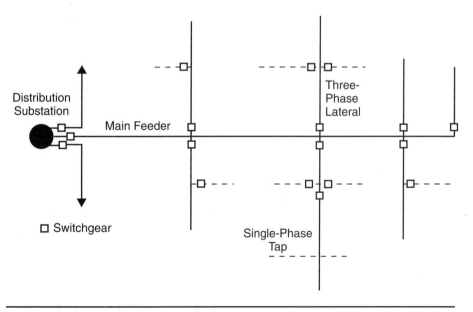

Figure 2–12 Radial feeders.

TABLE 2–1   **Six Main Segments of a Distribution System**

Segment	Function
Subtransmission Circuits	Subtransmission circuits transmit power from the large transmission substations to the distribution substations. Examples of subtransmission voltages are 13.8 kV, 27.6 kV, 34.5 kV, 46 kV, and 69 kV. At these voltages, the structures and insulation are small enough to allow building lines along roadways. Some utilities may consider subtransmission lines to be part of the transmission system.
Distribution Substation	The transformer in the distribution substation steps down the subtransmission voltage to a distribution voltage. The substation consists of: • Switchgear on the subtransmission circuit • A transformer • Voltage regulation equipment • A distribution voltage bus • Multiple feeders connected to the bus • Distribution voltage switchgear for each feeder Many distribution substations are operated remotely from a central control room. The central control room has access to substation data such as feeder voltage and loading and has the ability to operate the substation switchgear. Supervisory Control and Data Acquisition (SCADA) is the communications technology used to operate a distribution substation remotely.
Primary Feeders	The primary (low-voltage) feeders leaving the station can be underground or overhead and are normally three-phase. A distribution feeder can be a radial feeder that branches off and ends at the end of a street or road. A distribution feeder can also be networked into a grid with other feeders allowing it to be fed from two directions. The loop between feeders can have a normally open switch keeping them separate or can be looped with automatic switchgear.
Distribution Transformer	The distribution transformer feeding the customer steps down the primary feeder voltage to a utilization voltage. Depending on the type of distribution system, the transformer can be overhead, on a concrete pad, or below grade in a vault.
Secondary Systems	A secondary system can range from a single service fed from one transformer to a secondary bus network fed from many transformers.
Customer Connections	The service to the customer can come directly from the transformer or from a secondary bus. The service can be overhead or underground. The responsibility for the utility service usually ends at the electric revenue meter.

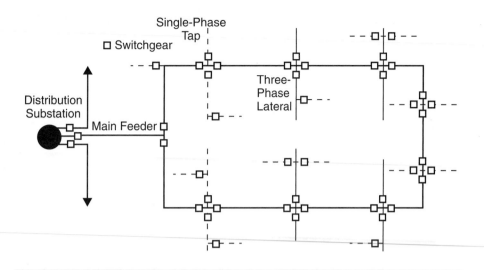

Figure 2–13 Loop primary.

Three-phase or single-phase branches or lateral taps feed customers along the circuit. The conductor in the main trunk carries the most load, and the branches get smaller as they feed out from the trunk. The length of a feeder is usually limited by the voltage and connected load.

Loop Primary

2.5.4 A typical loop circuit (Figure 2–13) starts at the distribution substation, makes a loop through the area to be served, and ends by returning to the substation. It is similar to two radial circuits with their ends tied together. A loop primary keeps most customers' power on automatically when a fault occurs on the line.

Circuit breakers are installed in the loop so that sections of the loop can be automatically isolated with the opening of any two breakers. Relays sense an overload situation and cause circuit breakers to open on each side of the fault.

Lateral taps from the loop are usually radial. An underground tap is usually in a loop, but an open switch within the loop keeps the two sides fed radially.

Primary Network

2.5.5 A primary network (Figure 2–14) is used for heavily loaded downtown areas in a city. It is similar to a loop primary except that the loop is fed from more than one substation and from more than one feeder from each substation.

Overhead and Underground Systems

2.5.6 A distribution system is either overhead, underground, or a combination of both. Urban centers tend to have underground systems, and rural areas tend to have overhead systems.

The advantages of an overhead system are these:

- Lower costs for conductor and associated switchgear and transformers
- Easier and quicker detection and repair of a breakdown within the system

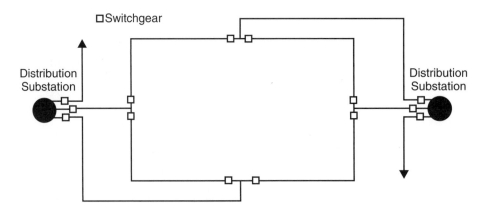

Figure 2–14 Primary network.

- Much lower cost to upgrade an existing overhead system because of less need to dig up finished streets, curbs, and lawns

The advantages of an underground power system are these:

- Almost no exposure to storms, trees, automobile accidents, insulator breakage, and insulator contamination
- More aesthetically acceptable to the public
- A necessity around airports, or where local laws require cable
- Long runs across water as submarine cable
- Less public exposure to the possibility of electric shock
- Generally, a longer system life expectancy

Two Types of Underground Systems

2.5.7 Generally, there are two types of underground systems: the duct and maintenance hole (manhole) system and the direct-bury system. The duct and maintenance hole system is used in cities where the presence of concrete and pavement would require very expensive digging for maintenance or upgrading. The cables are in concrete ducts, and equipment such as transformers and switching units is below the surface in maintenance holes.

The direct-bury system is used mostly in residential subdivisions where most of the cable is buried under grass. The cable must have an envelope of sand around it to prevent any pressure points on the cable because pressure points are often sources of cable failure. Ducts suitable for direct burial are also used to provide mechanical protection for the cable (e.g., at road crossings). The transformers and switchgear often have a "pad-mount design" and sit on the surface on a concrete pad.

TABLE 2–2   **Skilled Workers in a Distribution System**

People	Work
Design Engineers and Technicians	Set the design standards for structures, equipment poles, etc., considering their strength, electrical clearances, radio interference, lightning protection, and insulation.
Planning Engineers and Technicians	Monitor the system voltage and load. Decide on funding priorities for betterments. Carry out studies for fuse coordination, voltage regulation, voltage flicker, and load growth.
Customer Service Staff	Depending on the individual utility organization, customer service staff is the front-line customer contact regarding the following: • High bills • Meter reading • Conservation information • New service and service upgrade requirements • Collections for nonpayment of bills
Line Crews	Construct, maintain, and troubleshoot the overhead and underground distribution system. Numerous individual tasks could be listed here.
Forestry or Tree Crews	Responsible for keeping the lines clear of vegetation by trimming trees that are in close proximity to live circuits while keeping customers relatively happy with the quality of their work.

Managing a Distribution System

2.5.8 Most line work is in the distribution system. A variety of skilled people are needed to keep a distribution system functioning, as shown in Table 2–2.

Review Questions

1. The utilization of electrical energy comes from its four main effects. What are three of the four effects electrical energy can produce?

2. What physical act is required to generate power in almost all commercial generators?

3. What are three common energy sources used to drive a turbine?

4. What is the advantage of a cogeneration power plant?

5. Name four alternative electrical energy sources.

6. If the voltage on a transmission line could be doubled, how much more energy would it be able to transmit?

7. What is the purpose of communications systems between substations?

8. Name the six main segments that make up a distribution system.

9. Name three advantages of an overhead distribution system versus an underground system.

10. Name three advantages of an underground distribution system versus an overhead system.

CHAPTER 3

Electrical Units

Topics to Be Covered

Topics to Be Covered	Section
Introduction	3.1
Electrical Potential	3.2
Electrical Current	3.3
Electrical Resistance	3.4
Electrical Power	3.5

3.1 Introduction

What Is Electricity?

3.1.1 All materials are made up of atoms. Each atom has a nucleus, and each nucleus has electrons in orbit around it in the same way as the planets orbit the sun. The positive charge of the nucleus and the negative charge of the electrons keep the electrons in orbit and keep the electrical charge of the atom neutral.

The electrons of good conducting material, such as copper or aluminum, are dislodged fairly easily. With an external force, the electrons can be bumped from their own orbits into the orbits of adjacent atoms. An atom that loses an electron will then have a net positive charge and will be susceptible to gaining another electron. The atom that gains an electron will then have a net negative charge and will be susceptible to losing an electron. A charged atom has potential and is called an *ion*.

The transferring of electrons from one atom to the next is *electrical current*. In other words, electrical current is the flow of electrons.

Summary of Electrical Units

3.1.2 *Electricity* is a current or flow of electrons. Electrical current will only flow in a circle (circuit) and must always return to its source. The *ampere* is the unit used to measure the rate of flow.

Electrical current must have a pressure pushing it. Pressure, an electron moving force, which is also called an *electromotive force* (emf), is measured in *volts*. Pressure is needed to overcome any resistance, which impedes the current flow in a circuit. Resistance or impedance is measured in *ohms*.

A combination of electromotive force (volts) and current (amperes) is a measure of the rate of work being done. The unit of work is a *watt* (1 volt × 1 ampere), which is more commonly measured in blocks of 1,000 watts or kilowatts.

When the rate of work is at 1 kilowatt and it lasts 1 hour, 1 *kilowatt-hour* of work is completed. The quantity of electricity used is measured in kilowatt-hours.

3.2 Electrical Potential

Voltage Basics

3.2.1 To introduce electrical concepts, reference is often made to the properties of a water system. For example, water flows in a garden hose when some force or pressure is pushing the water from a high-pressure area to a low-pressure area. Electricity also needs a pressure or a potential difference to have a current flow. Water pressure comes from a water pump, and electrical pressure comes from an *electrical generator.*

Electrical potential is measured in *volts*. The symbol for electrical potential is E (from electromotive force) or V (from volts).

Measuring Voltage

3.2.2 To measure the amount of *potential* or voltage that is available in a circuit, a *voltmeter* is used. In the lines trade, voltage checks are frequently made because an improper voltage is the first indication that something is wrong. To measure voltage, the voltmeter leads must be connected across (parallel) two different potentials. Most voltmeters are rated up to 750 volts. Measurement of higher voltages is done at substations using *voltage transformers* (VT) to bring a representative voltage into the control room.

A powerline worker has no real reason to measure higher voltages but does need to check whether a circuit is hot by testing for voltage. A *potential tester* is used to determine if the circuit is alive or dead. A *potential test* is an essential step before placing protective working grounds on a circuit.

Safety with Electrical Potential

3.2.3 Where there is a difference in potential, receiving an electrical shock is also a possibility. Any electrical potential is always looking for a path to a different potential.

If a person puts one hand on each post of a car battery, he or she normally would not feel anything because the potential is only 12 volts, which is not high enough to overcome the resistance of a person's skin. Most people can feel 40 volts from hand to hand. A common voltage, such as 120 volts, is a high enough potential to drive a fatal current through a person's body.

Powerline workers are exposed to much higher voltages. Safe contact can only be made with a high-voltage circuit when the resistance between the circuit and a person is high enough to prevent a current flow. Such resistance is provided by live-line tools or rubber gloves.

TABLE 3–1 **Voltage Standard**

Nominal Voltage	Extreme Low Voltage	Normal Low Voltage	Normal High Voltage	Extreme High Voltage
		Single Phase		
120/240	106/212	110/220	125/250	127/254
240	212	220	250	250
		Three-Phase Four-Wire		
120/208Y	110/190	112/194	125/216	126/220
277/480Y	240/418	258/446	288/500	293/508
347/600Y	306/530	318/550	360/625	367/635
		Three-Phase Three-Wire		
240	212	220	250	254
600	530	550	625	635

Maintaining Good Voltage

3.2.4 Voltage in a circuit is susceptible to many influences that cause it to sag or surge. The quality of electrical service requires that a customer's voltage be kept within an acceptable range. Voltage that is too high or too low will damage a customer's motors, appliances, and electronic equipment.

The American National Standards Institute (ANSI) standard for proper voltage is a range of +6 percent to −13 percent. Table 3–1 shows a typical voltage standard for a North American utility. When a voltage is found to be lower or higher than extreme voltage, power should be shut off to avoid damaging customer equipment.

Voltage Drop

3.2.5 When a circuit has no load on it, no current is passing through it, and there is no significant drop in the circuit. When a load is added to the circuit, some of the voltage is "used up" in pushing the current through the resistance.

A voltage drop is equal to $I \times R$, where

$$I = current$$

$$R = resistance$$

Typical Utility Voltages

3.2.6 A large variety of standard voltages is used in the electrical utility business. A person working on distribution needs to be alert when choosing transformers, surge arrestors, switches, and insulators.

Powerline workers can differentiate between familiar voltages within a utility by referring to *utility operating diagrams*. When the voltage of a circuit is in doubt, reference can always be made to a nameplate on an existing transformer. Insulators and cutouts are not reliable indicators of the system voltage because of standardization of materials and prebuilding for future voltage conversions.

When a circuit voltage is given, it is normally the "nominal" phase-to-phase voltage. Common North American voltages shown in Table 3–2 are phase-to-phase voltages. Where applicable, a phase-to-ground voltage follows the slash.

TABLE 3–2   **Typical Utility Voltages**

Transmission Line Voltages (kV)	Subtransmission Line Voltages (kV)	Distribution Voltages (kV)	Utilization Voltages (V)
765	13.8	34.5/20	240/120
500	23	27.6/16	208/120
345	27.6	25/14.4	416/240
230	34.5	13.8/8	480/240
138	46	12.5/7.2	480/277
115	69	8.3/4.8	600/347
69		4.16/2.4	

Note that distribution voltage equipment is also commonly called medium voltage equipment, and utilization voltage equipment under 1,000 volts is commonly called low-voltage equipment.

3.3 Electrical Current

Current Basics

3.3.1 The flow of electrical current, as noted previously, can be compared with the flow of water in a garden hose. A garden hose conducts water while a wire or conductor conducts the flow of electrical current. Just like a large pipe can conduct more water than a small pipe, a large-diameter electrical wire can conduct more electrical current. It is the flow of current that does the work. For example, when electrical current meets resistance, heat is produced.

Electrical current is actually the flow of electrons jumping from one atom to the next. While electricity is known to travel at the speed of light, which is 186,000 miles per second (300,000 kilometers per second), the electrons themselves do not actually travel at that speed. The actual speed of electron travel in a conductor is about 0.003 millimeters per second. It is the electrical charge or voltage that travels at the speed of light.

The symbol for electrical current is I, from the French word *intensité*. The unit of measure is the *ampere*, which is represented by the symbol A.

Measuring Current

3.3.2 Current is measured with an *ammeter*. An ammeter is usually described as a meter that is connected in series with a circuit and measures the current flowing through it. This means that the circuit must be opened and reconnected to go through the meter so that current can be measured. To measure current with a *multimeter*, such as the one shown in Figure 3–1, requires that the circuit be opened. This type of meter may be suitable for electronic work but not for line work. Currents measured by powerline workers are very high, and the typical type of ammeter used is a clip-on meter, like the one shown in Figure 3–2. This type of ammeter should be used because it is convenient and can measure the current without having to connect the meter in series with the conductor. The magnetic field around the wire induces a representative current into the clip-on ammeter

Figure 3–1 Multimeter.

Figure 3–2 Clip-on meter.

coil. A clip-on ammeter is not voltage sensitive and can be used on all voltages as long as a line worker uses the meter while wearing rubber gloves or using a live-line tool suitable for the voltage of the circuit.

Electrical Current Needs a Circuit

3.3.3 Electrical current will not flow unless it is in a circuit. The current that leaves the source must make a complete "circle" and return to the source. An electrical circuit, therefore, needs a return path to the source. Depending on the type of circuit, the return path can be a ground, a neutral, or another "hot" wire. A break anywhere in the circuit, including in the return path, opens the circuit and the current flow stops.

Opening a ground wire or a neutral on a live circuit is dangerous because an electrical current could be interrupted. When a current is interrupted, a voltage will appear across the open point in the circuit.

Safety with Electrical Current

3.3.4 It takes a certain amount of voltage to break down the initial skin resistance of a human body before a current path is established. Once a current path is established, it is the amount of current and the path the current takes through the body that does the damage.

In Figure 3–3, it can be seen that 100 milliamperes (mA) can cause damage to a human body. Considering that a typical household circuit is fused at 15 amperes or 15,000 milliamperes, the potential for a lethal electrical shock is available on all electrical circuits.

Note that a ground fault interrupter (GFI) on a utilization circuit will open a circuit before any dangerous current can flow. A device as sensitive as a GFI is not available on utility circuits.

Load Current

3.3.5 Load current in a circuit is the current needed to supply the load demands of the customer. When an ammeter is used to take a reading on a circuit, the reading measures the load current at that moment, along with a small amount of current due to line loss.

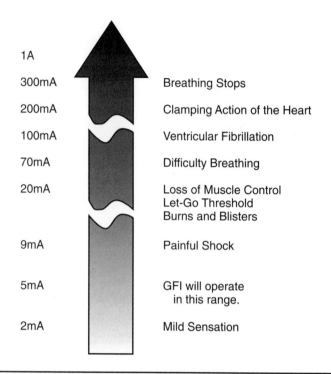

1A	
300mA	Breathing Stops
200mA	Clamping Action of the Heart
100mA	Ventricular Fibrillation
70mA	Difficulty Breathing
20mA	Loss of Muscle Control Let-Go Threshold Burns and Blisters
9mA	Painful Shock
5mA	GFI will operate in this range.
2mA	Mild Sensation

Figure 3–3 Typical effects of electrical current on the human body.

Voltage is *supplied* by an electrical utility, and load current is *drawn* by the customer. A utility can control the voltage, but it cannot control the load current because load current is based on customer demand.

Peak Load Current

3.3.6 The load current in a system fluctuates with the seasons and the time of day. Peak load current is measured by recording ammeters found at substations and portable recording ammeters installed on lines. Peak demand for power tends to occur on the coldest and hottest days of the year at the time of the evening meal.

An electrical system must be built to meet these peak demands even though they may occur infrequently. More trouble calls occur during peak load conditions because any weakness—such as an overloaded transformer, an overloaded circuit, or a low voltage—will appear then.

Utility conservation programs try to reduce peak loads by offering reduced rates during off-peak hours, by installing demand meters that penalize customers with high peak loads, or by encouraging the efficient use of electricity to bring down the total base demand.

Cold Load Pickup

3.3.7 When trying to restore power, especially during peak load periods, a fuse or breaker will sometimes trip out even though the cause of the original outage has been fixed. It is difficult to pick up a cold load after a circuit has been out of service due to the loss of diversity and the initial inrush of current into the circuit.

Diversity in a circuit refers to the normal situation in which everyone on the circuit is not using the furnace, air conditioner, appliance, or water pump at the same time. After a circuit has been out of service for awhile, much of this equipment could be set to come on at the same time when power is restored. The load current on the circuit could be as much as two times the diversified load current. An outage of 30 minutes may be enough to lose load diversity, and it could take as much as 45 minutes to restore the circuit to normal diversity.

There is a short period of high inrush current to load such as transformers, motors, and heaters. The initial inrush current is considerably higher than the current needed to maintain these loads.

Educating customers to switch off much of their electrical load when the power goes off can go a long way to solving the cold load pickup problem. After power is restored, customers could switch their appliances back on one at a time. Meanwhile, without customer help in reducing load, a trouble crew has to rely on a time-consuming process of sectionalizing the circuit to pick up the load in smaller chunks.

Fault Current (Short-Circuit Current)

3.3.8 When a circuit is faulted or short-circuited, all the current which the electrical system is able to supply to the faulted location goes to that fault. Fault current can be explained by using an automotive electrical system as an example. The normal usage of the starter and lights would draw load current equivalent to what a battery is designed to deliver. However, if a wrench were dropped across the battery terminals, an explosive fault current would go from one terminal to the other. All the current available in the battery would feed the fault.

Similarly, in an electrical system, a fault current due to a short circuit can be extremely high. The resultant flash and heat generated by the fault current can be very dangerous to a worker in the vicinity. Eyes are the most vulnerable to a large flash, and safety glasses should be worn any time there is a potential for a flash.

The highest fault current is near the source of a circuit, such as close to a substation or secondary conductors close to a distribution transformer. Using the car electrical system as an example again, a short circuit at the battery is much more explosive than a short circuit at a taillight. The electrical system cannot supply nearly as much power to a fault at a taillight because the small wire and the distance to the taillight add resistance, preventing a large current flow.

3.4 Electrical Resistance

Resistance Basics

3.4.1 Just as a garden hose provides resistance to the water flowing in it, an electrical wire also provides resistance to the flow of electrical current. *Resistance* in a conductor causes electrical energy to be converted into heat. This will be useful or wasteful, depending on whether the heat is a desired product or a line loss.

Some of the current intended to run a motor or light a building is converted to heat because there is resistance in every part of an electrical circuit. Resistance can also be added to a circuit intentionally, such as when a heating element is used in an electric range.

The symbol for electrical resistance is *R.* The unit of measure is *ohms,* which is represented by the Greek letter Ω (omega). A circuit has a resistance of 1 ohm if 1 volt causes a current of 1 ampere to flow.

Measuring Resistance with an Ohmmeter

3.4.2 Resistance is measured with an *ohmmeter,* which is normally found as one function of a multimeter. The ohmmeter is not normally used in the lines trade, even though it could be used to check continuity at a meter base or to check for a dead short or open circuit at a customer location. The ohmmeter feature of the multimeter shown in Figure 3–1 is not suitable for line work. Sooner or later the leads will be put into a live meter base or other location while the dial is set on the ohmmeter function and it will destroy the ohmmeter/multimeter, as well as expose the operator to a serious flash. *Insulation testers* are like ohmmeters and are more suitable for line work.

When an ohmmeter is hooked to two different wires and the meter reads "0," there is no resistance between the two wires being measured and they must be connected together or shorted somewhere. When an ohmmeter reads "∞" (infinity), the resistance is high and the two wires being measured can be considered insulated from one another.

Measuring Earth or Insulation Resistance

3.4.3 *Earth resistance testers* or *insulation resistance testers* are like ohmmeters except that they put out a higher voltage than a regular ohmmeter. A higher output voltage is needed to test the relatively higher resistance of earth or the very high resistance of an insulator or cable insulation. These testers are commonly called *meggers* (which is easier to say than "megaohmmeter"). Earth resistance testers can have various scales, such as 0–1 ohm, 0–300 ohms, or 1–1,000 ohms. It is important to have a low-resistance grounding network at station sites, transformer locations, and customer premises. Ground rods are driven until the earth resistance tester verifies that the grounding network meets specifications. An ideal grounding network at a transformer should read 15 ohms or less before connecting it to the neutral. Most utilities want a minimum of 25 ohms and require that more grounds be driven and connected together until that value is reached.

Insulation resistance testers can have scales that read megaohms and infinity. For example, when a 500-volt insulation tester is used at a meter base to check between two wires or between a wire and ground, a person would know that there is no short or partial breakdown when the insulation tester reads infinity.

Ohm's Law

3.4.4 The relationship between volts, amperes, and ohms is expressed in an equation known as Ohm's law (Figure 3–4). The current flowing in a circuit is equal to the circuit voltage divided by the resistance. This is the most used electrical theory formula for the lines trade. The equation is generally shown in a pie format as a visual aid in remembering how it is used, where

E represents voltage (*E*lectromotive force).
I represents current (*I*ntensité).
R represents *R*esistance.

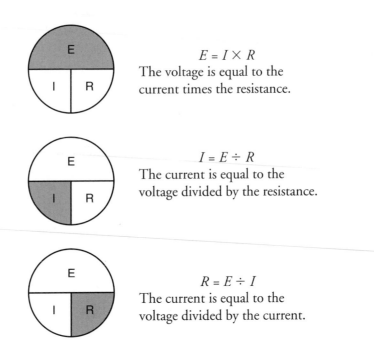

$E = I \times R$
The voltage is equal to the current times the resistance.

$I = E \div R$
The current is equal to the voltage divided by the resistance.

$R = E \div I$
The current is equal to the voltage divided by the current.

Figure 3–4 Ohm's law.

Examples Using Ohm's Law

1. The resistance of an electric heater is measured at 15 ohms. What is the voltage if the resistance of the heater is 8 amperes?

$$E = I \times R$$
$$E = 15 \times 8 = 120 \ volts$$

2. A clip-on ammeter reads 10 amperes on a 120-volt circuit in a home. What is the resistance of the circuit?

$$R = E/I$$
$$R = 120/10 = 12 \ ohms$$

3. How much current would a 240-volt heater with 30 ohms of resistance draw?

$$R = E/I$$
$$R = 240/30 = 8 \ amperes$$

Conductance

3.4.5 *Conductance* is the opposite of resistance. The term *conductance* is probably not used by the lines trade. Technically, instead of discussing the resistance of various types of wood pole treatment, the conductivity could also be expressed as conductance.

The symbol for conductance is *G*. The unit of measure is *mho* (transposition of "ohm"). An mho is probably only discussed during training and has no real application in line work.

$$Conductance\ G = \frac{1}{R}\ resistance$$

$$Ohms\ resistance = \frac{1}{mhos\ conductance}$$

Impedance

3.4.6 *Impedance* is another term for the opposition to current flow. In the lines trade, the terms *resistance* and *impedance* tend to be used interchangeably. Technically, the flow of current in an AC circuit is impeded by reactance as well as resistance. Reactance is explained in Chapter 4.

In a heater or incandescent bulb, there is only resistance to the flow of electrical current. When AC current flows into a coil, there is additional opposition to the current flow caused by *inductive reactance*. Some electrical loads, such as motors, electronic equipment, and fluorescent lights, are inductive loads. A portion of the load current flows in and then back out of the load without doing any work. The inductive reactance created by these loads causes additional impedance to current flow.

Similarly, capacitive loads, such as the capacitive reactance created by long lengths of paralleling conductors, also oppose current flow. Inductive reactance, capacitive reactance, and resistance provide the total impedance to current flow in a circuit. The symbol for impedance is Z and the unit of measure is ohms. Impedance can be substituted for resistance in Ohm's law as $E = I \times Z$.

In an electrical utility circuit, resistance makes up the bulk of the total impedance in the circuit. The reactive current usually makes up less than 10 percent of the current in a distribution circuit. The opposition to current flow in an AC circuit, therefore, is resistance and reactance. The combination of resistance and reactance is called impedance, but in this book you will find the terms *impedance* and *resistance* used interchangeably.

Conductor Resistance

3.4.7 In an electrical system, a short run of a large conductor provides the least resistance to electrical current. A wire table that shows the current-carrying capacity of different sizes of conductors is not used often in the utility business because there are other factors to be considered. The expected load current to be carried, the fault current the conductor can be exposed to for short periods of time, the length of the feeder, acceptable line loss, and expected voltage drop all have to be balanced with affordability when choosing a conductor size.

High Resistance and Insulation

3.4.8 Electrical current flows because there is a pressure (voltage) pushing it through any resistance toward an area of less pressure. It is like the common saying, "Electricity is always trying to find a path to ground." For example, electrical current flows through the resistance of a heating element because the pressure from the supply voltage pushes the current through the element to the low or zero pressure of the neutral end. A high resistance is needed to stop a current flow to ground. Current flows in the intended circuit as long as there is no low-resistance path to any other objects at a different pressure or voltage. High-resistance materials are used to insulate an electrical circuit from ground and other conductors.

Overhead conductors are generally bare and insulated from other objects by porcelain glass or polymer insulators. The longer the path through which the current has to flow and the higher the resistance of that path, the lower the current. Insulators have a number of curves along their surface. This increases the length of the path that current has to flow to ground. Increasing the size of an insulator increases its resistance and allows it to withstand a higher voltage.

Underground conductors are insulated by a rubber or polyethylene covering. The insulation needs to be well protected because even a little damage will cause the voltage (pressure) to stress the damaged location and eventually cause a short circuit in the cable.

High voltage can stress any insulation and cause it to fail. For example, air is normally an insulator, but it can become a conductor when it is electrically stressed and becomes ionized. Air is ionized when electrons in orbit around the atoms are displaced because of being stressed by voltage. An electrical arc and lightning are visible examples of air that has become conductive.

The Effect of Rain on Insulators

3.4.9 Contrary to popular belief, water is not a good conductor of electricity. When it rains and water flows on clean insulators, the resistance of the insulators is not reduced substantially.

When it rains on contaminated insulators, the dirty and wet insulators are less resistive and can eventually short out the circuit. Insulators can become dirty when near industrial areas, saltwater, or roadways spread with salt in winter. The failure of contaminated insulators is delayed due to the irregular shape and skirts on insulators, which keep parts of the insulator dry and make a longer leakage path for current to flow.

Insulators are cleaned using high-pressure water or corncob and nutshell blasting to mechanically remove grime from the insulators. This work is done with the circuit energized.

Rain or water around electricity is very dangerous if a live conductor has fallen to the ground. Water will absorb the salts in the earth and become very conductive. Dry ground is not a good conductor, but when the same ground gets wet, it becomes a very good conductor. Water will greatly reduce the resistance of any dirty surface.

Safety and Electrical Resistance

3.4.10 If an ohmmeter is used to measure a person's body from one dry hand to another dry hand, the resistance would be approximately 100,000 ohms. Most of this resistance comes from the skin. For some people, a 120-volt source is not high enough to overcome the resistance of dry, calloused hands. If a person is perspiring, the resistance is reduced to approximately 35,000 ohms. Once contact is made, the skin resistance can break down in a very short time. After skin resistance breaks down, there will be much less resistance through the internal organs of the body. The internal resistance of a body ranges between 100 and 400 ohms.

There can be many variables involving a person's resistance when electrical contact is made. The clothing and gloves being worn can increase the contact resistance and make a difference when electrical contact is made. When studies and calculations are made involving the resistance of a human body during an electrical contact, an average of 1,000 ohms is normally used.

Because people may have made contact with a 120-volt source and were not hurt, some mistakenly think that 120 volts will not hurt them; however, fatalities occur every year when contact is made with that voltage. The amount of resistance being imposed, often hand to hand, is not enough to prevent a small amount of current flow, considering that 100 milliamperes can be fatal.

Second Point of Contact

3.4.11 A human body does not have enough resistance to prevent a fatal current flow through it when contact is made with a primary voltage. A more important consideration is what other objects a person is touching when contact is made with a live circuit.

Current must have a circuit before it can flow. Before current will flow through a human body, it must enter the body at one contact point and leave the body at another contact point that is at a different potential. An electrical accident usually occurs because one part of the body is in contact with a live circuit and another part of the body is in contact with earth, a neutral conductor, a deenergized load, or another live wire. If the body is not touching a second point of contact, no current can flow through it.

For example, some people claim they can touch a 120-volt wire and not feel anything. The source may be 120 volts, but a person is not exposed to all the available voltage unless another part of the person is well grounded. A person may not feel anything if standing on a wooden floor or wearing good boots. The same person standing barefoot on wet ground would probably receive a fatal shock.

Keeping away from a second point of contact is a fundamental rule for working on or near live circuits. A body cannot become part of a circuit unless there is a potential difference across it. If a powerline worker makes contact with a live conductor while not in contact with any second point of contact, no current can flow through the body. This is the basis for barehand work.

3.5 Electrical Power

Heat from Current Passing through a Resistance

3.5.1 When current passes through a resistance in a circuit, heat is released. The amount of heat produced varies with the amount of current squared (I^2). If the current doubles, the heat produced quadruples. A low resistance draws more current, and more heat is produced.

Joule's law of electric heating states that the amount of heat produced during each second by electrical current in a conductor is proportional to the resistance of the conductor and to the square of the current.

$$J = I^2 \times R \times t$$

where J = the amount of heat in joules
I = the amount of current flowing
R = the amount of resistance in the circuit
t = the time the current is flowing

The same formula can be converted to the basic unit for electrical energy, which is a *watt-second.*

$$1 \text{ watt-second} = 1 \text{ Joule}$$

When current travels through the resistance of a human body, heat is also released. Catastrophic electrical burns are immediately apparent as visibly blackened skin where contact is made and where current leaves the body.

The consequence of a less-serious electrical burn may appear on the body as a small entry burn and a small exit burn. However, the current flow that caused these burns flowed through the body along the lower-resistance blood vessels and nerves. The heat from the current flow will cause damage that can be much more serious than the external injuries might suggest. In other words, most of the damage is not visible, and even so-called minor electrical burns should have medical attention.

Electrical Power and Energy Basics

3.5.2 Electrical energy is the product measured at a customer's meter. Electrical energy is electrical power × time. In other words, electrical energy and electrical power are not the same thing.

Electrical power is the product of volts and amperes and is measured in *watts* (W). The common equations for calculating power are:

$$W = E\,I$$
$$W = I^2 R$$
$$W = \frac{E^2}{R}$$

where W = watts
E = voltage
I = current

Electrical energy is the product of watts and time. A watt-second is 1 watt × 1 second. A kilowatt-hour is 1 kilowatt × 1 hour.

Power Formulas Derived from Ohm's Law

3.5.3 There are many electrical equations based on Ohm's law. The equation wheel in Figure 3–5 shows the interrelationship of these equations.

P = power in watts
I = intensity of current in amperes
R = resistance in ohms
E = electromotive force in volts

Large Units of Electrical Power

3.5.4 A watt is the basic unit of power, but it is very small. In the electrical utility business, kilowatts (kW) and megawatts (MW) are the most common units (see Table 3–3).

In the lines trade, the terms *kilovolt-ampere* (kVA) and *megavolt-ampere* (MVA) are used when discussing power. To transmit AC power, more volts × amperes (VA) are needed to deliver the actual wattage used by a customer. In an AC circuit, a counterforce causes a reactance that impedes the flow of electrical current. In other

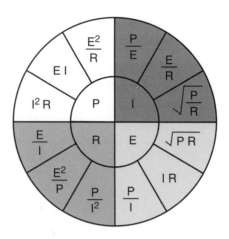

Figure 3–5 Ohm's law equation wheel.

words, slightly more than 1 kilovolt-ampere is needed to deliver 1 kilowatt of power. The chapter on AC power will explain this in greater detail.

The Kilowatt-Hour

3.5.5 As a unit, the watt is the amount of power being used at a given instant. It is also necessary to know how long the power is used to determine the amount a customer is charged for energy. Customers are billed based on the kilowatt-hour

TABLE 3–3 **Putting Power into Perspective**

1 kilowatt (kW) *= 1,000 watts*	Hardware store portable generators have ratings such as 750 W, 2.5 kW, or 3.5 kW. A typical toaster oven is 1.5 kW.
1 horsepower (HP) *= 746 watts*	With 100 HP = 74.6 kW, a 75 kVA transformer is needed to run a 100 HP motor. However, in reality, a motor is only about 80% efficient, and a 100 kVA transformer would be needed.
1 megawatt (MW) *= 1,000 kilowatts*	Some of the older hydraulic stations on small rivers have generating units rated at about 1 MW. The utilization station at a small factory is often rated at 1, 2, or 3 MW. 1 MW = 1 million joules per second.
1 gigawatt (GW) *= 1,000 megawatts*	The largest generating units are about 1 GW and are found in newer thermal or nuclear plants.
	Hydraulic plants such as the R. H. Saunders/Robert Moses generating station across the St. Lawrence River have 32 units: 16 in Canada and 16 in the United States. Each unit is rated at 57 MW, which means the total plant output is 57 MW × 32 units = 1.8 GW. The summer peak load of New York City is about 11 GW.

TABLE 3–4 Putting Kilowatt-Hours into Perspective

1 kilowatt-hour	1 kilowatt-hour will run a 1,000-watt microwave oven or a 1000-watt hair dryer for 1 hour.
	1 liter of gasoline has the energy equivalent of approximately 10 kWh. (1 U.S. gallon of gasoline has the energy equivalent of approximately 37 kWh.)
1,000 kilowatt-hours	An average household in North America is considered to use 1,000 kWh hours per month, and this figure is often used when comparing electric bills between utilities.
	One cord of dry hardwood has the energy of approximately 6,000 kWh.
	One barrel of crude oil has the energy equivalent of approximately 1,700 kWh.
1 billion kilowatt-hours	Annual statistics for the sale or generation of electricity are expressed in billions of kWh. The total generating capacity of the world is approximately 12,000 billion kWh. The following are some statistics from countries in the 1990s:
	United States 2,300 billion kWh Canada 500 billion kWh France 410 billion kWh

(kWh), where the kilowatt is the rate at which energy is used, and the hour is the length of time the power is used.

$$kWh = kW \times hours$$

Kilowatt-hour meters are installed to measure the kilowatt-hours used by customers. A large variety of revenue metering is used to measure other variables, but the primary charge for power used is the kilowatt-hour.

Kilowatt-Hours in Perspective

3.5.6 One kilowatt-hour is a small unit (see Table 3–4). When utilities, and even countries, are compared, the amount of energy generated is shown in billions kilowatt-hours.

Review Questions

1. What physical matter is flowing in an electrical current?

2. How is high voltage, over 750 volts, measured safely?

3. How can a person get into trouble when measuring voltage with a multimeter?

4. Why does a person normally not feel anything when hands are placed on each post of a car battery?

5. What means can be used to positively identify the nominal voltage of a primary circuit?

6. Do electrons travel at the speed of light in an electrical circuit?

7. Does electrical current stop once it gets to the load it is feeding?

8. Why is opening a ground wire or a neutral on a live circuit dangerous?

9. If a circuit is carrying 100 amperes, what portion of that current could induce ventricular fibrillation and probably death?

10. What is the difference between load current and fault current?

11. How would a line crew normally restore power when the switchgear will not pick up the load because of cold load pickup?

12. Where along a line would an accidental short circuit be most explosive?

13. When an ohmmeter is hooked to two different wires and the meter reads "0," what does that indicate?

14. Why does keeping away from a second point of contact reduce the risk of an electrical accident?

15. How much current would a 240-volt heater with 20 ohms of resistance draw?

CHAPTER 4

Alternating Current (AC)

Topics to Be Covered	Section
Introduction	4.1
Characteristics of AC	4.2
Reactance in AC Circuits	4.3
AC Power	4.4
AC or DC Transmission	4.5

4.1 Introduction

Why Alternating Current?

4.1.1 Alternating current (AC) became the standard form of electrical power over direct current (DC) in the pioneer days of electrical power. There were major arguments about which form of electrical power should be delivered to customers. Thomas Edison promoted the case for DC power.

Alternating current has one major advantage: the easy transformation from one voltage to another. Easy transformation allows the voltage to be stepped up for efficient transmission of electrical energy over long distances.

Another advantage to AC power is that every time the voltage and current reverse direction, the magnitude of the voltage and current is zero. This assists in extinguishing arcs when opening switchgear. AC does, however, introduce some complicating phenomena to electrical circuits that are not found in DC circuits.

4.2 Characteristics of AC

AC Basics

4.2.1 Current flows in a conductor as long as a potential difference is present. To have a potential difference, one end of the circuit is at an opposite pole (*polarity*) to the other end. These polarities are labeled as *positive* and *negative*. The direction of the current flow in a circuit is determined by the polarity of the source terminals.

With DC, the polarity does not change and the current flows in one direction only. With AC, the polarity at the source alternates between positive and negative and the current direction changes with every change of the source polarity (see Figure 4–1).

For example, the current in a single-phase circuit flows toward the load while the current in the neutral flows away from the load. In the next moment, the roles are reversed: The current in the neutral flows toward the load, and the current in the phase wire flows away from the load. The voltage on the phase wire is positive with respect to the neutral when it flows in one direction, and the voltage is negative when it flows in the other direction. The voltage on the neutral is unchanged and is close to zero with respect to a remote ground.

Frequency

4.2.2 In North America, alternating current supplied by electrical utilities travels 60 times in each direction in 1 second. In some other parts of the world, 50 cycles per second is common. The term *cycles per second* has been replaced by the international standard term for frequency, which is *hertz* and is represented by the symbol *Hz*.

Unlike voltage or current, the frequency in a circuit stays constant right from the generator to the customer. When the frequency starts to drop, it is an indicator that the generator supplying the electrical system is overloaded and slowing. A small reduction in frequency will trigger the electrical system to trip out of service. A typical range for frequency is 59.97 to 60.03 hertz. Some systems are set up to start load shedding when the frequency reaches 59.3 hertz.

Generation of AC Power

4.2.3 When a loop is rotated within a magnetic field, an electric current is induced in the loop. With AC generation, one half of a loop travels in one

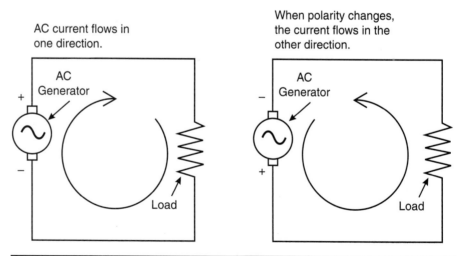

Figure 4–1 Direction of current flow.

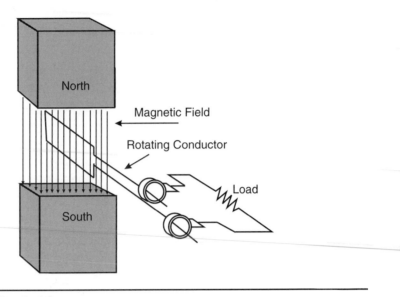

Figure 4–2   Simple AC generator.

direction through the magnetic field while the other half travels in the opposite direction. The current flow induced in the two halves of the loop, therefore, also travels in opposite directions within the magnetic field but ends up traveling in the same direction within the loop. The coil or loop shown in Figure 4–2 is in a position where it is traveling across through the magnetic field at 90 degrees to the magnetic lines of force, which is where the maximum current is generated.

In large commercial generators, many electric magnets are mounted on the rotating part (rotor), and many loops (coils) are mounted on the fixed part (stator).

Rise and Fall of Voltage and Current

4.2.4 When a loop or coil travels through a magnetic field, the induced current is at maximum when the coil cuts straight across the magnetic field lines of force at 90 degrees. When a coil travels in the same direction (parallel) as the magnetic field lines of force, no current is induced.

The current and voltage rise from zero to maximum value and drop back to zero while they travel in one direction and then repeat the zero-to-maximum rise on the return (Figure 4–3). In other words, AC and voltage change in both polarity and magnitude.

AC Represented by a Wave

4.2.5 The rate of the rise and fall of the voltage and current and the direction of flow can be represented on paper by drawing a sine wave (Figure 4–4). A sine wave is a wave shape that follows a mathematical form.

The wave above the zero current line represents the value of the current traveling in the positive direction, and the wave below the zero current line represents the value of the current traveling in the negative direction.

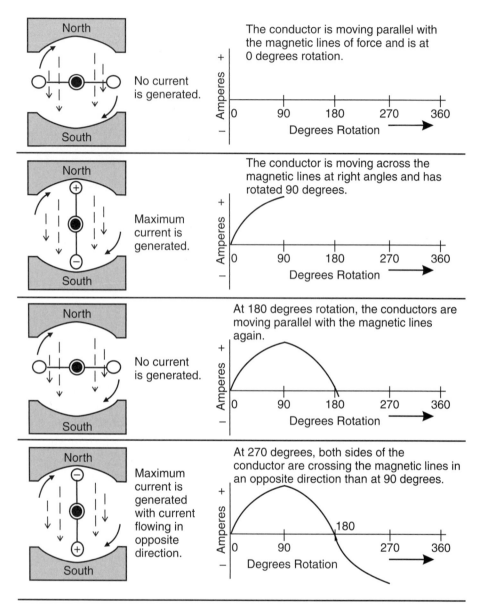

Figure 4–3 Rise and fall of current.

Sine Wave as a Graphical Representation

4.2.6 A sine wave displays how AC power behaves over time. The sine wave is a graphical representation of the rate that the current and voltage values rise and fall and of the direction the current travels during one cycle. The wave is about 3,100 miles (4,989 km) long on a 60-hertz line. Over the shorter distances that linemen do their work, the potential (voltage) on each part of a conductor is virtually the same at any instant in time. In the next instant, the potential along the wire is different, rising and/or falling as the wave rises and/or falls.

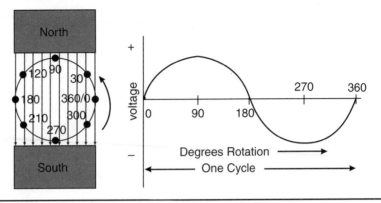

Figure 4–4 AC current represented by sine wave.

A sine wave is plotted against time, but it makes more sense to think about an electric charge on a wire in terms of distance. Except when speaking in terms of 10 miles or more, a typical conductor is at a virtual equipotential with the peaks and troughs of the sine wave occurring virtually simultaneously. Electric load and impedance of the circuit will reduce the magnitude of the peaks and troughs over distance. Transformers, voltage regulators, and other equipment can reduce/or increase the magnitude of the peaks and the troughs so that customers receive the proper voltage at their place of business or home.

Values of AC and Voltage

4.2.7 With the values of AC and voltage continuously changing, what values do we actually read on an ordinary ammeter or voltmeter?

- The *instantaneous value* is the actual value of the voltage and current at each instant in the cycle. This value is not measured with an ordinary meter.

- The *peak value* is the highest instantaneous value that the voltage and current reach in both directions during the cycle. While this value is not measured by an ordinary meter, this value must be considered by design engineers when planning the insulation needed for different voltage systems.

- The *average value* is obtained by calculating the average of all the instantaneous values in half a cycle. The average value works out to be 0.636 of the peak value. This also is not the value measured with an ordinary meter.

- The *effective value* of AC and voltage is the value of a DC and voltage that would have the same heating effect. The effective value is 0.707 of the peak value (Figure 4–5). This is the value measured with the ordinary ammeter and voltmeter. The effective value is often referred to as the root-mean-square (rms) value. In AC applications, the effective value of voltage and current is the value used for calculations and measurement.

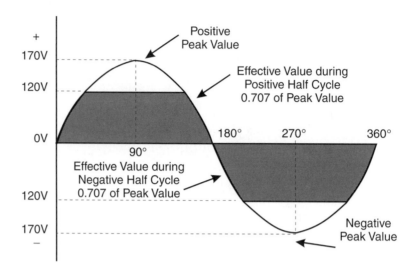

Figure 4–5 Effective value in AC.

Voltage and Current in Phase with Each Other

4.2.8 When both the voltage wave and the current wave reach their maximum and zero values simultaneously, the voltage and current are considered to be *in phase* with each other. In an electrical system, the voltage and current are generally not exactly in phase.

When current is flowing into certain loads, such as a motor load, the current wave will peak after the voltage wave peaks. This current is *out of phase* and *lags* the voltage.

When the current is flowing into a capacitor, the current wave will peak before the voltage wave peaks. This current is *out of phase* and *leads* the voltage.

Circuits in Phase with Each Other

4.2.9 An electrical power system of a utility is part of a large power pool or grid fed from many sources and locations. A generator must generate power so that the magnitude and the direction of voltage and current are synchronized with the other generators supplying power to the same grid. In other words, the voltage from all power sources must be in the same position on the sine wave before feeding power into the grid. All generators must be in phase with each other. If an out-of-phase generator is connected into the grid, it will act as a short circuit.

4.3 Reactance in AC Circuits

Loads Fed by AC Circuits

4.3.1 There are three kinds of loads fed by an AC circuit:

1. Heating and lighting are *resistive* loads. A resistive load can do work. The amount of work being done can be measured by a kilowatt-hour meter.

2. The energy used to magnetize a motor or a transformer is an *inductive* load. An inductive load does not generate heat or light and is not measured by the kilowatt-hour meter.

3. The energy used to supply a capacitive effect at capacitors, paralleling conductors, or in cables is a *capacitive* load. A capacitive load does not generate heat or light and is not measured by a kilowatt-hour meter.

Reactance in an AC Circuit

4.3.2 A resistive load opposes the flow of current, but so do inductive and capacitive loads. All three types of loads oppose the flow of current and add to the total opposition to current flow in a circuit. This disturbance imposed by inductive and capacitive loads in a circuit is called *reactance*. The symbol for reactance is X.

Reactance can be an *inductive reactance* (X_L) caused by loads, such as motors, transformers, fluorescent lights, and computers, or it can be a *capacitive reactance* (X_C) caused by capacitors or paralleling conductors.

Impedance in an AC Circuit

4.3.3 Resistance is the only opposition to the current flow in a DC circuit. In an AC circuit, the opposition to current flow consists of resistance *and* reactance. This combination of resistance and reactance opposing the current flow is referred to as *impedance*. Impedance is measured in ohms and is represented by the symbol Z. Impedance can be used interchangeably with resistance in calculations using Ohm's law

$$Z = IR \qquad Z = \frac{E}{I} \qquad I = \frac{E}{Z}$$

where E = effective voltage in volts
I = effective current in amperes
Z = total impedance in ohms

Resistance in an AC Circuit

4.3.4 Light and heat are resistive loads and do not cause any other disturbance to the circuit. Either AC or DC can supply a resistive load. Ohm's law applies to a resistive AC circuit in the same way that it applies to a DC circuit. For practical applications in the lines trade, resistance can be used for most calculations involving AC circuits, and the result will generally have less than a 10 percent error.

Induction in an AC Circuit

4.3.5 Voltage can be generated into a conductor:

- By moving a conductor within a magnetic field.

- By having a conductor near a moving magnetic field.

Voltage (electromotive force) is induced into a conductor when a conductor is moved through a magnetic field. There is no voltage generated unless the conductor is moving.

Voltage can also be induced into a conductor when a magnetic field from a nearby live AC circuit moves through the conductor. Only an AC circuit would have a moving or fluctuating magnetic field. Induced voltage is always in a direction that opposes the direction of the current flow. Induced voltage is, therefore, the opposite polarity of the source circuit.

With AC, the magnetic field is moving (expanding and collapsing) and any nearby stationary conductor will have a voltage induced on it. This phenomenon is familiar to

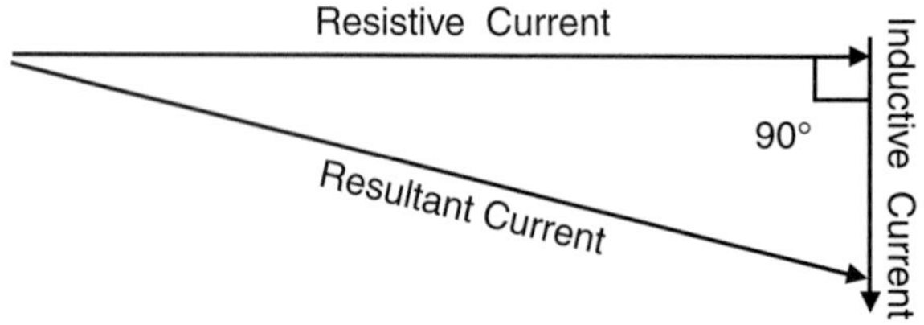

Figure 4–6 Effect of inductive current acting at 90 degrees.

the powerline worker, because induction from live circuits is a concern when grounds are installed on an isolated circuit. Some of the magnetic field around a live conductor cuts through the live conductor itself and induces some voltage onto itself. This *self-inductance* creates a counter-electromotive force (voltage) within the conductor.

When the conductor is part of a coil, such as in a motor or transformer, the magnetic field around the conductor cuts through adjacent wires in the coil, which increases the self-inductance in the conductors forming the coil. This opposition to the current flow delays the rise and fall of the current but not the voltage. The counter-electromotive force generated by the continuously changing voltage and current is called *inductance*.

Figure 4–6 shows the relationship between resistive current, inductive current, and the total current in a circuit. Inductive current acts on a circuit as though it flows at 90 degrees to the resistive current. When the resistive current is added to the inductive current, the resultant current vector is longer, which means that the resultant current is higher.

The symbol for inductance is *L*. The unit of measurement for inductance is a *henry*, but a henry is not a unit a powerline worker would use.

Inductive Reactance

4.3.6 The opposition to current flow within a conductor or coil is called *inductive reactance*, represented by the symbol X_L and measured in ohms. The formula is shown only to illustrate the factors that influence the magnitude of inductive reactance. It is not a formula a line worker would need.

$$X_L = 2\pi fL \; ohms$$

where X_L = inductive reactance in ohms
π = 3.14
f = frequency of the circuit in hertz
L = inductance in henrys

Amperage Lagging Voltage

4.3.7 Distribution feeders tend to have a combination of resistive load and inductive load (electric motors). The inductive load sets up an inductive reaction in the circuit, and this opposition to the current flow causes it to lag behind the rise and fall of the voltage. In other words, as represented by a sine wave, the voltage will peak before the current peaks. The power output of the circuit is reduced because

$$Power = volts \times amperes$$

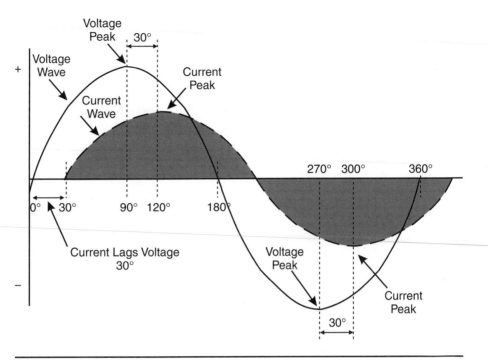

Figure 4–7 Current lagging voltage.

Figure 4–7 shows the current lagging the voltage by 30 degrees, which means the current is 30 degrees out of phase with the voltage.

Applications of Inductive Reactance

4.3.8 Two applications of inductive reactance used in substations are the current-limiting reactor and the shunt reactor. A *current-limiting reactor* is a coil of cable that sets up an inductive reaction in a circuit. The current-limiting reactor is designed so that a large inductive reactance is created during a high fault current condition. The inductive reactance impedes the flow of damaging fault current in the substation.

To balance large capacitive loads caused by parallel conductors of a long transmission line, *shunt reactors* are installed in substations. The reactors produce an inductive reactance that cancels out an equal amount of capacitive reactance in the transmission line. A reactor looks like a power transformer and is connected into the circuit as a shunt (a parallel load). The only connections to the shunt reactor are to high-voltage bushings. There are no output connections, such as the secondary of a transformer.

Capacitance

4.3.9 The major sources of capacitance in a system are paralleling conductors on long transmission lines, underground cable, and capacitors installed specifically to put more capacitance into the electrical system. The tendency of a circuit to store electricity when a potential difference exists between conductors is called *capacitance.* Capacitance occurs when an electrically charged conductor (plate) electrostatically

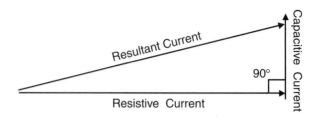

Figure 4–8   Effect of capacitive current acting at 90 degrees.

induces an equal in magnitude but opposite polarity charge on a nearby conductor (plate). The two conductors are not in contact but are separated by some kind of insulation.

When a capacitor is part of an AC circuit, the plates are charged and discharged alternately. The capacitor tends to store the acquired charges and cause a counter-electromotive force (voltage) to oppose the continuing voltage change.

Figure 4–8 shows the relationship between resistive current, capacitive current, and the total current in a circuit. Note that capacitive current is in the opposite direction to the inductive current shown in Figure 4–6.

Capacitive current acts on a circuit as though it flows at 90 degrees to the resistive current. When the resistive current is added to the inductive current, the resultant current is higher. When capacitive current is added to a circuit with inductive current, the two types of reactance cancel each other because they act in opposite directions. The symbol for capacitance is *C.* The unit of measurement for capacitance is a *farad,* but a farad is not a unit a line worker would use.

Capacitors

4.3.10 Capacitance normally occurs in a circuit. A parallel conductor is like a capacitor where the two conductors are separated by air and the conductors electrostatically induce charges on each other. Underground cable is like a capacitor where the inner conductor is separated from the outer sheath by insulation and a charge is built up between the conductor and the sheath.

A capacitor, as illustrated in Figure 4–9, is constructed to induce capacitance in a circuit. It consists of two strips of aluminum foil rolled up together with insulating oiled paper between them. As a capacitor, one electrically charged aluminum roll of foil (plate) will electrostatically induce an opposite polarity charge in the other foil (plate).

Capacitive Reactance

4.3.11 When a capacitor is charged up, a counter-electromotive force (emf) equal to the source voltage is built up on the opposite plate. Current will flow into the capacitor only while the voltage is rising. When the voltage approaches peak value, the counter-electromotive force on the opposite plate is also approaching peak value, which causes the current flow to decrease. There is no current flow when the voltage is at its peak (90 degrees). In a capacitor, the current reaches its peak before the voltage. A capacitor opposes a *change* in voltage, which is what the voltage is doing continually in an AC circuit.

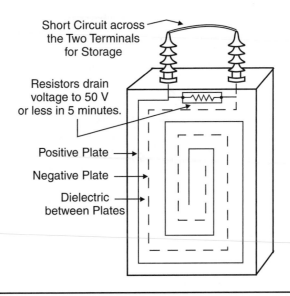

Short Circuit across the Two Terminals for Storage

Resistors drain voltage to 50 V or less in 5 minutes.

Positive Plate

Negative Plate

Dielectric between Plates

Figure 4–9 The construction of a capacitor.

This delaying or opposing of changes to the voltage is called *capacitive reactance*. Capacitive reactance (X_C) is measured in ohms. The formula is shown only to illustrate the factors that influence the magnitude of capacitive reactance.

$$X_C = \frac{1}{2\,\pi f\,C}\,ohms$$

where X_C = capacitive reactance in ohms
π = 3.14
f = frequency
C = farads

**Current Leads
the Voltage**

4.3.12 Because change to the voltage across the capacitor plates is delayed, this capacitive reaction causes the current wave to lead the voltage wave. Figure 4–10 shows the current wave leading the voltage wave by 15 degrees.

**Applications of
Capacitive
Reactance**

4.3.13 Capacitors are installed on electrical systems to draw a leading current from the circuit to counteract the more predominant lagging current in utility circuits. When the lagging current, due to motor load, is partially balanced by the leading current, due to the installed capacitor, there is less total reactive current. With less reactive current, there is less total current; and, therefore, there would also be less voltage drop and line loss. The most common use of capacitors, therefore, is as a voltage booster.

Because most customer load has a heavy inductive element to it, an increased load on a transmission or distribution line means that there is an increase in the inductive load. As the voltage starts to decrease, an increase in capacitance is needed to keep the voltage up.

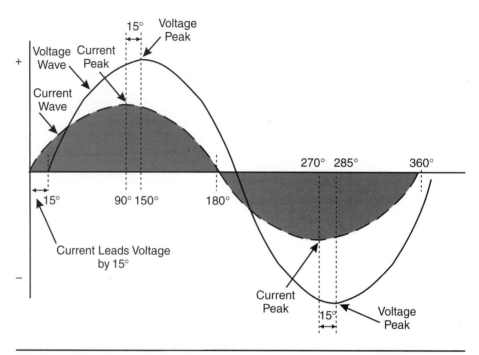

Figure 4–10   Current leading the voltage.

Effect of Frequency on Reactance

4.3.14 The formulas for inductive reactance and capacitive reactance show that the inductive reactance increases when the frequency goes up and capacitive reactance decreases.

$$X_L = 2\ \pi f L\ ohms$$

$$X_C = \frac{1}{2\ \pi f C}\ ohm$$

There is somewhat less inductive reactance in a 50-hertz circuit than in a 60-hertz circuit. A 60-hertz transformer has 10 to 15 percent less material than a 50-hertz transformer. A higher frequency sets up a greater magnetic flux linkage, and, therefore, a smaller iron core can be used. The electrical system in an aircraft is 400 hertz, which allows even less iron and less weight for electrical equipment using an iron core. Anyone in the lines trade who has worked with transformers in the few locations that still have 25-hertz circuits can verify that a 25-hertz transformer is much heavier than the 60-hertz transformer of the same kilovolt-ampere rating.

A 50-hertz circuit would have more capacitive reactance than a 60-hertz circuit. The increased capacitance could be significant on long transmission lines.

Summary of Resistance, Inductance, and Capacitance

4.3.15 Resistance opposes the *flow* of current in an electric circuit. Inductance opposes a *change* in current. The nature of an AC circuit is that its current is always changing by rising and falling in magnitude and reversing direction. Loads such as those with wire coils in them are inductive and increase the amount of inductive reactance in a circuit.

Capacitance opposes any change in *voltage.* The nature of an AC circuit is that its voltage is always changing by rising and falling in magnitude and its polarity is continually reversing. Capacitive loads such as capacitors increase the amount of capacitive reactance in a circuit.

4.4 AC Power

Active Power

4.4.1 The total power produced in a DC circuit is calculated by multiplying total voltage by total amperes. Because there is no reactance in a DC circuit, all the power the circuit supplies is useful power or *active power.*

Active power is also referred to as effective power, true power, or real power, because it is the power that gives light, gives heat, and turns motors. Real power can also be expressed as voltage × resistive current.

In AC circuits, power alternates at the same rate as the voltage and current are alternating. The power measured at a customer's meter is referred to as active power. Therefore, the total active power supplied by a circuit is equal to total effective current × total effective voltage, or

$$P = IE$$

Active power is measured at a customer meter and is measured as *watts* or in blocks of 1,000 watts, which is *kilowatts.*

Apparent Power

4.4.2 The total power supplied by a circuit is called *apparent power* because in an AC circuit all the power does not perform actual work. Apparent power is a combination of *active* power and *reactive* power.

$$Apparent\ power = \sqrt{(active\ power)^2 + (reactive\ power)^2}$$

Apparent power is measured in volt-amperes or kilovolt-amperes (kVA). The term *kVA* is common terminology for the lines trade when referring to transformer sizes. Using the term *kVA* for apparent power is more suitable than using the term *watts power* when referring to transformer size because a transformer has to supply the apparent power needed by the load.

Reactive Power

4.4.3 *Reactive power* is the element in the apparent power formula that does not do any work. In a circuit, reactive power is transferred back and forth between the reactive load and the circuit. Reactive power is not used up. Reactive power is equal to voltage × reactive current or I^2X. It is measured in volt-amperes reactive or kilovolt-amperes reactive (*VAR* or *kVAR*).

In most distribution circuits, the net reactive power is inductive due to a portion of the motor loads, fluorescent lighting, and electronic loads. Reactive power is normally very small compared to the active power available in the circuit.

Inductive reactive power is necessary to create electromagnetic fields in equipment such as transformers and motors. Capacitive reactive power is necessary to create electrostatic fields in capacitors. Volt-amperes reactive will increase current

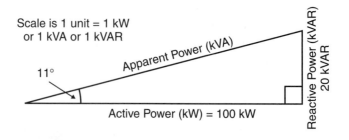

Scale is 1 unit = 1 kW
or 1 kVA or 1 kVAR

Apparent Power (kVA)

11°

Active Power (kW) = 100 kW

Reactive Power (kVAR)
20 kVAR

Figure 4–11   Power triangle.

flow in a circuit but do not represent energy consumption. Volt-amperes reactive store energy in one part of the cycle and return it in the next part of the cycle.

The Power Triangle

4.4.4 The mathematical relationship among the three kinds of AC power can be illustrated by a vector diagram (Figure 4–11). In a vector diagram, the length of each side represents the magnitude of each type of power.

The sides of the triangle in Figure 4–11 represent the magnitude of active power and reactive power. The hypotenuse represents the magnitude of apparent power. If two sides are known, the remaining side can be measured or calculated. In Figure 4–11, active power is represented by 100 units, and reactive power is represented by 20 units. The resultant power can be calculated, as shown in the following equation, or measured from the vector drawing.

$$Apparent\ power = \sqrt{100^2 + 20^2} = 102\ kVA$$

Power Factor

4.4.5 The ratio of active power to apparent power is called the *power factor* and is normally expressed in percents. If there is no reactive power in the circuit, the power factor is 100 percent. Keeping the power factor high in a circuit reduces line loss, voltage drop, and even generation. The power factor is measured at some customers' locations by revenue meters, and customers are penalized for a low power factor.

The angle between apparent power and active power represents the amount of reactive power in a circuit. A power factor can be measured from the power triangle or calculated in two ways:

$$Power\ factor = \frac{active\ power}{apparent\ power}$$

or

$$Power\ factor = \frac{R}{Z}$$

In the example in Figure 4–11, the angle is 11 degrees. The power factor is equal to the cosine of 11 degrees = 0.98, or 98 percent, or, when using a formula:

$$\frac{Active\ power}{Apparent\ power} = \frac{100}{102} = 0.98 = 98\%$$

**Power Factor
Correction**

4.4.6 In a circuit with a low power factor, the apparent power needed to supply the load on the circuit becomes unacceptably high. With too much reactive current in a circuit, more power must be generated to supply the load. More current must flow in the conductor, which causes more line loss (I^2R) and a greater voltage drop.

Because the reactance in most distribution circuits is due to inductive loads, the easiest way to correct the power factor is to install a nearly equal amount of capacitive volt-amperes reactive to balance the inductive volt-amperes reactive. Installing capacitors on the circuit would reduce the apparent power needed to supply power to the customer and, therefore, would reduce line loss and raise the voltage.

In industries with large inductive loads, the industry is billed for the apparent power used as well for the active power. These industries do their own power factor correction in the plant by installing capacitors.

Figure 4–12 illustrates that adding 5 kilovolt-amperes reactive capacitors to a circuit with 8 kilovolt-amperes reactive inductance will reduce the total inductive reactance in the circuit to 3 kilovolt-amperes reactive.

4.5 AC or DC Transmission

AC or DC

4.5.1 Most transmission lines transmit AC. Alternating current transmission became universal because AC was easily transformed to higher or lower voltages. For long distances, however, DC high-voltage transmission can be more economical because there is no reactive current being generated or transmitted.

The transformer made it possible for generation, transmission, and distribution to be performed at ideal voltages. High-voltage transmission lines made long-distance power transmission possible from remote hydraulic generation sites.

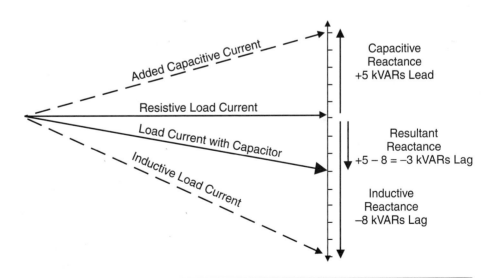

Figure 4–12   Capacitors reduce load current in circuit.

High-voltage direct current (HVDC) transmission has become popular for transmitting a large amount of power over long-distance overhead lines and long submarine cable crossings. Improvement in converter equipment has made DC transmission an increasingly popular option. Converters are called *rectifiers* when changing AC to DC and *inverters* when changing DC back to AC.

Effect of AC Frequency on Transmission of Electricity

4.5.2 The frequency of AC has an effect on the ability to transmit power. A standard 50- or 60-hertz circuit can transmit power for long distances if allowances are made for the inductive reactance and capacitive reactance by installing capacitors and reactors, respectively.

If the frequency was increased to an impractical 1,000 hertz, the inductive reactance would be so high that it would block the transmission of power after a very short distance. At 1,000 hertz, the skin effect on the conductors would also increase and cause the current to be concentrated on the outer surface of the conductor. The amount of current the conductor can carry would be severely limited.

Direct current transmission has no frequency and, therefore, has the opposite effect of high frequency AC. Induction and skin effect are eliminated, and, therefore, DC is a very efficient way to transmit power.

Main Applications of DC Transmission

4.5.3 The main applications of DC high voltage transmission are these:

1. Long-distance transmission of large amounts of power.

2. Long lengths of underground or submarine cable.

3. Tying together two AC systems with different frequencies.

4. Tying together two different AC systems at locations where it is difficult to maintain control of voltage, frequency, and power flow.

5. A long length of distribution line to feed a small remote load, which would otherwise need a high-voltage transmission line and substation or its own generation.

Advantages of DC Transmission

4.5.4 The advantages of DC transmission are these:

1. The power factor of the line is at unity, and, therefore, there is no need for reactors or capacitors to correct the power factor.

2. There is less corona loss and no skin effect in the conductor.

3. There is no charging current to energize a DC line.

4. More power can be transmitted per conductor. Ground return can be used instead of a conductor because the ground return is not subject to the impedance an AC circuit would have. If a two-conductor circuit needs work, work can be carried out on one conductor and the other conductor with ground return can continue as an independent circuit.

5. There is less short-circuit current on a faulted DC line, and the fault does not add to the fault current in the connected AC system.

6. A DC line can feed longer distances because there is no reactance in the circuit.

Disadvantages of DC Transmission

4.5.5 The disadvantages of DC transmission are these:

1. Converters are expensive, and they need reactive power to operate. This requires the installation of capacitors to keep the AC system feeding the DC circuit at an acceptable power factor. Modern electronic converters solve many of the earlier problems involving conversion.

2. Converters generate harmonics, and, therefore, filters must be installed to limit the effect on the AC system feeding the converters.

3. The steady state of DC current makes design of high-voltage DC switchgear difficult. This limits the ability to operate between DC circuits. Alternating current switchgear takes advantage of the fact that the current wave goes through its zero point and there is momentarily no energy to maintain an arc.

Description of DC Transmission Lines

4.5.6 A DC transmission circuit requires a conductor from the source to the load and a return path back to the source. The circuit, therefore, usually consists of two conductors. A two-conductor DC line is referred to as a two-pole circuit. Some underground or submarine DC circuits consist of one conductor and use the earth or seawater as a return path.

There is a converter at each end of the circuit. The converter at the sending end is a rectifier, which changes the AC to DC, and the one at the receiving end is an inverter, which changes the DC back to AC. A converter can be used as a rectifier or an inverter, which allows the circuit to feed in either direction.

Circuit breakers are installed on the AC side of the converters. It is easier to break the arc of AC because the magnitude of the voltage and current becomes zero, 120 times a second, on a 60-hertz circuit.

Resistance to Current Flow on DC

4.5.7 Direct current is fairly constant and is surrounded by a constant or stationary electric field. The energy of this field is in the form of potential energy. There is no electromagnetic energy or its associated induced current. There is no reactance on the DC line itself. The only impedance to current flow is the resistance of the conductor. In other words, the power factor of the DC circuit is 100 percent.

The converter on each end of a DC line draws reactive power from the AC system, and capacitors are needed for power factor correction.

DC Underground or Submarine Cable

4.5.8 The length of AC underground or submarine transmission lines would be limited because reactors would be needed every 25 to 50 miles (40 to 80 kilometers) to offset the capacitance generated by the cable. Similarly, when underground distribution is used in rural areas over long distances, reactors are installed at regular intervals to offset the capacitance of the cable. There is no similar concern about reactance in a DC cable. Direct current cable is the only choice for long-distance submarine power transmission.

Working on DC Circuits

4.5.9 On a two-pole transmission circuit, one pole can be grounded and worked on while the circuit stays in service. The other pole and the earth make up a circuit. The location and number of grounds must be such that the ground current does not flow back up the grounds through the circuit to get back to the source. Standard potential testers used on AC circuits will not work on a DC circuit because potential testers measure the electric field around a conductor.

Review Questions

1. What is the biggest advantage of AC power?

2. What is monitored in a circuit to ensure that it stays constant right from the generator to the customer?

3. What changes occur to AC as it goes through a cycle?

4. In relation to the peak value of AC power, what value do an ordinary ammeter and voltmeter measure?

5. What kind of AC load uses the energy needed to magnetize a motor or a transformer winding?

6. What kind of AC load uses the energy needed to supply a capacitive effect at capacitors, paralleling conductors, or in cables?

7. What three types of loads oppose the flow of current and form the total impedance to a circuit?

8. Distribution feeders tend to have a combination of resistive load and inductive load, creating a lagging power factor. What equipment is installed to counter a lagging power factor?

9. What are the three types of power in an AC circuit?

10. What are three applications of DC transmission lines?

CHAPTER 5

Three-Phase Circuits

Topics to Be Covered	Section
Introduction	5.1
Characteristics of Three-Phase Circuits	5.2
Delta-Connected Systems	5.3
Wye-Connected Systems	5.4
Three-Phase Power	5.5

5.1 Introduction

Three-Phase Basics

5.1.1 Electric current needs a circuit (a complete circle) before it can flow. A single-phase wye circuit can be a phase and a neutral with the current flowing through the "hot" wire and returning to the source through the neutral.

Most utility circuits consist of three phases. A three-phase circuit is not three different single-phase circuits but one circuit with all three phases interconnected. Each phase helps to complete the circuit by acting as the return path for the other two phases.

A live conductor in a circuit is called a *phase* because when three-phase voltages and currents are generated, each of the three conductors gets its voltage and current at a certain phase of a cycle. An electrical phase is often represented in drawings and text by the Greek letter phi (Ø).

5.2 Characteristics of Three-Phase Circuits

Why Three Phase?

5.2.1 The effect of three-phase power as compared to single-phase power is similar to the effect of a six-cylinder engine as compared to a single-cylinder engine. A six-cylinder engine produces a smoother six small pulses per cycle while the single-cylinder engine produces one large pulse per cycle.

103

The values of the voltage and current in each of the three phases overlap with the other phases; therefore, three interconnected phases provide a smoother power than the relatively more pulsating power of a single phase. Three-phase current supplies a rotating magnetic field. Even though the power on each individual AC phase pulsates when it goes through the AC cycle, the sum of the power in all three phases at any point is constant.

Large generators and large motors are more efficient and are considerably smaller as three-phase units compared to equivalently powered single-phase units. In a three-phase motor, the magnetic field automatically rotates, bringing the rotor along with it.

With the same voltage and current per phase, a three-phase system needs only one additional wire (without a neutral, there is a 50 percent increase in conducting material) over a single-phase system but increases the circuit capacity by 73 percent. A three-phase circuit can carry twice as much load as a single-phase circuit while maintaining the same voltage.

Generation of Three-Phase Power

5.2.2 A simplified three-phase generator, as illustrated in Figure 5–1, shows three coils mounted on the armature at 120 degrees apart. Each coil generates an AC and voltage, but the power generated in each coil reaches its peak and direction at 120 degrees apart.

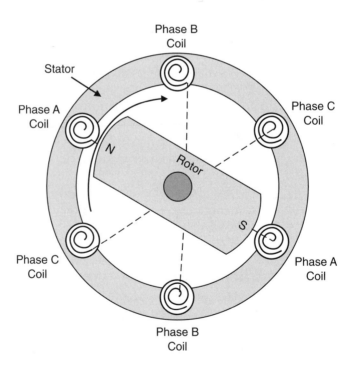

Figure 5–1 Simplified three-phase generator.

Commercial generators mount many coils on the stator and many magnets on the armature. The individual coils are wired so that they are connected together as three circuits 120 degrees apart. Each of the three circuits becomes a phase of a three-phase circuit.

Phases 120 Degrees Apart

5.2.3 When three phases are 120 degrees apart, as shown in Figure 5–1, the values also can be shown in graph form as in Figure 5–2. The first vertical line in Figure 5–2 shows the values being generated in Figure 5–1. Phase A, at 90 degrees, is generating at the maximum value; phase B, at 210 degrees is climbing toward the zero value; and phase C, at 330 degrees, is approaching the maximum return or negative value. The second vertical line shows what is happening to the power generated in each phase when phase A is 120 degrees (one-third of the way) into the cycle, phase B would be 240 degrees (two-thirds of the way) into the cycle, and phase C would be at 360 degrees (at the end, which is also the beginning) of the cycle.

A three-phase circuit is like having three separate AC single-phase circuits with identical voltage that reach their peak values at a different time. At 60 hertz, the second phase reaches its positive peak at 1/180 (0.00556) seconds after the time the first phase reaches a positive peak, and the third phase reaches its positive peak 1/180 (0.00556) second later. The first phase again reaches a positive peak 1/180 (0.00556) second after the third phase, starting the next cycle. Even though each phase has the same voltage, they are out of phase with each other and there is a voltage difference between them.

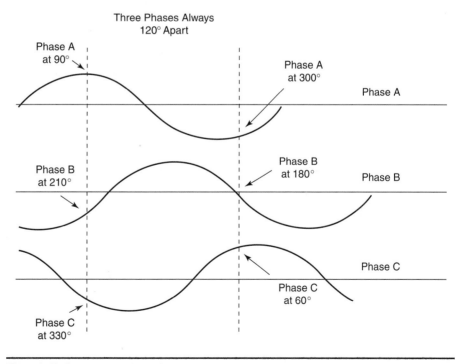

Figure 5–2 Relationship of three phases.

When the load on each phase is identical, the instantaneous power output of the three phases added together is constant. When one phase of a three-phase circuit reaches a peak voltage, another phase is close to zero volts and the third phase is on the return flow. Each phase is 120 degrees out of phase with the other phase. The voltage and current in each phase are 1/180 second, or one-third distance in a cycle behind another phase.

Phase Designations

5.2.4 In the lines trade, it is frequently necessary to trace individual phases to ensure that the correct phase is connected to the correct terminal. Individual phases are named and marked at various locations on the system to keep them apart. Utilities use various designations and markers, some of which are these:

1. Red phase, white phase, and blue phase
2. Red phase, yellow phase, and blue phase
3. A phase, B phase, and C phase
4. #1 phase, #2 phase, and #3 phase
5. X phase, Y phase, and Z phase

Phase Rotation

5.2.5 When a three-phase motor is part of a customer's load, it is necessary to have the three phases in a sequence, or the motor will run backward. If the hookup to the customer had a B phase, A phase, and C phase sequence, the motors would run backward. Switching any two phases at the transformer will put the phase rotation back in sequence. For example, with a B, A, and C sequence, switching A phase and C phase would give a proper B, C, A (which is A, B, C) sequence.

A test can be made with a rotation meter before the customer load is connected. If the rotation meter shows the supply phases are in proper sequence and the motor runs backward anyway, the customer will need to reverse two leads on the motor.

Three-Phase Connections

5.2.6 A three-phase circuit starts at a generator. After generation, these three phases are connected to the input and output sides of transformers throughout the transmission and distribution system. A three-phase circuit is interconnected at the transformers in two ways (Figure 5–3).

1. The three phases can be connected in parallel. One end of each of the three coils is connected together to a common point, and the other ends of the three coils are the three-phase connections. This is referred to as *wye-connected* (named after the letter Y). A vector drawing showing the three phases interconnected is in the shape of a Y.
2. The three phases can be connected in series, which is referred to as *delta-connected* (named after the Greek letter delta Δ). A vector drawing showing the three phases interconnected is in the shape of a delta.

Wye and Delta Systems

5.2.7 All circuits worked on by the lines trade are fed from a transformer bank somewhere in the system. When the circuit source is from a transformer bank with

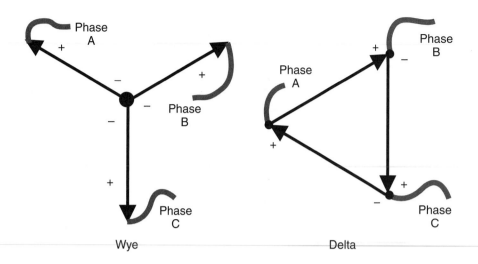

Figure 5–3 Wye and delta configurations.

a delta-connected output, the circuit is a delta system. Similarly, a wye circuit comes from a transformer bank with a wye-connected output.

A three-phase delta circuit consists of three wires. Each wire is a phase 120 degrees out of phase with the other wires. Transformers are connected phase to phase. Lateral taps branching off with two phases are used as single-phase circuits, which feed single-phase transformers and customers.

A three-phase wye circuit consists of four wires. Three wires are phase wires 120 degrees out of phase with each other, and the fourth wire is the connection to the common point, which is the neutral. Lateral taps branching off, consisting of a phase and a neutral, are single-phase circuits, which feed single-phase transformers and customers.

Connections to the three coils of three-phase transformers or motors are always made based on the standard wye or delta shape, as shown in Figure 5–4.

5.3 Delta-Connected Systems

Delta- or Series-Connected Three-Phase System

5.3.1 A delta system is a circuit fed from a delta-connected secondary of a three-phase transformer bank. The transformer bank provides a three-phase delta output with the three phases interconnected as one circuit.

To operate, each coil of a transformer must have a potential difference across it. On a delta connection, this can be achieved by connecting each coil phase to phase. The phase-to-phase connections are not at random, but each coil is connected so that the end of one coil is connected to the end of the other until all three are connected all the way around. In other words, the three phases are connected in series.

The current does not circulate around the delta. The current in each leg is traveling in a different direction at 120 degrees out of phase with each other.

Figure 5–5 shows how delta connections are made when the coils are in a delta shape and when the coils are side by side.

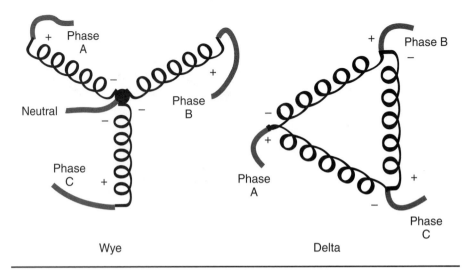

Figure 5–4 Wye and delta connections in wye and delta shape.

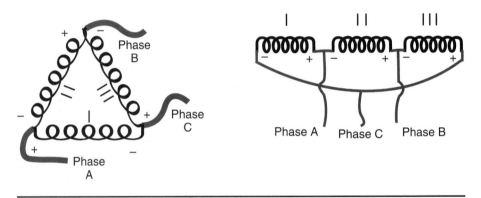

Figure 5–5 Delta configurations.

Voltage in a Delta System

5.3.2 The voltage across each coil is the same as the voltage measured from phase to phase. There is a voltage across each coil or between any two phases because each phase is in a different part of the AC cycle. The three phases are, in fact, always 120 degrees apart.

Current in a Delta System

5.3.3 For this discussion, the phase current is the current in each coil and the line current is the current in each conductor leaving the transformer bank. The current leaving each junction point is the resultant of the current in two phases 120 degrees apart. The current through each coil is equal to the full-phase current, but the line current leaving each junction point is 1.73 × the phase current in each of the two coils feeding the phase.

Return Flow in a Delta Circuit

5.3.4 To complete a circuit, electrical current must return to the source. In a delta circuit, the return flow to the source is in the opposing phase conductors. There is no return flow through the ground. There is a potential difference between the three phases of a delta circuit, but there is no "theoretical" potential between a phase and ground because going from phase to ground does not complete a delta circuit.

Using the same theory, a metal car body is the return path to the battery in an automobile. Theoretically, if a person avoids touching the car body, that person can touch the spark plug and not get a shock. If some of the return current takes a path to ground down one tire and up another tire, however, a person would still be exposed to a shock.

If one of the phases of a delta circuit became grounded, the voltage between the other two phases and ground becomes equal to phase-to-phase voltage. Unless a circuit breaker is equipped with a ground fault relay, a grounded conductor on a delta circuit will continue to be at a phase-to-phase voltage with the other two phases.

Ground Fault Protection in a Delta Circuit

5.3.5 Many, but not all, delta circuits have protection against ground faults. The nature of a delta circuit would not notice a phase-to-ground fault; therefore, a grounding transformer and relays must be installed.

A grounding transformer is installed in a substation between one phase of a delta circuit and ground. There is normally no voltage difference between a delta phase and ground, so there would be no current flow through the transformer. During a phase-to-ground fault, the current flowing back to the source will flow through the transformer and send a signal to the ground fault relay. The relay will detect this current and trip out the circuit.

5.4 Wye-Connected Systems

Wye- or Parallel-Connected Three-Phase System

5.4.1 A wye system is a circuit fed from a wye-connected secondary of a three-phase transformer bank. The transformer bank provides a three-phase wye output with the three phases interconnected as one circuit.

When connected in a wye configuration, each coil of a three-phase transformer is connected between a phase and the neutral. One end of each coil is connected together at a common point, which is the neutral. A voltage will be available at the other ends of the three coils when measured between any two phases. There is also a voltage between each phase and the common point. The three coils are connected in parallel.

Figure 5–6 shows how wye connections are made when the coils are in a wye shape and when the coils are side by side.

Voltage and Current in a Wye System

5.4.2 Two different voltages are available in a wye system: phase-to-phase voltage and phase-to-ground voltage. The phase-to-phase voltage is $\sqrt{3} \times$ the phase-to-neutral voltage. The phase-to-phase voltage is the resultant (vector or algebraic) sum of two phase-to-neutral voltages that are 120 degrees out of phase with each other.

The phase current going through each coil in a transformer is the same as the line current that flows into each phase of the wye circuit. The current flow in a wye circuit is $1 \div \sqrt{3}$, or at 58 percent of an equivalent delta circuit.

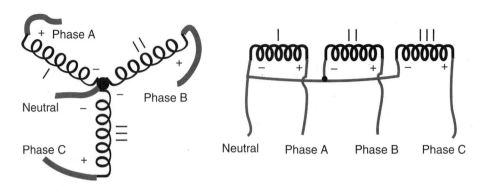

Figure 5–6 Wye configurations.

The Neutral in a Wye System

5.4.3 The neutral is the common point of each transformer winding in a wye system. If the loads on the three phases were equal to each other, there would be no current on the neutral. The neutral carries the sum (algebraic or a vector sum) of the three phase currents back to the source. With the three phases at 120 degrees, the three currents cancel out each other. The neutral wire can be smaller than the phase wires because it is sized to carry the unbalanced load between phases.

The worst-case scenario for an unbalanced wye circuit would be a phase-to-ground fault. Most neutrals are multigrounded, so fault current that enters the ground would return to the source through the ground and the neutral. For the duration of a phase-to-ground fault, the neutral current gets very high and the voltage between the neutral and ground also rises. On a single-phase line, the neutral—and to a lesser extent the ground—is the only path back to the source to complete the circuit.

Some three-wire circuits are actually wye circuits, which do not carry a neutral. The need for a neutral is minor when the load is balanced among the three phases. Transmission and subtransmission lines have relatively balanced loads and are often wye circuits without a neutral. In some utilities where there is good earth, the neutral is omitted on a distribution feeder because the earth is able to complete the circuit for unbalanced load and fault.

Earth Return System Neutral

5.4.4 At some locations, mostly in rural, thinly populated areas, no neutral conductor is strung on the wye-distribution system. A single-phase circuit would consist of only one conductor strung on a pole. This system uses the earth as the neutral. A similar approach is used in the electrical system of a car. The metal body of the car is used as the ground wire and is attached to the negative pole of the battery.

The advantage of the earth return system is that with fewer conductors, fewer pole-top fittings, and ease of construction, these lines require less capital to build. One disadvantage is that the down-ground wire on a distribution transformer pole is the transformer primary neutral. Anyone getting across a break in the down-ground is exposed to full primary voltage. It is important to ensure that the down-ground has good physical protection installed where it is accessible to the public.

Converting from Delta to Wye

5.4.5 Many delta circuits have been converted to wye circuits. There are economical and safety differences between the two systems.

When the output connections of a distribution substation transformer are converted from delta to wye, the phase-to-phase voltage will be increased 1.732 ($\sqrt{3}$) times. For example, a delta-connected transformer bank that has a phase-to-phase voltage of 2,400 volts across each coil of the transformer secondary can be converted to a wye connection by having one end of each 2,400-volt coil connected to a common point. Now, the phase-to-phase voltage of the newly connected wye circuit will be 4,160 volts, and the phase-to-neutral voltage will be 2,400 volts. (*Note:* Usually a conversion involves going to an even higher voltage fed from a new substation transformer.)

For the same load, the current in each wye-connected phase is reduced to 1 ÷ 1.732, or 58 percent. A lower current results in less line loss and less voltage drop.

During conversion, an existing distribution transformer that was connected as phase to phase on the delta circuit can now have the same primary voltage by connecting it phase to neutral on a wye circuit. (*Note:* Usually a conversion involves going to an even higher voltage and installing dual-voltage transformers to reduce the time of customer outage during the changeover.)

Single-phase wye-connected transformers require only one cutout and surge arrestor instead of the two needed on a delta transformer. Similarly, a single-phase lateral on a wye system needs only one line switch.

The multigrounded neutral on a wye system is an excellent ground and is available for transformers and secondary services regardless of possible poor local grounding conditions. On a delta system, the ground at a transformer is dependent on the driven ground rod at the transformer and at the customer.

Fuses and circuit breakers trip out quicker due to over-current when there is a good return path to the source. Phase-to-phase short circuits on both wye and delta circuits trip out a fuse quickly because of the good return path to the source through the other phases. Phase-to-ground faults have a good return path to the source on wye circuits through the multigrounded neutral. A tree contact would blow a fuse much quicker on a wye system than on a delta system.

5.5 Three-Phase Power

The Combined Power in Three Phases

5.5.1 When voltage and current are in each phase of a three-phase circuit, power is also being delivered. The power delivered by each phase will be 120 degrees out of phase with the other phases. In other words, the power delivered by one phase could be at its peak when the power delivered by another phase is one-third farther into the cycle and the power delivered by the third phase is two-thirds farther into the cycle.

Therefore, the total power in a balanced three-phase system is not simply three times the power of one phase. The square root of three, which is 1.73, times the power in one phase will give the power in three phases. When the load is unbalanced, the load in each phase must be measured individually and the average value is put into the equation. The power factor must be known to calculate the true power delivered by a three-phase system.

Field Calculations

5.5.2 Converting amperes in a circuit to kilovolt-amperes (kVA) and converting kVA into amperes per phase are sometimes valuable tools in the field. Field calculations are valuable when balancing three-phase circuits. The ampere loading of a phase should be converted to kVA to determine which transformers to transfer over to another phase.

Before working live line on a transmission circuit where jumpers are going to be installed, it is valuable to know the expected load on a phase. The controlling station can give the total load on the circuit, which can be converted to amperes per phase using field calculations.

Apparent power (kVA) is used in the field instead of true power (kilowatts) because apparent power is what a feeder carries. True power is measured by revenue meters. To determine the total load on a transformer, field calculations can convert amperes per phase to kVA.

Calculations Involving Power

5.5.3 Table 5–1 gives formulas used to calculate power in three-phase and single-phase circuits. Calculations for field applications use the kVA formulas.

Calculations involving three-phase power use line-to-line (phase-to-phase) voltage. The value of the square root of three is normally 1.73.

Calculations with "Handy Numbers"

5.5.4 To do the power calculations quickly in the field, a "Handy Number" can be used for approximations (Table 5–2).

Approximate kVA = amperes × "Handy Number"
Approximate amperes per phase = kVA ÷ "Handy Number"

Examples Using "Handy Numbers"

5.5.5 *Question* One phase of an 8.3/4.8-kilovolt feeder has 80 amperes more load than the other two phases. To balance the feeder, how many kVA should be transferred to the other two phases?

Answer Using a "Handy Number," which is 5 for a 4.8-kV single-phase line, × 80 A = 400 kVA. Therefore, 400 kVA should be distributed between the three-phases, 400 ÷ 3 = 133 kVA should be transferred to each of the other two phases.

Question Load on each of the three phases of a 120/208 50-kVA pad mount transformer bank are 150 A, 170 A, and 140 A. Is the transformer overloaded?

TABLE 5–1   Power Formulas

To Find	Direct Current	Single-Phase AC	Three-Phase Wye AC
Kilowatts (kW)	$\dfrac{I \times E}{1{,}000}$	$\dfrac{I \times E \times PF}{1{,}000}$	$\dfrac{I \times E \times 1.73 \times PF}{1{,}000}$
Kilovolt-Amperes (kVA)		$\dfrac{I \times E}{1{,}000}$	$\dfrac{I \times E \times 1.73}{1{,}000}$
Amperes (when kW are known)	$kW \times \dfrac{1{,}000}{E}$	$kW \times \dfrac{1{,}000}{E \times PF}$	$\dfrac{kW \times 1{,}000}{1.73 \times E \times PF}$
Amperes (when kVA are known)		$\dfrac{kVA \times 1{,}000}{E}$	$\dfrac{kVA \times 1{,}000}{1.73 \times E}$

*PF = power factor

TABLE 5–2   Examples of "Handy Numbers" for Some Voltage Systems

	Calculating Approximate Loads with "Handy Numbers"			
	Three-Phase kV	*Handy #*	*Single-Phase kV*	*Handy #*
	230	400		
kVA = Amperes ×	115	200		
"Handy Number"	69	120		
or	46	80		
Amperes per Phase =	25	40	14.4	14
kVA	12.5	22	7.2	7
"Handy Number"	8.32	14	4.8	5
	0.208	0.36	0.12	0.12

To calculate the "Handy Number" for other voltage systems:
For three-phase lines, the *"Handy Number"* = L – L voltage × 1.73 ÷ 1,000
For single-phase lines, the *"Handy Number"* = L – N voltage ÷ 1,000
where L = Line and N = Neutral.

Answer   The average load on the three phases is 150 + 170 + 140 ÷ 3 = 153 A. Using the "Handy Number," which is 0.36 for 120/208-V service, × 153 = 55 kVA. The transformer is only slightly above its rating, but the load should be balanced more between the three phases to prevent one transformer winding from being overloaded.

Review Questions

1. What advantages are there for a three-phase versus a single-phase circuit?

2. What does it mean when the voltages of each phase of a three-phase circuit are 120 degrees apart?

3. What can be done at a three-phase transformer bank if a customer's three-phase motor is running backward?

4. What determines whether a three-phase circuit is considered a wye or a delta circuit?

5. What is the voltage-to-ground on a 4,160-volt delta circuit?

6. Why does a source breaker see a phase-to-ground fault on a delta circuit?

7. If the phase-to-phase voltage on a wye feeder is 25 kilovolts, what is the phase-to-ground voltage?

8. What condition would put a very high current on the neutral and also raise the voltage between the neutral and ground?

9. Name two advantages for converting a delta circuit to a wye circuit.

10. A control room operator tells you a 115-kilovolt circuit is carrying 70 megavolt-amperes. How much current would a temporary jumper have to carry?

CHAPTER 6

Awareness when in an Electrical Environment

Topics to Be Covered   **Section**

Introduction   6.1

Connecting a Load in Series with a Circuit   6.2

Connecting a Load in Parallel with a Circuit   6.3

Electrical and Magnetic Induction   6.4

Voltage Gradients   6.5

Working with Neutrals   6.6

Vehicle Grounding and Bonding   6.7

Electromagnetic Fields   6.8

Minimum Approach Distance   6.9

6.1 Introduction

Working on or Near Electrical Circuits

6.1.1 When working on or around electrical circuits, people are exposed to electrical influences from sources that are not always obvious. The topics in this chapter apply knowledge of electrical theory to the various tasks involved when working in an electrical environment. An increased recognition of a potential electrical hazard will allow for safer work in an electrical environment. To be considered qualified to work closer than 10 feet (3m) to a distribution circuit, you should be able to recognize these hazards and know the types of barriers that must be put in place to control these hazards.

Making Contact with an Electrical Circuit

6.1.2 When working on or near energized circuits, a body can make two types of electrical contact. A person making contact is like an additional electric load to the circuit, and a load can be connected in series with the circuit or connected in parallel with the circuit. Some distinct differences exist in the way voltage and current acts on a load connected in parallel versus a load connected in series.

115

6.2 Connecting a Load in Series with a Circuit

**What Is a
Series Circuit?**

6.2.1 Two or more loads within a circuit are considered to be *in series* when one (common) current is flowing through all the loads. When the current has only one path (Figure 6–1) to take through two or more electrical loads, then the loads are in series with each other. In other words, when a component is connected end to end into a conductor, it is connected in series.

**Characteristics
of a Series
Circuit**

6.2.2 In a series circuit, an equal amount of current runs through the complete circuit and all connected loads. An ammeter reading would show the same value any place in the circuit. If any change is made to the current flow in any part of the circuit, the change to the current applies throughout the circuit.

$$I_{Total} = \text{The current through any part of the circuit}$$

In a series circuit, a voltage drop occurs across each load. The voltage drop across each load is dependent on the resistance of the load and can be calculated using Ohm's law ($I \times R$). A large load or resistance would have a large voltage drop across it. A break in the circuit would introduce an infinite resistance to current flow and would result in a total voltage drop. This means that the total circuit voltage (recovery voltage) is available across the break. It is, therefore, a basic line-trade procedure to always jumper any conductor that is carrying current before it is cut.

The sum of all the individual voltage drops is equal to the applied voltage of the circuit. The voltage drops some as it goes through each load in the circuit and is "all used up" when it gets back to the source.

$$E_{Source} = IR_1 + IR_2 + IR_3 + IR_{etc.}$$

Current through each of R_1, R_2, and R_3
is equal to the current in the circuit.

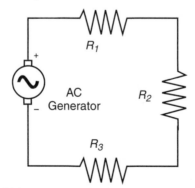

Voltage across R_1, R_2, and R_3 varies,
depending on the value of R.

Figure 6–1   Loads connected in series.

The total resistance in the circuit is equal to the sum of all the individual resistances within the circuit.

$$R_{Total} = R_1 + R_2 + R_3 + R_{etc.}$$

Loads Placed in Series

6.2.3 Few applications of series-connected loads are in an electrical utility. Series street-lighting circuits are still present in some utilities. The supply transformer keeps the current constant throughout the circuit, and the voltage varies depending on the number and size of the lights in the circuit. There are series-connected loads at the utilization level, but they are mostly within such electrical equipment as appliances and electronic devices. Some strings of Christmas-tree lights are connected in series. In a series-connected string of lights, when the element of one bulb fails, it opens the circuit and the lights go out along the whole string. The input voltage is equally divided over all the bulbs in the string. For example, strings have 10 bulbs, 25 bulbs, or 40 bulbs; the voltage rating of the bulbs from a 120-volt source is 120 divided by the number of bulbs in a string. Similarly, a person with a 240-volt service could connect two 120-volt lights in series to allow the use of standard 120-volt bulbs.

Making Series Connections

6.2.4 The line trade is involved in connecting equipment such as switches, reclosers, and voltage regulators in series within the circuit. Any time a person is involved with cutting or joining a conductor, a person risks getting into series with the circuit. When a power conductor is cut, all the current flow is interrupted. The resistance across the open point is infinite; therefore, the voltage drop (*IR*) is at full-line voltage. This full-line voltage (recovery voltage) appears across the two ends of the cut conductor. Installing a jumper across an open point keeps the current flowing and keeps the potential across the cut at 0 volts.

The Human Body in a Series Circuit

6.2.5 A person's body can complete a circuit when it bridges an open point within the circuit. When a body completes a circuit, it is exposed to the full-line voltage of the circuit and all the current the voltage is able to drive through the resistance of the body. Every time a person makes a cut or joint in a current-carrying conductor, one can accidentally put oneself into series with the circuit. Even on an isolated and grounded circuit, enough current flow can be in the conductors to cause a lethal shock. Only body resistance, clothing, and gloves limit the current flow when a body is put into series with the circuit. If the voltage is high enough across the open point, this resistance will be overcome, a person's body will complete the circuit, and a current flow will be established through the body.

Examples of Accidents Involving Series Contact

6.2.6 Accidents occur when a person's body completes a circuit, as in the following examples:

- A powerline worker received electrical burns when he opened the neutral of a live circuit without installing a jumper bypass across the open point. His body was in series with the neutral conductor. This occurred even though the neutral was multigrounded.

- A powerline worker received electrical burns when he removed a loop on a grounded transmission line. Grounds were installed on each side of the loop, but no bypass jumper was installed.

- Attaching to (getting in series with) a live secondary bus with one hand and an isolated service drop with another hand caused a powerline worker to be "frozen" on the line. The voltage across the open point was equal to the service voltage.

- Forgetting to install a jumper before cutting a conductor while doing rubber-glove work or barehand work results in an electrical flash and exposure to a lethal voltage across the open point.

Protection from Series Contact

6.2.7 Any time people bridge themselves across an open point in a circuit, they are exposed to the full-line voltage of the circuit and all the current the voltage is able to drive through the body. When a power conductor is cut, all the current flow will be interrupted. The resistance across the open point is infinite and therefore the voltage drop *IR* will be at full-line voltage (recovery voltage).

Every time a *cut* or *joint* is made to a current-carrying conductor, one can accidentally put oneself into series with the circuit. Even on an isolated and grounded circuit, current flow in the conductors can be sufficient to cause a lethal shock. Installing a jumper across an open point keeps the current flowing and keeps the potential across the cut at 0 volts.

Although not practical, electricians say that the best safety procedure is to keep one hand in your pocket while working. It should, however, be a habit to make or break a connection without having hands on each side of the open point. For example, when making a connection, have both hands on one wire until contact is made between the two wires. Even with a jumper in place and as a matter of habit, line workers should never put their hands across an open point in case some earlier step has been forgotten.

A piece of cover-up or an insulated aerial bucket provides protection from electric shock in cases of accidental contact. However, a bucket or cover-up will provide no protection from contact made by hands across an open point. Wearing rubber gloves provides protection, but no backup protection is available if the only thing preventing a current flow from hand to hand is the integrity of the rubber gloves.

6.3 Connecting a Load in Parallel with a Circuit

Making Parallel Contact

6.3.1 Powerline workers frequently put themselves in a parallel path to ground when working on a wye circuit. For example, when working with rubber gloves on a live conductor, a person is parallel to other loads on the circuit. The rubber gloves may prevent a dangerous current flow through the worker. On a delta circuit, a person must make phase-to-phase contact to make a parallel connection with other loads on the circuit.

What Is a Parallel Circuit?

6.3.2 When more than one path is available for current to flow through (Figure 6–2), the loads in each path are connected in parallel with each other. The current divides into each branch of the circuit. The magnitude of the current in each branch depends on the resistance within that branch.

Characteristics of a Parallel Circuit

6.3.3 The same voltage appears across each path connected in parallel because each path is connected between the same two wires supplying the source voltage. Each branch is independent of the others. Each branch has the same voltage, but the current and resistance can change in a branch, which will not affect another branch.

$$E_{Source} = E_1 = E_2 = E_3 = E_{etc.}$$

The total current in a circuit with its loads connected in parallel is equal to the sum of the currents flowing into each path.

$$I_{Total} = I_1 + I_2 + I_3 + I_{etc.}$$

The current within each path is dependent on the resistance or load in each path. Most current takes the path of least resistance, but *each* path will have *some* current flow through it. The magnitude of the current through each path is inversely proportional to the resistance. The branch with the least resistance takes the most current. The total current in the circuit is always more than the current in the branch with the least resistance. This means, therefore, that the total resistance of the circuit is less than the smallest resistance in the circuit.

$$\frac{1}{R_{Total}} = \frac{1}{R_1} + \frac{1}{R_2} + \frac{1}{R_3} + \frac{1}{R_{etc.}}$$

Current through R_1, R_2, and R_3 varies, depending on the value of R.

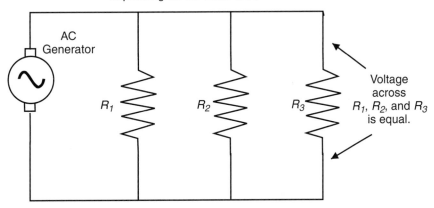

The neutral or other phase is the return path to the source.

Figure 6–2 Loads connected in parallel.

A *short-circuit fault* is the lowest-resistance load in a circuit and, therefore, attracts the most current flow. However, every other element connected in parallel still takes a portion of the current.

Calculating the Total Resistance in a Parallel Circuit

6.3.4 The total resistance of a parallel circuit is not the sum of the resistance as in a series circuit. The total resistance is calculated using the following formula:

$$\frac{1}{R_{Total}} = \frac{1}{R_1} + \frac{1}{R_2} + \frac{1}{R_3} + \frac{1}{R_{etc.}}$$

Example Calculation

In Figure 6–3, three transformers are connected in parallel. Calculate the equivalent or total resistance of the circuit, given a source of 5,000 volts and three parallel branches with a resistance of 250, 500, and 100 ohms.

Substituting the resistance values into the formula:

$$\frac{1}{R_{Total}} = \frac{1}{250} + \frac{1}{500} + \frac{1}{100}$$

$$\frac{1}{R_{Total}} = \frac{2}{500} + \frac{1}{500} + \frac{5}{500}$$

$$\frac{1}{R_{Total}} = \frac{8}{500}$$

$$R_{Total} = \frac{500}{8} = 62.5 \; ohms$$

Note that the total resistance of this parallel circuit is smaller than the resistance in any one branch. The larger transformer has a large load current but a smaller resistance.

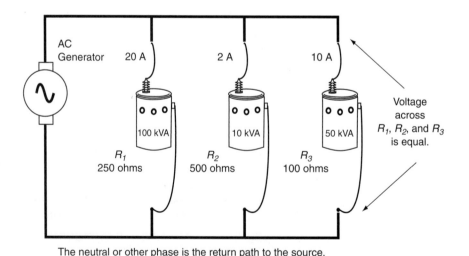

The neutral or other phase is the return path to the source.

Figure 6–3   Calculating total resistance in a circuit.

Loads Connected in Parallel

6.3.5 Almost all loads are connected to an electrical system as parallel-connected loads. Loads on a distribution feeder are fed through transformers. All transformers on a feeder are connected in parallel to each other. All transformers on a feeder are also connected to the same voltage, and the current flowing into each transformer is inversely proportional to the load.

Loads at the utilization level in homes and factories are connected in parallel. When an appliance is plugged into a socket, it is connected to the same voltage as other appliances plugged into that electrical service.

Leakage Current

6.3.6 In a wye circuit, anything that is in contact with both the ground and a live conductor is a parallel connection and has some current flow through it. Even high-resistance objects, such as insulators, have some current flow through or along them. This small leakage current is in inverse proportion to its resistance and is measured in microamperes.

Live-line tools, rubber gloves, and insulated booms are all subject to some leakage current. The care taken to keep these tools clean and in good condition is intended to keep the leakage current below a certain threshold.

Leakage Current Working Barehand

6.3.7 When working barehand from an aerial basket, the truck boom is a parallel path to ground. The resistance of the boom is very high, but some current flow still travels through the boom to ground. A *boom contamination meter* is used to confirm that the leakage current is at an acceptable level. The leakage current is never at 0. A typical acceptable leakage current for an insulated boom is less than 1 microampere for each 1,000 volts to ground. A person in an aerial basket is exposed to even less current because the metal grid below the feet is bonded to the conductor. In other words, the potential of the hands is the same as the potential below the feet. On high-voltage circuits, a conductive suit is worn to reduce the uncomfortable voltage gradients around the body and to keep all of the body at the same potential.

The Human Body in a Parallel Circuit

6.3.8 Any time a person makes contact with a hot conductor, whether with rubber gloves or with a live-line tool, that person will be exposed to some voltage and some current. In a wye circuit, high-resistance objects—such as insulators, live-line tools, rubber gloves, insulated booms, and anything that is in some kind of contact with both the ground and a live conductor—create a parallel connection on the circuit and will be subject to some leakage current. The magnitude of the current will depend on the resistance of the object in contact.

- Because some current flow will always be present when a parallel contact is made, a person is protected by keeping the current flow through the body to ground below a dangerous threshold. Current flow through a person will be kept below dangerous values when resistance is increased between a live conductor and the second point of contact by the use of rubber gloves, live-line tools, cover-up, and insulated platforms.

- Current flow through a person's body will be kept below dangerous values when there is no potential difference between one part and another part of the body. When switching or operating stringing equipment, the use of a ground gradient control mat will ensure that hands and feet will stay at the same potential. When there is no potential difference, there is no current flow.

- Even when working from an insulated basket, there is leakage current flowing down the rubber gloves and down the insulated boom. The current flow is very small, probably less than 10 microamperes, and it is below the threshold at which one would feel anything. If a person fails to wear rubber gloves or reduces the resistance of the electrical path through the body in any way, the body will take a greater share of the current flow.

Examples of Accidents Involving Parallel Contact

6.3.9 Accidents occur when a person's body is a parallel path to a current flow, such as the following:

- A powerline worker received a lethal shock when he made an inadvertent contact with a live circuit while standing on a pole waiting for the circuit to be isolated. The 4,800 volts in the line were high enough to overcome the resistance of his leather work gloves and the wooden pole. The amount of current going through him, as a parallel path to ground, was well above the usually fatal 100 milliamperes.

- An uninsulated vehicle boom made contact with the bottom of a transformer cutout while a powerline worker was getting material from the truck bin. The truck was grounded to a temporary ground probe but the circuit did not trip out. He was a parallel path to ground and received fatal electrical burns.

- While a powerline worker was opening a gang-operated switch, the operating handle became alive when an insulator broke and a live lead dropped onto the steel framework of the switch. The powerline worker was standing on a ground-gradient mat that was bonded to the operating handle and his back was in contact with some brush growing next to the ground-gradient mat. The brush was a parallel path to a remote ground, and the powerline worker received electrical burns on his back.

Protection from Parallel Contact

6.3.10 Because there is always some current flow when a parallel contact is made, a person is protected by keeping the current flow through the body to ground below a dangerous threshold. Current cannot flow unless there is a circuit. A person must prevent a circuit from being completed through his body. For example, a person in contact with a single live conductor, while working from an insulated aerial device, is part of an open circuit. Other than a small leakage current, the current has no place to flow to because there is no second point of contact. Removing or keeping away from a second point of contact is a key element in all live-line work procedures.

Current flow through a person is kept below dangerous values when resistance is increased between a live conductor and the second point of contact by using rubber gloves, live-line tools, cover-up, and insulated platforms. Current flow through a person's body is kept below dangerous values when there is no potential difference between any part of the body and another part of the body. The use of a ground-gradient control mat when switching or operating stringing equipment ensures that the hands will stay at the same potential. When there is no potential difference, there is no current flow.

6.4 Electrical and Magnetic Induction

Three Electrical Effects without Any Contact

6.4.1 A person can be affected in three ways by electrical phenomena without being in contact with a live conductor. All people, not just utility workers, are exposed to *static electricity*. Static electricity is noticed when one touches a doorknob after walking across a carpet. The spark to the doorknob is a DC charge, which is quite different from the type of induction experienced working near live AC circuits. An object or person near a live AC circuit is exposed to *electromagnetic induction*. Electromagnetic induction is comprised of *electric-field* induction and *magnetic-field* induction.

Static Electricity

6.4.2 Although static electricity is not the same as the induction experienced by electrical-utility personnel working near live lines, it is a phenomenon that can be a hazard in some work settings. Static electricity is a DC charge. It is called static because it is a stationary electric charge. This charge can be generated by rubbing together two nonconducting substances. When a static charge is discharged, a current flow travels between a charged object and the body that makes contact. Static buildup occurs on fast-moving conveyor belts and when removing synthetic clothing, walking on carpets, and sliding out of a car seat and contacting the metal door. A spark from static electricity can cause a fire, especially when the spark occurs in the presence of flammable vapor, dust, or gas. The following are two examples of how to eliminate fires due to static:

- The hoses at gasoline pumps are conductive to prevent a static discharge.
- When fueling a helicopter, a bond is installed between the fuel pump and the helicopter.

Electric-Field (Capacitive) Induction

6.4.3 An isolated, ungrounded conductor strung near a live conductor has an induced voltage on it. It is called *capacitive induction* because, as illustrated in Figure 6–4, the live conductor acts as one plate of a capacitor, the isolated conductor acts as the other plate of the capacitor, and the air between is the insulation between the two plates. The isolated conductor has a voltage on it induced from the live conductor. The isolated conductor is not part of a circuit if the switches are open at each end, and, therefore, no current flows. If the isolated conductor is grounded to earth at one location, the voltage is drained from the conductor and a minor amount of current flows down the ground. The magnitude of the induced voltage is higher in the following instances:

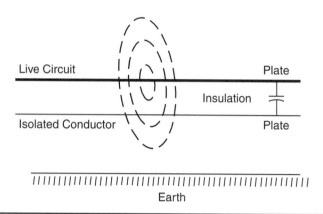

Figure 6–4 Capacitive effect between conductors.

- The voltage on the live conductor is high.

- The distance between the two conductors is decreased.

The length of the parallel between the live conductor and the isolated conductor is not a big influence on the amount of voltage induced on the isolated conductor but is a big influence on the amount of current induced on the conductor.

Electric-Field Effect on an Isolated Conductor

6.4.4 The voltage induced on an ungrounded isolated conductor from a neighboring high-voltage circuit can be very high. Contact with such a conductor can result in a lethal steady-state shock that continues as long as contact is maintained. Installing a set of grounds on the conductor discharges the induced voltage effectively. Bonds between vehicles, ground probes, conductors, and so on eliminate exposure to potential differences among them.

Electric-Field Effect Working in a High-Voltage Environment

6.4.5 When working in a high-voltage environment, such as climbing a transmission tower or working in a high-voltage substation, a person's body acts as the second plate of a capacitor even though the body is not necessarily well insulated from ground. An electric field induces a voltage on a body. The voltage becomes apparent every time a grounded object is touched and the voltage is discharged to ground. The resultant spark (spark-gap effect) consists of a high-voltage but low-current discharge. One hazard from an electric field is an involuntary movement or a fall due to the surprise of a shock. Wearing conducting-sole boots reduces this hazard when working on transmission towers or working in high-voltage stations. When approaching a live transmission line, the electric field gets more intense as a worker gets closer to a live conductor; in other words, the kilovolts per inch (or per cm) increase as a person gets closer to the conductor. When working barehand, a line worker is shielded from the high-intensity electric field with a conducting suit that includes a hood to fit over the hard hat, conducting-sole boots, and conducting work gloves. This shield or conductive "blanket" around the worker keeps all parts of the body at the same potential and forms a *Faraday cage,* which prevents current from the electric field from flowing through the conductive cover suit. Similarly, a person using rubber gloves on a high-voltage distribution line, such as a 34.5 kV line, might feel a vibration or "bite" in the rubber gloves. The rubber glove acts as insulation between two conductive plates, the first being the 34.5 kV and the second the worker.

Magnetic-Field Induction

6.4.6 An isolated and grounded conductor paralleling a live current-carrying conductor has current induced on it. This occurs because each conductor acts like a coil in a transformer and the air between acts like the core of a transformer. Current flowing through a live conductor acts as the primary coil. A nearby grounded conductor acts as the secondary coil. Induced current can only flow when a circuit has been created in the isolated conductor. As illustrated in Figure 6–5, the installation of two sets of grounds (bracket grounds) on the isolated conductor creates a circuit with current flowing along the conductor, down one set of grounds through earth (or neutral) and up the other set of grounds. The magnitude of the induced current is higher in the following situations:

- The current on the live conductor is increased.
- The distance between the two conductors is decreased.
- The length of parallel between the two conductors is increased.

Because the amount of induction from a magnetic field depends on current and not voltage, this induction is also a hazard on lower-distribution voltages.

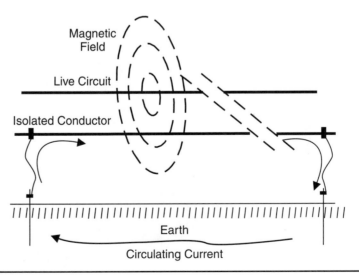

Figure 6–5 Magnetic field effect between conductors.

Working in an Environment with High Induction

6.4.7 A powerline worker is exposed to induction from a magnetic field when working on an isolated and grounded circuit that is parallel to a live circuit. When only one set of grounds is installed at the point of work, a circuit has not been created for the current to flow. When the conductor is grounded in two locations, a circuit is created and current flows through the conductor and through the grounds. If this circuit is interrupted by removing a ground or cutting a conductor, a high voltage is available across the open point. That is why it is important to install and remove grounds with a live-line tool.

Transpositions

6.4.8 Many transmission and subtransmission circuits constructed before 1955 had *transpositions* installed in them (Figure 6–6). A transposition involved changing the position of the three-phase conductors by crossing a conductor from one side of the structure to the other side. When the different phases crossed each other, the induced voltages on the phases canceled out each other. They were installed because large electromagnetic fields interfered with open-wire telephone circuits. In Figure 6–7, the A phase crosses under the other two phases to go from one side to the other. Three of these transpositions (one barrel) are needed to bring the three conductors back to the original ABC configuration.

Figure 6–6   Transposition on subtransmission circuit.

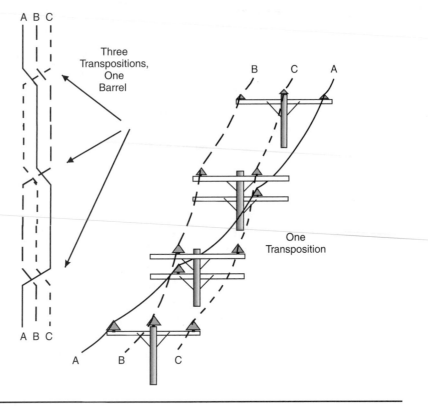

Figure 6–7 Transposition.

6.5 Voltage Gradients

Ground Faults **6.5.1** There is a hazard to anyone working at a location where a ground fault results in electrical energy flowing into earth. A ground fault is a short circuit caused when an object in contact with earth contacts a live conductor.

The following are examples of ground faults:

- Electrical current flows into earth when a utility pole becomes alive due to contact with a live conductor or because of a faulty insulator.

- Electrical current flows into earth when a live conductor comes in contact with a tree or a truck boom.

- Electrical current flows into earth when a portable ground is accidentally installed on a live conductor.

- Electrical current flows into earth when an underground cable is dug up or punctured.

- Electrical current flows into earth when a live conductor is lying on the ground.

- Electrical current flows into earth when the operating handle of a gang-operated switch becomes alive because of a switch-insulator failure.
- Electrical current flows into earth at the reel stand or tensioning machine when the conductor being strung contacts a live circuit.

Voltage Gradients

6.5.2 At the point where the current enters earth, the current breaks up and flows in many paths, depending on the makeup and resistance of the earth. The voltage available is highest where the current enters earth. The earth acts as a network of resistors, and the voltage drops as the current flows through these resistors. The voltage at the current-entry point is higher than the voltage one or two paces away from the entry point. Therefore, a difference of potential in the earth occurs around the current-entry point.

It is easiest to visualize these voltage gradients as ripples in a pond emanating from where a stone has entered. The ripples are strongest at the center and get weaker as they get farther from the center. The difference in the intensity of the ripples represents the difference in the voltage levels. Figure 6–8 shows the voltage between the ripples lessening as the distance from the contact point is increased. Voltage gradients are also known as *ground gradients, potential gradients,* and *step potentials.*

One form of protection from ground gradients is work from a ground-gradient mat (equipotential mats) that is bonded to the device that mat become energized. Figure 6–9 shows a person standing on a fabric-style ground-gradient mat that electrically bonded to the switch being operated. If the cap and pin breaks off the

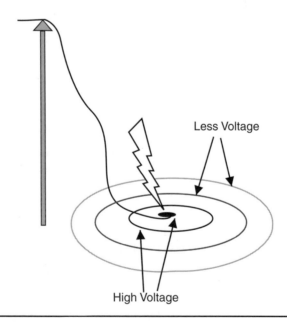

Less Voltage

High Voltage

Figure 6–8   Voltage gradients.

Figure 6–9   Operating a switch from a ground mat. *(Kri-Tech Power Products Ltd.)*

post insulator and energizes the steel structure, the person will be safe because no voltage difference would exist between the hands and the feet.

Figure 6–10 shows a person working on a ground gradient mat that is bonded to a pad-mount transformer. If ground fault on a cable or elsewhere raises the potential on the transformer tank, the person would be safe because no potential difference would occur between the hands and the knees.

A Voltage-Gradient Example

6.5.3 The line trade is exposed to a ground-gradient hazard when a pole is being installed in a live circuit. If a pole contacts a live circuit and also contacts the ground, a voltage gradient is set up at the base of the pole. The details involved with setting a pole in a live line are used in the remainder of this section to explain the specific hazards involving ground gradients.

Setting a Pole in a Live Distribution Line

6.5.4 A work procedure to set a pole in a live line requires insulated cover-up on the conductors and/or on the pole. With the use of cover-up and an observer, a modern vehicle can set poles in a live line without making contact with a bare live circuit. The procedure requires that the boom-equipped vehicle setting the pole be grounded so that the circuit trips quickly if the boom or its load makes accidental contact with the circuit. If the vehicle becomes alive, anyone near the truck is exposed to ground gradients. The boom operator stays on the operating platform or uses a ground-gradient mat. The circuit breaker or recloser can be put in

Figure 6–10 Working at a pad-mount transformer from a ground mat. *(Kri-Tech Power Products Ltd.)*

a nonreclose position to ensure that the circuit remains isolated should it be tripped out due to an accidental contact.

A person controlling the butt of the pole wears rubber gloves to provide a barrier against touch potentials (Figure 6–11). Pole tongs or cant hooks are also used to keep a person away from the base of the pole because the highest ground-gradient potentials are where the pole touches the ground. A person using rubber gloves to guide the pole into the hole could still have feet spanning two different voltage levels. At higher voltage levels, guide ropes tied to the butt of the pole can be used to get even farther away from the current-entry point.

Step Potential and Touch Potential

6.5.5 Electrical current flows into earth when an object such as a pole accidently makes contact with a live conductor. Where the pole touches earth, a rise in voltage is relative to any earth farther away from the base of the pole. The current takes many paths as it flows away from the pole. The voltage at the base of the pole is higher than the voltage farther away. The voltage or potential gradient around the base of the pole can be pictured as the ripples in a puddle after dropping a stone in the middle. There is a voltage difference between each pair of ripples, and the voltage decreases as the ripples move farther from the center.

A step potential refers to having one foot on a high-voltage ring near the base of the pole and the other foot on a lower-voltage ring farther away from the pole. A *step potential* is defined as the voltage differential between two points on the ground separated by the distance of one pace or 1 meter. A touch potential refers to touching the pole where the hands are at one potential while the feet on the

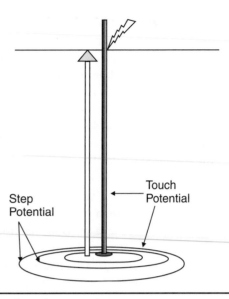

Figure 6–11   Step and touch potentials.

ground are at a different potential. A *touch potential* is defined as the voltage differential between both feet on the ground and an object being touched by hand.

Magnitude of Step and Touch Potentials

6.5.6 The magnitude of the step and touch potentials depends on the voltage of the circuit, the conductivity of the pole, and the quality of the ground. The higher the voltage of the circuit, the easier it is for the current to overcome the resistance offered by the pole and the ground. A high voltage, therefore, is more likely to generate high touch and step potentials. The magnitude of the current flowing to ground depends on the type of earth at the base of the pole and can also be dependent on the contact with the grounded derrick handling the pole. The resistance of a wood pole varies with the moisture, weather, and pole treatment. On low-distribution voltages, a wood-pole contact does not normally trip out the circuit, and the wood resistance may reduce the step and touch potentials at the base of the pole to a minimal hazard. A steel pole, a concrete pole, or a wood pole with a down-ground installed, on contact with a live conductor, has a touch potential at the base of the pole at almost the full-line voltage. The current flow into earth depends on the resistance of the ground that the base of the pole is touching.

The Size of the Step-Potential Gradient

6.5.7 Electricity needs a circuit before current can flow. Normally, current flows through a conductor to the load and returns to the source through another phase, neutral, and earth. When a fault to ground occurs, the current flows through earth back toward the source through the easiest paths available. The return flow can be into earth, back up any ground wires to the neutral, along fences or creek beds, and so on.

When setting a pole, the vehicle should be grounded. The return path for much of the current is back to the vehicle and up to the neutral. In other words, during a ground fault there is no way to know where and how far the ground gradients will travel. In good, moist earth, there is less resistance, and, therefore, the voltage drops very quickly, before the current travels very far from the pole. When the voltage drops quickly, there is a high-voltage difference between the potential rings close to the base of the pole. On a high-resistance surface, such as gravel, sand, rock, or dry snow, the potential gradients drop off more slowly and farther from the base of the pole. There is less voltage difference across each step.

Voltage Gradients on a Pole

6.5.8 Voltage gradients can also occur along a wood pole when a live conductor contacts a pole. For a person on a pole, the voltage at the contact point is higher than the voltage at a spot farther from the contact point. Anyone on the pole would have a potential difference between the hands and the feet. On a very conductive pole, such as a steel structure, there is less potential difference between the hands and feet because both are in contact with the same object at the same potential.

6.6 Working with Neutrals

Voltage and Current on a Neutral

6.6.1 A neutral or a metallic cable sheath tends to be treated as a nonenergized conductor by the line trade. This is probably because the voltage on a neutral is normally below the threshold of sensation. The neutral voltage is usually below 10 volts. There is, however, a current flow in the neutral, and when the current is interrupted, a recovery voltage appears across the open point.

Sources of Neutral Current

6.6.2 In an electrical circuit, all the current must return to the source. On a single-phase wye circuit, all the current returns by way of the neutral and the earth. The neutral and the earth are parallel paths for current to flow back to the source. Depending on the type of earth, about two-thirds of the current flows through the neutral and the remaining one-third flows through the earth. The bigger the load on the single phase, the greater the amount of current that returns to the source. On a *balanced* three-phase wye circuit, all the current returns to the source on the other phases. However, the loads on distribution circuits are not perfectly balanced between the three phases. The neutral and the earth carry the unbalanced portion of the current back to the source. The more unequally the phases are loaded, the greater the current flow through the neutral. In an electrical system where feeders are tied between stations, the neutral can also carry current between substations.

The neutral on a secondary service also carries current. On a three-wire 120/240-volt service, the current returns to the source transformer on the opposite leg of the two 120-volt legs. When the load is not balanced equally between the two 120-volt legs of the service, all the current will not return to the source through the opposite leg. The neutral and, to a lesser extent, the earth serve as the path for remaining current to flow back to the source.

Sources of Neutral Voltage

6.6.3 When there is a current flow, there also has to be some voltage pushing it. Therefore, if the current flow is reduced, the voltage is reduced. As the current gets higher, the voltage gets higher. Normally, on a neutral, the voltage is below 10 volts and not felt by a worker.

- The voltage on a neutral increases if the neutral resistance is increased. Based on Ohm's law ($E = I \times R$), the voltage increases if the resistance or current is increased. A poor electrical connection in the neutral circuit raises the voltage.

- There can be a very high voltage on a neutral, in relation to earth, during a line-to-ground fault. A line-to-ground fault on one phase is like a large unbalanced load between the phases. A large portion of the return flow to the source is through the neutral and earth. A high-fault current will result in a high voltage on the neutral.

- There can be a very high voltage on a neutral when a phase is struck by lightning. The high voltage on the phase couples (is linked together electromagnetically) with other phases and the neutral. Electrical coupling with the neutral tends to bring the phase voltage down, but electrical coupling also raises the voltage on the neutral before the voltage is dissipated to ground on the multigrounded neutral.

An Open Neutral

6.6.4 An open or broken neutral is a major hazard in the line trade. There is normally no apparent voltage on a neutral. A neutral is usually grounded on each side of a break at transformers or other equipment. There is, however, a high voltage across the break. On a multigrounded neutral, the voltage is kept low. If the current is interrupted by opening or cutting the neutral, all the voltage pushing the current appears across the open point. A break in the neutral introduces an infinite resistance to current flow and results in a total voltage drop. Applying Ohm's law shows that the total circuit voltage (recovery voltage) is available across the break. It is, therefore, a basic line procedure to always jumper any neutral before it is cut.

Precautions for Working with a Neutral

6.6.5 A powerline worker must take special precautions that apply only to a neutral. The first precaution is to properly identify which conductor is the neutral. On older constructions, the neutral position is not always standard. On some two-phase delta constructions, one phase is in a position that would normally be the neutral position in a wye system. Placing a ground on the neutral is a positive identification method. If a neutral is to be cut or joined, a bypass jumper must be installed. This avoids exposure to the voltage that is available across the open point. Stay away from all conductors, including the neutral, during a lightning storm.

6.7 Vehicle Grounding and Bonding

The Vehicle as an Electrical Hazard

6.7.1 Vehicles with booms are exposed to accidental or inadvertent contact when used in the vicinity of live circuits. A vehicle can become an electrical hazard to people on the ground at a job site in three ways (Table 6–1).

TABLE 6–1   The Vehicle as an Electrical Hazard

If	Then
A person on the ground is in contact with a utility vehicle while the uninsulated portion of a boom accidently contacts a live circuit.	The person is a parallel path to ground and will take some share of the current flowing to ground.
A person on the ground is near a utility vehicle while the uninsulated portion of a boom accidently contacts a live circuit.	The person is exposed to ground gradients at each location that current is entering the earth.
An uninsulated boom is used to lift or handle an isolated and grounded conductor in a high-induction area.	Unless the boom is bonded to the grounded conductors, the boom can be at a different potential to the conductors being handled.

How Vehicles Can Become Alive

6.7.2 Most utilities have procedures to protect people on the ground in case a vehicle should become alive due to inadvertent contact with a live circuit. Many types of mishaps can cause a digger derrick or the uninsulated portion of an aerial device to become alive, such as the following:

- A live conductor can fall onto a boom.
- A digger derrick can make contact while installing a pole or other equipment.
- The lower boom of an aerial device can inadvertently make contact with a tap running laterally from the circuit being worked on as shown in Figure 6–12.

Ground-Gradient Hazards Near the Vehicle

6.7.3 When the vehicle becomes alive (Figure 6–13), there are ground gradients in the vicinity of the vehicle's outriggers, tires, attached trailers, and anything else in contact with the vehicle. If the vehicle is grounded to the system neutral, there is a voltage rise on the neutral and a ground-gradient hazard at all the down-ground locations along the line. If a ground rod or pole down-ground is used to ground the vehicle, there is a voltage gradient around them as well.

Protection from Shock

6.7.4 The only real protection available to people working around a vehicle when a boom makes contact with a live conductor is to stay on the vehicle or stay away from the vehicle. Staying on the vehicle or on a ground-gradient mat bonded to the vehicle keeps a person at the same potential as the vehicle. As long as the person avoids contact with anything not connected to the vehicle, there will be no current flow through the person to another object. Keeping a safe distance from a vehicle that can become alive prevents contact with the vehicle and keeps one a safe distance away from high-ground gradients. Truck barricading promotes the need to stay away from the vehicle. High-resistance footwear provides additional protection by increasing the resistance of a person as a parallel path to ground. High-resistance footwear also provides protection from ground gradients.

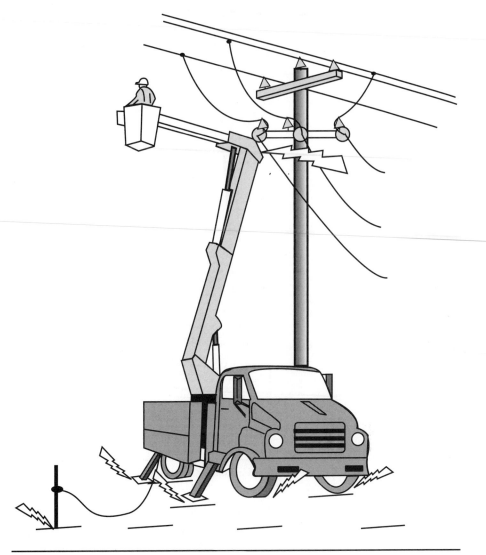

Figure 6–12 Boom contact with lateral tap.

Grounding the Vehicle

6.7.5 When there is contact between a utility vehicle's boom and a live conductor, anyone touching the vehicle is a parallel path to ground and has some current flowing through him or her. Even when the vehicle is grounded to an excellent ground, like a neutral, the amount of current going through the body could still be fatal. Grounding the vehicle to the neutral promotes a fast trip-out of the circuit should the vehicle become alive, and it also promotes the collapse of the voltage in the system. A fast trip-out reduces the exposure time to the hazard, and a collapse of the voltage reduces the voltage to which people are exposed.

On lower-voltage wye distribution systems, the vehicle must be grounded to a neutral to trip the circuit. The resistance of a ground rod or anchor rod is normally not low enough to generate a fault current high enough to trip out the circuit. On

Figure 6–13   Ground-gradient hazard near vehicle.

a delta circuit, the vehicle should be grounded to a ground rod. Most delta circuits are protected by ground-fault relays that trip out a circuit when there is a line-to ground fault. On higher-voltage distribution and subtransmission circuits, the voltage is normally high enough to overcome the resistance of a well-driven ground rod and cause the circuit to trip out.

Choice of Ground Electrodes

6.7.6 The purpose of grounding a vehicle is to promote a fast trip-out of a circuit if a boom contacts a live conductor. A vehicle should be grounded to the best ground electrode available at the work site so that any fault current has a good return path to the source. A complete circuit is needed for the current flow to be high enough to trip the protective switchgear. Typical ground electrodes, listed in order of priority, are these:

- A permanent ground network such as a station ground, a neutral, or a steel tower.

- A ground rod or an anchor rod in earth.

- A temporarily driven ground rod.

TABLE 6–2 **Boom Contact with Live 7.2-Kilovolt Conductor**

Vehicle Ground	Fault Current Generated	Truck-to-Ground Voltage	Current through Person
Vehicle Not Grounded	200A	5500V	6A
Vehicle Connected to Ground Rod	700A	5000V	6A
Vehicle Connected to Neutral	5000A	200V	0.2A

A permanent ground network ensures that the fault current has a good path back to the source to complete the circuit. Ground rods and temporary ground rods place a relatively high resistance element in the circuit.

Typical Values during a Boom Contact

6.7.7 Table 6–2 gives some typical ampere values that can occur when a digger derrick makes contact with a 7,200-volt conductor at a location where the circuit is capable of supplying a 6,000-ampere fault current. In this example, a person with a resistance of 1,000 ohms is touching the vehicle. When reading Table 6–2 remember the following:

- A person's heart can go into fibrillation after 50 milliamperes or 0.05 amperes of current goes through the body for a very short time.

- A location with a 6,000-ampere fault current available will probably be near the source of a feeder. Depending on the size of the recloser or the relay settings, the protection will probably need more than a 700-ampere fault current to operate.

Examples of Using a Ground Rod to Ground a Vehicle

6.7.8 A temporarily driven ground rod may not always trip out a circuit.

Transmission Lines Example

An accidental boom contact is made with a transmission line or subtransmission line. The vehicle is grounded to a temporary ground rod. The rod will probably provide a resistance low enough to trip out the circuit. The resistance of a temporary ground rod varies with the soil conditions but would seldom be less than 25 ohms and frequently is 100 ohms. Using Ohm's law and an example calculation of a 50-ohm ground rod for working on a 230-kilovolt circuit, the fault current generated would be:

$$I = \frac{E}{R} = \frac{133,000}{50} = 2,660 \ amperes$$

where
  $R = 50$ ohms
  $E = 230 \div 1.732 = 133 \ kV$ phase to ground

The fault current generated by the ground rod in this example is more than enough to trip out the circuit, especially a circuit protected by a breaker with relays that sense phase differential and ground currents.

Distribution Lines Example

An accidental boom contact is made with a distribution circuit. The vehicle is grounded to a temporary ground rod. There is a likelihood that the resistance of the rod is too high to trip the circuit quickly or at all. Using Ohm's law and 50 ohms of resistance for the temporary ground rod on a 4,800-volt circuit, the fault current generated would be as follows:

$$I = \frac{E}{R} = \frac{4,800}{50} = 96 \; amperes$$

In this example, a fault current of 96 amperes will not trip out a circuit protected by a fuse larger than 50 amperes because it takes 100 amperes to blow a 50-ampere fuse.

Boom in Contact with an Isolated and Grounded Conductor

6.7.9 A circuit is *not dead* when it has been isolated and grounded. There is often current flowing in the grounds, and there is often a voltage difference between the circuit and a remote ground. When a truck boom or crane is used on a job where a circuit is isolated and grounded, the boom should be bonded to the portable line grounds. On a right-of-way that has high induction from live neighboring circuits or in the rare case of accidental reenergization, bonding ensures that there will be no potential difference between the vehicle, boom, winch, and conductors.

Examples of Hazards Using a Boom around Isolated Conductors

6.7.10 The following examples of hazardous incidents are rare occurrences, but they have all happened:

- A person working on a conductor handles the winch of a crane (Figure 6–14) and bridges the grounded conductors and an unbonded crane. An unbonded vehicle is a remote ground in relation to the grounded conductors. In an area with high induction, there is a high voltage between the grounded conductors and the winch.

- When a vehicle is bonded to grounded conductors, the vehicle and the grounded conductors are at the same voltage. In a high-induction area, the bond sets up a voltage between the vehicle and any remote ground. A person standing on the ground and touching the vehicle could receive a shock. Grounding and bonding the vehicle, as well as bonding, reduces the voltage difference between the ground and the vehicle.

- When using an aerial device to install grounds, especially on a multicircuit line, the vehicle is often grounded/bonded to the same ground electrode as the portable line grounds. If the grounds are mistakenly installed on a live circuit, the truck also becomes energized, endangering those on the ground near the vehicle. People on the ground should stand clear of the vehicle until the grounds are installed.

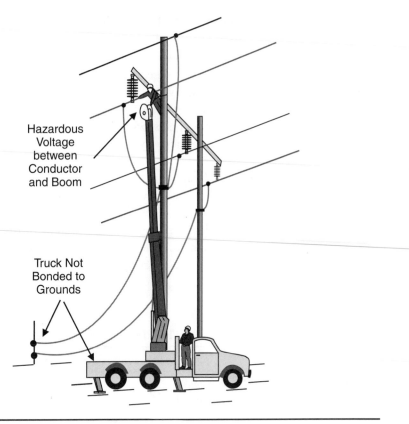

Hazardous
Voltage
between
Conductor
and Boom

Truck Not
Bonded to
Grounds

Figure 6–14   Vehicle boom as a remote ground.

6.8 Electromagnetic Fields

**Why the
Interest in
Electromagnetic
Fields?**

6.8.1 Before the 1970s, the only risks thought to be associated with electricity were electric shock or flash burns. There is now a question about the possible relationship between electromagnetic fields (EMFs) and some types of cancer. Most of the evidence comes from epidemiological studies. *Epidemiology* is a science that looks for statistical evidence of health patterns in people and the factors that may be responsible.

**What Are
EMFs?**

6.8.2 Wherever there is electricity, magnetism appears, and vice versa. Electricity and magnetism both travel in the form of waves and in fields (in the same way that gravitation has a field), and they spread everywhere. EMFs are energy waves with both an electric component and a magnetic component. Energy radiates out from a source and can travel without the need of any material to conduct it. Electromagnetic waves can travel through a vacuum and at the speed of light, and they have a wavelength, frequency, and amplitude (or field strength). A wavelength is the distance between one peak on the wave and the next peak. The frequency, measured in hertz, is the number of wave peaks that pass by in 1 second.

Electromagnetic waves from power frequencies of 50 or 60 hertz are just one portion of a large band or spectrum of electromagnetic waves. The 50- or 60-hertz waves from powerlines are very long waves (5,000 kilometers) and are referred to as extremely low frequency (ELF) waves. When EMFs are discussed in the media, the term usually refers to electric and magnetic fields in the power-frequency range that has a powerline as its source. The term *EMF*, however, is also used for electromagnetic fields with higher frequencies, which radiate much farther than power-frequency waves.

Electromagnetic Spectrum

6.8.3 All rays—including X-rays, ultraviolet light, visible light, infrared light, microwaves, radio waves, heat, and electrical powerlines—are electromagnetic waves. The properties that differentiate these various sources are the frequency and the wavelength. Table 6–3 shows some of the types of radiation that make up an electromagnetic spectrum. The lines dividing the different types of radiation overlap because the division between them is not accurately defined.

TABLE 6–3 **The Electromagnetic Spectrum**

Source	Effects	Frequency (Hz)	Wavelength
ELF (Extremely Low Frequency) DC Is 0Hz Powerlines Are 50–60Hz	Low Energy No Thermal Effects	3 to 300	Powerlines are 6,000 km.
VLF (Very Low Frequency) AM Radio	No Proven Health Effects	3,000 to 30,000	AM radio waves are about 300 meters.
VHF (Very High Frequency) FM and TV	Can Cause Heating	10^7 to 10^9	Television waves are 0.3 to 5.5 meters.
Radar Microwave	High Induced Currents	10^9 to 10^{12}	Microwaves are about 12 centimeters.
Infrared Visible Light Ultraviolet	Energy Waves Can Be Seen Photochemical Effects	10^{12} to 10^{15}	Visible light waves are from 0.75 to 0.04 micrometers.
Ionizing Radiation Ultraviolet Radiation X-Rays Gamma Rays	High Energy Radiation Burns DNA Damage	10^{15} to 10^{22}	X-rays are about 0.03 to 0.00001 micrometers.

Sources of Power-Frequency EMF

6.8.4 All live electrical wires, equipment, and appliances have an *electric field* and a *magnetic field* around them. Combined, these two fields are referred to as EMF. (EMFs should not be confused with *emf*, which refers to electromotive force.) The electric and magnetic fields behave differently and are measured separately, as seen in Table 6–4.

TABLE 6–4   Comparison of Electric and Magnetic Fields

Electric Fields	Magnetic Fields
The electric field is a voltage field. The higher the voltage source, the higher the electric field. An electric field is present around any live conductor and is independent of the current flow in the circuit.	The magnetic field is a field of magnetic lines of energy. The higher the current in a source conductor, the higher the magnetic field. If there is no load on the circuit, then there will be no magnetic field.
An electric field is measured in volts per meter (V/m).	A magnetic field is measured in microteslas (μT) or milligauss (mG).
The strength of the electric field drops off with the inverse of the distance from the source squared ($E = \frac{I}{r^2}$), where r is the radius from the source.	The greater the distance from a live source, the less the strength of an EMF. The strength of the magnetic field drops off with the inverse of the distance from the source ($H = \frac{I}{r}$), where r is the radius from the source.
Shielding from electric fields occurs if there are trees, walls, and such, blocking the way and draining the electric current to ground.	Magnetic fields are only weakened, but not stopped, by barriers such as trees, etc. They are similar to the effect of a magnet where the lines of force can go through material.
The electric field from a powerline would not normally penetrate into a building.	Magnetic fields from a powerline can penetrate a building.
When a person is within an electric field, there is a voltage induced on the body. Workers feel the existence of electric fields when they are working in a substation or on a high-voltage transmission line. Hair tends to stand up as a person gets close to a high-voltage source. A small arc can occur when the voltage on a person's body is discharged to a grounded object.	A magnetic field can induce a current flow in lengths of conducting material such as in a wire fence. A current, however, can flow only if there is a circuit. A fence kept insulated from the ground would have no current flow on it unless it was grounded in two places to form a circuit between the two grounded locations. An isolated fence would have a voltage on it.
An electric field can induce a weak electric current flow in the body by moving charges in the body. The redistribution of charges causes small currents, but these currents are typically much smaller than those produced naturally by the brain, nerves, and heart.	A magnetic field will pass through a body but, because a person's body is not normally in series with a circuit, there should be no current induced in it from magnetic waves.
An electric field can cause a fluorescent tube to light up when it is held under a high-voltage powerline.	A magnetic field can be induced on a circuit built near a high-voltage line. You could actually steal power if a circuit built near a powerline were connected to a load. You would have a small amount of current and no control over the voltage, which would make this option impractical.

Methods of Reducing the Strength of EMF

6.8.5 There are ways to reduce the strength of EMF coming from live power conductors:

1. Increasing the heights of poles and towers increases the distance from the ground to the powerlines.

2. A circuit converted to a higher voltage, given the same amount of load, would carry less current and, therefore, have a lower-strength EMF.

3. There is a canceling effect from three-phase lines and multicircuit configurations. The EMF from the current returning on one phase cancels the EMF from the current traveling in the other direction on another phase. A closer spacing between conductors reduces the EMF. For example, a triplex service or house wiring has a reduced EMF due to the closeness and canceling effect of the returning current.

4. Underground powerlines have a reduced electric field because of the shielding from the cable sheath and the surrounding earth. There is also a reduction in magnetic fields for underground lines, due not to shielding but to the EMF-canceling effect of the neutral and other phases in the closer conductor spacings allowed underground.

5. Transpositions in a powerline reduce the EMF. Transpositions were originally put into circuits to reduce the effect of EMF on open-wire communications circuits. As a prudent avoidance measure, the EMF from electric blankets and waterbed heaters is reduced with transpositions when they are manufactured because the wires are continually crossing over each other.

6. Methods using metal shielding to reduce magnetic fields from powerlines are available, but they are considered an expensive method for shielding large areas.

Measurement of EMF

6.8.6 To measure the strength of EMF, two instruments are needed: one for the electric field and another for the magnetic field. The strength of an electric field is measured as volts per meter (V/m) or in larger units of kilovolts per meter (kV/m). The strength of the electric field depends on the voltage of the source conductor and the distance at which the measurement is taken. The instrument must be held away from the body because the body acts as a shield and distorts the readings.

The strength of a magnetic field is measured in teslas (T) or gauss (Gs). The gauss is common in the United States, and the tesla is used internationally. A tesla is a measurement of the magnetic-field intensity or the density of magnetic lines. The strength of the magnetic field depends on the amount of current flowing in the source conductor and the distance at which the measurement is being taken. Measurements must be done in different locations over a period of time because the load current of the circuit changes during the day. Tesla units are too large to measure common exposure; therefore, the microtesla is used.

1 tesla = 1,000,000 microteslas

1 tesla = 10,000 gauss

1 gauss = 1,000 milligauss

1 microtesla = 10 milligauss

When taking measurements, it is important to understand the difference between an *emission* and *exposure*. A measurement taken at a conductor will give the emission, but exposure to the emission is normally much farther away. Exposure must be measured at a location where people would be normally. The measurements will not mean much to the average person unless the numbers are used to compare the EMF strength from various sources, as shown in Tables 6–5 and 6–6.

TABLE 6–5 Sample Measurements of Electric-Field Strength

Location of Measurement	Typical Values (V/m)
Under a transmission line, the field strength depends on the voltage of the line and the height of the conductors.	One to 10kV/m (1000 to 10,000V/m)
On the edge of a transmission-line corridor.	100 to 1,000V/m
Near an overhead distribution line.	2 to 20V/m
In homes.	200V/m close to an appliance to less than 2V/m in other locations in the home.
Exposure to powerline workers, cable splicers, and substation workers.	Typical 100 to 2,000V/m with peaks as high as 5,000V/m.

TABLE 6–6 Sample Measurements of Magnetic Field Strength

Location of Measurement	Typical Values (μT)
Under a transmission line, the field strength depends on the line loading and the height of the conductors.	10μT
On the edge of a transmission-line corridor.	0.1 to 1.0μT
Near an overhead distribution line.	0.2 to 1.0μT
In homes.	150μT near appliances to less than 0.02μT in other areas in the home
Exposure to powerline workers, cable splicers, and substation workers.	Average 0.5 to 4μT with as high as 100μT

Dose

6.8.7 One problem in researching the health effects of EMF is to determine which dose to measure. The word *dose* means exposure that produces an effect. For example, if a risk is due to EMF exposure, what type of dose would produce harmful effects?

- Is a weak field safer than a strong field?
- Is it exposure to the peak electric field or exposure to a constant electric field that is harmful?
- Is it the going into and coming out of an electric field?
- Is it exposure to the peak magnetic field or exposure to a constant magnetic field?
- Is it the going into and coming out of a magnetic field?

Natural Levels of Electric and Magnetic Fields

6.8.8 Electric and magnetic fields exist naturally on earth. This EMF source is obviously not at 50 or 60 hertz, but it is a DC source with a fluctuating voltage and current level. It is the fluctuations that cause electric and magnetic fields to occur.

Earth's atmosphere has a naturally occurring electric field that fluctuates on the surface around 130 volts per meter. Large electric current through Earth's core creates a magnetic field on the surface that can range from 30 to 60 microteslas. The magnetic field is stronger at the North Pole and South Pole than at the equator.

A thunderstorm is the ultimate demonstration of naturally occurring electric and magnetic fields in action. The electric-field strength is high enough to break down the insulation value of air and discharge as lightning. The high current within the electric arc generates a large EMF that can be noticed as interference on radio and television reception.

Health Risk

6.8.9 The health risk of EMF from 50- or 60-hertz sources has been the subject of more than 500 studies over a 30-year period. Some biological effects are produced by very high levels of electric and magnetic fields, but no agreement has been reached on whether lower levels are any hazard to health. Nor has there been any definitive proof one way or the other that exposure to EMF is a health risk. Experience shows that if there is a risk, it will be extremely small. Compared to smoking, diet, or sunlight as causal factors in cancer risk, the risk of cancer from EMF is extremely small. Electric utilities will likely continue to monitor future studies and keep their staffs informed of developments.

Limits of Exposure

6.8.10 The World Health Organization, the International Radiation Protection Organization, and other organizations have published threshold limits of exposure to EMF from power-frequency sources (50 and 60 hertz). There are limits for the general public and for workers. For example, one organization has a threshold limit for workday exposure to EMF as 10 kilovolts per meter for electric fields and as 5 gauss for magnetic fields. Utility workers should check for the limits their own utilities have adopted for exposure to EMF.

Working Near a Cellular Antenna or Microwave Dish

6.8.11 Powerline workers can be exposed to electromagnetic microwaves (MW) or radio frequency (RF) waves radiating from PCS (personal communications services, such as digital cellular phone service) antennas and microwave dishes that are installed on utility-owned structures. It is most hazardous in the area immediately in front of transmitting antenna at distances of less than 10 feet (3 m). Figure 6–15 shows where RF/MW frequencies are in the electromagnetic field spectrum.

An immediate health effect to a high exposure to RF energy is heating. Like a microwave oven, RF energy has the ability to excite molecules and create heat in any exposed tissue. An early symptom of overexposure is similar to a person showing signs of heat exhaustion. The heating effect may not be noticed by a person until damage is done. Damage can range from raising of body temperature to burned tissue and organs. Injuries from RF exposure is not cumulative as it would be from an ionizing radiation source.

When there is work to be done on a structure with an RF antenna or microwave dish, the employer must calculate the minimum safe distance for that antenna. Calculations are required to determine the distance required to receive less than the Maximum Permissible Exposure (MPE), which is measured in milliwatts per squared centimeter (mW/cm^2) of tissue. Health effects of overexposure to RF/MW fields depend on the frequency and intensity of the fields, the duration of exposure, the distance from the source, and any shielding that is used. If a minimum safe distance cannot be maintained to do the required work, other safeguards, such as a shutdown, may be required.

First aid is similar to heat stroke: Remove casualty from exposure area, provide cool drinking water, and apply cold water or ice to burned areas. There could be internal tissue damage without visible skin injury, so it is advisable to seek medical attention.

Induced Current from an RF/MW Transmitter

6.8.12 An RF transmitter can also induce electromagnetic induction on nearby objects. The effect is the same as induction from a power line. A voltage can be induced on a person, and a shock can result when touching a grounded object. Sparking may occur across a gap between two metal objects that are close together as the induced current is trying to flow to ground.

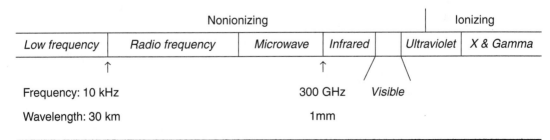

Figure 6–15   Frequencies on the electromagnetic spectrum.

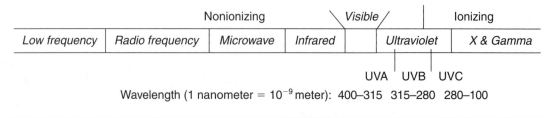

Figure 6–16 Ultraviolet light on the electromagnetic spectrum.

Ultraviolet Radiation

6.8.13 Ultraviolet (UV) radiation is a form of electromagnetic radiation. On the electromagnetic spectrum, UV radiation comes between visible light and X-rays. It is divided into three wavelength bands according to its effects on living tissue: UV-A, UV-B, and UV-C (see Figure 6–16).

The sun is the main source of UV radiation, and it is known that in the short term it can cause sunburn and in the long term skin cancer. An electric arc is a UV hazard where the eyes are most vulnerable because of the high intensity and short time exposure.

Reduce exposure through clothing and apply sunscreen with a sun protection factor (SPF) of 15 or higher of the type that is effective for both UV-A and UV-B rays. Plastic safety glasses are also good UV filters for protecting the eyes.

6.9 Minimum Approach Distance

Minimum Approach Distance as a Barrier

6.9.1 Maintaining a *minimum approach distance* to live exposed conductors is the most common barrier a powerline worker uses to avoid electrical contact. Government regulators and utilities have tables listing the minimum approach distance from various voltages for different levels of qualified people and equipment. The minimum approach distances in Table 6–7 apply to work in the vicinity of a live circuit, and they also apply to live-line work.

The flashover voltage for a live-line tool is the same as it is for air. A fiberglass live-line tool may be better insulation than air, but the distance needed on a tool is an air gap between the hands on a live-line tool and the live conductor. Rubber-glove work and barehand work may appear to be exceptions to the minimum approach table, but the table still applies, in reverse. Rubber-glove and barehand procedures depend on the powerline worker being insulated from ground or other phases.

The table should apply to the distance from the powerline worker to any exposed objects that are second points of contact. Unless they are covered with rubber or fiber barriers, a minimum approach distance is kept from other phases, the neutral, a grounded structure, or any other grounded objects.

TABLE 6–7   Typical Minimum Approach Distances

Maximum Phase-to-Phase Voltage (Max. Phase-to-Ground Voltage)	Minimum Approach Distance Phase-to-Ground Exposure	Minimum Approach Distance Phase-to-Phase Exposure
0.05 to 1.0 kV	Avoid Contact	Avoid Contact
Up to 15 kV (8.7 kV)	2 ft., 1 in. (64 cm)	2 ft., 2 in. (66 cm)
Up to 36.0 kV (20.8 kV)	2 ft., 4 in. (72 cm)	2 ft., 7 in. (77 cm)
Up to 46.0 kV (26.6 kV)	2 ft., 7 in. (77 cm)	2 ft., 10 in. (85 cm)
Up to 72.5 kV	3 ft. (80 cm)	3 ft., 6 in. (1.05 m)
Up to 121 kV	3 ft., 2 in. (95 cm)	4 ft., 3 in. (1.29 m)
Up to 145 kV	3 ft., 7 in. (1.09 m)	4 ft., 11 in. (1.50 m)
Up to 169 kV	4 ft. (1.22 m)	5 ft., 8 in. (1.71 m)
Up to 242 kV	5 ft., 3 in. (1.59 m)	7 ft., 6 in. (2.27 m)
Up to 362 kV	8 ft., 6 in. (2.59 m)	12 ft., 6 in. (3.8 m)
Up to 550 kV	11 ft., 3 in. (3.42 m)	18 ft., 1 in. (5.50 m)
Up to 800 kV	14 ft., 11 in. (4.53 m)	26 ft. (7.91 m)

The distances in Table 6–7 apply to a qualified, competent worker:

- working near a bare, exposed live circuit or equipment.

- keeping a length of clear live-line tool for the voltage being worked on.

- keeping any objects that are second points of contact at the distances listed while working with rubber gloves or bare hand.

Factors Considered for a Minimum Approach Distance

6.9.2 The minimum approach distance tables consider the hazard of an electric discharge from a live conductor to a person, and they consider an inadvertent movement by a worker in the vicinity of a live conductor. A minimum approach distance, therefore, consists of an *electrical-factor distance* and an *ergonomic* or *human-factor distance*. (*Note:* The formula shown is an overview of the factors calculated, the actual formula used is more complex.)

$$Minimum\ approach\ distance = A + (F \times B)$$

where
A is a human-factor distance that takes into account a momentary inadvertent reaching into the prohibited zone.
F is the minimum electrical clearance that would prevent a flashover from the highest transient voltage from an internal source.
B is a safety factor to ensure there is no chance for a flashover across the minimum electrical clearance.

The Electrical Factor ($F \times B$) in a Minimum Approach Distance

6.9.3 Design engineers use standard electrical clearances when determining the distance allowed between a phase and a grounded object for a pole framing or transmission tower design. An electrical-clearance distance is considerably less than the minimum approach distance a person must maintain. A minimum electrical clearance, which is represented by F in the preceding formula, is just greater than the flashover distance from the highest possible internal transient voltage. An internal source for a transient overvoltage would be a switching surge. An external overvoltage surge, such as lightning, could flash over the minimum electrical-clearance distance; therefore, live-line work is not carried out with a lightning storm in the vicinity. In the formula, the electrical-clearance distance F is multiplied by a safety factor B to provide extra confidence no flashover will occur across an electrical-clearance distance between the circuit and ground. The safety factor used tends to be approximately 1.25 times the electrical-clearance distance. A nearby surge arrestor should shunt a transient overvoltage to ground to provide an additional assurance of no flashover across a normal electrical-clearance distance.

The Human Factor (A) in a Minimum Approach Distance

6.9.4 The human-factor minimum approach distance is a space needed to prevent a person from encroaching into the electrical-factor ($F \times B$) distance. A human-factor distance is subjective and has not necessarily been studied scientifically. It could be said that it is unlikely that a powerline maintainer would inadvertently encroach more than 3 feet (1 meter) toward a live conductor. If 3 feet (1 meter), representing A, are added to the electrical factor ($F \times B$), in the formula, a minimum approach distance can be established for each voltage.

At transmission-line voltages, 3 feet (1 meter) added to the electrical-factor distance would establish a realistic minimum approach distance table and allow transmission-line work procedures to be carried out. At transmission-line voltages, no cover-up is available, and maintaining a safe approach distance is a necessary barrier for work on or near live transmission lines.

At distribution voltages, the human-factor distance is larger than the electrical factor distance. It is often necessary to go closer than 3 feet (1 meter) to an exposed conductor. A human-factor distance of less than 3 feet (1 meter) requires extra barriers, such as the use of cover-up, an insulated platform, or a dedicated observer to reduce the risk of inadvertent contact.

Review Questions

1. What are the two types of electrical contact that a person can make?

2. Why does a full-line voltage (recovery voltage) appear across the two ends of a cut conductor?

3. When making a cut to an isolated and grounded conductor, is it necessary to install a jumper across the cut?

4. *True or False:* Any time a person is in parallel with any load in a circuit, that person is exposed to some voltage and some current regardless of the amount of resistance being offered to the current.

5. Name the two forms of induction that make up electromagnetic induction.

6. Give an example of static electricity.

7. When working in a high-voltage environment, what form of induction causes a spark from one's body every time a grounded object is touched? What type of personal protective equipment will reduce this hazard?

8. Why is induction from a magnetic field a hazard on distribution lines as well as a hazard on high-voltage transmission lines?

9. What is the hazard when working at a location where a ground fault results in electrical energy flowing into earth?

10. Which ground gradient would spread out farthest: one in moist earth or one in rocky ground?

11. Why is there a voltage across a break in a neutral?

12. Why is a person not safe when touching a vehicle that is making contact with a live circuit, even though the vehicle is grounded?

13. What is the purpose for grounding a line truck?

14. When a truck boom or crane is used for transmission-line work where a circuit is isolated and grounded, should the truck be bonded to the portable line grounds?

15. What two factors are used to make up minimum approach distance tables?

CHAPTER 7

Constructing Powerlines

Topics to Be Covered	Section
Before a Work Order Is Issued	7.1
Constructing a Pole Line	7.2
Constructing an Overhead Transmission Line	7.3
Constructing an Underground Distribution Line	7.4
Underground Transmission Lines	7.5

7.1 Before a Work Order Is Issued

Planning for Maintenance and Capital Projects

7.1.1 Work in a utility is generally divided into two main categories: capital projects and maintenance.

Maintenance is usually part of operations and maintenance (O&M) and is funded from revenue. O&M includes billing, trouble calls, low-voltage complaints, inspections, pole-top maintenance, and so on.

Capital work tends to be funded through borrowing. The philosophy behind borrowing the funds for a capital project is that the company or owners benefit from the project for a given number of future years and the future rates should pay for it.

A large part of both O&M and capital cost is the overhead that is applied to each job. The overhead pays for engineering, accounting, safety professionals, supervision, and so on.

Utilities set priorities for maintenance and capital programs needed to keep the electrical system operating and to ensure that the quality of power delivered to the customer service entrance is at an acceptable level and meets standards.

Maintenance and capital projects are prompted by circumstances or data such as the following:

1. Peak load voltage and current surveys at substations and on individual feeders.

2. Problems with power quality, such as voltage flicker.

3. Customer demand, such as subdivision layouts and road-widening projects.

4. Nonstandard clearance between the conductor and the ground.

5. Underground cable replacement.

6. Rehabilitation projects, such as deteriorated pole replacement, conductor prone to breakage replacement, defective component replacement (e.g., aluminum dead ends porcelain cutouts).

Types of Line Inspections

7.1.2 Maintenance work must be prioritized so that the allocated funding can be put where it is most needed. Inspections, along with trouble calls, provide information used by engineering to prepare the maintenance program.

Inspection of the distribution and transmission are carried out because it is a good utility practice, but also to comply with applicable government regulations.

An inspection can vary from a simple patrol to very effective inspections, such as an infrared survey, vegetation survey, helicopter patrol, insulator testing, corrosion survey, pole testing, and ground resistance testing.

A very effective inspection that finds hot spots not otherwise visible takes advantage of infrared cameras. Warmer objects show up in infrared photos or video images as a lighter color than other objects that are cooler. Poor electrical connections and splices heat up, and an infrared inspection will show these objects as a lighter color. To be effective, the survey is carried out when the line is loaded, so that the heating effect is enhanced on any suspect joints and connections. Often, arrangements can be made to have system control transfer extra load to a circuit to be surveyed.

Many inspections use global information system (GIS) technology to reference data to geographic coordinates. The system allows users to continuously record what is being found, to locate each structure, and to store information electronically.

Thorough helicopter inspections can use binoculars and cameras with a vibration reduction feature that can zoom in very close to individual hardware components. A foot patrol can pick up items such as erosion, loose or missing nuts on anchor bolts, corrosion 1 foot below ground line at suspect locations, broken counterpoise, and ground wire. Measurements can be taken if a ground clearance appears low. Dangerous trees can be identified.

A device can be installed on a transmission-line conductor and operated remotely to travel the length of a span and gather data on the amount of galvanizing left on the steel core of the power conductor.

Underground transmission cables are also patrolled, sometimes weekly, mainly to check for any potential construction involving digging taking place along the cable route. Less frequently—typically annually—maintenance vaults, cable tunnels, stop joints in vaults, cables attached to bridges, alarm systems, earth-resistance measurement, and insulating oil are inspected.

Underground distribution systems have inspections where visible equipment such as vaults, pad-mount equipment, risers, and so on are inspected.

Many utilities also own communications systems used for telemetering and operating their systems that are inspected and maintained.

Types of Maintenance	**7.1.3** Utilities are constantly looking for the most effective way to carry out their planned maintenance programs. The type of maintenance a utility wants to avoid is corrective maintenance (CM), which is unscheduled and usually means something needs immediate attention. Lack of scheduled maintenance can mean a disconnect switch will not open, a voltage regulator is stuck in one position, or electrical connectors have failed. A utility also wants to avoid unnecessary maintenance, such as overhauling a recloser that when taken apart looks as good as when it was installed.

Preventative maintenance (PM) on substation equipment and line equipment such as voltage regulators and reclosers is often based on maintenance schedules either recommended by the manufacturer or "time based." Many utilities use loading history and/or number of operations as an indicator of the condition of their equipment.

Fixing hot connections and splices found by an infrared survey could be called *predictive maintenance* because it allows a utility to do repairs before a complete failure occurs.

Reliability-centered maintenance (RCM) focuses on preserving the purpose of the line or equipment. Maintenance is prioritized so that the devices and lines with safety or potential outage problems that affect the most people get priority over devices and lines with less impact. A line or device that services customers that can be back-fed from another line or device gets less priority than a radial feed to a customer. Reliability-centered maintenance also concentrates on doing maintenance on specific failure modes of lines and equipment—for example, on distribution overhead, prioritizing on failure modes means changing connectors that are prone to failure before replacing deteriorated guy guards.

A utility must set priorities when repairing deficiencies found during patrols. For example, 1 broken insulator or 8 flashed insulators in a string of 14 insulators on a 230 kV line would normally not require an immediate repair, but 8 broken insulators would. Similarly, during an infrared survey standards must be followed regarding when a hot connector or splice needs immediate replacement or when it can be scheduled at a convenient time. Chronic problems, such as corrosion at the ground line for many structures, would require a major maintenance project that is planned and budgeted in advance.

One example of a maintenance program is the inspection and maintenance of distribution lines in a given geographic area on a 5- to 10-year cycle. A utility may have a list of typical deficiencies that is prioritized based on the need to repair.

Decisions regarding which prioritized deficiencies are repaired are based on the funding available in the program.

A prioritized list of items to report may look similar to the following:

1. Public hazards, such as inadequate clearance to flag poles, antennae, and buildings.
2. Replace defective components known to be prone to failure, such as brands of dead-end insulators known to be defective, porcelain in-span switches and/or cutouts, porcelain post insulators, and wood pins.
3. Replace bad crossarms.
4. Replace connectors known to be prone to failure.
5. Repair broken strands on conductor.
6. Replace defective surge arrestors.
7. Replace open wire services.
8. Repair broken ground wires and exposed ground rods.
9. Re-pull slack down guys and replace missing guy guards.
10. Straighten leaning poles.
11. Rebuild nonstandard transformer installation.

Capital Project Planning

7.1.4 For line work, capital projects tend to be jobs where "plant" is installed. *Plant* refers to items such as structures, anchors, and conductors. Capital projects can be initiated by customer requests for service, low-voltage and/or overloaded feeders, road moves, the need for rehabilitation, and so on.

Justifying Capital Projects

Typically, a utility has a capital budget without sufficient funding for all possible projects. Projects are identified and given a preliminary estimate and are typically put into a 5-year capital projects plan. A priority is established for each project based on the justification prepared by a planning engineer. A planning engineer would provide details, cost benefits, present-day value, and so on. Typically, a justification based on correcting low voltage or overloaded circuits get priority because it would be intolerable to provide voltage below standard. The next level of priority includes new industrial customers needing service, new subdivisions requiring service, and lines that must be moved for road projects. Rehabilitation projects tend to be very low-level priorities because the justification is subjective and it is usually possible to get another year of use out of a line.

Estimating a Project

When a budget is prepared, the cost of each project is estimated so that decisions can be made as to which projects can be funded. Generally, each needed project is identified, estimated, and put on a prioritized list. The amount of funds that will be allotted to the budget will determine how many projects will be planned for the year.

Estimates range from initial ballpark estimates used to study two or three alternatives when justifying a project. Initial budget estimates are also ballpark figures that might come from cost-per-mile numbers that a utility uses for different types of line construction. When more accurate estimates are needed, a project may be planned on paper in more detail by an engineer, including drawings and estimates made from such drawings.

Before a work order is issued, a more accurate estimate is prepared based on actual staking data and field input. An estimate for an overhead distribution line, for example, would be prepared as follows:

- *Calculation of the material cost for conductor for the length of the line.* Generally, an estimator would have per unit costs for slack stringing and for tension stringing. Per unit costs would be included if existing conductors must be set out on auxiliary arms.

- *Calculation of the material costs for all the poles.* Generally, an estimator would calculate the per unit costs of setting poles based on the type of digging and whether the pole is to be set in a live circuit.

- *Calculation of the material costs of the pole framing.* Typically, a construction specifications book will contain a material and labor cost for each drawing. Using the staking data, the framing for each pole can be added up and the costs for each will be related to the construction specifications. On a new transmission line, each structure is likely to have individual specifications.

- *Calculation of transport and work equipment costs.* Each truck or piece of equipment, such as a tension machine, will have a cost figure (usually cost per hour) attached to it.

- *Calculation of administration costs such as overheads, board and lodging costs if required, and so on.*

Designing a Line

7.1.5 The design of structures, framing, vaults, and so on must meet applicable regulatory standards (such as the National Electrical Safety Code in the United States). A line design consists mainly of electrical and mechanical engineering considerations.

In terms of electricity, a line design is all about keeping the power conductor, whether overhead or underground, insulated from electrical short circuits and isolated from public contact. Three types of electrical clearances are considered when designing a line:

1. *Clearances from the ground, buildings, highways, railways, other electrical circuits, and communications cables to meet regulatory standards.* The maximum conductor sag that can occur during high temperatures due to weather and electrical load or during heavy ice conditions is included in the

specified height. In other words, final sags and clearances must be calculated. Field measurements during stringing are not adequate to determine final sag.

2. *Design standards for minimum electrical clearances between phases and between live parts, the structure, and down guys.* These clearances are much smaller than the minimum approach distances used for safe work. For example, on a three-phase 25 kV transformer installation, a standard may show that the minimum clearance between the riser drop wires to the three cutouts is 15 inches (40 cm) and the minimum distance between a phase and the transformer tank is 9 inches (13 cm). Metal hardware on a wood distribution pole must be at least 3 inches apart or bonded together to reduce the risk of sparking and radio interference.

3. *Design standards for clearances to allow safer work.* Climbing clearances have been part of design for many years. Some other examples of when utilities must consider worker safety in design include lowering the neutral 10 feet (3 m), allowing clearance for a digger derrick to hang a transformer, using saddle clamps that can easily be clipped in with live-line tools, using hardware that can be installed easily with bulky rubber gloves or live-line tools, and using armless framing for easier lifting.

Mechanically, the design for structure and conductor strength is dependent on whether the line is in a heavy, medium, or light loading district. Loading district standards take into account the potential for extreme ice, wind, and combinations of ice and wind. In the United States, the National Electric Safety Code (NESC) specifies the grades of construction; Grade B is used for most powerlines.

For new transmission lines, typically, each structure is engineered for height, strength, and foundation requirements. Each span is calculated for maximum sag. Manuals or drawings for common structures—such as twin-pole H-frame, wishbone framing, spar structures, common towers, and steel/concrete poles—are available and are used for work on existing lines. Specifications books are used for most distribution work to show how a pole should be framed, a conductor sagged, a cable installed, a transformer connected, and so on. Specifications are written as they are for good reason, but it is good practice to provide field input to design engineers. Powerline workers who choose not to follow specifications are often in violation of regulatory laws, as well as engineering practices.

Design should consider workers so that all parts of a structure, insulator, and hardware assemblies can be reached for maintenance. Climbing space, ladders where applicable, and even permanent walkways or handrails may be designed to provide access for construction and maintenance.

Staking a Project

7.1.6 A layout, staking data, or survey is prepared for most line crew assignments. Different utilities have different job titles for the staking technician who does this work. Staking is specialized work. A person who lays out service to a new customer is normally not the same one who stakes out a line for a road-widening project or the same person or crew who surveys for a new transmission line.

Before setting up a new or changed service, a technician decides whether the feed is a primary or secondary service, what size transformer is appropriate, what new poles or cable are needed, where to locate the meter base, and what size the service conductors should be. Before a technician goes out on large and more complex distribution-line projects, decisions such as conductor size, general route, type of pole or cable, and so on will have been made by a planning engineer. Ideally, the field supervisor, who will be doing the job, will go out to the site with the staking technician and engineer to provide input. For overhead lines, the technician must decide pole heights, class of pole, anchor locations, and so on. For underground lines, the route that the cable follows will be based on existing underground plant and disturbance to surface areas, such as streets and sidewalks. Obtaining property easements may also be part of a technician's responsibility.

Staking out a line using Geographic Positioning System (GPS) receivers and inputting the data into an automated Geographic Information System (GIS) helps to produce construction drawings, specifications, and maps. Once the information is in the system, it is used to easily make changes, prepare plant inventory, make material lists, and prepare as-built drawings.

The construction drawings used by field staff will show details such as pole locations, pole heights, pole class, trenching locations, transformer locations, conductor/cable size, secondary bus, services, and so on. Any plant that must be removed (salvaged) is also shown on the drawings. Drawings will refer to the applicable specifications drawings for each pole framing, equipment structure, pad-mount construction, and so on needed to carry out a project.

Joint Use with Other Utilities

7.1.7 There are some major cost advantages in going with joint-use structures and trenches where costs are shared among power, telephone, CATV coax cable (Community Antennae Television System), and in some cases gas utilities. Conductors are placed on poles such that the higher-voltage conductors are at the higher levels, and telephone and CATV are at a lower level separated by standard measurements. One standard measurement is 40 inches between the lowest powerline conductor (often the neutral or secondary bus) and the communications cable. The same spacing should exist midspan. Because the strand (messenger cable) is strung tightly before the cable is lashed to it, it is easy for the strand to contact the lower power company wires during stringing.

Often a higher grade of construction is necessary for a joint-use pole line. Anchoring is critical as can often be seen when a heavy telephone cable is added to a powerline after the powerline is in place. Poor anchoring or construction practices can cause a small movement of a dead-end or corner pole, which can cause a large change in the sag in the powerline.

In trenches, the location and spacing for power cables in relation to communication cables and gas lines are part of a joint-use agreement. Transmission-line cables are usually the deepest utility in the ground, below water, sewer, and others.

Powerline structures have become highly desirable locations on which to place new cellular antennas. Because of the live conductors on powerline structures, powerline workers are usually involved in installation of these antennas, as well as any time work on them is required by a communications company.

Color-Coded Marking System

A color-coded marking system has been adopted almost everywhere to indicate which underground utilities are present. Any flag, tape, or spray paint in these colors is a good indication of the presence of other underground utilities.

Marker	Utility
Red	Electric
Yellow	Gas, Oil, Steam
Orange	Communications, Cable
Blue	Water
Green	Sewer
Purple	Irrigation
White	Proposed Excavation
Pink	Temporary Survey Tape

Transmission-Line Refurbishment

7.1.8 The need for transmission-line refurbishment is a source of much major capital work. Many of the first transmission lines built are still in service. While some maintenance has been done on these lines, the lines cannot last forever. The most pressing reason to refurbish a line is that the power conductor is losing its strength, usually because the steel core is corroded. Data collection work includes removing short lengths of power conductor or shield wire to send it out for testing that can determine the remaining strength and flexibility. Data collection also includes checking for corrosion of structure steel, especially just below the surface.

Major refurbishment projects include structure reinforcement, footing work, pole replacement, restringing, and grounding improvement. In many cases, a new higher-voltage line will be constructed on the existing right-of-way.

Planning a New Transmission Line

7.1.9 A new transmission line requires studies to determine the need for the line, the chosen route, and why alternative solutions and routes are unacceptable. A new transmission line involves a lot of property, as well as public meetings, environmental assessments, and government approvals.

A very large financial investment is involved in a new line. Typically, newly designed structures and new drawings are issued for such a project. Lines traditionally have been plotted on long roll plans that show the exact location of each structure, span lengths, angles, property lines, environmentally sensitive areas, and access roads. Profile drawings that show structure heights and conductor sag in relation to the terrain are prepared by using applicable software. A critical component of the design is obtaining assurance that the line to ground clearance meets standards regardless of temperature, load, and ice. It is not uncommon for a conductor on a line feeding an air-conditioning load to sag an extra 20 feet on a hot day.

Emergency Standards

7.1.10 Utilities have emergency plans in place for situations such as restoration work after a major storm. Typically, emergency stock is owned by one or more utilities. A minimum number of emergency restoration towers are kept in central locations. These towers can be installed temporarily to allow the stringing of a bypass around downed structures. Power can be restored on the bypass while repairs are made to the original line. Written procedures are in place to carry out emergency work.

Utilities cooperate with other utilities and emergency service agencies to form plans and carry out mock disaster exercises. Utilities register the minimum acceptable levels of standby and repair personnel, construction crews, and available equipment. This information is available to other utilities and is used when extra help is needed after major hurricanes, ice storms, and so on.

7.2 Constructing a Pole Line

Why Pole Lines?

7.2.1 Overhead lines are kept out of harm's way by stringing circuits high up on structures such as poles and towers. By far, most overhead distribution powerlines are pole lines. Poles can be wood, concrete, steel, laminated, aluminum, or fiber-reinforced polymer composite. Wood poles are most common because of their relatively low cost and ease of use.

Poles support transmission lines, subtransmission lines, distribution lines, and outdoor lighting.

Choosing the Right Pole

7.2.2 Poles are chosen based on their strength, available heights, life cycle, cost, and availability. Other considerations include climbability, field drilling, type of foundation needed, and equipment needed for pole setup.

Pole Strength

The pole strength specified for a job is critical, as can be seen after a storm. The appropriate pole strength will be based on number of conductors, height of conductors, guying, equipment to be installed, and whether the placement is a tangent, corner, or dead end. Pole strength also has to meet regulatory standards for the loading district and construction grade needed to withstand wind and ice loading. The critical point of strength (moment) for an unguyed pole is near the ground line. However, as seen after a windstorm, the moment on a pole with a double circuit of heavy conductors on top and a large telephone cable below tends to be just above the telephone cable. The circumference of a wood pole determines its strength and resistance to bending. The strength of steel, concrete, and other manufactured poles is engineered and more predictable than the variable strengths of a natural product such as wood.

Wood poles are divided into several classes, according to top circumference and circumference 6 feet (2 meters) from the butt: classes 1 through 10 for normal strengths and H1 through H6 for higher strengths. A utility would typically specify a minimum pole class for their loading district and then use a bigger pole class for railway crossings, heavy dead ends, corners, or equipment poles.

Steel, concrete, and composite poles are graded similarly for strength. Some utilities use tables that compare the class equivalents to wood class numbers.

Pole Length

Pole length is selected based on the number of circuits, equipment, communications cables, ground clearance, and possible future needs. A pole that is too long is better than too short because an extra 5 feet (1.5 m) is much more economical than having to change out poles later to add a transformer or to make room for telephone or television cable. Pole length is also selected so that the grade of a line will be relatively even, the intent being that there will be no uplift on a pole placed in a hollow. In mountainous country, back-to-back dead ends are used to prevent uplift on a pole.

Wood Poles

Historically, wood poles have been the most common type of utility pole in North America. Wood poles have been plentiful and economical, are climbable with spurs, have moderate weight, and are easy to bore holes into for mounting equipment. Some powerline workers prefer wood poles and see them as less conductive and therefore safer to set in live lines or when working with rubber gloves. Historically, some dry, untreated cedar poles have been quite nonconductive, but from a working perspective all poles should be treated as though they are very conductive.

To prevent or delay biological decay, many types of treatment have been developed, including creosote, tar, copper naphthenate, pentachlorophenol, chromated copper arsenates (CCA), and more. Some pole treatment has become environmentally unacceptable, some will cause skin rash, and some have hard pole surfaces that spurs cannot penetrate. There are poles treated with an oil emulsion in the outer layer after they were treated with CCA to make the pole easier to climb. There is also a CCA PA process calls for injecting a polymer-based additive that creates a softer outer shell for better climbability. A complicating factor is that many locations consider treated poles as hazardous waste after they have been removed. The most common location for decay is at about 1 foot (0.3 m) below the ground line, which is where a pole is most likely to break when a powerline worker does not support the pole when the work involves changing strain.

The life expectancy of a wood pole is about 35 years, but a pole test and treat program is needed to ensure that no poles are decaying quicker. Structures can deteriorate to below the required strength level. The decision to repair, treat, or replace a wood pole is made by a person trained to use one of the many instruments made for testing or by a boring/auger drilling inspection. One criteria is to replace poles when their strength falls to two-thirds of the required strength. Others will replace poles based on a specified amount of shell that is still sound. Retreatment is an economical way to allow poles to be in service longer. Because testing a pole for possible replacement does not account for the work that may be done on a pole, a tested pole is not necessarily safe to climb.

Concrete Poles

Concrete poles historically have been used in urban areas within North America but are found almost everywhere in many other countries. Concrete poles have a long life span with known strength characteristics, although along roadways where salt is used in winter it is not unusual to see the steel reinforcement rods exposed and rusting.

Concrete poles are classed alphabetically. Table 7–1 classifies which poles have a capacity for bending that is appropriate to the design requirements. The minimum ultimate transverse load shown in Table 7–1 is applied 2 feet below the top of the pole.

Because manufactured poles can be engineered to exact standards, poles can be ordered with very precise requirements, as shown in Figure 7–1.

One advantage to concrete and steel poles is that pole-top fires and direct lightning strikes are not as damaging as they would be to wood.

Steel Poles

Steel poles, like other manufactured poles, have known strength characteristics and have typically been classed the same as wood poles. The galvanized tubular steel poles increasingly common in distribution lines are lighter weight than wood poles of the same strength and can be set as a direct bury similar to a wood pole or concrete pole direct bury. Steel poles also have a smaller diameter pole butt relative to a wood pole of similar strength, which is advantageous when installing in a drilled rock pole hole.

Steel poles are subject to corrosion, especially when placed in areas with a history of corrosion with galvanized anchor rods and so on. Extra protective coatings are needed to provide additional below-grade protection. Retreatment is also carried out by identifying any "rust" and painting on a zinc-rich paint.

Transmission-Line Steel Poles

Very high transmission-line poles are not direct bury but are bolted to anchor bolts that are previously installed in large engineered concrete footings. Steel transmission-line poles are manufactured in sections that are set into each other. They are

TABLE 7–1   Concrete Pole Classes

Class	Minimum Ultimate Transverse Load		Class	Minimum Ultimate Transverse Load	
	(lbs.)	(KN)		(lbs.)	(KN)
C	1,200	5.3	J	4,500	20.0
D	1,500	6.7	K	5,400	24.0
E	1,900	8.5	L	6,400	28.5
F	2,400	10.7	M	7,500	33.4
G	3,000	13.3	N	8,700	38.7
H	3,700	16.5	O	10,000	44.5

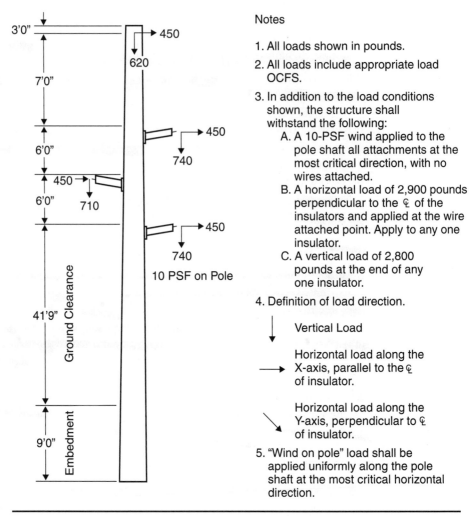

Notes

1. All loads shown in pounds.

2. All loads include appropriate load OCFS.

3. In addition to the load conditions shown, the structure shall withstand the following:
   A. A 10-PSF wind applied to the pole shaft all attachments at the most critical direction, with no wires attached.
   B. A horizontal load of 2,900 pounds perpendicular to the ₵ of the insulators and applied at the wire attached point. Apply to any one insulator.
   C. A vertical load of 2,800 pounds at the end of any one insulator.

4. Definition of load direction.

   Vertical Load

   Horizontal load along the X-axis, parallel to the ₵ of insulator.

   Horizontal load along the Y-axis, perpendicular to ₵ of insulator.

5. "Wind on pole" load shall be applied uniformly along the pole shaft at the most critical horizontal direction.

Figure 7–1   A typical load tree.

often designed to be self-supporting at corners and dead ends, and therefore they need extensive excavation, concrete, steel reinforcing, and long, large-diameter anchor bolts.

Pole Identification

A pole brand specifies the supplier, as well as the pole treatment, length, and class. (Other means are used to provide this information on steel and concrete poles.) Some suppliers bore a "through bolt" hole through the top of a wood pole. which indicates the alignment of the pole face. Many utilities place a nail of soft aluminum 10 or 15 feet up the pole, depending on the pole length, upon which are stamped the date of installation and the owner's name.

The Pole Foundation

7.2.3 The most common foundation for wood poles, steel poles, and concrete poles is a direct bury into a pole hole. Tables specifying depth settings for poles are provided by utilities. Typically, the setting depth for a wood pole in earth is equal to the pole height in feet divided by 10 plus 2 feet (X ÷ 10) + 2 feet. For example, the following is the setting depth for a 40-foot pole:

$$(40 \text{ feet} \div 10) + 2 \text{ feet} = 6 \text{ feet}$$

Exceptions to the hole depth are included in specifications books because poles are set in earth as well as in hard rock, shale, sandstone, sand, gravel, swamps, and marshes. One typical exception allows a pole set in rock to be set 1 foot shallower. However, one interpretation states that this applies to drilled holes in solid rock, not to blasted holes. When a pole set in a marsh is cribbed and the crib is filled with rock or gravel, the above-ground height of the crib is not to be considered as additional depth of the pole setting.

Most holes are dug with machinery such as a digger-derrick auger, backhoe, or sucker truck. Obtaining and paying attention to utility locations is essential because an auger has no mercy on buried gas, power, water, sewer, or communications lines. Occasionally, when all else fails, a crew must resort to "three-phase" equipment: the bar, spoon, and shovel.

There can be a lot of continuous transverse wind load on a line, and it is all too common to see a pole leaning on a recently built line. A well-known rule of thumb states that three ambitious people with tampers are needed for each lazy person on a shovel when back-filling a pole hole. A hydraulic tamper would be used more often if it was mounted on the truck deck for easy retrieval. When earth conditions are not ideal, rock, gravel, and so on should be used as backfill. Manufactured foam is also available to expand and fill voids. When there is not much room for backfill, such as in a drilled rock hole, fine grit such as limestone dust should be used.

Setting Poles

7.2.4 Poles are set most often with a radial boom derrick, although they can also be set with pike poles, a gin pole, a helicopter, or a backhoe.

The oldest method for setting poles is with pike poles. Depending on the length of pole, the process will require six to ten people. The pole is laid down with the butt next to the hole. Two or three digging bars are set in the hole as a backstop. The top of the pole is lifted high enough to get the "raising horse," an H-frame device, underneath it. The raising horse is moved toward the hole as the pole is raised. A lot of coordination is required as the highest pike poles are removed and inserted at a lower position on the pole while the lower pike poles and the raising horse hold the weight. Anyone removing a high pike pole has to hold it tight to avoid dropping the pike onto someone holding a lower pike pole. Figures 7–2 and 7–3 illustrate the method but are not a substitute for a written procedure if a crew must use this method in a back lot or island situation.

Another method for setting poles uses a temporary pole or existing pole as a gin, as illustrated in Figure 7–4. Rope blocks or a winch are hung on the pole used as a gin and the new pole is raised into position. Sometimes the pole is tipped in and sometimes it is picked up just above the balance point, then lowered into the hole.

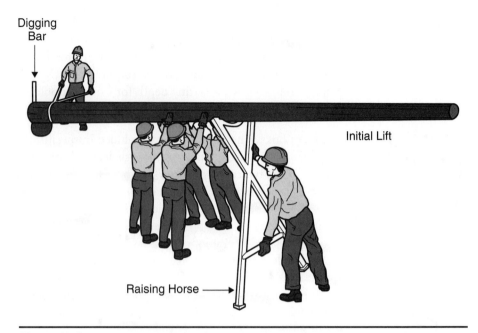

Figure 7–2   Setting a pole with pikes.

Figure 7–3   Raising the pole higher using pikes.

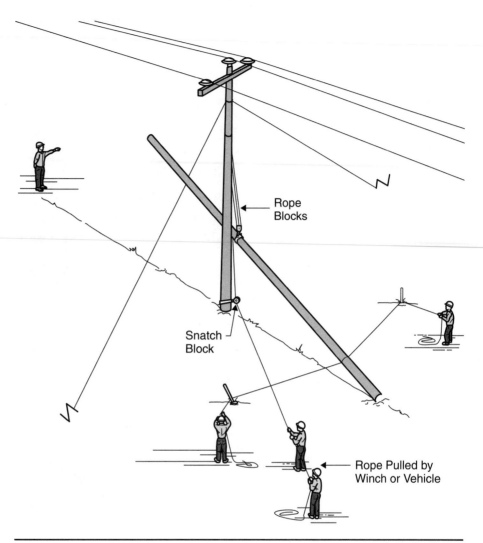

Rope
Blocks

Snatch
Block

Rope Pulled by
Winch or Vehicle

Figure 7–4 Using a gin pole.

There may still be applications of this method for pole replacement in subdivisions with back lot construction.

Setting a pole with a derrick is a straightforward process, unless it is being set in a live circuit. The winch is attached just above the balance point, and the pole is maneuvered into the hole while someone controls the butt.

The safest way to set a pole with a helicopter is to have the site rigged so that the structure can be set with no one in position under or within striking distance of the structure. Use of an eyebolt in the pole allows for the pole to be tied very securely to the sling connected to the helicopter load hook. When setting a new pole next to an existing pole, a specially designed bracket must be installed on the old pole to hold the new pole after it is lowered into position. The new pole can also be held in place

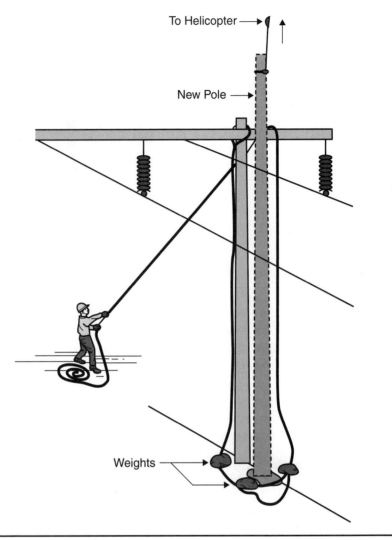

Figure 7–5 Preparation for a helicopter pole setting.

if a rope arranged with a loop is ready to receive the pole, as shown in Figure 7–5. The hole is usually dug in advance, although it is possible to stand the pole first, dig the hole, and then jockey the pole into the hole. If the pole is to be set on a new right-of-way, the poles are usually set up with rope guys already tied at the top and the bottom coiled and tied just above the ground line. After the pole is lowered into the hole, workers on the ground take the rope guys and tie them to predetermined anchor points or bull pins before the pole is released by the helicopter.

Problematic Pole Settings

The winch attachment just above balance point on a tall pole set into an existing line will be above the lower circuits or the communications cable when setting the pole. A lower attachment point will cause the pole to be top-heavy and trying to hold the bottom of the pole has a high risk for losing control of the pole. For a production job, using a crane to drop the pole in from above works very effectively.

A crane can also be used effectively to drop long transmission poles into place. Inserting a link stick in series with a winch reduces the risk of the crane becoming energized in a mishap. No one has to be anywhere near the pole as it is being lowered.

Setting a Pole in a Live Line

7.2.5 In addition to lifting a pole and setting it in a hole, two additional, and major, steps are needed to set a pole safely near a live circuit.

1. Use the equipment and procedures necessary to prevent the pole and equipment from making accidental electrical contact.

2. Use safety controls to reduce the risk of injury if that rare but hazardous dangerous contact is made.

Preventing Contact

To prevent contact, insulated cover-up is put on the conductors and/or on the pole. Even though cover-up is installed, the pole must be controlled. With a modern derrick, this is relatively easy when the winch can be attached to the pole just above the balance point. Rope guying may be needed with other installation methods. A dedicated observer positioned well for judging approach distances is standard, especially when installing a pole in three-phase lines.

No cover-up is available for transmission-line voltages. Larger clearances between conductors can allow a pole to be set in a live circuit. Depending on the installation method, extra rope guying to improve control may be needed.

Safety Controls

Safety controls refer to the extra steps taken to reduce the risk of injury if an electrical contact is made.

1. Ground the boom-equipped vehicle, setting the pole so that the circuit trips quickly if the boom or its load makes accidental contact with the circuit. If the vehicle becomes alive, anyone near the truck is exposed to ground gradients. The boom operator stays on the operating platform or uses a ground-gradient mat.

2. Have the circuit breaker or recloser put into the nonreclose position to ensure that the circuit remains isolated should it be tripped out due to accidental contact.

3. The workers most at risk, while setting a pole in a live circuit, are the workers controlling the pole butt. The designated observer can stand clear of any vehicles or objects that may become energized, and the boom operator can stay on the operating platform. The person controlling the butt is exposed to touch and step potentials. Rubber gloves can provide protection from distribution-voltage touch potential. Step potentials are generated where the pole touches earth. There is a rise in voltage relative to

TABLE 7–2   Summary of Hazards while Setting Poles in a Live Circuit

Hazard	Procedural Barriers
If a pole (wood, concrete, or steel) makes contact with a live circuit there will be touch potentials between the pole and earth. If the pole is also in contact with the earth, there could be high step potentials at the base of the pole (see Figure 7–6).	On distribution voltages, use rubber gloves along with pole tongs (cant hooks, pole handlers). The pole tongs keep a person away from the highest ground-gradient potentials where the pole touches the ground. On transmission-line voltages, use butt ropes and rubber gloves to guide the pole into the hole.
There will be touch and step potentials around the pole, truck, attached trailer, and ground rod when a bare pole contacts an exposed live conductor.	On distribution voltages, install protective cover-up on the conductors and/or on the pole. Use a dedicated observer to monitor the clearance between the boom pole and live conductors and to communicate with the boom operator. The boom operator must stay on the operating platform and other workers must stay clear of the truck in case the boom or its load make accidental contact.
Setting a very conductive pole (steel, concrete, or wet wood) in a high-voltage distribution circuit with limited open space in which to set the pole increases the risk of contact and a high fault current.	In addition to covering up the circuit, covering up the pole, using rubber gloves, and using a pole handler and/or butt ropes, a protective ground-gradient zone can be set up to provide protection for workers handling the pole butt. The ground-gradient matting (similar to tension stringing procedure) can provide an equipotential zone when a worker stays on the mat while handling the pole. The ground-gradient matting has to be bonded to the truck ground and, to the pole.
A circuit may not trip out when a truck boom contacts a live circuit.	Ground the truck to the neutral or other good ground to promote a quick trip-out of the circuit. The circuit breaker or recloser should be put in a nonreclose position and tagged to ensure that the circuit will remain isolated after it trips out. This will reduce exposure time to the hazard and facilitate a rescue if needed.

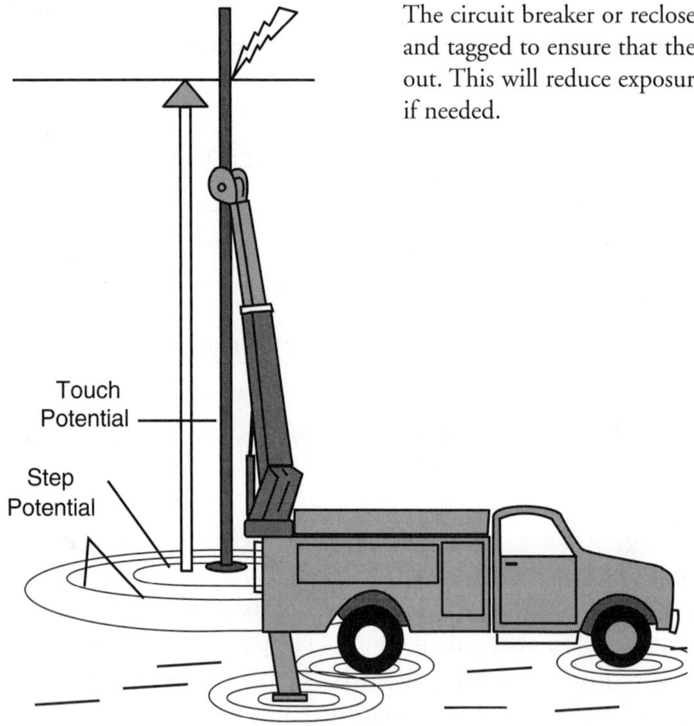

Touch Potential

Step Potential

Figure 7–6   Contact with a live circuit.

any earth farther away from the base of the pole. To keep a worker farther away from the high step potentials near the pole butt, tongs or butt ropes should be used to control the butt. Rubber gloves always should be worn while handling tongs because tongs are not usually electrically tested live-line tools. Ground-gradient mats bonded to the pole and derrick would provide even more protection from step potentials.

4. At transmission-line voltage levels, guide ropes tied to the pole butt can be used to get even farther away from the current-entry point.

5. If climbing to remove the winch from the pole, check to ensure that the pole is not in contact with a live conductor. Voltage gradients can also occur along a wood pole when a live conductor is in contact. The voltage at the contact point is higher than the voltage at a s pot farther from the contact point. Anyone on the pole could have a potential difference between the hands and the feet. On a very conductive pole, such as a steel structure, there is less potential difference between the hands and feet because all are in contact with the same object at the same potential.

Facing a Wood Pole

7.2.6 Every wood pole has a natural sweep along its length. The concave or inside of the sweep or bow is called the *face* and the convex side is called the *back*. Framing and equipment are put on the face of the pole.

Poles are installed so they end up being face to face and back to back in a line. Corner poles and dead-end poles are installed to face the anchor. Some variations occur, including facing poles uphill and facing the last two or three poles toward a dead end.

Guying a Pole

7.2.7 While some specially engineered steel or concrete self-supporting dead-end or corner poles are manufactured, most poles require anchors and guys to counter the pull of conductors in the opposite direction. Guys can be down guys, span guys, strut guys, or push-pull braces (see Figure 7–7). Down guys are the most common and are preferred.

Some typical guying arrangements are shown in Figure 7–8.

To determine the size and number of guys and anchors to be installed requires calculation of the expected load. The load on the guy is dependent on the following:

1. The dead-end or bisect tension of each conductor (under ice loading conditions).

2. The height of the guy(s) attachment above the ground.

3. The distance from the pole to the anchor.

Typically, generic calculations have been done and instead of calculating the load on a guy for each case, tables and graphs prepared by design engineers and found in specifications manuals provide the means to calculate the information needed.

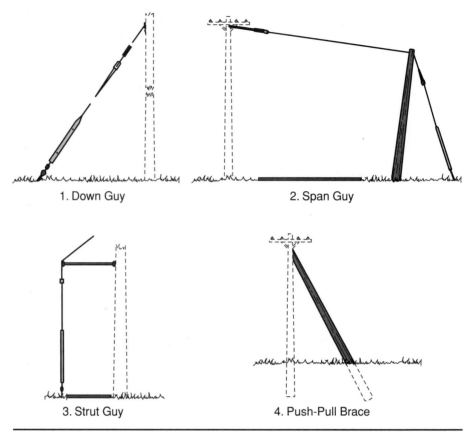

1. Down Guy   2. Span Guy

3. Strut Guy   4. Push-Pull Brace

Figure 7–7   Types of guys.

The tension on a down guy multiplies very quickly as the distance between the pole and the anchor decreases, as shown in Figure 7–9. The tension on a down guy is much higher than the conductor tension, and in most cases a guy already in service and under load would overload a standard chain hoist, grip, and pulling eye.

Guy steel tends to be 5/16-inch (8 mm), 3/8-inch (9.5 mm), and 1/2-inch (13 mm) galvanized steel or aluminium-clad steel. The guy holding a dead-end or corner transmission-line structure is considerably larger. It is important for the size of the guy steel to be properly identified. When a 3/8-inch preformed grip is used on 5/16-inch guy steel, it will not hold very much strain and may let go while someone is on the pole dead-ending conductor, and can result in a thrilling ride for anyone up the pole. The rule of thumb for determining the proper length of a guy is that it should be equal to the height of the guy attachment above the ground plus one-half the distance from the pole to the anchor.

Guy strain insulators are inserted into guy wires to reduce the risk of public contact with a guy that has become energized. There are differences of opinion among utilities regarding the use of guy strain insulators. Some utilities do not use any, others use them on distribution and not on transmission lines, and others use them

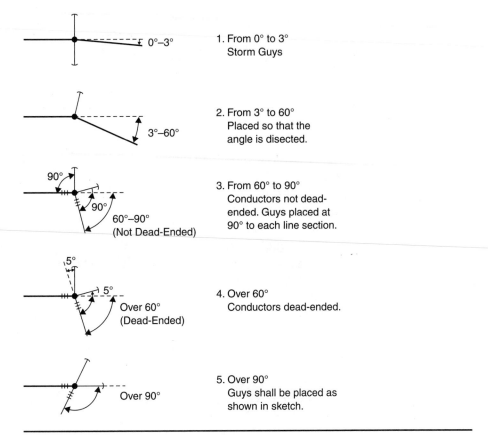

1. From 0° to 3°
   Storm Guys

2. From 3° to 60°
   Placed so that the
   angle is disected.

3. From 60° to 90°
   Conductors not dead-
   ended. Guys placed at
   90° to each line section.

4. Over 60°
   Conductors dead-ended.

5. Over 90°
   Guys shall be placed as
   shown in sketch.

Figure 7–8   Guying arrangements.

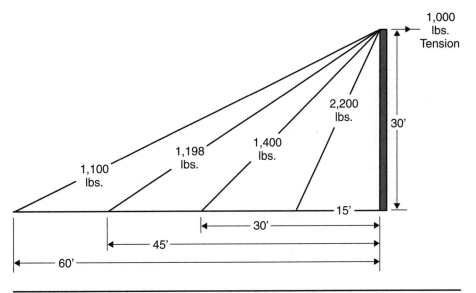

Figure 7–9   Guy lead length.

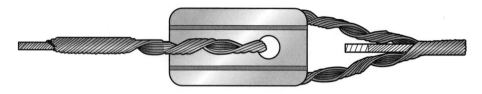

Figure 7–10   Porcelain guy strain insulator.

on all structures. Guy strain insulators can be made of wood, porcelain, or a fiber rod (Figure 7–10). A strain insulator is located in a guy so that it will be below the lowest live circuit and high enough above the ground so that it is above the reach of people, about 8 feet (2.5 m). A difference of opinion also exists regarding whether a down guy should be bonded to down grounds or not bonded at all.

When a guy is installed on a new line, the dead-end and corner poles are typically pulled over (raked) 1 to 1.5 ft (0.5 m) from plumb. If left straight and the anchor and guy settle a little, the pole will leaning to the line or into the corner. This arrangement will put a lot of extra strain on the guy assembly and, from a powerline worker's point of view, looks terrible.

Choosing and Installing an Anchor

7.2.8 The type of anchor specified for a job will be dependent on the soil conditions and on the type of load to be anchored.

Historically, a log dead-man (slug) was used where a log was buried into the soil and the anchor rod cut into the soil to angle it toward the pole. Other anchors that were used where there was good digging, but are now used less frequently, were plate anchors and expanding anchors, as illustrated in Figure 7–11.

Power-installed screw anchors are the preferred anchor where the soil conditions will hold the anchor and rocks do not prevent the installation. Different types are available for almost every type of load. They are installed by machine, and the result is an anchor that creeps up very little and causes very little soil disturbance. Utilities tend to use their local knowledge and experience to specify the type of anchor needed for local conditions. In sand or swampy areas, anchor rods can be

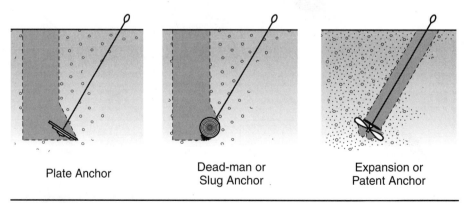

Plate Anchor   Dead-man or   Expansion or
                      Slug Anchor   Patent Anchor

Figure 7–11   Types of anchors.

lengthened until good solid earth is reached. For heavy critical anchoring, such as transmission-line dead ends, a more extensive study of soil conditions using a soil test probe should be carried out.

To install a power-installed screw anchor, the auger on the digger derrick is removed and a specially manufactured wrench is installed on the end of the Kelly bar. To install the anchor properly requires skill with a digger derrick so that proper alignment and down pressure are maintained as the anchor is screwed into the soil.

If a rock anchor is to be used, the rock must be solid. There are expanding rock anchors, rebar anchors, and rock eyes. The rock holes for expanding and rebar anchors are drilled in line with the intended guy. The rod is turned to expand the bottom of the expanding element in the bottom of the hole until it is tight. The quality of the rebar anchor depends on grout being applied around the rod in the rock hole. A rock eye (Figure 7–12) is installed at 60 degrees to the line, and the wedge in the bottom of the hole is expanded by hitting the top of the anchor with a sledge hammer. Grouting keeps out the elements. Where there is overburden, an extension rod is installed on the anchor. Guy wire should not be buried.

In poor rock, shale, or sandstone, there may be no other choice but to dig, break rock, or blast until solid rock is reached or a dead-man or plate anchor is installed.

The proper anchor rod for the application must always be chosen. The most common anchor rods are 5/8-inch, 3/4-inch, and 1-inch, as well as a 1-inch high strength.

Anchors must be very secure. If an anchor pulls or settles somewhat after the conductors are sagged or after the telephone company puts cable on the poles, a formerly good-looking job will now look bad.

In critical situations where a sudden release of the anchor could cause an accident, the anchor should be tested. A digger derrick and a dynamometer can be used to test anchors used on distribution lines. For more sophisticated testing, a specially designed hydraulic pull test, specified wait times, and a transit to accurately measure any creep should be used.

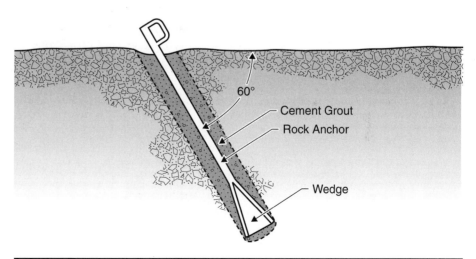

Figure 7–12 A rock eye.

Ideally, when locating an anchor, adequate distance is maintained between the pole and anchor to reduce extreme tensions on a down guy. The location of an anchor is more critical when a guy must go between conductors of underbuild circuits to reach the top of a pole. A graph drawn to scale showing the pole height and framing is the easiest way to locate options for anchors on multicircuit poles.

Choosing the Proper Framing

7.2.9 A majority of the material in a utility storeroom is kept on hand to meet the many specifications for framing a pole. Framing for tangent, various degrees of corners and dead-end poles using crossarms, armless framing, and aerial spacer cable framing are shown in specifications books. Drawings show the standards for installing equipment such as transformers, switchgear, regulators, capacitors, riser poles, and so on.

Powerline workers should not deviate from specifications because the specifications drawings are engineered and there are usually good reasons for the very specific details. A bill of material is part of most specifications drawings, typically including stock numbers. A technician often will enter the drawing numbers for a particular job into a computerized system that will, in turn, apply the costs, tabulate the materials needed, and order them. Stockkeepers then issue material, and stockroom inventory numbers are automatically kept up to date.

Drawings in the specifications books are created with software that breaks down the standards to the subassembly level. Subassembles are then mixed and matched and the various standard drawings are created. Figure 7–13 shows a typical specifications drawing for a switched capacitor bank.

600-KVAR BANK - 26.4-kV SYSTEM - SWITCHED

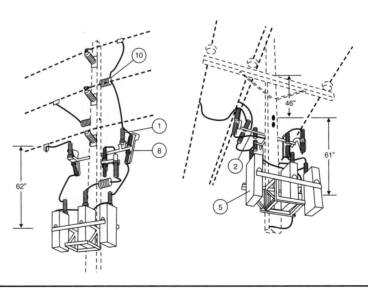

Figure 7–13 A typical specifications drawing.

1200KVAR BANK - 26.4-kV SYSTEM - SWITCHED

NO.	ITEM ID	QTY	DESCRIPTION
1	ARR 345	3	ARRESTER, LIGHTNING, POLYMER, 21 kV
2	BRCT 356	1	BRACKET, ARRESTER/CUTOUT, TRI-MOUNT
3	BOLT 3414	4	BOLT, MACHINE, SQUARE HEAD, 3/4X14
4	BOLT 3416	3	BOLT, DOUBLE ARMING, 3/4X14
5	CAP 003	1	CAPACITOR BANK, 1,200 kVAR, SWITCHED, FOR USE ON 26.4 kV
6	CONCT 1445	3	CONNECTOR, VISE TYPE, 6-2 SOL. 10-2 SOL.
7	COND 932	30	CONDUCTIOR, BARE COPPER, #4 SOFT DRAWN
8	CUT FUS 12	3	CUTOUT, FUSED, 150 kV BIL, 100 AMP, 27 kV
9	FUSLNK 449	3	FUSE LINK, TYPE T, 25 AMP
10	INSU VP 117	3	INSULATOR, VERTICAL POST, 34.5 kV
11	WASH RD 558	5	WASHER, ROUND, 2 IN. DIA. FOR 3/4-IN. BOLT
12	WASH SQ 559	8	WASHER, SQUARE, FLAT. 3 IN. FOR 3/4-IN. BOLT
13	WASH SD 561	5	WASHER, SPRING, DOUBLE HELIX, FOR 3/4-IN. BOLT

Figure 7–14 A typical materials list.

The software will automatically make up a bill of material and a cost of material. Figure 7–14 shows the material list for the specifications shown in Section 7.2.9B. Materials management includes ensuring that only approved materials are ordered but occasionally a particular hardware item gets approved but ends up being defective, usually a life cycle that is much shorter than a typical 40-year target for hardware. Very costly maintenance programs are then required to replace these items. Over the years, defective materials have included specific manufacturer's dead-end insulators, cutouts, post insulators, wood poles (premature rotting), guy strain insulators, and load break elbows.

Often, poles are framed on the ground before being installed. If the pole is to be installed in a live circuit, the down-ground should not be installed ahead of time. It is also important when moving the pole to avoid overstressing individual hardware items such as post insulators. When installing material and equipment on a pole, bolts should be installed so that the head of the bolt carries the heavy weight. Transformers should not be installed until the pole is vertical. Air pockets in the oil could cause a premature transformer failure.

Installing Insulators

7.2.10 Conductors on overhead lines are electrically insulated from ground by either sitting on insulators or being suspended from them. Insulators are either porcelain (ceramic), glass, or polymer. Other than glass, insulators and most other new equipment are sky gray in color. Some utilities will use a glass insulator to distinguish the neutral from the phases, especially when the neutral is on the crossarm.

Insulators are designed with skirts to increase the length of the path (tracking distance) electricity will need to get to earth. A combination of dirt and wetness will cause the insulators to flash over. On porcelain, a flashover leaves a visible white-glaze burn. Generally, a surface flashover is a more common failure mode than a puncture through the insulating material. Cement growth in porcelain dead-end insulators has been a cause of mechanical failures, and utilities have developed programs to change out these insulators. The design of the insulator is such that, depending on the wind direction, some parts will likely stay dry in rain and some parts will likely get washed in rain.

Insulator Types Used on Overhead Lines

1. *Pin-type insulators* are screwed onto threaded steel pins. Wood pins were used successfully in crossarms, but at voltages higher than 5V phase-to-ground deteriorated quicker than the crossarm and became a hazard to workers. Most pin-type insulators are porcelain (ceramic) and can be one or more pieces cemented together. Figure 7–15 shows a one-piece and a two-piece insulator. There is a practical limit to the size and expense of pin-type insulators and are therefore not used on lines over 70kV. For most pin-type insulators, the conductor must be tied in with wire.

2. *Suspension-type insulators* can be porcelain (ceramic) and glass. They come as individual disks that are rated at about 11kV each and are coupled together to the length needed for the line voltage. They are used horizontally to dead-end conductors or vertically on tangent structures. They are rated for strength in kilo-pounds (1 kip = 1,000 lbs.) or kilo-newtons (kn), typically 25 kip, 30 kip, 50 kip, and 80 kip. Figure 7–16 shows how a ball-and-socket design puts the insulating material under compression to create strength.

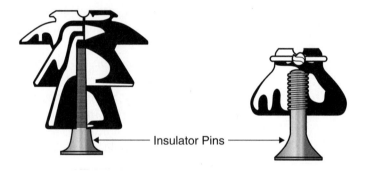

Figure 7–15   Pin insulators.

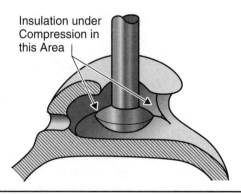

Figure 7–16   Suspension-type insulator design.

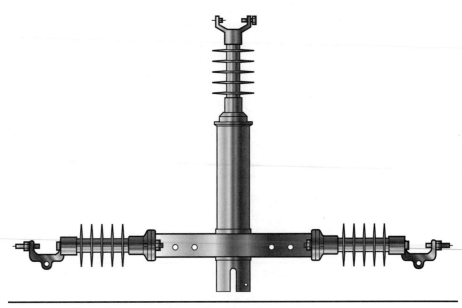

Figure 7–17   Vertical and horizontal post insulators.

3. *Strain-type insulators* are inserted into guys. Some distribution dead-end insulators are referred to as strain insulators. Otherwise, the terms strain and *suspension* are used in the field for the same insulators: suspension when used vertically with the conductor suspended below, and strain when used horizontally to dead-end a conductor.

4. *Post insulators* are positioned on a pole to support conductors in a vertical or in a horizontal, cantilevered position. The insulators are one piece and come in many lengths and strengths. The insulators come with tops where the conductor can be tied in or clamped in. Figure 7–17 shows a vertical post and two horizontal posts used in pole framing.

Insulators are often installed when poles are framed. Post insulators are especially vulnerable to damage because the insulators get dragged and bumped against objects as the pole is moved around.

Stringing Conductor

7.2.11 Stringing conductor can be one of the more complex jobs in lines work. Taking time to document a job plan may help you to recognize the many hazards that could be encountered. Complexities include road and railroad crossings, an extra-long span, a heavy corner, live underbuild, induction from nearby transmission lines, locations to ground, and so on.

The probability of making contact with a live circuit is relatively high when stringing in the vicinity of a live distribution circuit. When using tension stringing techniques, the consequence of a worker having an electrical contact is usually low because the setup of the stringing equipment, grounds, and ground-gradient matting will prevent injuries when accidental contact is made.

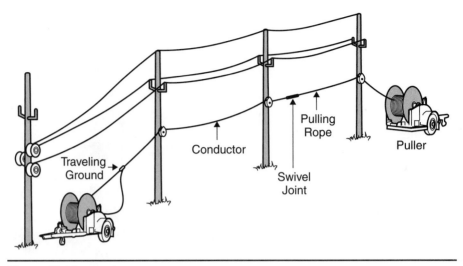

Figure 7–18   A pilot rope system.

The tension stringing principles for transmission lines are similar to this distribution procedure. Figure 7–18 shows a pilot rope system with a puller at one end and a tensioner at the other.

TABLE 7–3   Slack Stringing or Removing Distribution Conductors Near a Live Circuit

Hazards	Controls
While stringing a conductor in the vicinity of a live circuit, there is a chance of the conductor making an inadvertent contact.	Tension stringing techniques should be used when stringing over or at the same level and on the same side of the structure as a live circuit.
	If slack stringing underneath a live circuit, use tie-down ropes midspan to prevent a snagged conductor from whipping up and making contact with the live circuit.
Workers on the ground are exposed to possible electric shock while stringing in the vicinity of a live circuit.	If slack stringing, the reel stands should be grounded and put on a ground-gradient matting or on a grounded trailer. Anyone tending the reels must remain on the ground-gradient matting or trailer.
	An operator of a reel trailer, tensioner, or puller must stay on the operating platform or on a ground-gradient mat that is bonded to the machine.
	The conductor must be held with grips and protective grounds installed before changing reels or doing other work at the tensioner or puller end.
A conductor makes contact with a live circuit while a worker is tying or clamping it to an insulator.	Rubber gloves must be worn by anyone handling the conductor unless they are in a bonded zone.
The live circuit may not trip out when a conductor contacts the live circuit.	A stringing procedure and precautions taken should recognize that a conductor can become alive and that it may not trip out the circuit. Ground the stringing blocks to the system neutral at regular intervals. Use traveling grounds at the reel stand or tensioner end.

TABLE 7–4   **Typical Distribution Tension Stringing Procedure**

Step	Action	Details
1	Ensure that there is adequate spacing to allow stringing a new conductor.	1. To install a new circuit above an existing circuit, higher poles must be installed. The space above the live underbuild should be at least 5 ft. (1.5 m) and ideally 10 ft. (3 m). 2. To replace existing conductors, install auxiliary arms and set out the existing live conductors. The closest conductors should be at a minimum of 3 ft. (1 m) to the side. 3. To cross over live circuits mounted on the same pole, the necessary clearance can be smaller because the live circuit can be covered up. Crossing live circuits in-span requires more clearance, but additional protection can be obtained by installing cover-up.
2	Install stringing blocks. 	The *finger line* (throw line) is a small rope put through the stringing blocks and tied off down the pole. The finger line is used later to pull the pilot line or pulling rope through the stringing block. 1. Stringing blocks are normally installed when any necessary framing is done. Finger lines installed through the stringing blocks during installation will save additional setup. The finger lines must be tied off above public reach and clear of live underbuild. A clean finger line, in combination with rubber gloves, will tolerate momentary brush contact with live conductors. 2. On multisheave stringing blocks (see Figure 7–19), keep the finger lines in the center sheave. 3. Corner stringing blocks should, if possible, be set out so that the conductors do not have to be moved into place before sagging. 4. Install grounds, as required by your utility, on the first and last stringing block and at regular intervals. 5. *Note:* Friction from stringing blocks is a large factor in determining the pulling tension. *Pulling Tension = Line Tension + (% Friction of Block × Line Tension × Number of Structures)* For example, pulling tension for a 20-span pull, with a 3% friction of blocks and line tension of 500 pounds = 500 + (.03 × 500 × 20) = 800 pounds.

Figure 7–19   Three-sheave stringing block. *(Photo courtesy of TSE International. All rights reserved.)*

Step	Action	Details
3	Set up the puller.	1. To reduce the down weight on a structure, keep the puller back at a distance of at least one-third of the span length. 2. Set up the puller so that it is in line with the pull or so that the installation of snatch blocks will allow the pull to be in line. Figure 7–20 shows a drum puller with the pull rope loaded on the drum. 3. Ensure that the operator and anyone else near the machine will be on an operating platform or on a ground-gradient mat bonded to the puller.

(continued)

TABLE 7–4 **Continued**

Step	Action	Details

4. Install a barrier around the puller to keep away people during the stringing operation. The electrical hazard at the puller increases when the conductor comes into the puller.
5. Use a reinforced steel reel made specifically for winding up the pulling rope under tension. Other reels can be crushed by the elastic properties of the rope.
6. Have protective grounds ready to install on the conductor when it comes to the puller.

Figure 7–20   Drum puller. *(Photo courtesy of TSE International. All rights reserved.)*

| 4 | Set up the tensioner. | The *tensioner* is the reel carrier for the conductor and holds tension on the conductors by pulling back the conductors hydraulically or by applying brakes. |

1. Set up the tensioners so that the conductors will be in line with the first pole or structure.
2. Place ground-gradient mats so that the machine operator and people involved in changing reels are working from the mat bonded to the tensioner.
3. Install a barrier around the tension machine(s) to keep away people during the stringing operations.
4. Have protective grounds ready to install on the conductors when the pull is stopped. For additional grounding during stringing, install traveling grounds.
5. Wooden conductor reels can collapse and cause a sudden loss of tension. It is generally acceptable to tension directly from a wooden or metal reel at tensions less than 1,000 lbs. (450 kg). Use a metal axle all the way through a wooden reel to prevent a total collapse. Use a bull-wheel tensioner as shown in Figure 7–21 for higher tensions.

Figure 7–21   Bull-wheel tensioner. *(Photo courtesy of TSE International. All rights reserved.)*

TABLE 7–4 Continued

Step	Action	Details
5	String in the pilot line.	A *pilot line* is a small rope strung from the tensioner, through the stringing blocks to the puller, and used to pull back the heavier pulling rope. Figure 7–22 shows pilot line reels mounted on a pole. (*Note:* The pulling rope may be pulled out directly without the use of a pilot line.) If stringing wire through multisheave stringing block (for example, three sheaves), only one pilot line is needed to pull in one pull rope. 1. As the pilot line is strung and fed through the stringing blocks, it will likely make occasional contact with any live underbuild. The first 150 ft. (50 m) of the pilot line should consist of live-line rope or clean, dry, synthetic rope. Rubber gloves must be worn by the handlers of the rope. 2. Guard all road crossings during the stringing of the pilot line.

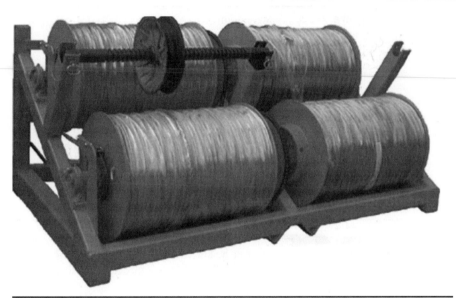

Figure 7–22 Pilot line reels. *(Photo courtesy of TSE International. All rights reserved.)*

6	Pull the pulling rope back to the tensioner with the pilot line.	The *pulling rope* is the rope used to pull in the conductor. It must be strong enough to pull in the conductor, have very little stretch, and be clean enough to withstand brush contact with live conductors. 1. Connect the pilot line to the pulling rope. 2. Using a tensioner, pull the pilot line from the puller back to the tensioner.
7	Pull in the conductor with the pulling rope.	1. Use a minimum length of pulling rope to make the pull. Work as close to the drum core as possible because, unless it is a bull-wheel puller, a large-diameter reel of pulling rope will require more pulling tension. 2. The pull rope will be connected to one conductor or to a running board that may have more than one conductor attached to it (as shown in Figure 7–23) when used on a transmission line. The connection to the pulling rope is made with a swivel joint (also shown in Figure 7–23). If the swivel is not performing well, a running board will start flipping over in a span, often more than once, which creates a lot of work to unwind.

(continued)

TABLE 7–4 Continued

Step	Action	Details

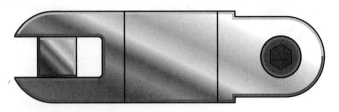

Figure 7–23 A swivel joint.

3. Establish radio communications between the puller, the tensioner, observers at road crossings, and workers following the running board or rope-to-conductor joint. If possible, use an exclusive radio channel for stringing. Only the puller can stop the pull, and only the tensioner can adjust the stringing tension or sag.

4. Apply tension at the tensioners. Hydraulic tensioners are put in the take-up mode to tension the conductors. Tensioners that use braking to hold the conductors must have brakes that are designed for continuous braking and that will not overheat and fade.

5. Pull in the pulling rope on the puller.

6. When the conductor arrives at the puller, install grounds at both ends.

| 8 | Problems that may be encountered while pulling in the conductor(s). | |

1. If the conductor sag is fluctuating and hard to control, the design of the pulling rope has too much stretch. The elastic-like action is causing the tension and sag to change constantly. Use a rope specifically designed for tension stringing.

2. On a multiconductor pull, the running board can flip over between spans even when a swivel is used. The pulling rope should be designed not to rotate.

3. If there is a long span within the pull, such as a wide road crossing or river crossing, and it is difficult to maintain the high tensions needed to maintain clearance from underbuild, that span should be strung separately. The weight of the long span will keep the sag in shorter spans excessively tight.

4. Conductor smaller than 3/0 will cut into the lower layers of a conductor reel. Unless a tensioner is equipped with a bull wheel to remove the tension from the reel, small conductor should not be strung.

5. If a tensioner is tensioning the conductor directly from a reel, the braking action must be reduced as the reel empties and the circumference gets smaller.

6. For heavy conductor on a long pull, tension can be lost when brakes heat and fade on the tensioner, so a tensioner with a hydraulic retarding system should be used.

7. If the puller seems to be pulling at a very high tension and it is not tight at the tensioner:
   - The stringing blocks may be too small in diameter and cause extra loss due to the bending and straightening of the conductor as it passes over each stringing block.

TABLE 7–4 **Continued**

Step	Action	Details
		• There may be too much friction on the stringing blocks, too many corner structures or changes in elevation for the length of the pull. Losses in efficiency are additive. Even a good stringing block with a 2 percent loss at each suspension point can, after 15 structures, increase the total tension of the pull approximately 30 percent. • A flexible mesh pulling grip on the pulling rope can let go when it is not properly installed. The diameter of the rope will decrease considerably under high tension. Use a fiber or wood plug in the core of the rope to maintain the rope diameter.
9	Change conductor reels at the tensioner as required.	All workers must be completely in the bonded work zone or completely out of the bonded work zone. 1. To allow reels to be changed at the tensioner, the ground-gradient mat setup should be big enough to accommodate the work. Protective grounds are installed on the conductor and bonded to the ground-gradient mat. If a vehicle boom is used from outside the bonded zone, the vehicle must be bonded to the work zone. The boom operator must stay on the platform, and all others must stay away from the vehicle. 2. However, *if* the pull is stopped, protective grounds are installed at the tensioner end, the conductors are temporarily dead-ended in grips, and the length of the pull is patrolled for any potential electric contact hazards, *then* the reels at the tensioner could be changed with a reasonable assurance that the conductors will not become energized.
10	Free the running board or conductor when it snags onto a stringing block.	1. While the conductor or pulling line is being pulled (in motion), no one should be aloft on a pole or structure or aloft in the vicinity (in a bucket), except during a small amount of adjustment needed to guide the stringing sock or board through a stringing sheave. 2. When handling conductors during a tension stringing operation, use rubber gloves or apply protective grounds and/or bonds to the conductors and structure at the point of work.
11	Sag the conductor.	1. Set the corner conductors in stringing blocks as close as possible to their final positions. 2. Sag the conductors using the tensioners, or bring the conductors in close to sag using the tensioners and finish sagging with chain hoists or a derrick winch.
12	For long pulls that require more than one setup, dead-end the conductors temporarily.	1. Temporary dead ends require standard anchoring and guy steel to hold the conductor tension. The use of rope guys or unsupported pole butts can lead to sagging into live underbuild. 2. Live underbuild conductors will need cover-up and/or setting out to provide clearance for the guying. 3. The slope of the guys must be adequate to prevent unacceptable downward stresses on crossarms, insulators, and so on.
13	Tie-in or clamp-in conductor.	1. Use rubber gloves or apply protective grounds and/or bonds to the conductors and structure at the point of work.

Stringing across Roadways

Reduce the risk of a vehicle making contact with conductors being strung across a roadway by considering the following:

- Road-crossing spans are often longer than other spans in the line being strung. A lot of conductor will gather in an extra-long span and cause excessive sag. Consider stringing the road-crossing span by itself instead of it being just another span in a long pull.

- On high-volume roads, consider using road authorities and their equipment to channel and control traffic. The presence of a highly visible police vehicle may add to the effectiveness of traffic control.

- If tension stringing, use backup barriers such as rider poles or a rope basket to catch conductors before they drop onto the road. Slow traffic by channeling vehicles into a single lane so that they can be stopped quickly if a conductor drops too low.

- If slack stringing, stop traffic before running a rope or wire across the road. Stopped traffic in each direction can serve as a barrier for traffic entering the work zone.

- A pole can break when a passing vehicle catches onto a conductor or when a running board catches on a stringing block. No one should be on a pole when the conductor is in motion. To free a running board from a stringing block, move the conductor only far enough for a person to go aloft to fix it.

Sagging Conductor

When the sag for a line is specified, the maximum tension on the conductor in relation to its *rated tensile strength* (RTS) and its potential vibration, potential galloping, elasticity, tension, clearance from the ground, and ruling span, as well as temperatures, wind, and ice conditions (the loading district) that are likely to be encountered. *Conductor creep,* which is the final stretching and strand settling (and may take 10 years), is also a factor in specifying sag.

The *final sags and tensions charts* are not the sags and tensions to be used by a line crew. These charts refer to the sags and tensions expected under loaded wind and ice conditions. Design specifications for structure heights, anchoring, ground clearance, and so on are based on final sags and tensions.

Lines must be sagged to the specifications in the *initial sags* or *string sags charts.* Sagging must be done accurately. If the section being sagged is long, measurements are needed in more than one span. The conductor can get quite tight where it is being pulled up before it starts to move at the end of the line or out of a long span. When the conductor gets close to sag, it should be taken up very slowly because if the conductor gets too high a lot of slack must be put back to get it to come down again near the end of the line.

Note: A lot of distribution conductor is not sagged to specifications. Line crews tend to sag until it looks good, which is usually too tight. Conductor sagged too

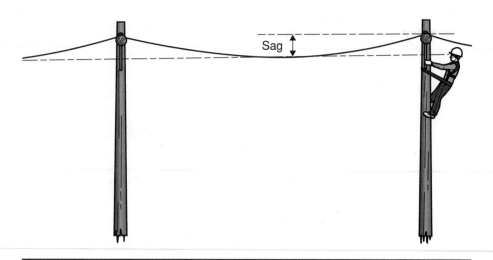

Figure 7–24   Measuring sag.

tight in the summer has led to structural (dead ends, corners, guying) failures in winter and, in other cases, to excessive vibration. The preceding information should indicate that there is a lot of science involved in determining the proper sag—and that looking good is not one of the parameters.

The most common method of sagging has been the *target method,* that is, using sag boards. Once the temperature and the length of the span chosen for the measurement are known, sag charts will give the specified sag for the conductor size. The sag measurement is taken from the conductor support to a spot down on the structure where a board (a rolled-up flag or other target) is placed. The same is done at the next pole in the measured span, and the two boards can be used to see when the bottom of the sag lines up with the boards. On long transmission lines, a scope—instead of a board—makes it much easier to see and be more accurate, especially for the shield wire.

The sag on transmission lines is often measured with surveying equipment where no climbing is involved.

Measuring tension with a *dynamometer* is the best method for sagging messenger/strand cable, which is strung at a high tension. It is probably not very accurate for power conductors unless the tension in more than the span is measured where the conductor is pulled up. Depending on the length of the pull, the tension must be checked at multiple spans.

The *return-wave method* can also be used to check the sag on an existing line. This method is applicable regardless of the span length, tension, size, or temperature or the type of conductor. Start a wave in a conductor by pulling on it with a telescopic stick or jerking down on a rope over the conductor. The wave travels to the next structure and is reflected back and forth until the wave is eventually damped out. Record the time it takes (there is a special stopwatch available for this purpose) for 3, 5, or 10 return waves. Long spans and large conductors can be more accurately counted than short spans and small conductors. The largest number of return waves minimizes errors in recording time. The initial impulse does not count as a return wave. Getting two equal results will give some assurance of accuracy. See Table 7–5. The return wave method is probably not the best while initially sagging because it does not give a continuous indication of where the sag is and because pulling has to be stopped each time a measurement is made. It is a very good method for checking sag on an existing line.

Chapter 15 covers conductor weights, calculating conductor tension, and other useful calculations when working with a conductor.

TABLE 7–5   Return-Wave Method Chart

Sag in inches (cm)	Return of Wave in Seconds		
	3rd Time	*5th Time*	*10th Time*
24 (0.61)	4.2	7	14.1
30 (0.76)	4.7	7.9	15.8
36 (0.91)	5.2	8.6	17.3
42 (1.07)	5.6	9.3	18.7
48 (1.22)	6	10	19.9
54 (1.37)	6.3	10.6	21.1
60 (1.52)	6.7	11.1	22.3
66 (1.68)	7	11.7	23.4
72 (1.83)	7.3	12.2	24.4
78 (1.98)	7.6	12.7	25.4
84 (2.13)	7.9	13.2	26.2
90 (2.29)	8.2	13.7	27.3
96 (2.44)	8.5	14.1	28.2
102 (2.59)	8.7	14.5	29.1
108 (2.74)	9	15	29.9
114 (2.90)	9.2	15.4	30.7
120 (3.05)	9.5	15.8	31.5
126 (3.20)	9.7	16.2	32.3
132 (3.35)	9.9	16.5	33.1
138 (3.51)	10.1	16.9	33.8
144 (3.66)	10.4	17.3	34.5
150 (3.81)	10.6	17.6	35.2
156 (3.96)	10.8	18	35.9
162 (4.11)	11	18.3	36.6
168 (4.27)	11.2	18.7	37.3
174 (4.42)	11.4	19	38
180 (4.57)	11.6	19.3	38.6
186 (4.72)	11.8	19.6	39.2
192 (4.88)	12	19.9	39.9

Pigtail Tie

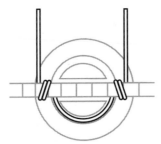

Start tie wire away
from you.

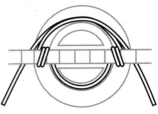

Make two close turns.

Lay in side groove.

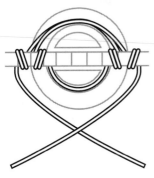

Make two more close turns.
Bring ends together.

Twist in pigtail.
Snug up twist with pliers.

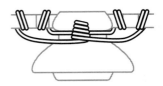

Trim off twisted ends.
Bend up twisted tail.

Long Tie

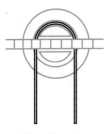

Start tie wire.

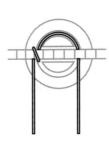

Make one close turn.

Lay in side groove.

Make two close turns.

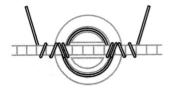

Make two long turns.

Make two close turns.

End bent back.

Figure 7–25 Typical types of insulator ties.

Tying or Clipping in Conductor

After conductor is sagged, it must be lifted out of the stringing blocks and tied in or clipped in to the insulator(s).

Tie wire or preformed ties are used on most top-tie insulators. Utility specifications and set patterns are available regarding how a conductor is to be tied in. Figure 7–25 shows two typical insulator ties, a pigtail tie for conductors over 3/0 and a long tie for smaller conductors. Other ties are available for corners and spool insulators; however, the local utility should specify its preference for conductor ties. Aluminum tie wire is used on aluminum wire and copper on copper. If a cover is on the conductor, a covered tie wire may be specified. Preform ties are very secure and protect the conductor from broken strands due to vibration.

Stringing Secondary Bus

7.2.12 Secondary bus is strung where it is more economical to install one transformer and feed 2 to 15 customers. Secondary bus is common on urban streets and in rural areas where more than 1 customer is located in a group. Bus can be open bare (or weatherproof) wire, open insulated wire, triplex cable, or aerial cable. Bus can be 120/240 volts, 120/208 volts three-phase, and, in industrial areas, 277 or 480 volts three-phase.

Open bare wire is the most economical to install and can be installed vertically on three-point racks or on crossarms. It is still found strung on crossarms in some cities in North America. It is also very common in Australia, New Zealand, and some other countries, where it is strung on crossarms. This kind of bus takes up a lot more space on a pole than open wire bus with insulated wire because it requires good spacing to prevent conductors from slapping together midspan.

Aerial cable is bus where insulated secondary wires are lashed to a messenger (strand). It is to most large communication cables (Figure 7–26). Messenger can be 3/0 AASCR, which can serve as the neutral and has the strength to be tensioned very tightly. Because the messenger wire is tight, services can be strung to

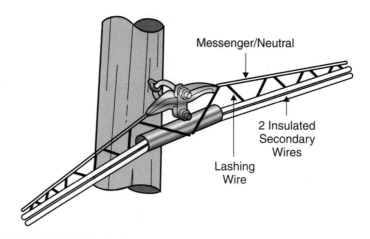

Figure 7–26   Secondary aerial cable.

customers from midspan and side guys are not needed. It is important to prestress and string the messenger cable to the specified tension. If a messenger cable loses tension after the secondary cables are lashed to it, the tension on the secondary cables becomes excessive, making it very difficult to get enough slack to make service connections. It is also a good idea to test the anchors to ensure that one will not let go while someone is aloft, as well as to remove some of the creep that would develop later. Preassembled aerial cable, which has the cable wrapped around the messenger instead of underneath, is also available.

Terminating a service midspan requires terminating the lashing wire on each side of a new service—dead end and pulling slack into the bus wires. If working on a hot secondary, it is wise to use cover-up because all the connections are close and the neutral and lashing wires are bare.

Equipment on Poles

7.2.13 Transformers, regulators, capacitors, and different types of switchgear are mounted on poles. The pole framing dimensions and electrical connections should be available in a specifications manual. As a general rule of thumb the "head" end of the bolt—not the threaded end—should carry the majority of the weight of any attachment. Heavy equipment, such as some regulators, require a better-than-average class of pole. Some locations will construct a platform between two poles to carry a large piece of equipment.

Every piece of equipment has a number assigned to it, and an installation is not complete until a number is attached to the pole. Some utilities are using Global Positioning System (GPS) numbers to identify the locations of their equipment. Numbers are used to help identify locations for troubleshooting and for routine work. Numbers are assigned to other equipment, such as voltage regulators and capacitors, for similar reasons.

The numbers on switchgear are especially important when preparing a switching order using a formal lockout/tagging procedure. Switchgear numbers can be used to accurately relate field devices with the devices shown on operating drawings.

Stringing Service to the Customer

7.2.14 Services from a pole line can be strung and connected directly from a transformer pole, strung and connected to a bus, or run down a pole to an underground service. At the customer end, overhead service is connected to a stack and underground service—if a socket-base meter—is brought up to the bottom lug of a meter base.

Neutral supported cable, such as triplex and quadruplex, is the most common service drop and is used as bus in many locations. Because they are accessible to the customer, the connectors at the customer end must be taped or covered well. For very large services, a double run of service wires can be installed. When installing a double run, it is fairly critical to have both wires exactly the same length; otherwise, the shorter wire with slightly less impedance will carry a larger share of the load.

When dead-ending the service at the utility pole, the tail of the service wire is often long enough to reach and contact live conductors on the pole. Tie a rope to the end of the service wire to maintain control.

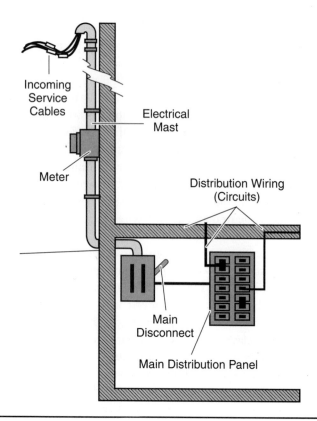

Figure 7–27   Service entrance.

At the customer end, the meter should be removed or the disconnect switch opened. A typical residential service layout is shown in Figure 7–27. The wires in the stack can be checked with a 500-volt tester to ensure that the stack contains no short circuits. Always check the voltage at the customer end after connecting a service.

7.3 Constructing an Overhead Transmission Line

Deciding the Route

7.3.1 The decision making to establish a route for a new transmission line involves technical, environmental, and political issues. Technically, the route must go from one terminal to another. The most direct route, with a minimum number of corners and dead ends would be the most economical, but parks, homes, highways, pipelines, wetlands, and more affect the route.

Environmentally, a route must avoid wetlands, certain other habitats, and densely populated areas. Permission is needed to clear all trees and brush and to remove from the right-of-way all trees that could contact the line if they were to fall.

Many people will object to any route chosen. They will express concerns through the political process about the health effects of the magnetic fields, the visual pollution, and impact on property values. Political backing is needed when property is bought or easements obtained for a line and for access to each structure.

Designing the Line

7.3.2 Whenever a line is designed, a roll plan is produced. This plan shows the right-of-way measured from one end to the other (*chainage*) and the location of each structure. Another roll plan illustrates the profile of the line and shows the terrain, the height of each structure, and the sag in each span. A multitude of sub-assembly drawings and close-ups will show how foundations, structures, insulator strings, vibration dampers, shield wire attachments, electrical connections, and so on are assembled. Tower-loading diagrams will help when planning how to rig a tower for erection and for raising conductors.

An important consideration when designing a line is how to reduce the risk of the domino effect (cascading) occurring when one transmission-line structure goes down. Some types of structures, such as a wood-pole "H" frame, have very little ability to resist a longitudinal force. Thus, additional dead-end or anchor structures are strategically inserted into the line. Some types of towers—such as a rigid square-based latticed tower; a V, Y, or delta tower; and some types of steel poles—are deemed to have acceptable longitudinal strength to avoid cascading. The swing of a suspension insulator string or the conductor slipping through a suspension clamp also reduce force on adjacent structures.

Clearing the Right-of-Way

7.3.3 Transmission lines transverse almost every kind of terrain, including mountains, deserts, forests, lakes, farm fields, and cities. The right-of-way must be cleared for construction and made suitable for maintenance for years to come. Temporary roads must be built into individual structures, although the use of helicopters allows structures to be built in all kinds of terrain with no need for access roads. Trees must be cleared and, if practical, the right-of-way should be grubbed and compatible ground cover should be planted.

Line crews must be informed about any special arrangements made with property owners. It has not been unusual for a line crew to drive through or over areas where agreement had been reached with the property owner that the area would be avoided.

Right-of-ways can go across very valuable property and have compatible secondary uses such as parks, vehicle parking, and some buildings is encouraged and a source of revenue for utilities. It is fairly common for powerlines up to and including 230 kV to be strung over industrial or commercial buildings, but not higher-voltage lines such as 345, 500, and 745 kV. Utilities have staff dedicated to handling requests for secondary use of transmission-line corridors.

Constructing the Structure Foundations

7.3.4 The foundation types for transmission towers include grillage, pad and pier, and augered, as shown in Figure 7–28. In addition to the foundation needing to provide a solid and level base, it also must counter large uplift and down-thrust loads, especially dead ends, corners, and towers subjected to wind and ice. The civil work involved with putting in a foundation has to be very precise and is normally carried out on construction projects by specialized crews.

Formerly, most steel-lattice structures had grillage footings, each with a good base width and a hole filled with the same material that was excavated. Today, the footing

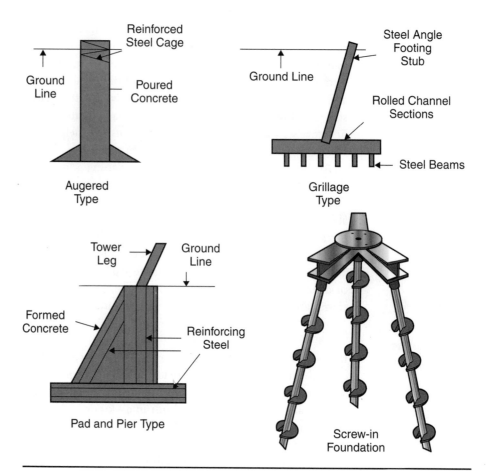

Figure 7–28 Types of transmission tower foundations.

almost always involves excavating a hole for each leg. Installing caissons, forming reinforcing steel, putting in bolts to which the structure will be attached, and pouring concrete. The layout has to be very precise, and the portion above ground must be formed to make a reasonably attractive finish.

The foundations of steel towers are grounded electrically to either *counterpoise* (wire such as 1/0 copper buried the length of the line) or *crow's foot counterpoise* (copper buried around the base of the tower in a crow's-foot pattern). The downgrounds on wood poles are grounded to ground rods at the pole base. Other methods of grounding wood poles, such as a "hot plate" (wire fastened to the bottom of the pole) or a "butt wrap" (wire wrapped around the buried portion of the pole), are not nearly as effective as a ground rod.

Assembling and Erecting Structures

7.3.5 There are many different transmission-structure designs for each transmission voltage. Pole structures include twin-pole wood (H-frame), twin-pole gulf port, single-pole wishbone, single pole with a variety of post insulator arrangements, and more. Steel-lattice structures can be single circuit with many different designs, double circuit with many designs, guyed V structures, and so on. Each design would also have heavy anchor structures for dead ends, heavy angle structures, and light angle structures.

The work involved in assembling structures depends on the type of structure and on the method of structure erection.

Steel-lattice structures are assembled in sections with a small crane used to lift and move the sections around as needed. When the structure is to be set by crane, the lowest section is placed on the foundation and the other sections are assembled nearby. If the structure is to be set by helicopter, assembly yards are usually strategically placed where the structures are assembled. Each steel member and plate is stamped with distinguishing numbers and/or letters that correspond to those on the structure drawings. The members are assembled with bolts and nuts with spring washers. The nuts are not torqued at this stage to leave some flexibility when the sections are bolted together later. Sometimes individual sections need some temporary reinforcement to prevent individual members from being bent.

Transmission-line structures are most often set by crane, but a sky crane helicopter is common for right-of-ways that are difficult to access. It is common to erect steel-lattice structures in sections where workers are placed at each leg of the tower to receive the next section. Spud wrenches are used to align two sections by inserting the pointed end into a hole on each side of the corner and then installing bolts into the vacant holes. Workers quickly realize that the last person to line up the holes has to struggle the most, so they usually compete to get their bolts in first. Good communication is needed because sometimes 1/2 inch or smaller adjustments have to be made by the crane. If the structure is to be installed in one piece on the footings, temporary reinforcement may be needed to prevent damage as the tower is being tipped up.

If steel-lattice towers are erected in sections by helicopter, it is best *not* to have workers on the structure, despite the need for communication. Ideally, temporary brackets have been installed in each section so each section can be set up while no one is on the tower. Wood and steel poles can be set into pole holes with a helicopter, much like the distribution poles described in Section 7.2.4 in this chapter.

Large steel-pole structures are visually more acceptable to the public than are steel-lattice structures. The very large steel poles come in sections with a slip joint between sections, as shown in Figure 7–29. The sections must be pulled together to form a specified overlap. Steel poles are heavy, and lining up each section has to be done very accurately. Each male and female section will have a mating mark to help with proper orientation and splice overlap. Such poles need more engineering than steel lattice because, like distribution poles, they flex and can be damaged very easily by improper rigging. If a circuit is to be strung on only one side, steel poles are sometimes set to counter the eventual deflection that would cause an unsightly lean toward the loaded side. The pole is actually bent (or cambered) to offset the calculated expected deflection so that it will look straight after the wire is strung. Wood poles can be framed in advance. In some cases, especially when erecting by helicopter, even twin pole structures can be assembled with the crossarms in place while leaving one crossbrace loose to allow plumbing the structure after it is set in the holes.

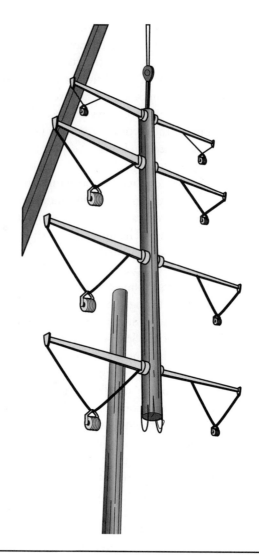

Figure 7–29 Top of a steel pole set on slip joint.

Other methods are used to erect steel-lattice structures because they are manufactured in many small pieces. In the past, poles or steel-lattice structures have been set with a gin pole. Today that would be a rare event, and the knowledge and skill needed to erect a steel-lattice tower with a gin pole are probably lost in most locations.

In brief, a gin pole (wood or steel lattice) is set up in the middle of a future tower. Four rope blocks are attached to the butt and tied to each tower leg. Four rope blocks are attached to the top of the pole, and the top of the pole can be moved to a location within the tower so that it is above the point for a lift of steel.

In places where fall arrest is used, the rope used by the fall arrest system is attached to the top of the structure before it is erected.

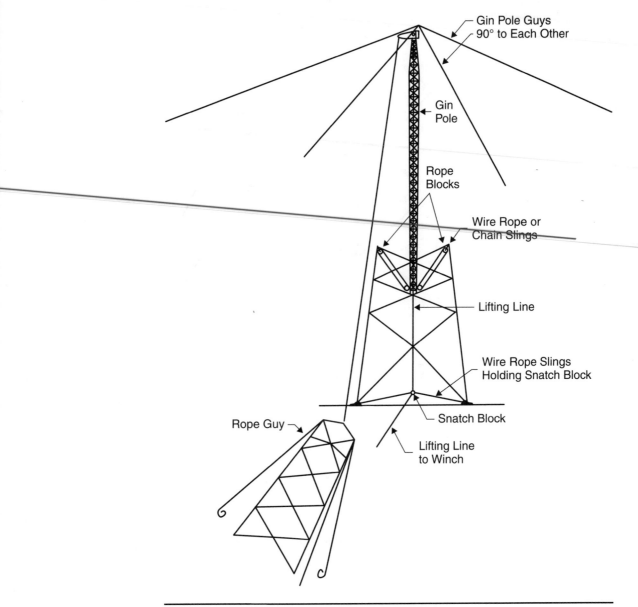

Figure 7–30 Building a tower using a gin pole.

Hang Insulators and Stringing Blocks

7.3.6 Transmission-line insulators are most often porcelain (ceramic), glass, and polymer in suspension. Post insulators and braced post insulators are common when a line is built on a narrow right-of-way or along a highway. When braced posts (Figure 7–31) are used, a post and suspension insulator supports heavier conductor in a fixed position and because the insulators do not swing, the braced posts can be used on smaller structures which would have with less visual impact.

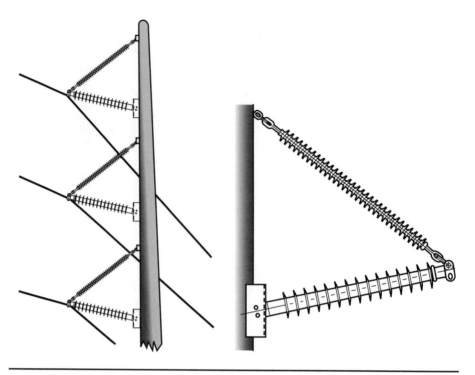

Figure 7–31 Brace post insulators.

Some structures are designed with a V arrangement of the insulator strings. A V arrangement is more likely to self-clean because the contaminants on both sides of each string are likely to be washed off by rain.

Insulators, stringing blocks, and, in some cases, ropes through the stringing blocks are sometimes installed before a tower is erected, but more often they are erected after the tower is erected. When sending up a string of insulators, a cradle or other device that can send the string up straight will prevent excessive bending of the string and damage to the ball, socket, and cotter key between the insulators. Polymer insulators are much lighter and easier to work with, but can be abused easily with rough handling.

Climbing up and down insulator strings when constructing a new line has been common in the past and may have been acceptable with porcelain insulation, especially if the feet were crowded in as close to the steel hub as possible. Some utilities do not allow anyone to come on older lines for fear that a skirt will break and cause a fall or severe cut. Toughened glass insulators shatter completely when broken, porcelain insulators typically break off in chunks, and ceramic insulators also tend to shatter. Climbing on polymer insulators can damage the skirts, and the damage can be overlooked easily.

Stringing blocks for stringing bundle conductor come in single, double, and triple sheaves. Figure 7–32 shows a single-sheave stringing block designed to accept a pilot line dropped in by helicopter.

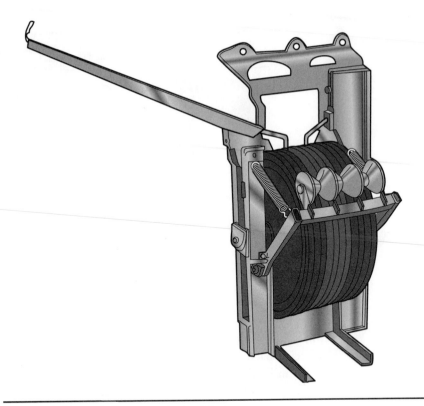

Figure 7–32 A helicopter stringing block.

The diameter of a stringing block must be such that it does not damage the conductor. The strands of a large conductor will flex and loosen excessively as it rolls through the block. Smaller-diameter stringing blocks may be acceptable for a resagging job where the conductor is under line tension and will not travel very far.

Install Rider (Guard) Poles

7.3.7 On new lines, virtually all conductor stringing is done under tension. In a perfect world the conductor could be strung and kept clear of highways and other critical spans. However, it is essential *not* to lose control of a conductor, so a backup system is necessary for preventing conductors from dropping down on roadways, railways, and circuits crossing below.

Guard structures or nets are installed at roadways, railroad crossings, and at locations where crossing circuits lie below. The guard structures are generally two- or three-pole structures with rider poles suspended horizontally between them. Single poles under each conductor with crossarms mounted on top in V formation are also common (V poles). Another type of rider that is effective for shield wire stringing or restringing (when power conductors are in place) is a length of 3/8- or 5/16-inch steel strung across the three power conductors and tied to the ground with rope on each end.

Having flaggers as a backup at all such sites is common practice.

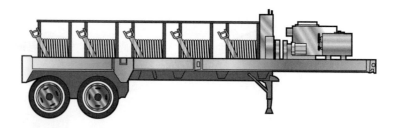

Figure 7–33   A pilot line winder.

String Conductor

7.3.8 Historically, conductors were strung along the ground and pulled up through stringing blocks at every structure. Relatively short pulls and logs laid down in strategic locations prevented too much damage to conductors.

Almost all conductors are now strung under tension. Thus, they never intentionally touch the ground. Pilot lines (ropes) are dropped, usually from a helicopter, and strung into the stringing blocks that are designed to accept rope as it is dropped from above. When the pilot line reaches its target, a pull rope (sometimes a steel winch) is attached and pulled back by the tensioner. The pilot line can be reeled back to the conductor/tensioner end with a machine such as the one shown in Figure 7–33.

The pull rope (or wire rope) is attached to the power conductor or running board. Running boards are available to string two, three, or four conductors with one pull. Ideally, the rope pulling the running board will be in the center sheave when it reaches the insulator string. If it isn't, however, the running board will center itself and each conductor will end up in its own sheave after the board has passed. Figure 7–34 illustrates a weight holding the running board level. The swivel between the pulling rope and the running board takes out the torsional forces that could flip the running board.

The puller pulls in the conductor while the tensioners hold enough tension to keep the conductors in the air. Figure 7–35 shows a tensioner setup.

When working with conductor joints and connectors, sharp corners and projections capable of producing a corona discharge must be made smooth.

Shield wire is strung in a similar manner. It is common to take advantage of optical ground wire (OPGW) when stringing in new shield wire. OPGW is fiber-optic cable surrounded by strands of steel-shield wire, so placing it in the shield wire position is ideal. The fiber-optic cable inside the shield wire can be damaged if is bent too sharply or twisted during stringing. Larger-diameter stringing blocks and special hardware for dead-ending and clipping are used to avoid excessive bending, and a swivel and weights hung near the pull rope prevent twisting (Figure 7–36).

Sag and Clip-in Conductor

7.3.9 Normally, transmission lines are sagged more precisely than distribution lines. Scopes and transits are used to make precise measurements. More checks are made, especially in extra-long spans and spans on hillsides. After the conductors

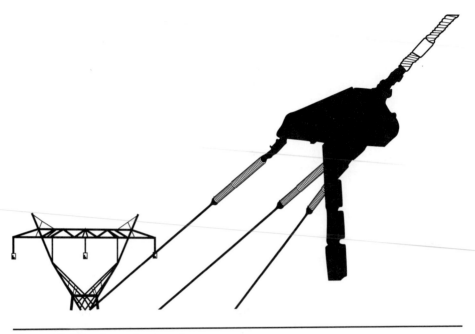

Figure 7–34   A running board.

Figure 7–35   A tensioner setup.

have been sagged, they are clipped in (clamped in) on the tangent and light angle towers between the dead ends. The conductor (or conductors, in the case of a bundled conductor) is removed from the stringing block and transferred to the saddle clamps. Vibration dampers (spacer dampers) are installed.

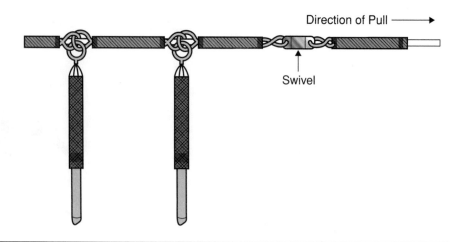

Figure 7–36   Pulling OPGW cable.

To lift the conductor out of the stringing block, a hoist is hung right above the conductor on the tower arm. Nylon slings are generally used at the tower end, and unless a shoe is made specifically to hook onto the conductor(s), a nylon sling is used at the conductor end. To get down to the conductor level, the powerline worker—while wearing a harness and fall arrest system, climbs down either the insulators, a rope ladder, or a rigid live-line ladder. If the hoist is hung upside down, all the up and down adjustments can be made at the conductor level. Because sometimes the chain will jam when lowering the conductor and can cause hoist failures, some locations do not allow the hoist to be hung upside down.

Vibration dampers must be installed at specified distances from the saddle clamp. The frequency of conductor vibration is highest near the saddle clamp, and it is important to place the vibration damper at the point and frequency for which it is designed. Spacer dampers are installed from carts ridden from tower to tower on the conductor. The carts are usually motorized and have hydraulic power for lifting the conductor past the insulator strings and for operating impact wrenches.

Dead-Ending Conductor

7.3.10 The highest tensions worked with in line work are dead-ending transmission lines. The rigging components and rigging configurations require planning, and probably some engineering. Calculations must be made of the expected load on each tower component, snatch block, sling, hoist, winch cable, and so on. The configuration of the rigging should be such that the angle through any snatch block will not increase the bisect tension of the anchor point beyond its load rating. For example, as explained in Chapter 15, a winch line that changes direction through a block at 90 degrees will put 1.5 times the line tension on the anchor point, sling, and snatch block.

The conductor is dead-ended with compression or implosive dead-end terminals.

It is common practice to sag conductors using pullers and tensioners and then to transfer the conductor to temporary anchors (tie-downs or helpers) to free up the machines and to allow tangent structures to be clipped in. Dead-ending work involves working with one span between the dead-end tower and the tie-downs at the next tower.

Major Transmission Projects with Existing Lines

7.3.11 To delay the need to build a new circuit, utilities are carrying out projects that will maximize the current-carrying capacity of existing lines. Work includes restringing or resagging power conductors and refurbishing existing lines.

Resagging a circuit improves the ground clearance and allows a line to carry more load. Reinforcement of structures, changing dead-end insulators, and changing saddle clamps and vibration dampers may be necessary. This is a job that can be carried out hot. The conductor is transferred to stringing blocks using live-line tools or barehand techniques from a tower or buckets. A hydraulic winch, much like the boom-tip winch of a digger derrick, is hung on the conductor using barehand techniques from buckets. Dielectric hydraulic hoses are connected to the tool circuit of a digger derrick that recently has had the oil electrically tested. The winch may have to be strung out to provide a two-, three-, or four-part line. Line workers working together in two bucket trucks install the grips and spread out the winch cable. When the conductor is pulled up, the slack between the grips is coiled up using barehand techniques. When the conductor is at the new sag, it is spliced and the conductors are clipped in. When required, dead-end insulators are changed out before resagging using live-line techniques.

Restringing usually involves putting the existing conductor in stringing blocks and pulling in the new with the old. The splice between the old and the new is the weak link that may require more that just boring out one-half of the small sleeve to accommodate the larger conductor. Shield wire and power conductor are restrung in this manner. Broken strands are not uncommon on old conductor, especially on old steel-shield wire. A strand will break and unravel until a length of it is dropping on and tripping out circuits that are being crossed over, despite the existence of rider (guard) structures. In another case, a broken strand will bunch up at the front of a stringing block to the extent that it will stop the puller, damage the structure, or both. Constant helicopter patrol is needed when stringing and restringing.

Commissioning

7.3.12 Before a new line is put into service, it goes through a commissioning process to ensure that the line was built to specifications. Because a new transmission line is a huge investment, commissioning is actually continuous as the line is constructed. Powerline workers are used for commissioning because they can closely examine almost every part of a certain number of structures. Detailed data about all structures are recorded on required forms. Utility representatives perform the following tasks and more:

- Watch the foundations being installed and ensure, among other things, that any grounding connections are made.

- Torque a representative number of bolts on each tower to ensure that they meet specifications.

Figure 7–37 Structure numbers. *(Photo courtesy of TSE International. All rights reserved.)*

- Observe splicing and dead-ending operations to ensure that the conductor has been cleaned and the work is done to specifications.

- Change as-built drawings as changes are made.

Sometimes, a commissioning team must number the structures. Numbers or labels are placed at the bottoms of structures and often include the circuit name or number. Numbers are also installed at the tops of structures to assist helicopter patrols, as shown in Figure 7–37. The trend today is to use a Global Positioning System (GPS) to determine the latitude and longitude of a structure and to use their intersection as the structure number. For example, a structure number might be 41° 08′ N × 76° 15′ W. Warning signs for helicopters are also put on top of structures two or three spans before a circuit that is crossing over or under that circuit.

7.4 Constructing an Underground Distribution Line

Why Underground Distribution?

7.4.1 The public always seem to be asking why utilities do not use more underground. It is true that the public tolerates extended outages less and less and that underground distribution does escape the extensive damage done by hurricanes and ice storms. Some municipalities legislate underground distribution for select parts of their jurisdictions. Underground distribution is very common in densely populated areas of cities, and most residential subdivisions built in the past 30 years or so have been supplied underground. Underground is more expensive than overhead, not so much because of the cost of cable compared to a pole line but because of equipment, such as pad-mount and submersible transformers and switching equipment. Conversion from overhead to underground is expensive because it also includes converting overhead services to underground.

Two Types of Underground Distribution Systems

7.4.2 The duct and vault system and the direct bury system are the two main types of underground systems.

The *duct and vault system* is used in cities where streets, sidewalks, and lack of space would be impractical for a direct bury system. In such systems, duct banks are installed between vaults and utility holes and encased in concrete, as shown in Figure 7–38. Switchgear and transformers are placed either under the street in large subterranean vaults or in buildings along the street. Duct banks are accessible at every utility hole and vault. Sections of cable can be installed or replaced for years to come without having to dig up streets.

The *direct bury system* is more economical to install than a duct and vault system and is used mostly in underground residential distribution (URD). For installation, direct bury systems need some available space between streets and buildings. The cable may be put in conduit for some extra protection but is usually not put in duct banks or encased in concrete. Cable on a reel can be purchased preassembled in a polyethylene conduit (*cable-in-conduit system*). Some cables will have only an envelope of sand around them. Transformers and switchgear are either pad-mount design and sit on the surface of a concrete pad that sits over a well where cables come up to feed the equipment or are submersible where the equipment is installed below grade level.

Civil Work: Trenching, Vaults and Pads

7.4.3 The trenching and digging needed to put a new duct system in a city require very extensive civil work and will cause a lot of disruption to the street. Locations for water, sewer, gas, other electrical circuits, communications cables, and even underground transportation systems must be considered when digging. Civil work involves breaking concrete/asphalt, extensive digging, concrete forms, placing conduit, pouring concrete, installing vaults, backfilling, and placing new street/sidewalk surfaces. Figure 7–39 shows one of the many types of duct bank designs. Ducts are mostly made of polyvinyl chloride (PVC) plastic or fiberglass, but existing ducts are

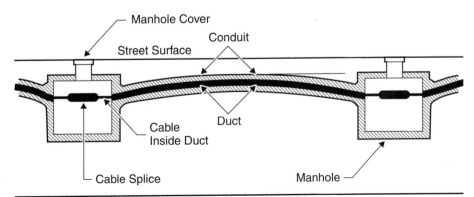

Figure 7–38 A duct bank.

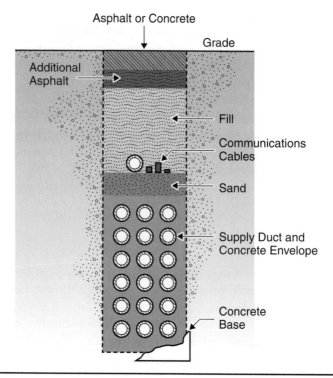

Figure 7–39 Typical duct bank trench. *(Photo courtesy of TSE International. All rights reserved.)*

also made of tile, concrete, or steel. Any bends or curves must be as large in radius as possible to keep the sidewall pressure on the cable to a minimum and to reduce the pulling tension on the cable during the cable installation.

Very large, specially designed vaults are constructed much like basements are, with elevations that are perfectly aligned with the street grade above and with foundations and covers that can support heavy overhead traffic. Figure 7–40 shows how a transformer vault might look. Typically, more circuits would be going in and out and switchgear may be in the vault.

The civil work for direct bury systems is not as technical as for a duct and vault system. In a new subdivision, direct bury can be as simple as digging an open trench and laying in cable with proper separation and such and ensuring that the cable has a complete sand envelope around it. One rock pressing against a cable can cause a concentration of the electrical field at that point and eventual cable failure. Different preferences for how a cable is laid in a trench depend on the utility. Choices to protect the cable include enveloping it in sand, in PVC stick conduit, in flexible PE (polyethylene) conduit, and big O pipe. Guided underground boring is also carried out where it is more economical or customer friendly to avoid disrupting streets, lawns, and so on. Smaller cable that is available preassembled in conduit can also be specified.

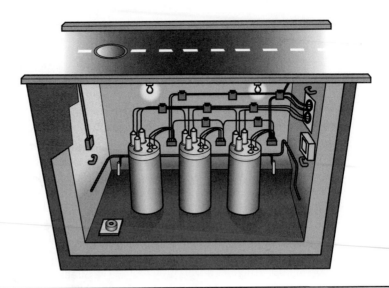

Figure 7–40   A typical transformer vault.

Sharing a trench with other utilities is common with direct bury systems. Each organization must follow the specifications for depth, vault size, duct size, minimum bend radius, and so on. Figure 7–41 shows a typical joint-use trench with typical dimensions.

The civil work for installing such equipment as transformers and switchgear on direct bury systems consists of installing and leveling prefabricated fiberglass, concrete, or polymer–concrete pads for pad-mount equipment and vaults for submersible (under grade level) equipment.

Some utilities serve each customer with a service straight from the transformer, while others run secondary bus to secondary pedestals or handholds, which are typically fiberglass boxes where services are connected to the bus. For secondary bus, conduit is installed between the transformer pads/vaults to secondary pedestals or handholds. The pedestals and/or handholds are installed, depending on the type, such that the top of the pedestal is at final grade or partly underground with the connections above ground.

Red warning tape is laid out about 1 foot (0.3 meter) below the surface and above the underground cable to be a warning to people digging above the cable. A bare ground wire strung along the top of the cable or duct bank can be used to more accurately locate cable in the future, as well as for gathering stray ground current.

Pulling and Laying Cable

7.4.4 As discussed elsewhere in this book, underground cables are delicate and any excessive bending or tension will damage them. A damaged cable may be in service for a while, but electrical stresses at locations where there are insulation

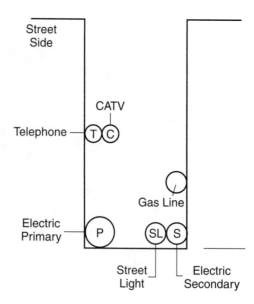

Figure 7–41 A joint use trench.

voids, a damaged semiconducting layer, and so on will cause premature failure. Therefore, it is essential when pulling in a cable to protect it by not pulling beyond the maximum allowable tension and not flexing it beyond the maximum allowable radius.

Maximum Allowable Cable Tension and Bending Radius

The maximum allowable tension for a cable is usually part of the manufacturer's cable specifications. The maximum tension allowed is dependent upon the conductor size and on how a pulling eye is attached to the cable. The core conductor(s) is the only part of a power cable that can take a fairly high pulling tension. Therefore, a crimp-on pulling eye is the best choice. A crimp-on pulling eye can be factory or field installed and is made to seal the cable against contaminants. If using a wire-mesh grip with a swivel eye, the pull will be on the sheath only, which can tear it away from the core. Therefore, the allowable pulling tension is very low, usually less than 1,000 pounds (500 kilograms). The manufacturer will also specify a minimum cable bending radius for the type of cable being installed.

Estimated Pulling Tension

An estimated pulling tension can be calculated before starting a pull or before the cable is purchased by entering certain known data into a computer program. The data will include the weight of the cable, number of cables in the duct, details about the length and clearances in the conduit, and sidewall pressure. Of course, the estimated pulling tension has to be less than the maximum allowable tension of the conductor. If not, a revision of the pulling layout is needed.

Preparing the Duct

Typically, a duct will contain a pulling wire or rope. If not, an air compressor can be used to blow a line carrier (bird) with a small nylon cord attached to it through the duct, as shown in Figure 7–42. The cord is used to pull in a bigger rope, which in turn brings in a bigger pulling rope or winch. Another method pushes a duct rodder from one vault to another, as shown in Figure 7–43. One way a duct can

Figure 7–42   A line carrier.

Figure 7–43   A duct rodder.

be checked is to pull a flexible steel mandrel of the correct diameter through the length of the conduit, as shown in Figure 7–44.

Rigging the Pull

To make a pull within the tension limits of the cable, the vault at the cable reel end must be rigged so that a minimum amount of cable bends and a variety of cable guides are made specifically for keeping the cable running smoothly with a minimum amount of tension as it comes off the reel. Vaults are manufactured with embedded eyes for use as anchoring points for snatch blocks. The cable guide shown in Figure 7–45 can plug into duct at the face of the vault wall to provide a smooth and low-friction change of angle. A quadrant block, as shown in Figure 7–46, allows the cable to make a smooth low-friction 90-degree turn.

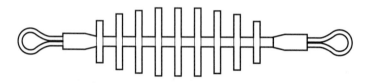

Figure 7–44   A flexible mandrel.

Figure 7–45   Cable feeding sheave.

Figure 7–46   A quadrant block.

If the reel is set up as in Figure 7–47 no extra rigging is needed, only muscle. If this method is used, at least one worker, and probably more, should help to turn the reel, with someone in the vault to guide the cable, someone applying lubricant, and possibly someone inspecting the cable for defects.

Making the Pull

Figure 7–48 shows how a puller and reel might be set up. The winch is attached to the end of the cable. The pulling machines have gauges or monitors to indicate the tension on the cable. An electric puller monitors pull tension by translating the number of amps the motor is drawing into tension. Applying a lubricant specifically made to be compatible with the cable to reduce friction is essential as

Figure 7–47 Cable at the reel end.

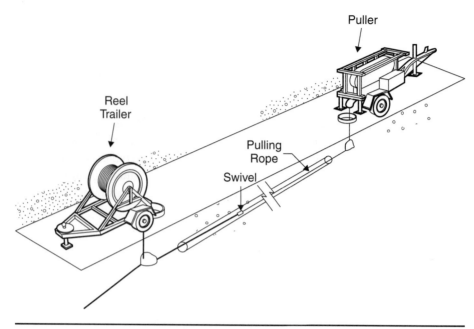

Figure 7–48 Pulling underground

the cable is pulled through the duct. A weak link can be installed at the pulling eye to act as a mechanical fuse and to break apart before a cable is overstretched. Figures 7–50 and 7–51 show a type of pullers that can be used to pull in the cable. The puller shown in Figure 7–50 can be put into different configurations to adapt to the setup at the vault.

Installing Equipment

7.4.5 Equipment such as transformers, switchgear, reactors, and capacitors are set on pads, lowered into vaults, or rolled into buildings.

Pad-mount equipment is very accessible to the public and is placed over the hole to the cable compartment below so as not to leave a space for vandalism. Before the equipment is installed, the primary and secondary cables are trained with the ends of the cable up through the hole.

Terminations and Splices

7.4.6 Electrically, the most technical part of underground work is making terminations and splices. Some terminations are made at substations, some in equipment such as transformers and switchgear, and some on riser poles for a transition to overhead. Terminations and splicing underground cable have to be done to exact standards (the principles are discussed in (Chapter 8). There are many cable types and termination types, and unless a person is lucky enough to work only with one kind all the time, it is probably best to have a written procedure on hand.

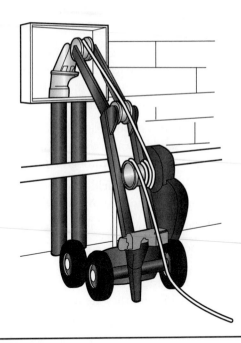

Figure 7–49 A cable puller.

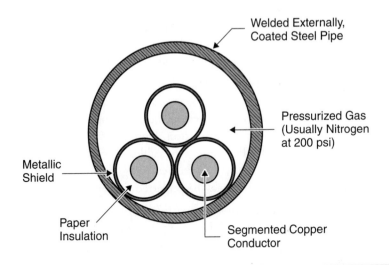

Figure 7–50 High-pressure gas-filled (HPGF) pipe.

Each cable must be traced and labeled. Each switching device must be labeled with a corresponding number on an operating drawing.

Most utilities require electrical testing of new cables, splices, and terminations before energizing. Use the specified voltage for testing because it is very easy to damage a cable by testing it with too high a voltage.

7.5 Underground Transmission Lines

7.5.1 Generally, underground transmission lines are used where there is no practical alternative, such as to feed the downtown core of a city, to build a line near an airport, to cross a river or channel, or to feed from a generating station to a step-up substation. Underground transmission lines have a lot of advantages, such as the following:

1. Where it is impossible to build overhead, underground can be laid under streets, under water, through high-density residential areas, along very narrow right-of-ways, and through some types of environmentally sensitive areas.

2. Electromagnetic field (EMF) concerns are diminished because underground conductors are laid together closely with a greater canceling effect.

3. There are fewer visibility concerns.

4. Underground lines are not affected by the scourges of wind and ice.

7.5.2 Underground transmission cables are classified according to their insulation and whether or not they are in pipes. The main types are these:

1. *High-pressure, fluid-filled pipe type (HPFF).* A high-pressure, fluid-filled pipe type cable, consists of three high-voltage cables in a steel pipe filled with an insulating fluid (oil). Each cable is made of copper or aluminum, insulated with oil-impregnated paper insulation, and covered with metal shielding (usually lead). The steel pipe provides mechanical protection, is a container for the oil, and helps cool the cables. HPFF cable is, historically, the most common underground transmission cable.

2. *High-pressure, gas-filled pipe type (HPGF).* High-pressure, gas-filled pipe uses pressurized nitrogen gas instead of oil. Oil is better insulation and, therefore, each cable laid in nitrogen-filled pipe will be made with about 20% more insulation. Figure 7–57 shows a typical layout for both HPFF and HPGF pipe-type cable. The cable is more difficult to cool and will have a lower current-carrying rating. Because the danger of oil leaks is nil, this cable may be preferred for sensitive areas.

3. *Self-contained, fluid-filled pipe type (SCFF).* In SCFF cable, one hollow cable is in each fluid-filled pipe; three pipes comprise a circuit. Each cable has paper insulation, a lead-bronze (or aluminum) sheath, and a plastic jacket. This cable is often used for water crossings.

4. *Extruded dielectric, polyethylene (XLPE)* pipe type. XLPE (solid dielectric) cable is like distribution cable, except it is single cable, with each cable put in pipe or concrete duct for extra mechanical protection; three pipes comprise a circuit. Each cable has a copper or aluminum conductor, a semiconducting shield, cross-linked polyethylene insulation, an outer semiconducting shield, a metallic sheath, and a plastic jacket. The insulation is much thicker than oil-impregnated paper insulation. This type of cable is the choice for new underground transmission lines. Such cables

were limited to 69 kV and 138 kV circuits, but higher-voltage XLPE is becoming available.

5. *Gas-insulated lines (GIL).* GILs are large gas-filled [sulfur hexafluoride (SF_6)] pipes with bare conductors suspended on insulators. A GIL is a good choice when very large conductors are needed, such as between a generating station and the step-up transformer substation.

Splices

There is a practical limit to the amount of cable a reel can carry, therefore, splicing locations must be planned. Splices for oil-filled pipe-type cables are in vaults constructed along the length of a line. The vault is typically about 15 feet (4 m) long with one or two vents to the surface, and it is strong enough to withstand the weight of overhead traffic.

XLPE splices can be in vaults, but some are put in temporary vaults filled with backfill.

Terminations

Transitions (risers or potheads) are made from underground to overhead lines or to substation potheads. The cable is terminated so that the high-voltage conductor is brought out from the cable in such a way that the cable is protected from moisture/contamination and, at the same time, has electrical clearance from the grounded sheath, pipe, and structure. Porcelain or polymer housings or potheads are used to make these terminations.

Cable Current-Carrying Capacity

The rating or *ampacity* of the cable system is dependent on the size of the conductor and how well heat can be dissipated. Backfill is depended upon to do a majority of the cable cooling and, therefore, it plays a large part in determining the cable load-carrying capacity. Corrective thermal backfill material is designed to move heat away from the line, and typically it is a graded sand that is compacted or a thermal backfill made from a weak concrete solution.

Civil Work: Trenching and Vaults

7.5.3 The civil work required to install transmission lines is similar to distribution except that the transmission line is typically deeper, the pipes or conduit are larger, and more concrete is used to protect the cable. Because of the cost and consequences of an error when installing a transmission-line cable, the project is a team effort, with on-site engineering, on-site utility commissioning staff, and cable manufacturer representatives.

Overhead transmission lines are placed at the top of a structure, and underground transmission lines are typically placed at the bottom, below water and sewer lines and every other underground utility. The trenches are dug with gradual slopes and turns, and depending on the type of cable or pipe to be laid, concrete forms are prepared to build duct banks.

One type of layout for oil-filled cables is shown in Figure 7–51. Pipes are welded, X-rayed, protected from corrosion with plastic coatings, and pressure and vacuum tested between vaults.

Figure 7–52 shows a typical layout for an XLPE cable duct bank. Extra ducts and communications cable are commonly installed. Above the concrete duct bank, a ground wire is sometimes strung to carry stray ground current.

Underground transmission lines, other than some submarine cables, are generally less than 10 miles (15 km) in length. In that length, vaults are needed for locating splices and accessing the duct banks.

The trench is closed with thermal backfill and soil and the streets and sidewalks are resurfaced.

Pulling Cable

7.5.4 Cables are pulled between vaults in similar fashion to distribution except that the cable will be much heavier and the consequences of an error will be much greater. The length of each pull is limited to the length of cable on a reel. As for distribution cable, there will be a maximum allowable cable tension. The calculations will determine the rigging needed to keep the tension below the maximum allowed.

Terminations

7.5.5 At each end of a cable will be a transformation to either three separate overhead phases or three separate potheads. The termination for underground transmission line is at a pothead of a transition structure, or at a pothead in the wall of an underground vault or substation. Figure 7–53 shows a termination on an overhead transmission structure, and Figure 7–54 shows a typical riser in a substation.

Making a splice or termination on XLPE transmission-line cable is not unlike working on distribution. Making a splice or termination on pipe-type cable is usually done by people who specialize in such work.

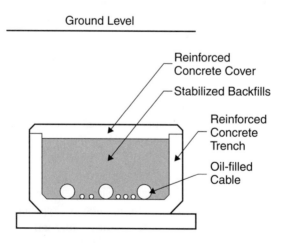

Figure 7–51 Transmission cable ducts.

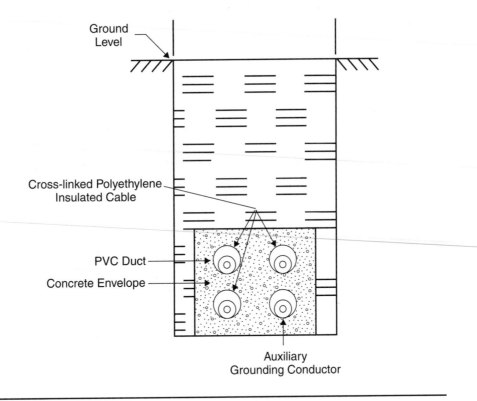

Figure 7–52   A typical layout for an XLPE cable duct bank.

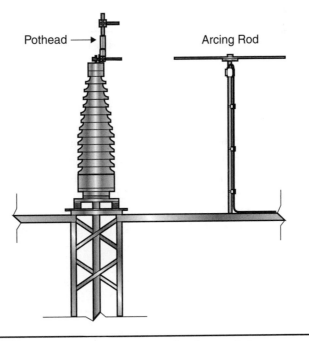

Figure 7–53   A typical termination on an overhead transmission structure.

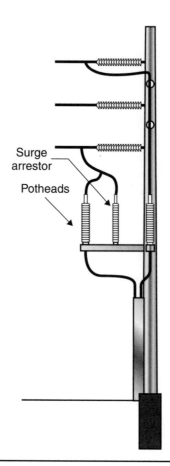

Figure 7–54 A typical riser in a substation.

Extensive electrical testing is carried out before a cable is energized.

Auxiliary Equipment

7.5.6 Underground transmission cable is closely monitored for temperature, contaminants, pipe pressure, corrosion, and potential dig-ins.

Pipe-type cables will have oil-pumping stations that keep oil flowing in force-cooled cable systems. Oil samples are routinely scheduled for analysis, especially for the presence of air or moisture. Alarm systems will indicate low oil or low oil pressure. Cables in pressurized gas filled–pipes are similarly monitored for pressure, contaminants, and so on.

Review Questions

1. What are three electrical clearances to be considered when designing a line?
2. Before digging, what other utilities should be located?
3. Which wood pole has the larger diameter: class 1 or class 5?
4. What depth hole is needed in earth to set a 60-foot wood pole?
5. What measures are taken to avoid a pole or truck boom contact when setting a pole in a live circuit?
6. What measures are taken to prevent injury to workers on the ground in case a pole or truck boom makes contact with a live circuit?
7. What two factors determine the size or number of guys and anchors needed to hold a pole?
8. Name three precautions needed to install a power-installed screw anchor.
9. What kinds of protection can be taken to prevent injury when stringing conductor near live circuits?
10. During a stringing operation, how is a person on a tensioner protected from electric shock if the conductor being strung makes electrical contact?
12. What procedures are needed to prevent a vehicle from contacting a conductor while stringing over a highway?
13. Describe two types of transmission-tower foundations.
14. What causes an uplift on a transmission-tower foundation?
15. When assembling a steel-lattice tower, what two references are needed to determine the location of each individual piece of steel?
16. How can broken strands cause problems when using old conductor to pull in new conductor?
17. What are the two main types of underground distribution?
18. What methods are used to ensure that the maximum cable tension is not exceeded when pulling it into a duct?
19. Name three types of underground transmission cables.
20. How does the backfill for an underground cable affect the current-carrying capacity of the cable?

CHAPTER 8

Working with Conductor and Cable

Topics to Be Covered	**Section**
Electrical Properties of a Conductor	8.1
Overhead Conductors	8.2
Working with Overhead Conductors	8.3
Underground Cable	8.4
Working with Underground Cable	8.5
Working with Fiber-Optic Cable	8.6

8.1 Electrical Properties of a Conductor

Conductor and Cable Work

8.1.1 Line work, whether overhead or underground, is all about working with conductor. Working with conductor involves stringing, splicing, making connections, tensioning, and so on. Stringing can be some of the most complex work done by a line crew because it includes stringing near other live circuits, working around road crossings, and rigging for heavy pull and high tensions. Cutting and splicing tensioned conductor has contributed to many electrical accidents.

Underground line includes laying of cable, working in confined spaces, pulling cable through conduit, locating faults, and so on.

Electric Current in a Conductor

8.1.2 When an electric current flows in a conductor, three basic effects occur:

1. A magnetic field is set up around the conductor.

2. Heat is generated to some extent.

3. A drop in voltage occurs to some extent.

Some kind of conductor is used in every electrical circuit. A conductor can be wound into coils, such as in a transformer coil; it can be a large aluminum pipe, such as in a station bus; or it can be in an electronic circuit board of a protective relay switch. This chapter describes conductors used in overhead and underground transmission and distribution circuits.

Conductor Selection

8.1.3 From an electrical perspective, the selection of a conductor is based on the ampacity and voltage requirements of the circuit. The larger the diameter of the conductor, the greater the capacity to carry large amounts of energy with the least amount of line loss. However, some compromise has to be made between a large-diameter conductor and the mechanical properties of a conductor.

A larger-diameter conductor increases overhead line tension, adds to sag, allows for more ice buildup, and provides more surface for wind. However, while a large conductor is sagged lower, it will not heat up as much for a given load and will, therefore, have less sag. The bare conductor chosen should typically have a maximum thermal load of 37.8°F, (100°C). Depending on the length of a span and the expected electrical load on a conductor, the mechanical strength requirements can be more critical than the electrical properties of a conductor.

On underground circuits, current-carrying capacity and voltage regulation are the dominant factors involved in specifying a conductor.

Ampacity of a Conductor

8.1.4 Ampacity can be defined as *the current in amperes that a conductor can carry continuously without exceeding its temperature rating*. When a conductor temperature reaches the annealing point, its strength, brittleness, and elasticity are permanently changed.

Two factors affect the amount of heat in a conductor:

1. There is a resistance in the conductor itself. This resistance impedes the current flowing in the conductor and causes heat to be produced based on this formula:

$$Watts = I^2R$$

In other words, a large-diameter conductor has less resistance to electrical current, which means that less heat is being generated within the conductor.

2. Heat generated in a conductor can transfer by convection or conduction to the surrounding environment. With an overhead conductor, heat transfers to the air; therefore, on a cold day, a conductor can carry more current than it can on a hot day. Underground cable has thermal barriers that slow the cooling of a conductor, including for example, conductor insulation, the soil surrounding the cable, or poor air circulation in a duct.

3. The ampacity of a conductor is not normally the governing factor for choosing a conductor size. The conductor size chosen is normally much larger to reduce the voltage drop to a distant load.

Capacity Rating of a Transmission Circuit

8.1.5 Each transmission circuit has a continuous current rating. A normal electrical load causes some heating of the power conductors, and the conductor sag increases as the load increases. Overloaded conductors heat and sag into crossing circuits or trees, depending on the span length and conductor type. A conductor sag can change about 30 feet (10 m) with load and weather changes. The circuit is rated to a maximum permissible loading based on conductor size and sag.

As the load on a circuit and the ambient temperature change, a control-room operator uses precalculated tables to prevent the line from being overloaded and the conductor sag from dropping below regulatory standards. By now, computer programs that give a real-time thermal rating for a circuit have probably replaced the paper tables everywhere. These programs continually calculate the maximum permissible loading as the load, temperature, and wind change. Some utilities now have sensors on transmission lines that will give the actual conductor temperature.

A utility also has transmission-line capacity ratings for emergency loading when other circuits are lost. An emergency rating allows additional sag as a temporary measure.

Capacity Rating of a Distribution Circuit	**8.1.6** It is not normal to have a capacity rating for each distribution circuit. On rare occasions, an overloaded distribution circuit may sag into a neutral or secondary, but normally a switchgear tripping out a voltage problem would indicate a possible overloaded conductor.

Secondary buses and services are not as closely monitored as a distribution feeder, and a trouble crew will be alerted to problems during a low-voltage trouble call. An underground system should be monitored more closely because an overloaded cable will heat up, shorten the life of the cable, and eventually lead to failure.

Voltage Rating of a Conductor	**8.1.7** The voltage to be used on a bare overhead conductor is not a factor in specifying conductor size until it is used on high-voltage transmission lines. On high-voltage lines, a minimum diameter is needed to avoid corona loss. Extra-high-voltage circuits use two, three, or four cables bundled together with spacer dampers to form a group, which creates a virtual large conductor.

On underground cable, the voltage rating is based on the property of the insulating material. The cable insulation, as well as other design considerations, must be suitable for the voltage of the circuit. Voltage induces electrical stresses on the insulating material and an inadequate amount of insulation, a sharp bend in the cable, or external pressure from a rock will eventually cause a rupture in the insulation. Insulation will break down faster because of AC voltage stress than because of DC voltage stress. The DC voltage rating of a specific cable insulation is three to four times higher than the AC voltage rating. The stresses induced on the insulation by DC voltage are constant, while the stresses induced by AC are multidirectional and fluctuating.

Voltage Drop in a Conductor	**8.1.8** When current passes through a conductor, resistance opposes the flow and a voltage drop results. The amount of voltage drop can be calculated using Ohm's law ($E = IR$). The amount of resistance offered by a conductor depends on the conductor's diameter and length.

Voltage-drop calculations are normally done with a computer or by using voltage-regulation tables. Table 8–1 illustrates the impact of conductor size and length in

TABLE 8–1   **Voltage-Regulation Table**

	Percent Voltage Drop per Mile for 4.8-kV, 50-A Load, at 0.9% Power Factor				
	1 Mile	*2 Miles*	*3 Miles*	*4 Miles*	*5 Miles*
#4 ACSR	5.6%	11.2%	16.8%	—	—
#2 ACSR	3.8%	7.6%	11.4%	15.2%	—
1/0 ACSR	2.7%	5.4%	8.1%	10.8%	13.5%
3/0 ACSR	1.9%	3.9%	5.8%	7.8%	9.7%

a single-phase line with a 50-ampere load. The table also illustrates why voltage regulation is a bigger consideration than ampacity when choosing a conductor.

For example, the voltage at an unloaded distribution transformer is 120 volts. What would be the voltage of an unloaded transformer 3 miles downstream if the primary conductor is 3/0 ACSR (aluminum conductor, steel-reinforced)?

Table 8–1 shows that there would be 5.8 percent voltage drop over a 3-mile length of 3/0 ACSR, which results in the following:

$$120 \text{ V} - (0.058 \times 120) = 113.04 \text{ V}$$

Voltage Drop in a Three-Phase System

8.1.9 To use Table 8–1 to calculate the voltage drop for a *balanced* three-phase circuit, the voltage drop for a single-phase circuit is divided by 2 because the flow back to the source is no longer on the neutral. The result is then multiplied by the square root of 3, which is the voltage drop per phase. Because the square root of 3 divided by 2 is 0.866, the voltage drop on one phase of a balanced three-phase system can be calculated by multiplying a single-phase voltage drop by 0.866.

For example, the voltage at an unloaded three-phase transformer bank is 120 volts per phase. What would be the voltage of an unloaded transformer bank 3 miles downstream if the primary conductor is 3/0 ACSR?

Table 8–1 shows that there would be a 5.8 percent voltage drop over a 3-mile length of 30 ACSR. The voltage drop for a single-phase line is thus:

$$120 \text{ V} \div 1.058 = 113.4 \text{ V}$$

which is a drop of

$$120 - 113.4 = 6.6 \text{ V}$$

For a three-phase line, the voltage drop would be:

$$6.6 \times 0.866 = 5.7 \text{ V}$$

Specifying Conductor Size

8.1.10 The current-carrying capacity of a conductor is not normally the controlling factor when specifying a conductor for an electrical utility circuit. Other factors include the following:

- A conductor must be large enough to keep the voltage drop to an acceptable limit.
- A conductor must be large enough to limit line loss and keep the fault current available at the end of the line high enough for the protective switchgear to see a fault.
- A conductor must be large enough to accept future load growth.
- A conductor on transmission lines must be large enough to limit corona loss.

On a very short length of line, ampacity can be a limiting factor because voltage drop or line loss will not be as noticeable. For example, a main line consisting of 336,000 circular mils (kcmil) AL has a voltage regulator with #2 copper input and output leads. This is acceptable because the #2 copper has the ampacity to carry the load current and the short length will not affect the voltage regulation appreciably.

Conductor Sizes

8.1.11 Learning to recognize a conductor size on sight is a common skill for powerline workers. When in doubt, a conductor size should be confirmed with a gauge to avoid using the wrong sleeve or connector. The numerical systems used to size conductors can be quite confusing. The numbers used to indicate conductor size have no practical application to the line trade. Fortunately, most utilities standardize on a relatively small number of conductors and provide tables for their weight, die sizes, and grip sizes.

The American Wire Gauge (AWG) system is formed by defining a 40 conductor as 0.46 inches in diameter and a #38 wire as 0.005 inches in diameter. There are 38 sizes of wire, spaced in a geometric progression, between these 2 sizes. Conductor sizes are expressed by numbers. Common sizes used in the line trade are #4, #2, #1/0, and #3/0.

Conductors larger than 4/0 are referenced to their cross-sectional area (CSA), expressed in circular mils. The size of a conductor is not calculated by using the formula for determining the area of a circle: πr^2. One circular mil is defined as a circle with a diameter of 1/1,000 or 0.001 inches. Based on this definition, a conductor size can be determined by measuring the diameter of a conductor in mils (1/1,000 or 0.001 of an inch) and then squaring that number. The size of a conductor is normally expressed in thousands of circular mils, or kcmils.

However, only the conductive material is used when discussing conductor size, so type of stranding and steel wires in a conductor will change the calculated diameter. For example, a 336.4-circular-mil ACSR conductor with 26 strands of aluminum and 7 strands of steel is measured as 0.720 inches in diameter, which when squared would indicate that this conductor should be a 518.4-circular-mil conductor.

In the metric system, a conductor size is referenced to the area of its cross-sectional area (CSA), expressed in square millimeters. The conductor size can be calculated using the formula for the area of a circle (πr^2). The aluminum and steel cores of ACSR conductors are measured separately and shown as 40/20 mm^2 for 40-mm^2 aluminum and 20-mm^2 steel core.

Corona Loss

8.1.12 An electric field around a conductor can be strong enough to break down or *ionize* the molecules in the air and cause sparks or a *corona* around the conductor. Under certain weather conditions, corona can be seen around a conductor on a dark night as a purple glow or as sparking. Corona can also be heard as a crackling or hissing sound, especially on a foggy or damp morning.

When the air between phases, or between phase and ground, is electrically stressed, the air becomes ionized (the air becomes conductive) near the surface of the conductor. The electric field generates a cloud of tiny electric discharges into the air surrounding the conductor.

Corona generates ozone gas (O_3), which is an ionized form of oxygen and is recognized by a distinct caustic smell. Ozone decomposes organic materials, such as rubber, and affects materials that are subject to oxidization. Older rubber cover-up was subject to ozone damage when the cover-up was left on a line for any length of time.

It takes energy to make corona, and corona loss results in power loss and causes radio and television interference. The design of a circuit, its conductor, and its hardware minimize corona loss:

- Voltage stress of the air between phases or between phase and ground is reduced by designing the circuit to have enough spacing between conductors. The higher the voltage, the greater the spacing required.

- Voltage stress is reduced at the surface of the conductor by spreading the stress over a larger area. High-voltage circuits, therefore, need a larger-diameter conductor. Extra-high-voltage circuits use bundled conductors to spread the voltage stress over a greater air space. Corona rings or grading rings used on extra-high-voltage circuits also spread the stress over a larger area.

- Voltage stress is reduced at the surface of conductors by smoothing any rough or sharp points where voltage stress of the air concentrates.

Skin Effect

8.1.13 Alternating current does not travel equally distributed throughout the conductor. Electrical current interacts with its own magnetic field. The electromagnetic field around the conductor also cuts through the conductor itself, and the created inductive reactance causes a counter-electromotive force (cemf). The cemf is greater at the center of the conductor than along the outside. The main current flow becomes concentrated along the outer surface of the conductor.

Large-diameter conductors or tubular conductors are used to overcome the higher impedance to current flow caused by the skin effect. Skin effect increases with an increase in frequency. Although the frequency of a powerline is a standard 50 or 60 hertz, the skin effect is increased when the circuit has high-frequency harmonics superimposed on it. Higher-frequency harmonics increase the amount of induction created by the electromagnetic field and increase the skin effect. For the same reason, harmonic distortion causes an increase in the heating of transformer and motor windings.

Vibration and Galloping of a Conductor

8.1.14 Conductors that are strung to high tension are subject to aeolian (caused by wind) vibration. Unless transmission lines have special vibration-resistant conductors, vibration dampers are installed in each span. Vibration dampers can be armor rod wrapped around the conductor at the suspension clamp, stock bridge dampers, torsional dampers, spacer dampers, and fiber helix dampers. One method of reducing vibration in a span is to have torsional or stockbridge dampers installed at a specified distance relatively close to the suspension clamp to reduce high-frequency vibration and to have another damper farther out from the suspension clamp to reduce lower frequency vibrations.

Typically, when conductors on distribution lines are strung tighter than 20% of the rated tensile strength (RTS) they are subject to aeolian vibration. Preformed spiral plastic dampers are often installed at the suspension points of a distribution line affected by aeolian vibration. Strand or messenger cable that is tensioned properly but has no cable lashed to it is very vulnerable to vibration.

Under conditions such as ice loading and a moderate wind, conductors can "gallop" or "dance" where the power conductors or shield wire in a span rise up and drop down violently. The wires rise and fall from a few feet to a distance equal to full sag. Severe galloping can have the conductor go up the same distance as the full sag and has in the past destroyed supporting structures. Galloping is usually vertical where shield wire and power conductor can clash, and on some occasions, galloping can also result in phase-to-phase contact. Subspan galloping can also occur where multiple oscillations occur in a single span, as illustrated in Figure 8–2.

There continues to be much study on ways to reduce or eliminate galloping. Some solutions have been air-flow spoilers, midspan dampers, spacer dampers, detuning pendulums, and such circuit design changes as shorter spans.

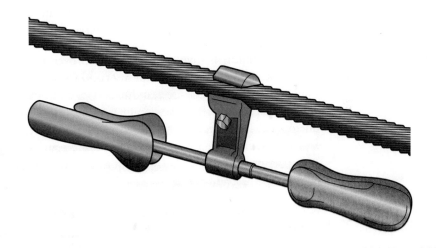

Figure 8–1   A stockbridge damper.

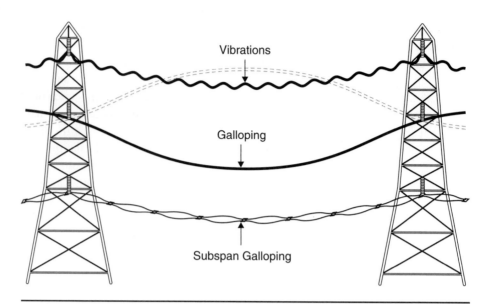

Figure 8–2 A comparison of galloping, vibration, and subspan galloping.

8.2 Overhead Conductors

Types of Overhead Conductor

8.2.1 Overhead transmission-line conductors are always bare. They are made up mostly of aluminum stranding with some kind of steel reinforcement. An overhead distribution conductor can be bare, covered with weatherproofing, or insulated with a jacket. Weatherproof covering is apparently a carryover from earlier days when local or municipal electric codes called for conductor insulation. The weatherproof covering provides some protection from low voltages, but today it only provides some additional electrical protection from tree contact. A powerline worker should treat weatherproof-covered conductors as though they are bare.

Secondary buses and services are mostly insulated. The live legs and neutral are often wrapped together to form a spun aerial cable or triplex cable.

Advantages of Aluminum

8.2.2 Aluminum is involved in almost all overheated splices and bad joints, so why use it? Almost all overhead power conductors strung today are made from aluminum, aluminum alloy, or aluminum with steel reinforcing. The conductivity of aluminum is about 62 percent that of copper, but the weight of an aluminum conductor is about half of a corresponding copper conductor with an equal resistance and length. in other words, aluminum has a conductivity-to-weight ratio that is twice that of copper. The light weight and cost advantage of aluminum have made aluminum the preferred conductor for overhead applications.

Types of Bare Conductors

8.2.3 The bare conductors available are a compromise between a conductor's tensile strength and its conductivity. Other properties considered in a conductor design are conductor weight per unit length, thermal expansion, elasticity, surface shape drag, fatigue resistance, and ability to dampen vibration and resist galloping.

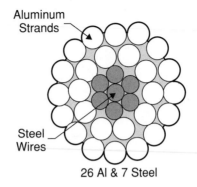

Aluminum
Strands

Steel
Wires

26 Al & 7 Steel

Figure 8–3   An ACSR conductor.

Examples of some types of conductors include the following:

1. For transmission and distribution lines, the strength and weight of *aluminum conductor, steel-reinforced* (ACSR) (as shown in Figure 8–3) allow longer spans, less sag, and, therefore, shorter structures. The reinforcing wires may be in a central core or distributed throughout the cable. A galvanized or aluminized coating reduces corrosion of the steel wires.

A large variety of stranding arrangements are available. For example, a 336.4k-circular-mil ACSR can have a ratio of aluminum strands to steel strands of 6/1, 18/1, 20/7, 24/7, 26/7, or 30/7. Each conductor would have a slightly different diameter. An increase in diameter increases the resistance to wind and ice and decreases the resistance to electrical current.

2. *All-aluminum conductor* (AAC; also called *aluminum-stranded conductor,* ASC) is a conductor with high corrosion resistance but relatively poor tensile strength. It is used in distributions in which shorter spans do not require steel reinforcement for strength. Corrosion resistance of aluminum has made AAC a conductor of choice in coastal areas where even the best galvanized steel can start corroding in 2 years.

3. All-aluminum-alloy conductor (AAAC) (Figure 8–4) looks like AAC, but it is a conductor with higher-strength, individual, aluminum-alloy strands. The individual strands will be much stiffer to bend than the aluminum in AAC. Compared to an ACSR of the same diameter, AAAC has lighter weight, comparable strength, better current-carrying capacity, and better corrosion resistance.

4. *Aluminum conductor, aluminum-alloy-reinforced* (ACAR), is composed of aluminum stranding and aluminum-alloy stranding (Figure 8–5). The aluminum-alloy strands provide a conductor with a balance of electrical and mechanical properties. ACAR can have any combination of the two types of strands to provide the best choice between mechanical and electrical characteristics for each application. In appearance, ACAR will look like AAC and AAAC, but ACAR is a combination of the two and will have easy-to-bend stands and hard-to-bend strands.

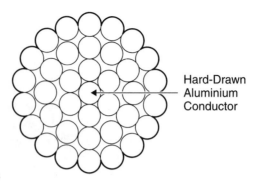

Figure 8–4   All-aluminum-alloy conductor (AAAC).

5. *Aluminum-alloy conductor, steel-reinforced* (AACSR) is an aluminum-alloy conductor with steel strands added for more strength. AACSRs have approximately 40 to 60 percent more strength than comparable ACSRs of equivalent stranding and only an 8 to 10 percent decrease in conductivity. It is a very high-strength conductor used for extra-long spans or for use as a messenger/neutral cable for spun secondary.

6. An *ACSR with trapezoid-shaped aluminum wires* (ACSR/TW) is a compact conductor, as shown in Figure 8–6. With a conductor diameter equivalent to conventional ACSR, there is a 20 to 25 percent increase of aluminum area. This provides a significant decrease in the resistance and an increase in the current-carrying capacity of the conductor, as well as a reduction in vibration to levels where vibration dampers are not needed. Less diameter for a given load allows using less sag and longer spans, it also means smaller ice and wind loads.

Figure 8–5   Aluminum conductor, aluminum-alloy-reinforced (ACAR).

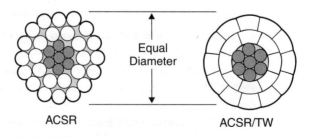

Figure 8–6   Compact trapezoidal conductor.

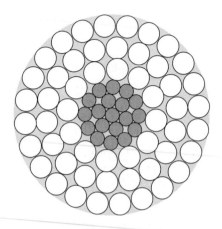

Figure 8–7   Aluminum composite conductor reinforced (ACCR).

7. *Aluminum composite conductor reinforced* (ACCR) (Figure 8–7) is similar to ACSR except that the core is a composite material instead of steel. The composite core is probably the most recent innovation for conductor. The core consists of a number of individual composite wires that look like the steel wires in ACSR, but each composite wire provides strength at about half the weight of steel, good conductivity, and corrosion resistance. Each composite wire contains many thousands of ultra-high-strength, micrometer-size fibers.

An existing line can be restrung to approximately double its ampacity with no increase in conductor diameter, less weight, and no requirement to upgrade the structures.

A variation of ACCR conductor is aluminum conductor composite core (ACCC/TW), which is wrapped with trapezoid-shaped aluminum wires similar to those used in ACSR/TW (see item 6) around the composite core wires (Figure 8–8).

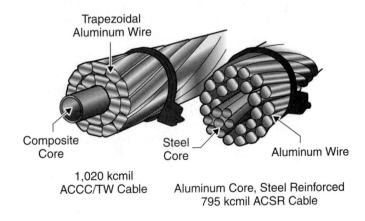

Trapezoidal
Aluminum Wire

Composite
Core

Steel
Core

Aluminum Wire

1,020 kcmil
ACCC/TW Cable

Aluminum Core, Steel Reinforced
795 kcmil ACSR Cable

Figure 8–8   Composite core conductors.

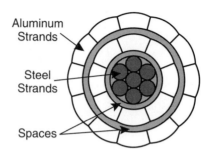

Figure 8–9   A self-dampening conductor.

8. An *ACSR self-dampening conductor* (Figure 8–9) is self-dampening and vibration-resistant. It is constructed of steel wires in the core surrounded by layers of trapezoid-shaped aluminum wires. It is designed to keep a small gap between the layers of wire while under tension. The interaction of the different natural vibration frequencies of the steel core and aluminum layers provides an internal dampening effect.

9. *Vibration-resistant* (VR) or *twisted* (T-2) *conductor* (see Figure 8–10) is composed of two identical conductors twisted together, giving the conductor a spiraling figure-eight shape. VR conductor is used in areas subject to vibration and galloping due to wind or ice. The spiraled shape presents a continuously changing conductor diameter to the wind, which disrupts the force of the wind on the conductor. This type of conductor can be sagged to full allowable tension without the need for additional vibration protection. During repair or splicing, each of these two conductors must have its own grips and hoist installed. Any splices should be about 15 feet (3 meters) apart. *Oval conductor* is another vibration-resistant conductor that also provides continuously changing diameters to the wind.

10. *Aluminum-weld* (AW) (also called *aluminum-clad) conductor* has aluminum cladding bonded onto each individual strand of high-strength steel wire. It has the strength of steel with the conductivity and corrosion resistance of aluminum. A wire size of "7 No. 5" means there are 7 strands of number-5 wire. Aluminum-weld conductor is often used as overhead ground wire (shield wire), as a messenger

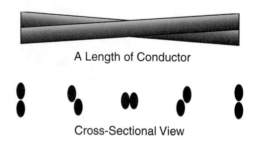

Figure 8–10   A vibration-resistant conductor.

Figure 8–11 An aluminum-clad conductor.

(strand) wire, and even as guy wire in corrosive areas. Similarly constructed is *copper-weld* (CW) (also called *copper-clad) conductor*, which is used as a buried ground wire (counterpoise) along a transmission line.

Tree Wire or Aerial Spacer Cable

8.2.4 Tree wire and aerial spacer cable (Figure 8–12), which are basically the same type of conductor, have insulated jackets that protect the conductor from tree abrasion. The jacket, however, is not considered insulation but rather a cover. The cover prevents an immediate short circuit when the conductor makes contact with trees or other grounded objects. If the contact with a grounded object is prolonged, the insulated cover deteriorates and eventually fails. It is estimated that tree cable reduces the need for tree trimming by 60 percent.

The insulation on unshielded cable, such as a covered conductor, cannot be depended on for personal safety. The cable must be treated as a bare conductor for working purposes because the cover may have deteriorated without the deterioration being readily visible.

Bundled Conductors

8.2.5 A bundled conductor (Figure 8–13) is an arrangement of conductors in which each phase has two or more conductors in parallel. The conductors are held a short distance apart by dampers (Figure 8–14). Bundled conductors are frequently used for high-voltage and extra-high-voltage transmission lines. From an

Figure 8–12 Tree wire on an urban street.

Figure 8–13 A four-conductor bundle.

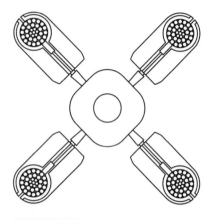

Figure 8–14 A spacer damper supporting a four-conductor bundle.

electrical point of view, a bundle of conductors is one very large conductor and has all the advantages of a very large conductor.

A bundled conductor operates at a lower temperature, lower resistance, and lower line loss than does a single conductor with the same total amount of material. The inductive reactance in the circuit is reduced. For example, a two-conductor bundle has only about 50 percent of the reactance of a single conductor having the same circular-mil area as a bundled pair. The greater the spacing between each conductor in the bundle, the lower the reactance. There are less corona and radio noise from a bundled conductor because corona loss from a conductor is related to the voltage gradient at the conductor surface.

Secondary Bus and Service Drops

8.2.6 Overhead secondary bus and service drops under 600 volts can be aluminum or copper, many sizes, open wire, aerial cable, and neutral-supported aerial cables.

Open-wire bus and service drops are typically three wires strung separately and spaced apart. They can be bare, have a weatherproof covering, or be insulated. Open-wire bus is still being strung, generally with insulated wire. Except for very big industrial service drops, almost all service drops are now triplex or quadruplex. Open-wire service drops with weatherproof conductor are electrical hazards to the public because these services often have exposed live wires at the customer service rack.

Aerial cable lashed to a messenger (strand) is popular in some areas. One major advantage is that side guying the poles for service drops is unnecessary. The tension on the messenger is tight enough to keep the poles straight. The messenger can also serve as a neutral and is typically 3/0 AACSR. Terminating a service midspan requires terminating the lashing wire on each side of a new service drop's dead end and pulling slack into the service wires. If working on a hot secondary, it is wise to use cover-up because all the connections are close and the neutral and lashing wires are bare.

Neutral supported cable, such as triplex and quadruplex, is the most common service drop and is used as bus in many locations. When used as bus, a lot of sag occurs in the span, which may encroach on the space reserved for communications cables. As a service drop, the connectors at the customer end must be taped or covered so that live connections are not exposed.

8.3 Working with Overhead Conductors

Making Splices and Connections

8.3.1 Work with conductors normally involves splicing and making connections. To avoid unnecessary line loss and a possible burn-off, splices and connections must be made on cleaned conductor to ensure a low-resistance connection.

Avoid unnecessary line loss and possible burn-off, ensure splices and connections are made on cleaned conductor. High-resistance oxides form very quickly on aluminum and copper conductors. Aluminum oxide is a high-resistant transparent film that forms immediately on the surface of aluminum when exposed to air. Even aluminum conductor that looks clean and bright must be cleaned. Use oxidation-inhibiting joint compounds to prevent reoxidation in the connections. The abrading action of the fired wedge connector will remove some of the oxide from conductor during installation, but utilities will insist that the conductor be cleaned before any connection is made.

Over time, aluminum is prone to creep or flow out of a tight connector and eventually to cause the connection to be loose. The design of an aluminum connector has to maintain a relatively low average stress, along with sufficient elasticity or spring-type loading, to provide a constant pressure even when there is some aluminum flow out of the connector. Many old bolted connectors, such as parallel groove clamps and split bolts that are good for copper, will eventually fail on aluminum. There are approved bolted connectors for aluminum, but they are not common. Approved connectors tend to be compression connectors, fired wedge connectors, and compression terminals with bolted pads.

Copper oxide, which is the green coating on the wire, is somewhat conductive, and that is why copper connections rarely burn off. Approved connectors that join aluminum and copper together have a divider (often with a cadmium surface) between the two metals. The copper should be on the bottom to prevent the copper oxide from leaching over and corroding the aluminum. Note in Figure 8–15 how copper and aluminum can be kept apart with an H-type connector.

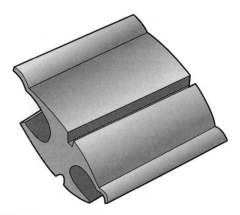

Figure 8–15   An H-type connector.

**Making a Tap
Connection**

8.3.2 A huge variety of connectors are available for transmission and distribution, ranging from split bolt connectors to large compression connections.

Connections on transmission lines, especially at terminals and for loops (jumpers) at dead ends tend to be compression fittings with lugs or pads. When the pads are put together, they are cleaned and then bolted together. Belleville (spring) washers, which are bevelled, are used to keep constant pressure on the connection by compensating for the expansion and contraction of the bolts and connection. It is important that they be properly torqued so that they are compressed to only 80 percent of their height; if no bevel is left in the washer, the connection is too tight and expansion could cause a failure.

Fired-on wedge connectors are available in sizes suitable for a service entrance, up to and including relatively large conductors on transmission lines (Figure 8–16). Once the correct-size installation tool (gun), correct-size cartridge, and the correct-size connector are chosen, the connection has a relatively fail-free history. The tool is powder actuated, and incorrect use can and has resulted in injuries. The short discussion in this text is not a substitute for the training that comes with use of the tool. A worker must know how and when to use either of the two platforms, choose the correct color shell, use the take-off clip, and clean and lubricate the tool.

On distribution lines, there are split-bolt, parallel-groove, squeeze-on, compression, and many other types of connectors. To make a good connection with

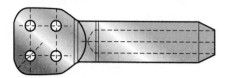

Figure 8–16   Installing wedge clamp.

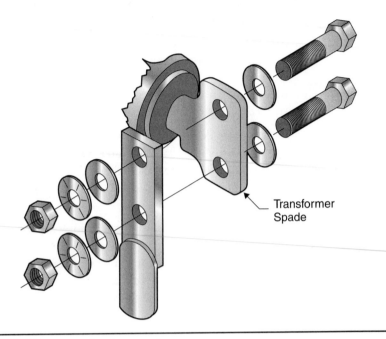

Transformer
Spade

Figure 8–17   Lug and pad connection.

these connectors, it is necessary to use special tools, proper torque, and proper die sizes.

Connections to equipment, such as to a transformer or regulator, are bolted, and conductors typically are not installed directly into equipment lugs or pads. Transformers with secondary spade connectors are connected with wires terminated with compression lug and pads (Figure 8–17). Connections are similar to those made for a transmission-line pad, with cleaning, no oxide compound, bolts, and Belleville washers. Wire connected to the bolted lugs of older transformers tends to be copper with an aluminum-to-copper transition elsewhere.

Making a Connection to a Live Circuit

8.3.3 Equipment or another line often must be connected by making a hot connection. The most common connector is a hot-line connector, which should always be installed on a stirrup (bale 1) and not directly on the conductor. A poor connection directly on the conductor can cause the connector to heat up and the conductor to burn apart.

Fixed connectors, such as fired-wedge connectors or compression connectors, are also connected to live circuits, usually with rubber gloves or with live-line barehand methods. Any time a connection to a live circuit must be made or broken, a jumper or lead first must be installed with a shotgun stick. Taking a shortcut by using rubber gloves or working barehand to make or break a connection has been the cause of serious accidents. All too frequently unforeseen situations have occurred, such as breaking too much load, connecting into a short circuit, a connector failure, a worker's body accidently making contact between the two elements, or a high-charging current energizing a line or transformer.

Working with Small Conductor

8.3.4 A live primary conductor, such as a brittle #6 copper or #4 ACSR with the steel core rusted away, can break with very little disturbance.

- Do not do any live-line work on this conductor. In the past it has broken from the shock of firing on a wedge connector, from using a hot stick to knock ice off the conductor, and while removing a live-line clamp.

- Do not stand under this conductor when any work is being done on it.

Making a Splice

8.3.5 Splices, terminals, and connections, especially for large conductor, are compressed onto a conductor with hydraulic presses and dies.

Two ends of a conductor can be joined or spliced, either as a full-tension splice or as a splice intended only as an electrical connection. Electrical-connection splices are like the insulinks used at a service entrance.

It is very easy to select the wrong sleeve or die when making a splice because of the complex method of designating conductor sizes and because each manufacturer uses different terms and designations for dies and presses. The information stamped on sleeves can include very specific information, such as the catalog number, the customer stock code number, manufacturer-specific die numbers, and conductor-diameter range. While in the field, some of this information is difficult to translate into other manufacturers' die sizes and such. The information is very precise—for example, a splice for a 336.4 ASC 19 strand conductor needs a different sleeve and different dies than does a splice for 336.4 ACSR 26/7 strand conductor. A smooth body conductor of a given size may not hold in a sleeve for a regular conductor of the same size.

Splicing a conductor together with a full-tension splice involves a sleeve, a press, dies, cleaning, and no-oxide inhibitors. Sleeves are hollow tubes made with an alloy that is compatible with the conductor. These sleeves allow conductor to be inserted into each end, then squeezed or pressed so that the conductor is joined. Larger ACSR conductor has a separate steel sleeve for the steel core and an aluminum-alloy body that is pressed on to provide electrical conductivity. The procedures described in Table 8–2 for making a two-piece compression splice is generic and one-piece sleeves, dead ends, and terminals are similar.

The Banana and Birdcaged Splice

8.3.6 A finished splice, especially on smaller conductor, may have bowed (and may now look like a banana). Such splices can be straightened on a flat surface with a hammer. Surprisingly, little force can straighten a compression sleeve while it is being pressed, after which it will be in a "plastic" state. Applying a little light machine oil to the die faces also reduces bowing.

The birdcaging or separation of individual strands after making a joint occurs because the sleeve and conductor are made of different materials with different properties and expand or deform at different rates when under compression. The birdcaging becomes more exaggerated when the grips holding tension on the

TABLE 8–2   Procedure for Making a Two-Piece Compression Splice

Step	Action	Details
1	Choose the correct sleeves and dies.	The material used to splice a large ACSR conductor consists of a steel sleeve for strength and an aluminum splice body to carry the electrical current. Refer to company documents or manufacturers' catalogs to ensure that the correct size and type of sleeves are chosen for the conductor size and type.
		Each steel and aluminum sleeve is stamped with the die size and usually the conductor type and size, along with information related to the manufacturer. It is important to use the dies specified on the sleeve because no standard is interchangeable among manufacturers.
2	Slide aluminum sleeve onto one end of the conductor.	Slide the aluminum splice body over one end of the conductor far enough to allow the installation of the steel sleeve. This is the most embarrassing step to forget, especially when working hot on a tensioned conductor and not noticing the absence of the aluminum splice body until after the steel sleeve is pressed. To fix the situation will require a piece of conductor and two splices.
3	Expose the steel core.	The aluminum strands on each end of the conductor being spliced are cut back, square with the conductor, half the length of the steel sleeve plus at least another 1/2 in. (1 cm) because the steel sleeve will expand lengthwise as it is compressed. Ideally, a cable trimmer with a cable trimmer bushing is used to make a square cut. If using a hacksaw, it is critical *not* to nick the steel wires. Taping the aluminum where the cut is to be made will prevent the individual strands from bending while being cut.
		After the steel wire is exposed, make or keep it straight and clean it. A small piece of wire wrapped near the end of the steel will prevent the strands from unraveling.
4	Insert the steel core into the steel sleeve.	The steel must be measured and marked, often with tape to indicate when the steel core reaches the middle of the sleeve. If the steel sleeve has a crimp in the center indicating the middle, it will be fairly obvious when the center is reached. The rated strength of the splice will not be achieved if the steel ends are not in the center.
		The wire wrapped around the end of the steel stranding should slide back as the steel is inserted into the sleeve.
5	Press the steel sleeve.	Use one of the many suitable compression tools and the die size and type that are stamped on the sleeve.
		Make the first compression directly over the center, capturing both ends of the steel core. Press from the center toward each end and overlap each compression by about 10 percent. Depending on the type of die and other factors, the sharp edges may have to be filed off the completed sleeve and the sleeve may need straightening.
		If the sleeve is being installed on tensioned conductor, back off the hoist and remove the grips so that you have more room to work with the aluminum and birdcaging will be less likely when pressing the aluminum.
6	Clean the aluminum stranding.	If the conductor is very black, it can be cleaned using a caustic soda like lye. Before the steel sleeve is installed, each end of the wire should be inserted into hot water and lye. Eye protection must be worn. Ideally, a special "lye pot" made from a heavy-gauge steel is used for this method of cleaning conductor. The conductor should be rinsed after the cleaning.

(continued)

TABLE 8–2   Continued

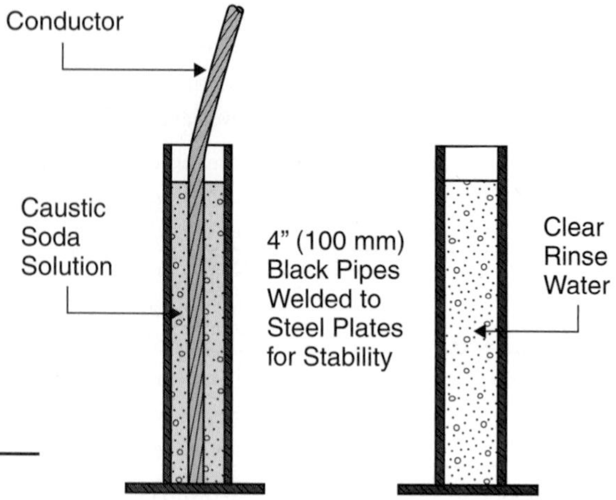

Step	Action	Details

Figure 8–18   A lye pot.

The standard method of cleaning is to unravel (without bending) the aluminum strands and to wipe each strand with an abrasive cleaning pad or fine steel wool coated with an oxide inhibitor. This can be very dirty work, especially when working hot barehand or with rubber gloves. Remember that the no-oxide inhibitor is conductive.

It is not normally necessary to unravel the last layer of aluminum strands next to the steel core.

Step	Action	Details
7	Slide the aluminum body over the sleeve.	Wrap the aluminum strands back into place so that it can be inserted into the sleeve. Measure and mark or tape the aluminum conductor so that when the aluminum body is slid into place it is directly over the center of the steel sleeve.
8	Insert the joint into the filler hole.	One or two filler holes are typically in the aluminum body of a two-piece sleeve so that the cavity around the steel sleeve can be filled with joint compound. Joint compound is conductive and helps prevent oxidation. Joint compound is added with a grease gun or caulking gun to supply pressure. The compound is added until it begins to flow out between the aluminum body and the conductor. An aluminum plug or pin is then hammered into the filler hole until it is flush with the sleeve body. Use one of the many suitable compression tools and the die size and type that are stamped on the splice body. The starting point and direction are important for preventing high-stress points in the joint.
9	Press the aluminum sleeve.	Make the first compressions on each side of the steel sleeve and move out toward the ends, overlapping each compression. Make no compressions over the top of the steel sleeve. The sleeve will expand out as the compressions are made, and any tape that marked the center should be removed. Pressing a one-piece sleeve is done in similar fashion except that the press can start on either side of the middle and can press full length each way. A terminal is pressed by starting at a point closest to the pad (tongue). Joints, especially on high-voltage lines, must have sharp edges filed off to make the joint smooth.

conductor are close. Birdcaging strands can be spread out somewhat along the wire by pushing and twisting with your hands. On high-voltage lines birdcaging can produce corona. A certain type of compression sleeve is designed to reduce bird-caging—as it is pressed first from the outer ends, a pressure relief hole located at the center allows the oxide inhibitor to bleed out while pressing.

Automatic Splices

8.3.7 Automatic sleeves for splicing or dead-ending aluminum distribution conductors are popular because they are easy to install. Tapered, serrated jaws inside the sleeve grip the conductor when tension is applied. As more tension is applied, the wedge action of the jaws clamp down more. This method of installation has to be quite precise. First, select the proper splice for the conductor by checking the conductor size and markings on the splice. The conductor must be straight when it is inserted, with any natural curve taken out. Mark the conductor to ensure that the conductor has reached the center of the sleeve. The conductor is inserted into the pilot cup (a plastic piece on the end of the sleeve to ensure centering) and into the pushed sleeve in a single smooth motion until it strikes the stop in the center. If the conductor does not go in smoothly, conductor strands are probably getting caught between the jaws inside the sleeve, which will prevent the jaws from working properly. Forcing and twisting the conductor will not work. Remove the sleeve and start again with a new one. Set the jaws initially by applying tension before letting off the hoist.

Automatic splices should not be used in some places and for some modes. They are intended to be installed on conductor under tension and are not suitable for being strung and run through stringing blocks. They also are not suitable as an electrical connection in a nontension mode, as a compression sleeve is sometimes used. A utility may restrict use of automatic splices in coastal areas because of corrosion concerns, especially if it also does not use ACSR because the steel core corrodes.

Note: Automatic splices are not to be reused.

Implosive Sleeves

8.3.8 Implosive sleeves, dead-end hardware, and connectors have an implosive charge wrapped around them. After the usual preparations and instead of using a press and dies to compress the sleeve, the implosive (not explosive) charge is set off and virtually crushes the sleeve and conductor into a solid piece of metal. The result is an amazingly smooth, compressed sleeve. A separate steel sleeve is used on ACSR conductor. The implosive sleeve does not expand outward, so there is no birdcaging. The sleeves can be used during stringing and will go through stringing blocks.

The actual implosion has a lot of energy and is very loud. People living nearby are usually alerted to what is taking place. On a construction project, all the joints prepared on a given day are imploded at one time. On a dead-end tower with three bundled conductors of four each, 12 implosions may be set off simultaneously.

Exothermic Connections

8.3.9 Exothermic or thermit welding (the names Cadweld, Thermoweld, and Techweld Cadweld may be more familiar) bonds two materials into an electrical connection by melting them together. An electrical connection is made by pouring superheated, molten-copper alloy into a mold that contains the conductors being joined. The heating is due to a chemical reaction in which temperatures reach 4,000°F (2,200°C).

Exothermic connections are common for electrical connections to ground rods or to fencing in a substation. The connector joins together materials such as copper, steel (plain or galvanized), clad steel, bronze/brass, and stainless steel.

Note: A wet mold can lead to an explosion, and hot molds can be fire hazards.

Tools for Making a Splice or Connection

8.3.10 A large variety of tools crimp or compress sleeves and connectors. There are hand-operated crimp-it, linket, and hydraulic presses. Hydraulic presses are available for almost all types of compression splices and connectors. The hydraulic pump can be powered by hand, foot, a regular electric motor, a gasoline engine, or a battery, as well as through an intensifier from a truck hydraulic system.

Generally, the dies will fit only the press for one manufacturer, so using the correct combination of tool, die, and connector is important for ensuring that the compression is made to the intended specification. A learning curve characterizes the process of mastering the terms used for the different presses—terms such as the Burndy designations for the OH25, MD6-8 Y35 shown in Figure 8–19.

The OH25 linkit press (Figure 8–19) allows a one-hand operation for compressing insulink and linkit connectors commonly used at service entrances. One compression on each side of the connector does the job. It works with a ratchet mechanism that cannot be reversed once it has started, so the wire has to be held in the center until started.

The MD6-8 (Figure 8–20) is a hand-operated press that can take considerable muscle. It is commonly used for splices and connectors on small conductor.

Figure 8–19 A linkit press.

Figure 8–20 An MD6-8 press.

Figure 8–21   A Y35 press.

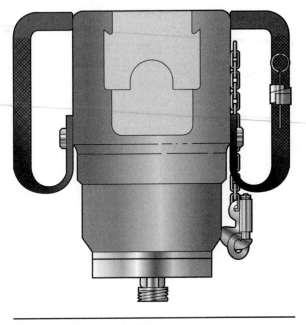

Figure 8–22   A Y48BH press.

A Y35 is an intermediate hydraulic press. The one shown in Figure 8–21 is pumped by hand, but the same press head can be operated from an intensifier on a truck hydraulic system. A lighter hydraulic oil will allow it to be operated more easily on a cold day. Be sure to use the heavier oil for regular situations.

A Y48BH press head can come with a hand pump, foot pump, and all the other power systems previously described. Such a press can apply 40 tons of force.

8.4 Underground Cable

Types of Underground Cable

8.4.1   There are high-voltage transmission-line cables, distribution-voltage cables, and secondary-voltage underground cables. Cables are generally identified or described according to insulation type. For example, there are paper-insulated lead-covered (PILC) cables, ethylene propylene rubber (EPR), and cross-linked polyethylene cables.

Transmission Cable

The most common high-voltage transmission cable has been the pipe-type oil-paper insulated cable. The insulated cable is put in a pipe, and the pipe is filled with an insulating oil. Oil-filled cables are referred to as *high-pressure fluid-filled* (HPFF) cable. Older cables tended to be *low-pressure oil-filled* (LPOF) cables, now called *self-contained fluid-filled* (SCFF) cable. Oil has prevented voids (a common cause of failures in other types of cables) in the insulation and allowed continuous checking of the cable condition, as well as monitoring of the pressure and condition of the oil at the cable terminal oil-pumping stations. Environmental concern about oil leaks has resulted in some of these cables being converted to high-pressure gas-filled (HPGF) cable.

Gas-insulated lines use a metal busbar, supported on insulated spacers in the middle of the pipe and the pipe is filled with an insulated gas such as SF6.

Working with transmission cable tends to be a specialized cable trade. A powerline worker's involvement may be limited to placing grounds at potheads as shown in Figure 8–23 or to doing other work where lines equipment is needed.

Figure 8–23   230 kV overhead to underground transition.

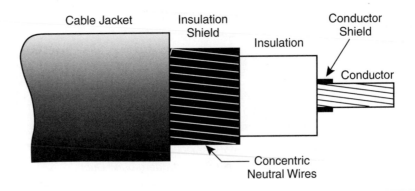

Figure 8–24   Underground cable design.

Underground transmission line is gradually being switched over to cross-linked polyethylene-insulated XLPE power cable, which is similar in design to XLPE distribution cable and much easier to splice and terminate.

Distribution Cable

Earlier distribution-voltage cables were PILC cables. The paper insulation was impregnated with oil, and the lead covering acted as a protective sheath. A lead-covered cable can withstand rainfall runoff or oil from the streets better than modern polymer cables can. There is, however, a concern about the environmental effects of lead and oil. A substitute copper-alloy sheath is available for this type of cable.

Polymeric insulation has taken over from PILC, with each manufacturer having its own additives and process to improve upon the insulation and cable design. A dictionary definition of polymer is not particularly helpful, but it is worth citing: "a synthetic compound consisting of large molecules made up of a linked series of repeated simple monomers." Common polymeric cables are cross-linked polyethylene (XLPE), tree-retardant cross-linked polyethylene (TR-XLPE), or ethylene propylene rubber (EPR).

Submarine Cable

Submarine cable is like underground cable but with an added protective shield around it.

Secondary Cables

Underground secondary cables are typically three or four insulated conductors bundled together. Each conductor is insulated, generally with a 600-volt polyethylene (PE) insulation plus a protective polyvinyl chloride (PVC) jacket.

Cable Design   **8.4.2** Underground cables have a common design requirement, which is to protect and ensure the continued integrity of the insulation. The electric field surrounding the conductor must be kept uniform so as not to become concentrated

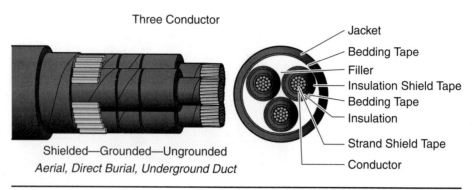

Figure 8–25   A three-phase cable.

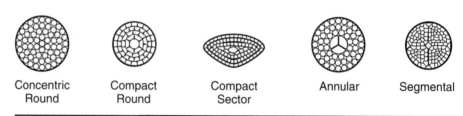

Figure 8–26   Conductor shapes.

in any part of the insulation. If the electric field becomes concentrated in one area, the electrical stress in that location will lead to eventual insulation failure.

Cables at each voltage can be single-phase or three-phase bundled into one cable. Figure 8–25 shows how a three-phase cable can be constructed.

The conductor inside all that insulation and protection can be aluminum or copper and various shapes. Figure 8–26 shows conductor shapes that are in use. The concentric round conductor is the most common. A cable with a compact round conductor, or the compact sector conductor of the same size as a cable with a concentric round conductor, has more conductive material and more ampacity. The annular and segmental conductors were designed to reduce the skin effect of the cable. The center of the annular and the space between the segments of the segmental conductors are nonconductive.

Cable Shielding   8.4.3 The insulation of a cable has a semiconducting shield at both the inside and the outside of the insulation (Figure 8–27). A semiconducting layer on each side of the insulation spreads the electric field uniformly.

The semiconductor layer next to the conductor is the *conductor shield,* which spreads an irregular electric field uniformly throughout the insulation. Electric stress would otherwise concentrate in certain areas because of the irregular shape of stranded conductor or bends in the cable.

The semiconducting layer on the outer surface of the insulation is the *insulation shield,* and it prevents a concentration of any electric field induced by the con-

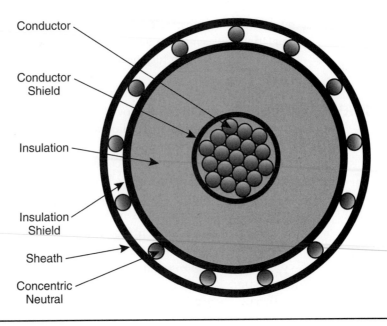

Figure 8–27 Cable shielding.

centric neutral wires. The insulation shield also spreads the electric field uniformly over any minor cable damage, thereby reducing any concentration of an electric field at the damaged point.

When making splices or terminations, the insulation shield must be stripped without damaging the very vulnerable insulation. Any voids or air pockets when applying the insulation shield (semicon) could result in a phenomon called *partial discharge* and could eventually damage the cable.

A metallic shield is applied over the insulation shield. This metallic shield can be designed so that it serves as a path for the return current (neutral). The metallic shield acts as a ground wire where it can provide a path for fault current and reduce any touch potentials when contact is made with the cable. The metallic shield (concentric neutral) can be bare or have another protective cover over it.

Cause of Cable Failure

8.4.4 One cause of a cable failure is when electric stress is allowed to concentrate in one area. The semiconducting cable shield and insulation shield normally spread out any electrical stress, but any sharp bends, voids, or sharp pressure against the cable concentrate the electric stress at that point.

Water treeing is also a cause of premature failure. Cable can have some water or moisture in it. The moisture enters the ends where the cable is cut during storage or installation. Moisture fills the very fine electric stress lines that occur at voids, sharp bends, and shield irregularities. The stress lines form in the shape or appearance of a tree; the root of the tree is at the cable, and the stress lines spread out from there toward the outer edge of the cable. Distribution submarine cable usually has a solid conductor instead of a stranded conductor to reduce the probability of water migrating between the strands. In TR-XLPE cable, a tree-retardant semiconduction compound is used that fills the area between the conductor strands to prevent moisture migration.

Cable Splicing and Terminations

8.4.5 Although there are a lot of cable types and a lot of different splicing kits and tools, the principles applied are the same for all. For a splice, this means exposing the inner core so that the core conductor(s) can be spliced and then rebuilding the cable so that a conductor shield, an insulation shield, a neutral, and a jacket are installed in such a way that there will be no added concentration of electrical stress on the insulation. For a termination, that means exposing the core conductor and making an electrical connection to some type of exposed terminal and then rebuilding the conductor so that the exposed end will have a long tracking distance back to the neutral and the semiconducting conductor shield in such a way that no added electrical stress will be put on the insulation.

Because there are so many different types of cable and splicing and terminating methods, a cable splicer must follow the manufacturer's or owner's specifications to the letter. Failure to use the proper splice for the type of cable, to handle the cable without adding undue bending stress, to keep the cable clean and dry, to use exact measurements, and so on will lead to eventual failure. Although there are splices that depend less on tape, the generic taped splicing procedure that follows illustrates a rationale that applies to almost all splices.

The same principles apply to making a termination. There are many ways of terminating cable, depending on the voltage, the size of cable, the manufacturer's products, and the purpose. Terminations are made at transitions from underground to overhead. On higher voltage, the transitions tend to be called *potheads,* as per the 44-kilovolt terminations in Figure 8–29. Figure 8–30 shows a taped termination that could be used to terminate at a pothead. On distribution, transition on poles tend to be called riser poles or dip poles. Terminations are also made into elbows (Figure 8–31) for dead front operating at transformers and switching kiosks and terminations are made into the switchgear at live front equipment.

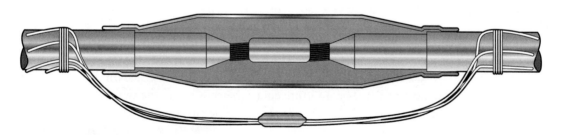

Figure 8–28   A cable splice with a single conductor.

8.4.6 The limiting factor for the ampacity of cable is heat. When the cable is direct buried, the ampacity depends on the *thermal resistivity* of the earth. If the thermal resistivity is low, the heat is carried away from the cable and the ampacity of the cable is higher.

Figure 8–29   A 44-kilovolt overhead underground transition.

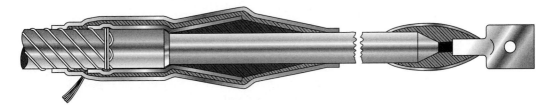

Figure 8–30   Cable termination.

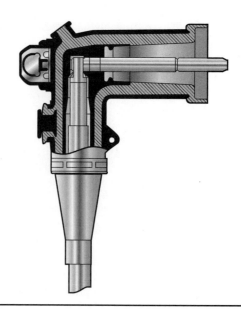

Figure 8–31   Elbow cutaway.

TABLE 8–3   Procedure for Splicing a Single-Conductor Concentric Neutral

Step	Action	Details
1	Train the cable into position.	The cable must be trained into position in such a way that it curves with the natural curve in the cable. A sharp bend can leave voids between the insulation and the conductor shield and also can leave electrical stress points at a sharp bend.
2	Cut the cable.	Cut the cable where the splice is to be made. Because the core is being exposed, it is at this stage where the tools, hands, and environment must be kept clean and dry.
3	Lay out the dimensions.	Using the manufacturer's or owner's specifications, prepare to remove the jacket and so on at the exact location on the cable.
4	Remove the cable jacket or sheath.	There are many types of cables and many types of jackets. The surface of the cable jacket or sheath should be cleaned to remove all pulling lubricants, oils, dirt, and so on that can later contaminate the splice. Cleaning a lead sheath can mean using a shave hook or rasp until it is shiny, and a polymer jacket can be cleaned by using an abrasive cloth. The finished splice will be overlapping onto the cleaned jacket.
		Use the special tools available for removing the jacket for the distance specified, with the understanding that the cable shield and the insulation must not be cut or damaged.
		Clean the removed jacket and sheath material from the work area.
5	Remove the metallic shielding.	The metallic shielding is often composed of wires that must be controlled. Tape hose clamps; other methods can be used. Depending on the location of the cable and other live cables, the metallic sheaths of the two cables being joined should be jumpered. Start each strand of the wire sheath at the end of the cable, usually with a knife, while being careful not to nick the cable insulation.

Step	Action	Details
6	Remove the semiconducting insulation shield.	The semiconducting material that makes up the conductor shield must be removed completely from the insulation. It is a good practice to leave 1/4 in. (50 mm) of the material where it meets the metallic shielding. It is easier to stop there than tight to the end and it serves as a reminder not to overlap it later with insulating tape or other material.
		The semicon material must be scraped off to leave the insulation clean. If cleaning with solvents or other cleaners, ensure that the cleaner is compatible with the cable insulation. When cleaning, wipe away from the end and toward the semicon.
7	Remove and pencil insulation.	The insulation is removed from the conductor core for a distance of half the sleeve or connector length, plus an allowance for a short length of exposed conductor between the insulation and the sleeve. Some materials are very hard to cut, and the application of heat from a hair dryer will ease the task. The insulation at the sleeve end is penciled to a specified distance with a knife or, preferably, a penciling tool.
		The space between the sleeve and the penciled end of the conductor is used to make an easier transition for the shielding tape.
8	Splice or connect the conductor.	When using a sleeve to join the conductors, use the sleeve, dies, and press specified for the type of conductor and in the splicing kit specifications. When splices are made between two different sizes or between copper and aluminum, sleeves made intentionally for that purpose must be used.
		If using a soldered sleeve, follow the instructions to prevent overheating and to allow for the proper cleaning of the joint.
		Make the joint smooth. Be sure to remove any sharp edges on the joint.
9	Apply new conductor shield—semiconducting tape.	The conductor shield is conductive, prevents any electric stress from concentrating in one area, and fills any small indent at the sleeve or connector. Start the semiconductive tape at about 1/8 in. (3 mm) up the penciled slope, and tape a smooth layer back across the joint to the same position on the other slope.
10	Clean the exposed cable insulation.	Remove all dust and contamination with an abrasive cloth or an approved solvent.
11	Apply insulating tape.	Use calipers to measure the diameter of the sleeve/connector on the core, then double the width of the caliper. The doubled distance will be the thickness that the insulated tape will be applied over the connector. Apply tape to build up the insulation while stretching it to three-quarters width. Apply tape over the sleeve so that it is built up to the thickness set by the calipers while sloping the tape back to the original cables.
12	Apply the insulation shield—semiconducting tape.	Apply the semiconducting tape, while overlapping by half for the full length of the splice until it covers the existing semiconducting layer on each end of the splice by 1 in. (2.5 cm).
13	Apply a protective jacket.	On a taped splice, the protective jacket would be two layers of PVC tape, half overlapped over the full length of the splice.
14	Connect the two ends of the metallic concentric neutral.	The neutral is joined with a specified sleeve or connector. If a jumper had been installed earlier it can be removed after the joint is made.

**Limits to
Ampacity**

A cable in a duct does not have direct contact with earth; therefore, the cable will heat up quicker and have a lower ampacity. The center cable in a trench is not able to dissipate the heat as well as the outside cables. The section of cable going up a riser pole, inside a metal cover and exposed to the sun, may limit the ampacity of the whole circuit.

**Electrical
Current in a
Cable Sheath**

8.4.7 The electromagnetic field in an underground cable can induce unacceptable levels of current and voltage on the metal sheath and concentric neutral wires. The magnetic field from the current-carrying conductor induces a current in the metal sheath or concentric neutral wires when the sheath is grounded at both ends of the cable. Figure 8–32 shows that when the sheath is grounded at both ends, a circuit is created for the induced current. The induced current in the sheath flows back to the source through earth. The current on the sheath can be high enough to cause heating and derate the ampacity of the cable.

**Voltage on a
Cable Sheath**

8.4.8 Planning engineers sometimes specify grounding a metal sheath at only one end to reduce heating caused by induced current. When only one end of the sheath is grounded, the circuit is open and no current can flow in the sheath. An additional conductor must be strung to serve as a neutral for the circuit.

At the end where the sheath is not grounded is a potentially high voltage between the sheath and the neutral (Figure 8–33). The voltage is generally less than 40 volts. Under fault conditions, the voltage across the open point between the sheath and the neutral could be several thousand volts and hazardous to anyone working at the termination.

Engineering specifications should include a requirement to flag the open circuit location as a hazard. A surge arrestor could also be specified to limit the voltage across the open point.

**Conductors
in SF6**

8.4.9 In some station designs where space is limited, bare conductors are suspended inside pipes that are filled with an insulating gas, sulfur-hexafluoride (SF6). The pipe containing the conductor can be above ground and is used as a bus in stations. This design has advantages similar to those of underground cable

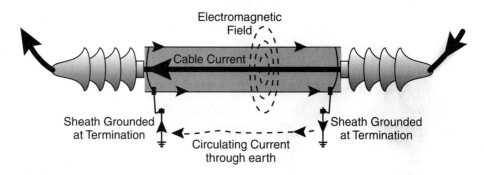

Figure 8–32   Circulating current in sheath.

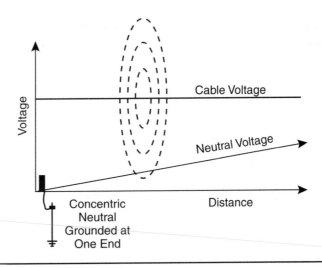

Figure 8–33   Voltage rise in concentric neutral.

because less electrical clearance is needed between phases, between phase and ground, and between circuits. The pipes are grounded; therefore, the bus can be laid out along the ground where workers may be in contact with it.

8.5 Working with Underground Cable

Maintain Sheath Continuity

8.5.1 In a looped circuit, any break in the sheath of a cable can have a high voltage across the break. When work is performed on or near cable, the metallic sheath (shield) continuity has to be maintained. The sheath should be treated the same way a neutral is treated on overhead systems.

Identifying an Isolated Cable in a Trench

8.5.2 When underground cables are exposed for work in a trench, it is necessary to distinguish between the cable to be worked on and other cables buried in the same trench. A specialized instrument with a transmitter and a receiver is used. The transmitter sends a pulsing DC voltage down the sheath of the cable. The pulses can be varied with different time delays that help to ensure that the signal received is the signal being sent. The receiver is a DC voltmeter that is connected between the cable sheath and a remote ground probe.

Even with this reasonable assurance that the proper cable has been identified, a cable is "spiked" before it is worked on. A spike (spear) is forced into the cable using a spiking tool fired by a cartridge or the spike is forced in with a hydraulic tool or turned in with a live-line tool. A spiked cable will cause a short circuit if the cable is live, and it provides a positive physical identification of a desired cable.

A cable-penetrating ground clamp can be used either as a tool for spiking jacketed cable or as part of a grounding jumper used to bond both ends of an opened cable during work operations.

Energizing a Faulted Cable

8.5.3 When energizing a faulted cable, the high fault current generated can become either a ground-gradient hazard near the fault or an explosive hazard in a confined space. The high fault current can also damage an entire length of cable beyond repair.

Very few transient faults occur on an underground cable. A blown fuse generally indicates a cable fault and that a test for the existence of a fault should be administered before reenergizing.

Locating and Tracing an Underground Cable

8.5.4 An underground cable is only visible at the two ends that come out of the ground. Maps and water witching are unreliable tools for locating cable. Cable locators consist of a transmitter, which induces an electromagnetic field (radio frequency or audio frequency) on the target conductor, and a receiver that traces the field. The methods presented in this section do not apply well to cables in duct banks under city streets. However, cables in duct banks tend to be more protected from faults and better data are available on their routes and locations.

The receiver, a directional antenna, is swept from side to side. The strength of the electromagnetic field increases as the receiver gets closer to the cable. The electromagnetic field can be distorted by other cables, a turn, a change of depth in the target cable, or other metal, such as property stakes. Use the "Null" mode to locate the cable and the "Peak" mode to verify the location.

Putting an Active Signal on a Cable

Consider the following cautions:

- Ensure that the circuit to be tested is isolated. Reduce the risk of applying leads to a live circuit. Take out a formal clearance, test and ground, apply the test leads, and then remove the grounds.

- A cable is a capacitor, and it will have a voltage on it long after a high-voltage test is completed. Ground while making the connections for a test, and ground the cable before removing the test equipment. After a DC test is applied, it takes a long time to drain the charge off the cable. Wait 15 minutes, then ground it.

- Put up a barrier at both ends of a cable while it is being tested.

Locating a Faulted Section of Cable

8.5.5 When one section of cable has a fault, a fuse or breaker somewhere in the system can trip out many sections of cable. To find the faulted section of cable, a line crew has to progressively open, test, and close each section of cable until it finds the fault, unless fault indicators have been installed.

A fault indicator will give a visual "flag" after the high magnetic field from a fault current triggers the unit. The fault indicators are put on the cable at various strategic locations (Figure 8–37). The system can be traced from the source through each fault indicator until one is found in the "no-trip" position. The fault indicator in the no-trip position did not have a fault go through it therefore, the fault is upstream.

TABLE 8–4   Three Methods of Putting an Active Signal on a Cable

Method	Steps	Additional Information
The transmitter is attached right onto the sheath or to an isolated core conductor with the *direct-connect method* (Figure 8–34).	1. The transmitter can be connected to the sheath if the cable has an insulated cover over it. To trace a cable with a sheath that is continuously grounded (e.g., lead cable), use the lowest possible frequency. 2. Ground the far end of the cable to complete a circuit so that the signal current returns to the transmitter ground through earth. 3. Set to a low frequency (less than 10 kHz). A lower frequency is less likely to spill over (couple) to other buried utilities and the signal travels farther.	1. This is the most accurate method, because the signal (tone) is isolated to one cable. 2. Can be connected to the sheath of a live cable *but not to a live cable conductor.* 3. When attaching the transmitter to a sheath at a riser pole with many cables, the signal current will take the easiest path, which may not be the target cable.

Figure 8–34
Tracing cable direct-connect method.

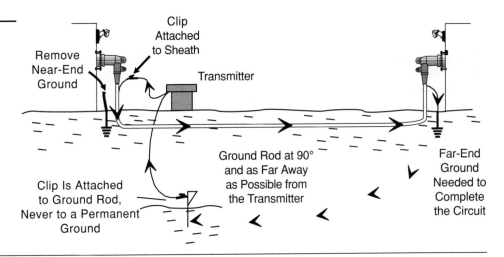

| The *general-induction method,* induces a signal into a cable from a transmitter set on the ground directly over the cable (Figure 8–35). As an operator with a receiver passes over the cable, the receiver picks up the tone so its route can be traced. | 1. The sheath must be grounded at both ends.
2. The receiver should be at least 15 paces away from the transmitter to avoid receiving a signal directly through the air.
3. Try a medium frequency (30 kHz to 90 kHz) to reduce interference from other sources. A high frequency can be used to sweep a large area when looking for all buried utilities. | 1. The transmitter can also induce a signal on other cables, pipes, etc., causing the receiver to pick up false signals. This is not a good method for congested areas.
2. For this method, the cable sheath has to have an insulated cover over it to prevent the signal current from following other ground paths.
3. This method is not suitable for cable deeper than 6 ft. (2 m). |

(continued)

TABLE 8–4 Continued

Method	Steps	Additional Information

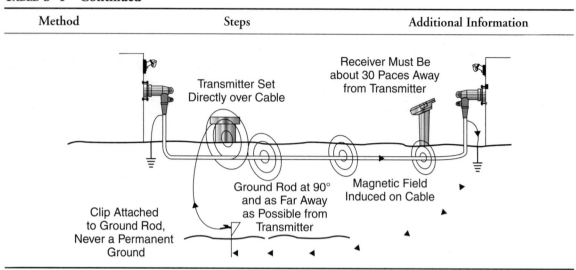

Figure 8–35 Tracing cable: General-induction method.

The *inductive-coupling method* uses a C-clamp (coupler) to concentrate the magnetic field signal onto the sheath or conductor (Figure 8–36).

1. To use the inductive-coupling method, the cable sheath must be grounded at both ends to form a complete circuit for the signal current. For secondary cable without a sheath, a ground is placed on each end.
2. Use radio frequencies. Audio frequencies will not work.

1. The C-clamp can be connected over the sheath of live cables or over live secondary cables.
2. The concentration of the signal on a cable ensures less spillover to other cables on a riser pole or in a trench.

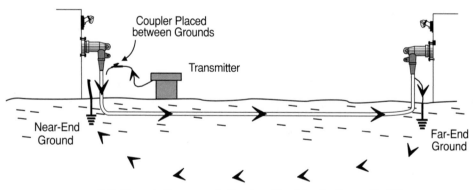

Figure 8–36 Tracing cable: Inductive-coupling method.

After a fault indicator has flagged a fault, it must be reset to the "no-trip" position. Some types are reset automatically by a normal electrical current, others are reset automatically after a specified time, and still others have to be reset manually.

Using an Insulation Megohmmeter to Verify the Existence of a Cable Fault

8.5.6 A cable fault will be caused either by some kind of insulation breakdown (anywhere from a dead short to a high-resistance fault) or a break in the conductor (open circuit). A megohmmeter (insulation megger, *not* a ground megger) can be used to test the insulation resistance of the cable and to verify if there is in fact a fault that cannot be pinpointed. This is a nondestructive test if the proper test voltage for the cable insulation is used—for example, use a 500-volt megger on a secondary cable rated up to 600 volts. Typical fixed DC voltages on a megohmmeter are 500, 1,000, 2,500, and 5,000 volts.

The faulted section must be grounded to drain any capacitance in the cable before any testing is done. Using rubber gloves, the concentric neutral can be isolated from ground at both ends to prepare for testing the cable. The insulation can be tested in the following ways:

1. Between the isolated neutral (sheath) and the grounded phase conductor.

2. Phase to phase.

3. Between the target conductor and other grounded conductors.

Table 8–5 shows typical readings.

The voltage is applied for about 1 minute until the charging effect has diminished and the reading is stabilized.

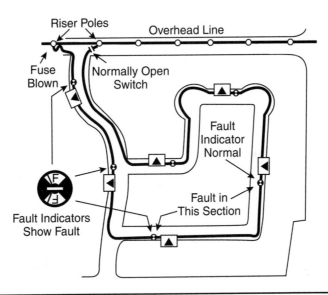

Figure 8–37 Fault indicators in an underground system.

TABLE 8–5   Typical Megohmmeter Readings

Meter Reading	Type of Fault	Notes
0	A shunt fault, where the fault path is from the high-voltage conductor to ground or to the sheath (a short circuit or dead short).	Look for sources of potential dig-ins, etc.
More than 0 (hundreds of ohms resistance)	A low-resistance shunt fault allows current to flow to ground with very little resistance. Overcurrent protection will trip out the circuit.	The location of this type of fault is relatively easy to pinpoint with standard instrumentation.
Less than 4 (thousands of ohms resistance)	A high-resistance shunt fault where often both the center conductor and neutral are still intact. (A cable is considered good if it reads 1 megohm for each kilovolt of cable rating, i.e., 5-megaohms 5-kilovolt cable.)	This is the most common fault because very fast circuit protection tripped the circuit before the cable was damaged more. Circuit protection may hold for a while when the cable is reenergized.
Infinity 4	Indicates a series fault where the conductor and/or neutral are burned open, or it indicates a cable without a fault.	Ground at the far end of the cable and measure again. A "0" resistance would indicate that it is not an open circuit.

Pinpointing the Location of a Cable Fault

8.5.7 After a megohmmeter reveals the most likely type of fault in a cable, choose the instrument suitable for finding that type of fault. The methods described here are most suited to direct bury cables and generally not suitable for cable faults in duct banks under city streets.

Short Circuit or Low-Resistance Fault

This is the easiest fault to find.

The cable tracing equipment described in Section 8.5.4 can be used. After all the cable grounds have been removed, a signal current from a transmitter is forced out where the cable insulation has failed. The voltage gradient above the fault is picked up by a probe or A-frame connected to the receiver. The A-frame is moved (Figure 8–38) and turned in the vicinity of the fault until the signal strength at each leg of the A-frame is equal (a "null" signal), indicating that the A-frame is directly over the fault.

Cable radar (TDR—Time–Domain Reflectometer) can be very effective as it sends a high-frequency pulse along the cable and measures the time it takes for the signal to be reflected back. Irregularities in the cable and their locations can be

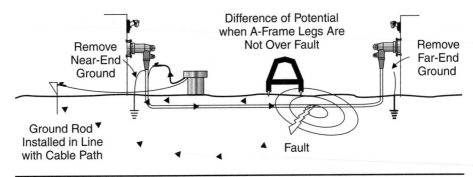

Figure 8–38 Pinpointing a cable fault.

shown in graph form on a monitor screen (Figure 8–39). Short circuits, open circuits, splices, transformers, and other irregularities will show up on screen in waveforms that trained operators can recognize. After training, a person can determine the distance to the fault with cable radar.

A *thumper* (surge generator, impulse generator, capacitive discharge set, banger) finds the short circuit by storing a high-voltage charge in its capacitor and then discharging it into the cable to cause a flashover and an acoustic shock wave at the fault location. The shock wave can be detected by vibration, sound, seismic detectors, or microphones.

High-Resistance Fault

High-resistance faults (the most common type) are also the most difficult to find. They are often caused by a faulted conductor burning back toward the source and surrounded by the insulation is "healed over." It may be easier to find a high-resistance fault from the load end of the cable

A high-resistance fault can be broken down into a low-resistance fault by a thumper or burner.

Caution: Aged cables that have been thumped excessively are likely candidates for a failure within the next year. The voltage chosen should be below the rated cable voltage and generated for as short a time as possible to reduce the risk of damaging the cable at other weak spots. A thumper should not be used on secondary cable in

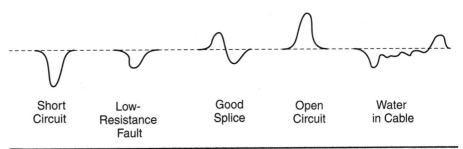

Figure 8–39 Typical time-domain reflected pulse shapes.

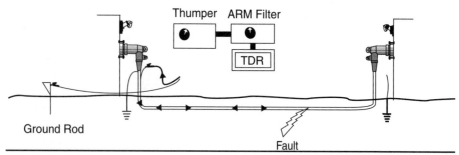

Figure 8–40   Arc reflection method.

case the signal finds its way into the customer's wiring and ground. A very low frequency (VLF) AC high potential (hipot) burns much quicker than conventional
DC burners.

The least damaging and most effective approach to finding a high-resistance
fault would be to connect a thumper, cable radar (TDR), and an arc reflection
method (ARM) filter (Figure 8–40). The thumper "turns on" the fault momentarily as the cable radar captures the image of the brief flashover at the fault location. The arc reflection method (ARM) filter is needed with this method to
prevent the thumper output from damaging the cable radar instrument. Damage
to the cable is limited because frequent thumping is not needed and the voltage
will not be much beyond the breakdown level as the fault breaks down before the
voltage rises too high.

Open Circuit

If an open circuit has no leakage to ground, TDR is effective for pinpointing the
location of the open point. An open circuit leaves a distinct blip on the monitor
screen (Figure 8–41).

**One Source of
an Erratic
Secondary
Cable Fault**

8.5.8 A fault on a secondary underground cable often starts out as a complaint of
erratic power. A voltage reading at the customer may show a normal voltage.

A break in the insulation of a secondary cable is often a high-resistance fault.
When water gets into an aluminum conductor, it slowly corrodes the aluminum
and turns it into an aluminum hydroxide, which is a high-resistance, white, pow-
dery material. The voltage may be normal until a load is put on the conductor
because the corroded higher-resistance cable will cause an increased voltage drop
as the load increases.

Use a 500-volt insulation tester to test the service. A reading of anything less
than 1 megohm is an indication of a faulty cable. The insulation tester shown in
Figure 8–41 has the ability to send a 250-volt, 500-volt, or 1,000-volt test voltage
for insulation resistance testing.

Testing Cables

8.5.9 A new or repaired cable installation is often tested before it is put into service. One method is to apply an "over-voltage" (hipot) test. Check with your util-

Figure 8–41   An insulation tester.

ity for the proper test voltage because a hipot test is a destructive test. There is a concern about shortening the life of the cable with this test method, and some utilities will not use this test.

A DC or the preferred VLF hipot test of a cable measures any leakage current in milliamperes between the phase conductor and the sheath or earth. The level of leakage current is not as critical if it remains at a steady level. If the leakage current increases rapidly during the test, it will indicate a potential fault. Stop the test if it begins to increase to avoid damage to the cable. Of course you will now have a high-resistance fault to pinpoint.

For distribution voltage cables, an insulation tester (megger) or phasing sticks are common devices used to test after repair or maintenance of a cable.

Using a Hipot Adapter on Phasing Sticks

8.5.10 A DC hipot adapter attached to a phasing tool can test a cable with an AC voltage when using an existing live AC source and converting it to DC. The DC voltage impressed on the cable will be at about the peak value of the source AC voltage.

The hipot adapter is installed on the meter stick (Figure 8–42). This stick is connected to a live source. The live source can be a transformer bushing or an open cutout at a riser pole. Some bushing adapters and elbow adapters allow making the connection.

The reel stick is attached to the cable to be tested. The cable must be isolated at both ends because a DC signal through a transformer will show up as a short circuit.

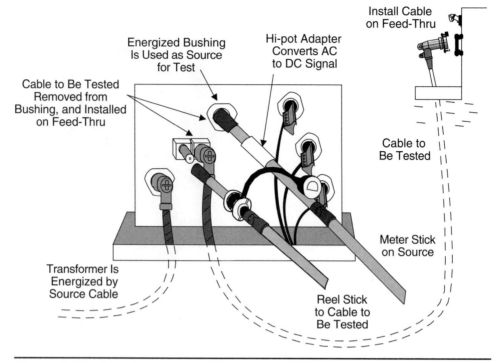

Figure 8–42 A handy hipot tester.

A long cable will take some time to charge up to peak voltage. A meter reading of 0 indicates a good cable, a high reading indicates a defective cable, and a fluctuating reading indicates a cable that is starting to break down.

8.6 Working with Fiber-Optic Cable

Why Fiber Optics?

8.6.1 Fiber-optic cable is an alternative to copper telephone, microwave, and radio communications between substations, switchgear, and so on. It is a superior communications cable because it offers a huge capacity in a very small cable. The optic fibers are made of glass and are nonconductive, so the communications signals are not affected by electric magnetic induction. Utilities have the infrastructure, skilled staff, right-of-ways, structures, and underground duct banks that make them ideal vehicles for getting into the fiber-optic business.

Fiber-optic cable is also used on hydraulic boom trucks. On very long insulated booms used for barehand work, lightweight fiber-optic cables can replace the hydraulic hoses that are used as a "communication" to change a boom position. These long hydraulic hoses present a hazard should the oil level in the hose fall, creating a conductive partial vacuum.

Because fiber-optic cable can carry an immense amount of communications, utilities are able to sell some of their overcapacity to telephone companies, cable companies, and corporations for their internal Internet communications. Some utilities are running fiber directly to their customers to compete with suppliers of high-speed communications.

What Is Fiber Optics?

8.6.2 Fiber optics use light pulses to transmit information down glass fibers. Digital information, which is composed of a series of 0's and 1's, is transformed into a series of light pulses that are either on or off. Fiber-optic cable is a "light guide" in which the source of light pulses and a light-emitting diode (LED), or laser, is transmitted at one end and received at the other end. Figure 8–43 illustrates electronical signal from a wire that is transformed to light and back again.

The inside of a fiber cable is coated with a mirror as seen in Figure 8–44. The light pulses in one end can be seen at the other end because the mirror allows the light signals to bend around humps, bumps, and corners. When a light pulse strikes the mirror surface, it keeps bouncing back into the cable.

Types of Fiber-Optic Cable

8.6.3 A cable consists of the core, the cladding, strengthening fibers, and the cable jacket, which is a coating or buffer (Figure 8–45). The cable is designed to

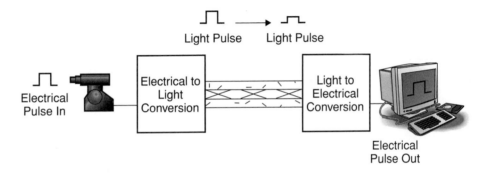

Figure 8–43   Fiber-optic transmission.

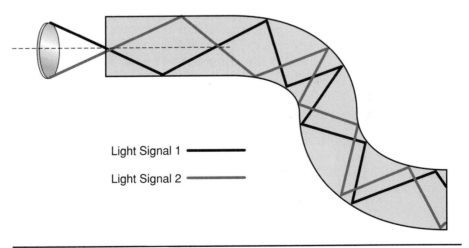

Figure 8–44   A mirror-lined fiber-optic cable.

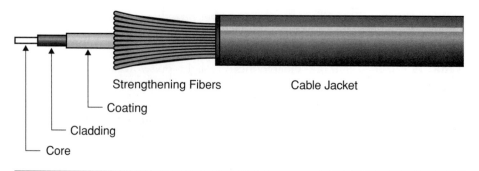

Strengthening Fibers   Cable Jacket

Coating

Cladding

Core

Figure 8–45   Fiber-optic cable construction.

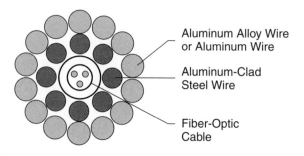

Aluminum Alloy Wire
or Aluminum Wire

Aluminum-Clad
Steel Wire

Fiber-Optic
Cable

Figure 8–46   Optical ground wire (OPGW).

protect the glass-fiber core and cladding. The optical fiber is a flexible filament of very clear glass that is just a little thicker than a human hair. The core is the light-transmission area of the fiber. The cladding is the layer that surrounds the core. The light in the core strikes the interface with the cladding at a bouncing angle and is trapped in the core.

Fiber-optic cables being installed in electrical utilities include the following:

1. *Optical ground wire* (OPGW) fiber-optic cable, which is strung as a replacement for a transmission-shield wire. The shield wire provides protection from lightning, carries fault current, and provides a communications channel.

2. *Wrap-type fiber-optic cable* is wound around shield wires and, in some cases, around conductor.

3. *All-dielectric self-supporting* (ADSS) fiber-optic cable as shown in Figure 8–47, typically is strung 10 to 30 feet (3 to 10 meters) below existing conductors. It can be strung very tight, but that brings it closer to a power conductor's midspan. It was intended to be dielectric cable, but it is not kept clean like a live-line tool, and eventually the electromagnetic field from the power conductors will induce current flow down the contaminated surface of the cable.

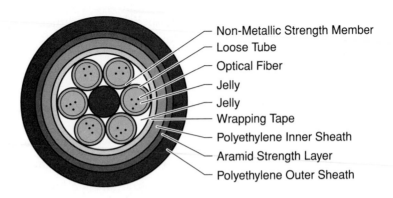

Figure 8–47 All-dielectric self-supporting (ADSS) fiber-optic cable.

4. *Duct-type* fiber-optic cable can be of various designs, including dry core or jelly-filled, single-sheathed, unarmored, and armored.

5. *Direct burial type* fiber-optic cable can be dry core or jelly-filled, single- or double-sheathed, and armored.

The fiber-optic cables typically used by utilities are loose-tube cables containing several individual cables (tubes), each with a fiber core within the main cable. The tubes are wound around a central member composed of aramid yarn (product similar to Nomex and Kevlar), which provides strength. The area around the loose tubes is filled with gel or water-absorbent powder. The loose-tubes design allows an individual tube to be accessed at intermediate locations without bothering other tubes and fibers. The outer buffer and outer jackets provide protection and strength. The ADSS cable shown in Figure 8–47 is an example of a loose-tube design.

Working with Fiber-Optic Cable

8.6.4 Working with fiber-optic cable is a very specialized undertaking. Some skills, such as stringing, climbing, and underground work, are common to both copper and fiber. This section provides only a brief overview. The specifications for dead-ending, stringing, and splicing will be included among a project's documents. Most of the technical documentation will involve care of the cable. Fiber-optic cable requires a lot of care. ADSS cable, for example, includes hardware such as special dielectric dead ends, dielectric suspensions, abrasion protectors, a dielectric vibration damper, a dielectric corona coil, and download cushion.

Installation methods are similar for both wire cables and fiber-optic cables. Fiber-optic cable has more strength than copper wire if pulled straight, but the fibers break when bent too far.

A swivel pulling eye is necessary because any pulling tension will cause twisting forces on the cable. Twisting will stress the glass fibers.

Most cables cannot be pulled by the jacket, unless a special cable grip or special-strength members made of Kevlar or aramid yarn are in place and are used.

Splicing requires very special tools and training that make the work easier than splicing together each tiny glass fiber.

Review Questions

1. What are three basic effects when an electric current flows in a conductor?

2. Why is the ampacity of a conductor higher in winter?

3. How does the sag in a transmission-line span affect the ampacity of a conductor?

4. Name two factors that influence the specification for the size of conductor needed.

5. If a person working on a transmission line leaves any rough or sharp points on a conductor or other live hardware, what effect will that cause?

6. Why is it important to clean aluminum conductor before making a connection or splice?

7. Can the insulation on unshielded cable, such as a covered conductor, be depended on for personal safety?

8. Why may sharp bends, voids, or sharp pressure against a cable cause an eventual failure?

9. Why should the cut end of an underground cable be sealed when it is stored on a reel in the yard?

10. What is the purpose of the conductor shield (semicon) and the insulation shield layers in an underground cable?

11. The magnetic field from the current-carrying conductor induces a current in the metal sheath or concentric neutral wires when the sheath is grounded at both ends of the cable. What can be done to reduce this current flow?

12. When the ground is removed from the sheath at one end to reduce heating in a cable, what hazard exists at the ungrounded end of the cable?

13. Before cutting a cable in a trench, how can a powerline worker be sure the correct cable has been isolated?

14. A customer fed by a secondary underground cable complains about erratic power. A voltage reading at the customer may show a normal voltage. What else should be checked?

15. How can phasing sticks be adapted to carry out a hipot test on a distribution cable?

Operating Switchgear

Topics to Be Covered	**Section**
Switching Characteristics and Switching Hazards	9.1
Switching to Provide an Isolation Guarantee (Lockout/Tagout)	9.2
Using Maps to Locate Switchgears	9.3
Operating Isolating Switchgears	9.4
Operating Protective Switchgears	9.5
Underground Distribution Switchgears	9.6

9.1 Switching Characteristics and Switching Hazards

Two Main Types of Switchgear

9.1.1 A powerline worker operates two main types of switchgear:

1. *Isolating switchgear,* such as a disconnect switch, an air break switch, or a load interrupter does not operate automatically during a fault but provides operating capability to isolate, sectionalize, or transfer loads at strategic locations. Some types can interrupt a load current, while other types have no ability to interrupt any load current.

2. *Protective switchgear,* such as a circuit breaker, recloser, or fuse, protects a circuit by providing automatic isolation when it is exposed to damaging faults. This type of switchgear can interrupt the extremely high current that occurs during a short circuit. Some protective switchgear, such as breakers and reclosers, will open and then close in again on a circuit for a prescribed number of times. If the fault is transient, customers will have power; if it is permanent, a line crew must be called out.

Arc Hazards

9.1.2 Excessive arcing can destroy a switch, trip out a circuit, and hurt powerline workers. All switching must be carried out without arcing. If, an excessive arc occurs and molten metal sprays out from the switchgear when switching, some kind of switching error has been made. The properties of an arc are illustrated in Figure 9–1.

265

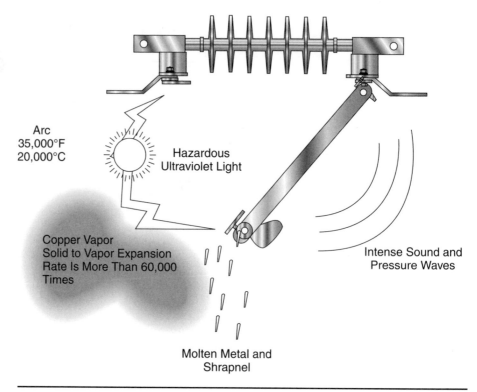

Arc
35,000°F
20,000°C

Hazardous
Ultraviolet Light

Copper Vapor
Solid to Vapor Expansion
Rate Is More Than 60,000
Times

Intense Sound and
Pressure Waves

Molten Metal and
Shrapnel

Figure 9–1   The properties of an arc.

Many types of switchgear are designed to extinguish an arc, but many disconnect switches have no ability to extinguish an arc. When an arc is established, the heat from the arc causes the air to become ionized. The *ionization of air* means that the air has become charged with atoms and that the air is changed from being an insulator to being a conductor. Once the air between the switch contacts becomes conductive, a follow-through current will flow across the switch gap.

An arc is more probable when opening than when closing a switch. Normally, a circuit can be closed without concern about an arc unless the device did not close the first time and a restrike occurs. It is the interruption of current that causes an arc.

Arcing generally occurs only when opening switchgear, especially opening switchgear that is not designed to open under load. Arcing will also occur when trying to close switchgear, usually a cutout, and because it did not make good contact immediately opening again.

An arc in the confined areas of underground switchgear can easily spill over to grounded cabinets or other phases, exposing a powerline worker to dangerous ground gradients and an explosive fault.

A potential arc length can be calculated. However, a lineworker should not be asked to open a device unless the following conditions are met:

- The switchgear is designed to interrupt load current.
- The switchgear is capable of accepting a load-bust tool.
- The switchgear will not be interrupting any load.

An arc length is dependent on the circuit voltage *plus* the current being interrupted.

Formulas that can be used as estimates for the expected arc length when opening a switch follow for when the current is *less than 100 amperes:*

$$Arc\ length\ in\ cm\ =\ 0.5x\ kV\ I$$

and when the current is *more than 100 amperes:*

$$Arc\ length\ in\ cm\ =\ 50x\ kV$$

Designs to Extinguish Arcs

9.1.3 The design of switchgear includes the requirement to quickly extinguish any arc that is created when a switch is opened. There are many methods used to extinguish arcs, including the following:

- When contacts are immersed in an insulating medium such as oil, vacuum, or SF6, an arc is extinguished quickly.

- When air is the insulating medium, an arc ionizes the air, which causes the air to become conductive. An air-blast breaker will blast high-pressure air at any potential ionized air and will blow it away.

- An arc can be transferred from the switch contacts to a spring-loaded horn gap, whip, or high-velocity interrupter, which separates the arc.

- A spring-loaded fuse link separates the two parts quickly when the fuse melts.

- A special coating inside the fuse holder reacts with the arc and produces a gas at high pressure, which expels the ionized gas out of the tube.

Zero-Awaiting and Zero-Forcing Interrupters

9.1.4 Most switchgears take advantage of the fact that in an AC circuit, no current flow occurs twice during each cycle.

A *zero-awaiting interrupter* is a switching device that requires AC passing through 0 before it can interrupt a load current. Examples of zero-awaiting switchgear are cutout fuse links, Bayonet links, and cartridge fuses.

A *zero-forcing interrupter* is a switching device that forces the current to zero. It forces the system current to 0 by inserting a large resistance into the circuit. An example of a zero-forcing device is a current-limiting fuse.

Interrupting a DC circuit is more difficult because it cannot use a zero-awaiting interrupter feature.

Remotely Controlled Switchgear

9.1.5 Remotely controlled switchgear keeps a safe distance between people and any switching hazards.

When there is a choice, such as at a capacitor bank, it is always safer to operate from the control box. A ground-gradient mat should be used when operating at a control box when the box is on the same structure as the switchgear. A fault within the switchgear could short to the equipment grounding system, which will raise the potential on the control box.

Operating Three-Pole Switches

9.1.6 If only one phase of a three-phase circuit trips out, the protective switchgear and relays will experience a large unbalanced load with two phases loaded and one not loaded. The current and the voltage on the whole system will become unbalanced. The unbalance due to one phase being out of service is not as severe to distribution circuits as it is to transmission circuits. Three-phase motors will heat up when one phase is out, but the thermal protection should prevent them from being damaged.

All transmission switchgear and a lot of distribution switchgear is gang-operated. All three phases will trip out, even if only one phase is faulted.

SCADA Systems

9.1.7 A *supervisory control and data acquisition* (SCADA) system is an automated distribution system that brings needed information and remote control of switchgears into a central control room. It brings the operation of a distribution system to a level similar to a transmission system. SCADA systems are widely used in such other industries as telecommunications, water, pipelines, refineries, transportation, and nuclear-power plants.

A communications system, such as a telephone line, fiber-optic cable, radio, or coaxial cable, brings information from *remote terminal units* (RTUs) in substations and from remote switchgear to a *central processing unit* (CPU) in the control room. The SCADA system gives an operator control room information such as system voltage, feeder loading, and the status of switchgears as open or closed.

A remote-controlled switchgear needs a remote-controlled motor that can open and close the circuit breaker or switch. The motor is set in motion by sending a signal to a motor-operating mechanism. The motor-operating mechanism has a low-voltage supply, a battery, RTU circuitry, and a communications connection to the control room.

Maintaining and troubleshooting a SCADA-controlled switch includes bypassing the remote control and operating the switch manually. A line crew can be asked to go to a remote unit and operate it on-site when there is a breakdown.

Understanding the Switchgear Being Operated

9.1.8 To avoid the creation of an excessive arc while switching, a person needs to know the purpose for operating the switchgear and whether the switchgear is capable of dropping load current.

Defective Pedestal-Type Insulators Supporting Switchgear

9.1.9 The failure of porcelain pedestal-type insulators during a switching operation can allow an energized part of the switchgear to contact the grounded switch frame. This can result in a large flash, falling hardware, and high-potential ground gradients.

These failures, which are due to cement growth, causing the cap to separate from the porcelain, occur most often where the pedestal-type insulators are mounted horizontally, either as bus supports or as supports for hook-stick-operated disconnect switches.

Most pedestal-type insulators should have been replaced by now with post-type insulators, which have a higher cantilever strength but also are not affected by cement growth.

TABLE 9–1   **Understanding Switchgear**

If	Then
A length of line, with a load on it, is to be isolated or interrupted.	A load current will be interrupted and an arc will have to be extinguished. Switchgears, such as a circuit breaker, a recloser, or a load interrupter disconnect switch, are capable of dropping load and quenching an arc.
	A disconnect switch without a load interrupter is not designed to interrupt any load. It may have a rating of 600 amperes, but that refers to the load it can carry through the switch continuously.
A length of line, with no load on it, is to be isolated.	The line can be isolated with an ordinary disconnect switch. The length of line that can be dropped with a disconnect switch depends on the voltage. For example, an air break switch, without a load interrupter, can, with permission, drop up to 3 miles (5 km) of 230 kV or up to 16 miles (26 km) of 50 kV.
Switchgear is opened to break parallel in a circuit that is being fed from two directions.	Some current and voltage will be interrupted. If the switch breaks parallel between different stations or two unequal lengths of line, a voltage difference (recovery voltage) will occur and a current flow will be interrupted upon opening the switch.
	A control room operator has the needed information to calculate the amount of current to be interrupted. Switchgears capable of interrupting load current can break parallel easier than an ordinary disconnect switch can.
Switchgear is closed to make parallel between two sources.	There can be a voltage difference and current flow created when the switch is closed. Unless there is a restrike, all switches should be capable of picking up the rated load current.
	Closing switchgears between two circuits fed from two different substations that are fed from two different transmission systems can be dangerous because a large voltage difference may create a large current flow through the switch. A system control operator should have control of such switchgears.
A loop must be opened or closed. (Opening a circuit fed from two directions but fed from the same circuit breaker is breaking a loop.)	Unless a loop is excessively long it can be closed or opened with an ordinary disconnect switch or a hot-line clamp.
	An example of a loop is where a new line is constructed next to an old one, such as at a road-widening project. The new circuit can be energized in parallel with the old circuit by tying it in at both ends and forming a loop. Any load on the old circuit must be opened before breaking the loop and isolating the old circuit.
A switch is to be closed, as a test, to determine if a line is still faulted.	Switchgears can be closed without an arc. A major arc will occur if a switch is closed in on a fault and the powerline worker immediately reopens the switch. It is important to let the normal protective switchgear trip out the circuit automatically.

Operating a Disconnect Switch with an Operating Handle at Ground Level

9.1.10 Many disconnect switches are three-phase gang-operated switches with operating handles that extend to ground level.

If an insulator or other component breaks (Figure 9–2) while operating the switch, the live leads could contact the switch frame and energize the operating handle. It is critical, therefore, to stand on a ground-gradient mat or ground-gradient network that is bonded to the operating handle. To dodge falling porcelain,

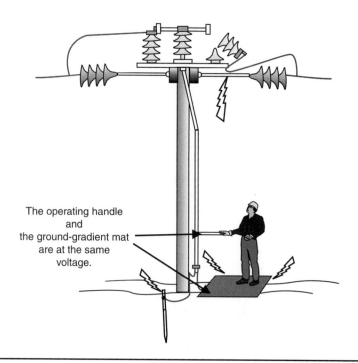

The operating handle and the ground-gradient mat are at the same voltage.

Figure 9–2   Use of a ground-gradient mat.

if necessary, jump clear either with both feet together or by hopping without ever having both feet on the ground at the same time.

When the mat and operating handle are bonded together, the two will stay at the same voltage no matter how high the voltage becomes. If there is no voltage difference between the operating handle and the mat, there will be no voltage difference between the operator's hands and feet. If there is no voltage difference, there is no current flow.

Switching from the Ground Using a Telescopic Switch Stick

9.1.11 The use of a telescopic switch stick (Figure 9–3) has the advantage of keeping a worker as far away as possible when energizing suspect equipment. Only the top foam-filled section has the insulation rating of a live-line tool.

When using a telescopic switch stick, a person can still be exposed to an electrical shock when a high-potential ground gradient is created around the base of a pole during a switching operation. This has happened when a fault traveled down ground wire because of a faulty surge arrestor or because a live part contacted grounded hardware when a pedestal insulator came apart.

Keep some distance away from any ground rod at the base of the pole and keep your feet together during the switching operation.

Confirm Proper Phasing between Two Sources

9.1.12 It is often necessary to do some phasing checks before making connections or switching at the open point between two live sources. In Figure 9–5, the meter reading on the phasing tester should read near 0 between phase 1 and phase A, and so on, when the two sources are in phase. In the field, draw a table (like the one in Figure 9–4) to record the results of your tests.

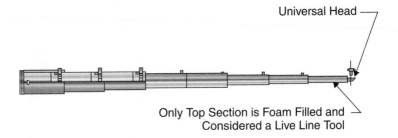

Universal Head

Only Top Section is Foam Filled and
Considered a Live Line Tool

Figure 9–3   A telescopic switch stick.

**Using a Phasing
Tester**

9.1.13 A phasing tester is like a high-voltage voltmeter. It has the ability to measure an approximate voltage between two different potentials on circuits over 750 volts and, with the proper extensions or model of tester, can measure up to 161 kilovolts. A phasing tester can be used as a potential tester, as a phasing tester where a reading near 0 volts between two phases indicates they are the same phase, as an insulator tester, and as a hipot tester when using a special adapter.

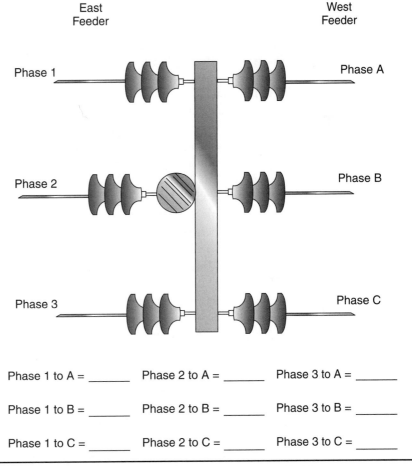

Phase 1 to A = _____   Phase 2 to A = _____   Phase 3 to A = _____

Phase 1 to B = _____   Phase 2 to B = _____   Phase 3 to B = _____

Phase 1 to C = _____   Phase 2 to C = _____   Phase 3 to C = _____

Figure 9–4   Check phasing before making connections or switching.

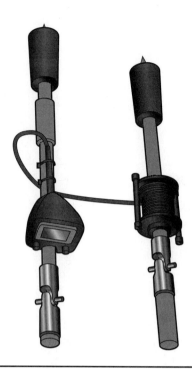

Figure 9–5   Phasing sticks.

At the contact end of each stick is a high-impedance resistor that lowers the voltage and current to a representative reading on the meter. From an operating perspective, keep a safe distance from the resistor sticks and cable. The resistors are protected by an epoxy covering, not a rated insulation; therefore, each stick should be in contact only with an individual phase (Figure 9–5). Below the resistor are standard live-line tools on which a normal minimum approach distance should be kept from the splice of the stick. On higher voltages, additional resistors are needed and are available as extension sticks.

The cable between the sticks should be kept as short as practical to keep from sagging into structures or other conductors. The cable insulation is originally rated at 15 kilovolts but should not be treated with the same confidence as a line hose.

To get more accurate readings, the cable and reel must be kept away from other electric field influences. When measuring line-to-ground voltage, the stick with the meter should be used at the ground potential end, and on phase-to-phase measurements connecting cable must be kept as far as practical from other conductors and structures.

Wireless phasing tools eliminate many of the operational steps needed to take a measurement (see Figure 9–6). The tools consist of a transmitter and a receiver and are rated up to 40 kilovolts. The transmitter is a voltage detector and measures the phase angle. This is transmitted to the receiver, which compares the information with the reading it is getting from the other phase or ground.

For measuring at underground installations, the overhead probes are removed and elbow adapters and/or bushing adapters are installed to allow testing dead-

Figure 9–6 Wireless phasing tool.

front equipment. There is also a DC hipot adapter that allows the tools to apply a DC voltage on a cable to test cables before energizing. One stick is attached to a live source and the other stick is attached to the cable being tested. The DC hipot adapter allows the cable to be tested with a DC voltage.

TABLE 9–2 **Specific Hazards Using a Phasing Tester**

Hazards	Controls
Creating a short circuit while using the phasing tester on a higher voltage than the tester is rated. *Note:* These hazards do not apply to wireless phasing tools.	Check the voltage rating of the phasing tester. Typically, depending on the manufacturer, the phasing tester is used up to 15 kV and is handled directly with rubber gloves. On voltages between 15 kV and 50 kV, special extension sticks are needed and the phasing sticks are held away from the powerline worker with attached universal live-line tools. At voltages above 50 kV and up to 161 kV, phasing testers specifically made for these voltages are used.
The insulated connecting cable between the cable reel and the other stick makes contact with a grounded object or person.	Typically the connecting cable insulation is limited to 15 kV. Keep excess cable on the reel and use rubber gloves and/or universal sticks to avoid contact. In case of accidental contact, the resistors within the phasing tool should keep current flow at a safe level. Meter-reading accuracy will be affected when the connecting cable is influenced by other grounded objects or phases. When doing phase-to-ground tests, keep the reel stick on the grounded object.
The upper end of the stick, where the resistor is enclosed, makes contact with a grounded object or other phase and shorts out.	The voltage at the upper end of the resistor, enclosed inside the stick, is not intended for continuous contact. Keep the sticks away from other objects when they are in contact with a live circuit.

9.2 Switching to Provide an Isolation Guarantee (Lockout/Tagout)

Lockout/Tagout Procedure

9.2.1 One of the most sacred procedures for utility work is the procedure that isolates an electrical circuit or electrical equipment from all electrical sources and ensures that the isolation will stay in effect while working on the line or equipment. A lockout/tagout procedure ensures that all potential electrical sources are locked and/or tagged. The condition established is called a "clearance," but a more accurate term would be *isolation guarantee*. The term "clearance" is also used for electrical clearances between objects in work specifications or clearances from buildings or roadways. The term "isolation guarantee" leaves less doubt about what a lockout/tagout procedure is trying to achieve.

An isolation guarantee should be a formal document signed by a responsible and qualified person stating that it is safe for a crew to apply grounds and go to work.

TABLE 9–3 Common Elements in a Lockout/Tagout Procedure

A lockout/tagout procedure for lines would not necessarily meet the regulatory locking requirements in a generating station. In lines, one person may be signed on as the holder of the isolation guarantee and be responsible to everyone on the job and that the line is isolated and grounded will remain isolated and grounded.

Common Elements	Details
1. There is a controlling authority (system control or dispatch) responsible for granting an isolation guarantee on a circuit or equipment.	1. The controlling authority is normally the system control (dispatch) for the system. 2. In some utilities, powerline workers are given control of the distribution system, especially for a switchgear that is not remotely operated. They will act as their own dispatchers and will prepare their own switching orders and will apply tags on applicable switchgears. There are some switchgears to open or close safely, such as a tie point between two substations, that may require information only available to system control personnel.
2. An application is made out by the work authority to isolate a circuit or apparatus when it is needed to provide safe working conditions.	1. An isolation guarantee for work is given to a competent individual who is deemed responsible for obtaining and maintaining a circuit in an isolated and grounded state. 2. The application (usually on a prepared form) for an isolation guarantee on a circuit is made out in advance so that the controlling authority can study it in relation to other applications and can determine the impact on the system (especially for transmission lines). 3. The application can be done verbally when an outage is needed on short notice. Both parties should write down the verbal application on an application form. 4. There is a joint responsibility for the controlling authority and the work authority to ensure that the proper element is identified for an isolation guarantee.

Common Elements	Details
3. Switching is carried out and tags (cards) are placed on the switchgear providing isolation.	1. A switching instruction or switching order form (as seen in Table 9–4 is prepared as a plan for the switching sequence needed to provide the isolation guarantee for the work. 2. If verbal switching instructions are used (radio, etc.), the message should be repeated back for confirmation. 3. After operating any switchgear, it must be visibly checked to ensure that it is in the correct position. 4. A switchgear that serves as an isolation point for an isolation guarantee for work on a circuit over 750 V must have a visible open point and be tagged. 5. In addition to tagging, reduce risk of an inadvertent operation of a switchgear by using an additional safety measure, where applicable, such as a lock, removing a switch element, removing a loop, disabling a motor-operated disconnect, or opening an extra disconnecting device.
4. The controlling authority certifies and signs a formal document that the circuit is isolated from all sources and will remain isolated until the isolation guarantee is formally surrendered by the work authority.	1. A formal communication, confirming that the isolation guarantee is in effect, is made, often issuing an isolation guarantee number to keep the isolation guarantee distinct from others issued by the controlling authority. 2. Authority to install protective line grounds and go to work is given to the work authority by the controlling authority.
5. The work authority verifies that isolation is complete.	1. Potential checks are carried out to ensure the absence of a normal line voltage before protective line grounds are installed. 2. In some jurisdictions, the protective grounds are controlled and tagged by the controlling authority, while in others the work authority controls the placing of protective line grounds.
6. When work is completed, the work authority surrenders the isolation guarantee for the work.	1. The person holding the isolation guarantee ensures that all workers are clear and that protective line grounds are removed before surrendering the isolation guarantee.

Use a Switching Order

9.2.2 Reduce the risk of an operating error. Use a written switching order form whenever a sequence of switching is to be carried out.

When acting as a switching agent for a controlling operator (dispatch), the operator should have a written switching order; however, the powerline worker should also get a copy or write down the sequence when received by radio.

A typical switching order used to isolate a set of voltage regulators is shown in Table 9–4.

TABLE 9–4   **Switching Order Form**

	Switching Order			
Purpose	Isolate Voltage Regulator FR16			
Ordered By	District Control		**Time**	
Completed By	John Lineman		**Time** 10:30	

Sequence Number	*Device Being Operated*	*Operation*	*Tag #*	*Initials*
1	Auto/Manual Switch	Neutral Tap		JL
2	Input & Output Terminals	Voltage Test		JL
3	Auto/Manual Switch	Turn Off		JL
4	Bypass Switches - 3 phases	Close		JL
5	Load Switches - 3 phases	Open		JL
6	Source Switches - 3 phases	Open		JL
7	Source Risers	Remove		JL
8	Load Risers	Remove	N/A	JL

9.3 Using Maps to Locate Switchgears

Circuit Identification and Structure Numbers

9.3.1 When preparing or applying for an isolation guarantee on a circuit, the circuit must be identified by a name, number, or acronym.

Virtually all transmission and subtransmission circuits are identified with some kind of nomenclature. Transmission circuit nomenclature typically identifies the source substation and the destination substation. If there is more than one circuit, each must have a number. For example, in Figure 9–7 the source for the 230-kilovolt circuits that feed the Benton Substation is the Latchford Substation. The circuits are therefore labelled L1B and L2B. The four 46-kilovolt feeders coming out of the substation are labelled B1, B2, B3, and B4.

On distribution systems, often the source switch number identifies the circuit. Note that the single-line drawing in Figure 9–8 does not identify each circuit, but each line section can be identified by the source switch number.

On a right-of-way, especially one with multiple circuits, the nomenclature on each structure should include the name of the circuit owner, the circuit name, and the individual structure number. Some system control people ask for the actual structure numbers that are to be worked on during an isolation guarantee. This information can be cross-referenced on maps and drawings for assurance that the proper location and switchgear for the isolation guarantee are identified and that no work on structures will be done outside of the isolation guarantee zone. Live circuits have been grounded in the past because two lines being similar in appearance or because of a double circuit.

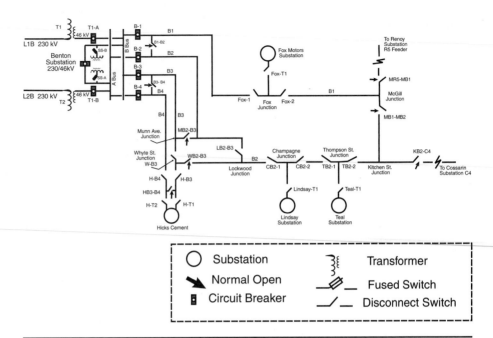

Figure 9–7   A typical schematic of a subtransmission system.

Structure numbers are identifiers for recording data into computer-aided drafting (CAD) software that is tied into facility management (FM) software, which is tied into Geographic Information System (GIS) software and many evolving variations. The facility management database would typically have access to information for each structure, including the owner of property that must be crossed and the type of structure, height, hardware manufacturer, and so on. Many utilities are using the latitude and longitude coordinates, as registered by their Global Postioning System (GPS) receivers, as their structure numbers.

Switchgear Nomenclature

9.3.2   When preparing or applying for an isolation guarantee on a circuit, the switchgear that feeds or is able to feed that circuit must be identified by a name, number, or acronym. Reliance on nomenclature and an operating drawing is especially critical on transmission lines and underground systems where it is not practical or possible to trace circuits physically. Relying solely on memory or physically tracing a circuit to identify isolation points on a distribution line to establish an isolation guarantee has a history of incorrect isolation and accidents.

Numbering and naming of switchgears are usually based on the circuit or source substation name. In many other locations, distribution switchgear numbers appear to be totally random. Note in Figure 9–8 that the switchgear numbers correspond to the feeder and/or junction names.

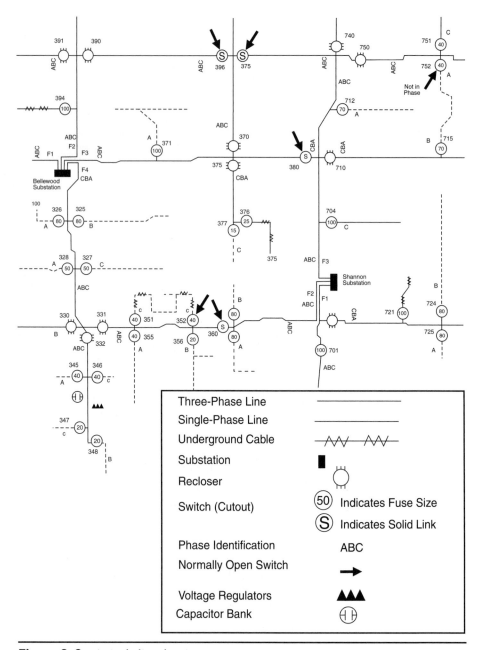

Figure 9–8 A single-line drawing.

Electrical Schematic Drawings

9.3.3 The most efficient type of drawing for operating a system is a schematic drawing. Schematic drawings have virtually no relationship to the geography but make it much easier to trace a circuit to its terminal points, view the relationship of one circuit with another, and locate junctions and switchgear. Schematic drawings can be found for almost all electrical apparatus, from showing the electrical circuitry of a car to the circuitry of a transformer to the circuitry of a large transmission system at a system control center. Figure 9–8 is a sample schematic drawing showing four 46-kilovolt feeders coming from a substation. Each feeder feeds customers and the high side of distribution substations. The dark arrow at a switch indicates a normal open point. These open points can be closed to feed back on another circuit.

A system control center uses schematic drawings almost exclusively for transmission lines and substations. It is common in the control room to have the schematic drawing on a wall and also on a computer monitor. A line crew should also have access to system drawings to follow and check the switching order (sequence) issued by a system control center or for one prepared by themselves. When dispatchers or system control refer to a schematic drawing to discuss work, they do not necessarily understand exactly where a line crew is located.

Standard symbols are used to designate a breaker, a disconnect switch, a load-break switch, and so on. Figure 9–8 shows the types of symbols used by some utilities for a line schematic drawing.

One-Line Distribution Drawings

9.3.4 One-line drawings are common for operating a distribution system. A one-line drawing shows the lines where they are geographically, but the background geography, such as roadways and lot lines, is either not present or is very faint in the background. Figure 9–8 shows a typical one-line drawing with no geographic background, but the lines generally follow the roads. The drawings concentrate on what is needed to operate the system; therefore distribution transformers and individual customers are not on these drawings. The symbols on the legend for single-line drawings are not consistent or standard among utilities. A legend will include enough information for understanding the drawing and identifying isolation points when needed.

Many utilities have one-line distribution drawings mounted on a wall. These provide the big picture of a system. These drawings are given priority for revisions. Changes occur daily, and line crews that take out an isolation guarantee must know about any change in normal feeds.

Detailed Geographic-Based Maps

9.3.5 Maps that show distribution and/or transmission lines, transformers, and customers on a geographic background are detailed and would be too cluttered to use as operating drawings. Such maps are used to make drawings of new projects, to prepare a layout for a new subdivision, to record property easements, and to locate customers. Geographic maps, along with software such as automated mapping/facility management software (AM/FM), are used as to create an inventory of the locations and type of plant or facility the utility owns.

A transmission-line map is a record of the type of structure, type of insulators, type of vibration dampers, and etc. The data are used for such situations as identifying the location of hardware of a certain manufacturer or type when it has been found to be defective and a replacement program is needed. Transmission lines are also recorded in even more detail on roll plans that show each structure, span length, sag, ground clearance, access road, property owner, and so on.

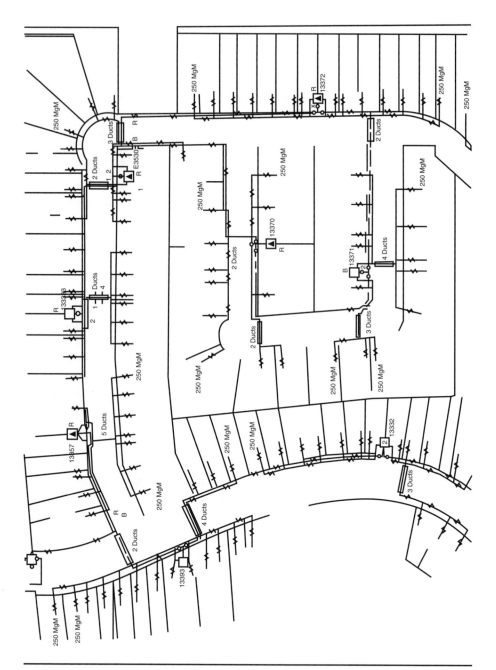

Figure 9–9   A typical geographic map.

Planning Maps

9.3.6 Utilities also have planning maps. For distribution systems, a planning map shows the length of each line segment, conductor sizes in each segment, phasing of each line segment and lateral, voltage regulator location, capacitor location, transformer location, size, and connected phase. Engineering staff use these maps to prepare voltage and current surveys, short-circuit studies, protective device coordination studies, phase balancing studies, load management studies, and maintenance and capital programs.

Another type of drawing is the overview transmission-line circuit diagram, which is similar to a distribution one-line drawing. The overview transmission-line circuit diagram shows transmission circuits geographically placed but no background geography, and they are useful for planning maintenance programs.

9.4 Operating Isolating Switchgears

Operating a Nonload-Break Disconnect

9.4.1 A disconnect switch is any solid-blade switch installed to provide a means to isolate or sectionalize a circuit. Unless a disconnect switch has a load interrupter, it has no capability to interrupt load current. A disconnect switch has no capability to open automatically under fault conditions.

Disconnect switches come in all voltages and can be single-phase bracket-mounted, single-phase in-span, or three-phase gang-operated. Depending on the type, disconnect switches are operated by hotstick, operating handle, or remotely by way of a low-voltage motor.

Figure 9–10 is a three-phase gang-operated switch with no load-break capability. This switch may show a rating of 600 amperes, but that means it is capable of carrying 600 amperes, not of breaking a 600-ampere load. The switch is operated with a handle at ground level, and the design of the switch installation should include a grid placed below and bonded to the handle. Some utilities require the use of a portable ground-gradient mat.

Figure 9–11 is an in-span disconnect that has no load-break capability unless it is opened with a load-break tool. A fused in-span disconnect does not have load-break

Figure 9–10 A subtransmission gang-operated disconnect switch.

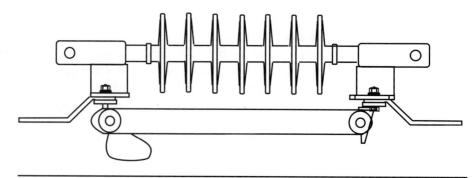

Figure 9–11   Single-phase in-span disconnect switch.

capability either. The fuse can isolate a fault automatically, but when the device is opened with a switch stick, it operates as a nonload-break disconnect. At distribution voltages, single-phase disconnect switches are normally equipped with hooks to allow a portable load-break tool to be used.

An ammeter check can be made to confirm that there is no load on a circuit before opening a nonload-break disconnect switch. Some utilities suggest that a nonload-break disconnect switch be operated by using the *inching method*. Because the switch should not be dropping any load, there would be no arc developing as the switch is opened slowly. If there is an unexpected load and an arc starts to develop, close the switch immediately. If a fairly long length of conductor (no load) is being de-energized by the disconnect switch, the switch should be opened in one fast operation.

Operating a Load-Break Disconnect

9.4.2 Disconnect switches with load interrupters come in all voltages. A load-break disconnect switch is designed to interrupt load current and can be operated without creating a dangerous arc. They can be three-phase gang-operated switches or single-phase switches. Depending on the type, load interrupters are operated by hot stick, operating handle, or remotely by way of a low-voltage motor. Load-interrupter switches can break load and are normally rated at 600 amperes or less. A load-interrupter switch has no ability to open automatically under fault conditions.

Figure 9–12 shows a common type of load interrupter. It extinguishes the arc within an interrupter housing by deionizing gases that are exhausted flamelessly through a muffling device.

Figure 9–13 is a type of load-interrupter switch that is used in substations. The power fuse provides overcurrent protection but cannot drop load current. The load-interrupter switch is used to drop load but cannot interrupt a fault current automatically.

Operating a Hot-Line Clamp

9.4.3 Hot-line clamps are not switches, but they are used as a convenient way to disconnect and connect risers between equipment and circuits. There is, obviously, no arc-extinguishing capability with either a hot-line clamp or a duckbill clamp. When

Figure 9–12 A three-phase load interrupter and power fuses.

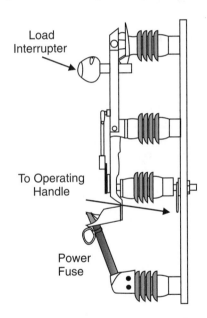

Figure 9–13 One pole of a load-interrupter switch.

inadvertently dropping load with a hot-line clamp, a very long arc can be established. The air within the arc becomes ionized and, therefore, conductive so that as the hot-line clamp is pulled away the arc will follow. If, when the live-line clamp is pulled away it then touches a structure, an explosive fault current arc will be established.

To reduce the risk of an unmanageable arc, a hot-line clamp should not be used to drop any load or even an unloaded transformer winding larger than 10 kilovolt-amperes. Hot-line clamps are sometimes used to drop a limited length of conductor (no load).

9.5 Operating Protective Switchgears

Circuit Breakers

9.5.1 Circuit breakers are the backbone protective switchgears in an electrical power system. They are installed to protect generators, transformers, transmission lines, subtransmission lines, and distribution lines. They provide sophisticated circuit protection and switching capability. Circuit breakers, including distribution reclosers and metal-clad breakers, can be set to open and reclose a number of times before they will finally lock out on a permanent fault. On a transient fault, the breaker will stay closed once the fault has cleared from the circuit.

Circuit breakers open automatically for faults such as overcurrent, low voltage, or a drop in frequency. Potential transformers and/or current transformers on a circuit send representative voltage and current values to relays. Relays are programmed to send a signal when readings indicate a problem on a circuit. The signal can go to an alarm in a control room and simultaneously activate an electric motor that opens the circuit breaker. The motors of a circuit breaker are supplied by a low-voltage source, such as a substation service. Figure 9–14 shows a typical oil circuit breaker.

Circuit breakers are named according to their arc-quenching medium. There are oil circuit breakers, air-blast circuit breakers, vacuum circuit breakers, and sulfur-hexafluoride (SF6) circuit breakers. Oil circuit breakers have been the most common circuit breakers and have been used for the longest time. The circuit-breaker contacts are immersed in insulating oil, which quenches arcs.

Air can be used as an insulation medium to quench an arc if the air is prevented from being ionized between contacts. Compressed air is piped to air-blast breakers and will "blast" an arc away from contacts. When these breakers are opened, the shotgun-type blast is extremely loud.

An arc occurs when the air is ionized and becomes conductive. When a vacuum is used as the insulating medium there is no air and therefore no arc. The contacts for a circuit breaker can be in a vacuum, and the remaining part of the breaker is immersed in oil. A separate vacuum container for the contacts prevents the oil in the rest of the circuit breaker from becoming contaminated.

SF6, an inert nonflammable gas with high insulating properties, is a common insulation for circuit breakers (Figure 9–15). Breakers using this gas are much smaller and can be used indoors. The operation is quieter than others and is ideal for substations in cities. SF6 is not toxic, but under arcing, toxic by-products are produced that require special handling during maintenance.

Metal-Clad Circuit Breakers

9.5.2 In urban distribution substations, a common circuit breaker is a metal-clad, draw-out breaker. This type is a multishot device with the ability to automatically interrupt a circuit for a fault and automatically reclose. It can be operated with a toggle switch or, more commonly, by remote control from a control room.

Typically, deep inside and along the length of a metal cabinet are bus bars that are fed from the secondary side of the substation transformer. Individual, metal-clad, draw-out circuit breakers are racked (pushed) into the substation bus bars. The output from each breaker feeds an underground distribution feeder. The breakers are mounted on a trolley or on wheels, or some other easy means allows them to be

Figure 9–14   A 46 kV oil circuit breaker.

Figure 9–15   46kV SF-6 circuit breaker

racked out. A draw-out circuit breaker can be in the in-service position, in a test position, a disconnected position, or completely removed. Because of the extremely high-fault current available and the limited space for operating, full face protection and flame-retardant clothing should be worn when racking out a breaker.

The breakers are designed with various arc-quenching mediums, such as vacuum and air.

Reclosers

9.5.3 On distribution lines and often in rural substations, a common circuit breaker is a recloser. It is a multishot device with the ability to automatically interrupt a circuit for a fault and reclose. Reclosers were originally self-sufficient hydraulic units that did not need a low-voltage supply or relays for operation. Figure 9–16 shows a simple single-phase hydraulic recloser. Today, there are large

Figure 9–16   A single-phase hydraulic recloser.

hydraulic reclosers with low-voltage supply to open and close the contacts, as well as electronic reclosers with sophisticated relaying, and all reclosers can be operated or modified to be operated remotely through a supervisory control and data acquisition (SCADA) system.

Reclosers can have their contacts enclosed in vacuum bottles, SF6, or oil. They can be overhead or underground (pad mount). They can be single-phase or three-phase units.

A recloser can be set to open at various current levels. For example, a recloser is often set to trip out when the current going through the recloser coil is twice its rating. Therefore, it takes a minimum of 200 amperes to open a 100-ampere recloser. This ensures a trip-out is probably for a fault and not a temporary overload.

Operating Hydraulic Reclosers

9.5.4 A hydraulic recloser is an oil-filled recloser that automatically opens when an overcurrent flows through its trip coil. A solenoid coil (see Figure 9–17) in the recloser is the fault sensor. When the current flowing through a coil is higher than the current rating of the coil, the electromagnetic action on a moveable plunger inside the coil opens the contacts. Larger hydraulic reclosers have a low-voltage supply to an electric motor, which allows the heavy contacts to be opened and

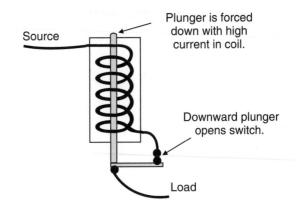

Source

Plunger is forced
down with high
current in coil.

Downward plunger
opens switch.

Load

Figure 9–17 A basic solenoid coil.

closed quickly. Any hydraulic reclosers that must be operated remotely (such as SCADA) would also have a low-voltage supply to operate the recloser.

The recloser will close and reopen a specified number of times and at a specified speed. If the fault has cleared, the recloser will close and reset itself for the next time a fault occurs. On a permanent fault, the recloser will go through the full sequence of specified operations before staying open.

A hydraulic recloser can be used safely to interrupt load current by pulling down the operating lever under the sleet hood. There is also a nonreclose handle right beside the open-and-close handle. The handle that opens and closes the recloser is often painted yellow.

Operating Electronic Reclosers

9.5.5 Electronic reclosers are controlled by a relay. Relays can be programmed for a range of minimum trip values, a number of operations to lock out, and a range of minimum response times to coordinate with upstream and downstream protective switchgears. The size of the plug in the resistors in the control box (Figure 9–18) determines the trip-current level.

An electronic recloser has a low-voltage supply, which allows the recloser to be operated from a control box. A low-voltage supply can be from a regular distribution transformer on the supply side of the recloser or from a bushing-current transformer mounted in the recloser. The low-voltage supply to the control box must also be in service to close the recloser.

The normal method of opening or closing these units is by the operating switch in the control box or remotely through the SCADA system. The main operating switch in a control box can open and close the recloser. The switch can be closed and held in the closed position to provide a cold-load pickup capability. Holding the switch blocks the instantaneous trip function. In other electronic reclosers, a cold-load pickup feature is programmed to prevent an instantaneous trip-out when closing after a lockout. The delayed trip will still open the circuit if an overcurrent situation lasts long enough. An electronic recloser has an open-and-close handle

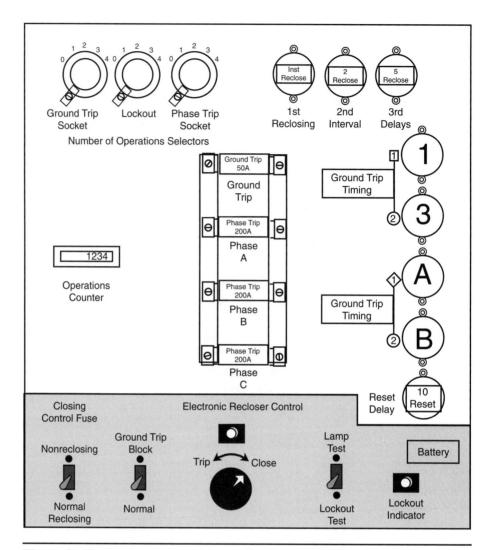

Figure 9–18 An electronic recloser control box.

and a nonreclose handle under the sleet hood, the same as a hydraulic recloser does. The recloser can be *opened* with the handle, but some electronic reclosers must be *closed* from the control box. The handle must be in the *up* position, or the remote control or SCADA control cannot close the recloser.

An electronic recloser can detect a fairly small phase-to-ground fault. This sensitivity can prevent reenergizing at the recloser because the ground-fault relay can interpret an unbalanced load as a phase-to-ground fault. Temporarily switching the *ground trip* toggle switch to the block position will prevent a small ground current from tripping out the circuit.

An operator should stand on a ground-gradient mat, or other grid, bonded to the control box when operating the main switch. The control box can become energized if the recloser malfunctions or the bushings flash over because the control cable bonds together the recloser and control box.

Operating Sectionalizers

9.5.6 A *sectionalizer* is a device that will isolate a faulted section of line when coordinated with an upstream multishot recloser or circuit breaker. A sectionalizer is a slave device that cannot interrupt a fault current and opens the circuit during a specified second or third interval while the upstream multishot device has the circuit de-energized (during dead time).

A *hydraulic sectionalizer* is an oil switch with a mechanism that will open automatically after a fault current goes through the coil a specified number of times. As with reclosers, sectionalizers come with various voltage ratings and current ratings. A hydraulic sectionalizer can safely be used to interrupt load current by pulling down the operating lever under the sleet hood, as with any oil switch. Hydraulic sectionalizers look very much like reclosers because they are both oil switches, but a sectionalizer does not have a nonreclose handle.

An *electronic sectionalizer* is a device that fits into a cutout in the same manner as a fuse chamber. The chamber is composed of a copper tube with a bronze casting in each end. Current flows through the copper tube when the unit is closed. A current transformer is mounted on the copper tube. The secondary of the current transformer is wired to an actuator on the bottom of the chamber that, when activated, drops the chamber and will look like an open cutout. An electronic sectionalizer is a slave device that opens during an interval when the upstream multishot device has isolated the circuit. An electronic sectionalizer is like any solid-blade switch: When it is to be operated manually, it requires a portable load-break tool to interrupt load current.

Operating a Distribution Cutout

9.5.7 A distribution cutout is a switch that can be used with a solid blade but is most often used as a fused cutout. It is common on distribution overhead lines for protecting lines and equipment such as transformers, regulators, and capacitors. A fused cutout is a one-shot device that can interrupt a high-fault current.

An expulsion-cutout fuse link is the most common and economical fuse used in a distribution system. When the spring-loaded fuse melts, the fuse chamber drops open to provide a visible open switch. When a fuse element melts, the current continues to flow in the form of an arc through the particles of the vaporized fuse element and ionized gases. The heat from the arcing burns back the remaining element, and the heat generates the release of a large amount of gas from the inside wall of the fuse chamber.

The resultant high-pressure gas and arc products are expelled from the tube. When a cutout is opened with a switch stick, the cutout is operated like a regular isolating disconnect switch that has no arc-extinguishing capability other than the air gap between the switch terminals. When opened with a switch stick, a cutout can only interrupt about 15 amperes safely. If a cutout is closed in on a faulted circuit during troubleshooting, it is important not to immediately open the cutout because it is likely to draw a large arc, possibly from terminal to terminal. The design of the fuse and fuse holder should be allowed to extinguish the arc.

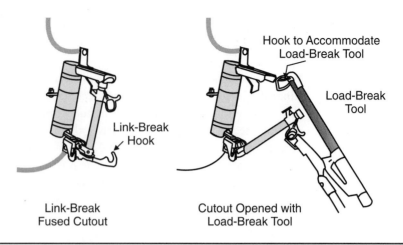

Figure 9–19 Dropping load with a cutout.

It is not unusual to close a fused cutout and find that there is still a fault on the circuit. When that happens, exhaust gases and molten metal will be expelled and directed down from the vent end of the fuse holder. Use a long length of switch stick and stay to the side of the fuse tube alignment.

A load bust tool can be hooked up to a fuse cutout or disconnect switch to provide a parallel path for load current through the tube of the load-break tool (see Figure 9–19). The initial downward pull on the tool charges an internal spring. At a certain point in the downward pull, the spring is released, resulting in a high-speed separation of the contacts. Any arc is extinguished inside the chamber by the fast elongation of the arc and the release of deionizing gases formed from the surrounding chamber material. A load bust tool is a bypass for the load current. The opening of the circuit and any resultant arc occur inside the load-break tool.

Two types of cutouts can be used to break load, but many utilities do not install them. A link-break fused cutout has a hook that can be pulled down with a switch stick to break the fuse link and allow the arc to be extinguished inside the fuse chamber. A cutout that has an arc chute is designed for load-break operation and can be operated with a switch stick.

A fuse holder should not be left hanging in the open position in a cutout for long periods of time. Rain and ice will collect inside and eventually damage the fuse holder. Remove the fuse holder and hang it upright on the pole.

A blown fuse in a cutout should be replaced with a fuse of the same size and speed to maintain coordination between other upstream and downstream fuses and switchgear. Feed the fuse cable clockwise around the stud and tighten it so that extra tension is not put on the link. The diameter of a 100-amp fuse link is designed only for a fuse holder up to 100 amps. A larger tube diameter is needed for larger fuses to operate properly.

Fuses

The replacable fuse link inside the tube of a cutout is a metal or alloy with silver, tin, lead, or copper that is designed to melt when a given amount of overcurrent for a given amount of time flows through it.

A fuse can carry load current without deteriorating, can carry some overload without immediate rupture, and must be able to interrupt a very high-fault current. The higher the current flowing through the fuse, the quicker it will blow. The amount of current a fuse is able to interrupt is based on its ability to extinguish an arc:

- An arc is extinguished by providing a fast separation of two parts of a melted fuse. One way to separate a blown fuse quickly is to have it spring loaded so that the two parts of the blown fuse will separate quickly.

- An arc inside a fuse chamber forms gases when it acts on a special coating on the inside walls of a chamber. The formation of gas forces the arc products out of the expulsion chamber and extinguishes the arc.

- An increase to the resistance of an arc path will extinguish an arc. Having a fuse immersed in oil or other insulation will cool and increase the resistance of the arc.

The melting and clearing time of a fuse should coordinate with upstream and downstream protective devices. Different speeds of fuses are available; for example, a K-link fuse is fast, and a T-link fuse is slower. The K-link and T-link fuses have specific time and current characteristics recognized by all manufacturers.

Solid-material fuses have a fusible element inside a heat-absorbing and arc-quenching material such as silica sand or borax. During a fault, the fuse vaporizes and the solid material cools the arc. These fuses can be fixed or dropout expulsion. The reduced expulsive emissions of boric acid fuses permit their use in enclosures, in substations, and in certain vulnerable overhead distribution applications.

The following list summarizes the types of fuses used in electrical utilities:

- Expulsion-cutout fuse links

- Under-oil expulsion fuses (bayonet style)

- Solid-material-filled power fuses

- Nonexpulsion (NX) current-limiting fuses

- Under-oil backup current-limiting fuses

Types of Current-limiting Fuses

9.5.8 An ordinary expulsion fuse is not current limiting. It will limit the duration of an arc but not the magnitude. A current-limiting fuse will limit the magnitude of the current flow by introducing a high resistance after the fuse element melts. A current-limiting fuse is used in locations where a very high-fault current is available on the electrical system. A current-limiting fuse will limit the magnitude of a fault current and will reduce the risk of transformers and

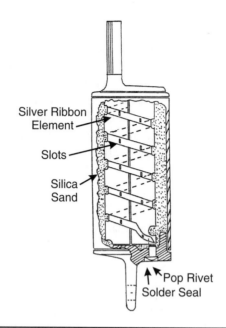

Silver Ribbon
Element

Slots

Silica
Sand

Pop Rivet
Solder Seal

Figure 9–20   A current-limiting fuse.

other equipment from failing explosively. A current-limiting fuse (see Figure 9–20) consists of a silver-ribbon element wound around inside an insulated tube of silica sand. The silver ribbon is perforated with holes along its full length. During a fault, the silver-ribbon element vaporizes along its length, starting at the perforations. The vaporized element is blown into the surrounding sand. The resulting arc heats the sand and turns it into a glasslike material that increases the resistance to current flow and chokes off the arc.

The two main types of current-limiting fuses are partial range and full range.

A *partial-range current-limiting fuse* (or backup current-limiting fuse) is designed to limit only high-fault currents. It is used in series with a fused cutout to protect equipment from the high energy levels available in a high-fault-current location. It is available in different sizes and speeds to coordinate with a cutout fuse link. For example, a 25K current-limiting fuse coordinates with a 25K cutout fuse link. An air-insulated, partial-range current-limiting fuse is installed right on top of a fused cutout (as shown in Figure 9–21). An under-oil submersible partial-range current-limiting fuse is used in series with low-current protective devices such as a bayonet-style under-oil expulsion fuse, cartridge fuse, or fuse link. If a transformer cutout fuse is found open, the current-limiting fuse if properly coordinated should not be damaged. Testing or replacing the current-limiting fuse before energizing the transformer with the cutout will reduce the risk of an explosive failure if the transformer is faulted.

A *full-range current-limiting fuse* (or *general-purpose current-limiting fuse*) is not used in series with another fuse but is the only fuse needed to protect equipment. It prevents a high-fault current from going through equipment, and it isolates

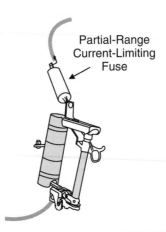

Partial-Range
Current-Limiting
Fuse

Figure 9–21 Application of a partial-range current-limiting fuse.

defective equipment from the circuit. It is most often used to protect underground or metal-clad equipment. A full-range current-limiting fuse can be air-insulated and used for high-amperage-rated applications in live-front switchgear or as an under-oil submersible current-limiting fuse (bayonet-style mounted fuse) used with dead-front equipment.

On underground systems, an under-oil submersible partial range current-limiting fuse is used in series with low-current protective devices such as a bayonet-style under-oil expulsion fuse, cartridge fuse, or fuse link.

Bypassing Protective Switchgear

9.5.9 There are different designs for recloser installations, many have a means to bypass the recloser to allow maintenance. When bypassing a recloser such as shown in Figure 9–22, *if* the operating sequence to isolate protective switchgear is not followed, *then* load could be dropped accidentally with a hot-line clamp or input or output switch, resulting in an uncontrolled arc.

The bypass should be fused to provide protection downstream. If a bypass fuse size is not specified, use a fuse size equal to the recloser coil rating.

To isolate, do the following:

1. Close bypass.

2. Open recloser.

3. Remove hot-line clamps.

Nonreclose Feature on Breakers and Reclosers

9.5.10 Putting a breaker or recloser in a nonreclose position gives a crew working on a circuit the assurance that the circuit will not be reenergized automatically if an incident on the job trips out the circuit.

The nonreclose position does not guarantee that a circuit will trip out during an accidental contact; it only ensures that a circuit will stay out of service after it is tripped out. Placing a tag at the breaker or recloser will prevent other utility personnel from closing the recloser without first checking with the crew working on the circuit.

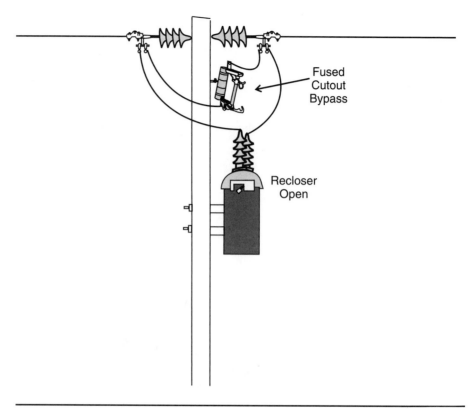

Figure 9–22 A recloser bypass.

9.6 Underground Distribution Switchgears

Types of Underground Switchgears

9.6.1 Switchgear in an underground distribution system is operated in confined areas where any arc could easily spill over to grounded cabinets or other phases. Some types should not be operated under load, and others require special tools to operate safely. There are dead-front and live-front types of switchgear in pad-mounted kiosks or as submersibles in below-grade vaults. There are also large vaults with overhead-style switchgear.

Switching distribution underground involves operating load-break-separable connectors (elbows), arc-strangler switches, bayonet-style under-oil expulsion fuses, vacuum switchgear, SF6 switchgear, and other devices with arc-quenching capability. A portable load-break tool is needed to operate some types of switchgear safely.

Often switching an underground system involves opening and closing ordinary overhead switchgears at a riser pole where the overhead-to-underground transition exists (Figure 9–23).

The original design of some types of underground switchgears (Figure 9–24) may have allowed operation under energized conditions, but field experience, higher fault-current levels, and higher distribution-voltage levels have changed this. Usually, an accident or incident investigation will restrict the manner in which some types of switchgears are operated. Some switching is carried out in a

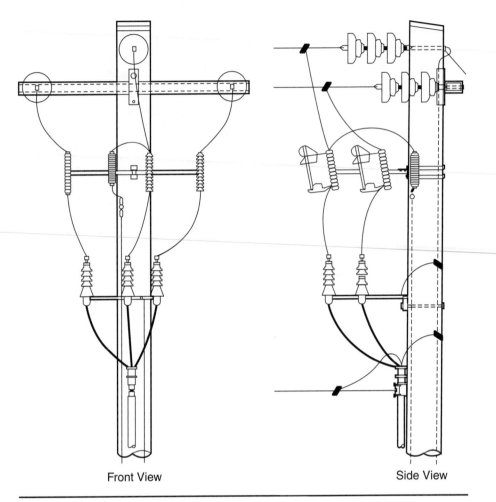

Front View   Side View

Figure 9–23   Riser pole.

vault or manhole where there is the additional hazard of creating an arc in a confined space. A line crew always checks for the oxygen level and for the existence of
flammable or toxic gas before and during switching inside a confined space. There
are utilities that require all energized switching to be done from outside a vault,
especially when the switching involves oil-filled equipment.

**Operating
Cable-Separable
Connectors
(Elbows)**

9.6.2 Separable connectors are the live-line clamps of an underground system,
although fused load-break elbows are available. Load-break elbows are used to isolate equipment or to sectionalize segments of cable. They are found at the input
and output of a transformer and at other locations where it is separating a cable
from equipment under live conditions is necessary. A load-break elbow can be
pulled from the load bushing with a live-line tool to interrupt a 200-ampere load current. The elbow must be pulled off in one quick motion, especially on high-voltage
distribution. If the lubricant between the elbow and the bushing has dried, an elbow
does not always come all the way off with the first pull. An arc between the load-break

Figure 9–24   Switching cabinet using elbows.

pin and the bushing contacts can spill over to the outside of the bushing to a grounded tank or cabinet. Pulling elbows has a history of flashovers. The root of the problem is that while the load-break elbow was being pulled from the bushing, a partial vacuum was formed across the mating interface. A partial vacuum reduces the dielectric strength across the mating interface. While a vacuum is a perfect insulator (as seen in vacuum-insulated switchgear), a partial vacuum is a poorer insulator than normal air pressure. Manufacturers have designed elbows with vent holes around the cuff of the elbow to prevent the partial vacuum from forming.

There are nonload-break elbows (Figure 9–25) that should not be operated alive. A nonload-break elbow can have a current rating as high as 600 amperes and is often used to terminate a main feeder into a switching cabinet.

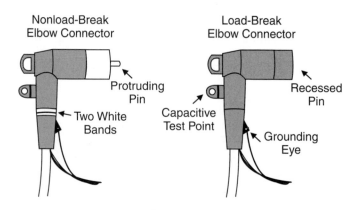

Figure 9–25   Load-break and nonload-break elbows.

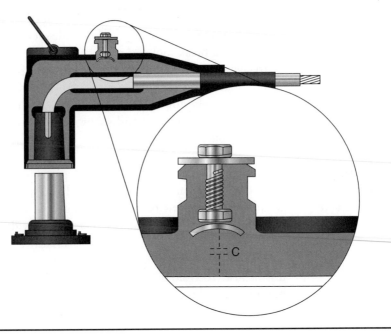

Figure 9–26 Capacitive test point.

The capacitive test point (Figure 9–26) on an elbow can be used to determine whether or not a circuit is energized. The cap over the test point is removed with a live-line tool, and a potential tester designed to pick up the capacitive voltage is used at the exposed test point. The test point is not a direct connection to the live conductor inside the elbow but has a potential because of capacitance. An ordinary voltmeter will not pick up a potential at the capacitive test point. The test point can also be used for phasing checks when using a phasing tool that has the multiple-functions feature.

Nx Switches

9.6.3 Nx (nonexpulsion) switchgear, also called an arc-strangler switch (Figure 9–27), is found in live-front switching cabinets and transformer vaults. It is operated with a live-line tool in the same manner as operating a fused cutout.

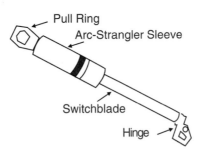

Figure 9–27 An arc-strangler switch.

The Nx switchblade is an arc-quenching load-break device that is available as a current-limiting fuse or as a solid-blade device. The load-break works like a portable load-break tool and must be cocked to operate.

To cock the barrel, the arc-strangler sleeve is pulled down and held in that position by a latch spring. When the switch is closed, the latch spring is depressed and the sleeve is held down by the switch itself. When the switch is opened, the arc-strangler sleeve is released and snaps up to activate the load-break feature of the switch barrel.

Operating Under-Oil Bayonet-Style Fuses

9.6.4 Figure 9–28 shows an elbow plugged into a bushing. The elbow is a load-break device but cannot interrupt a fault. In the figure, the elbow is in series with an under-oil bayonet-style fuse. The bayonet fuse is an under-oil expulsion fuse contained in a load-break holder. The fuse provides protection to the transformer by interrupting a fault, but it is not necessarily a good device to drop load.

Some utilities require that the transformer be isolated before removing or inserting the fuse. To avoid oil from being expelled when the fuse is withdrawn, relieve the pressure in the transformer tank by operating the external relief valve. To prevent dropping oil on the rubber elbows, pull the fuse out about 3 inches (5 centimeters) and hold it to let the oil drain from it. When it is removed, wipe the oil off the fuse.

Dry-Well Canister Fuses

9.6.5 Three-phase pad-mount transformers often have dry-well canister fuses. A current-limiting fuse that protects the transformer is mounted in an oil-tight dry-well canister. As with the bayonet fuse, the current-limiting fuse should not be used to isolate or reenergize the transformer. Even under an assumed isolated condition, the fuse should be removed with a shotgun stick.

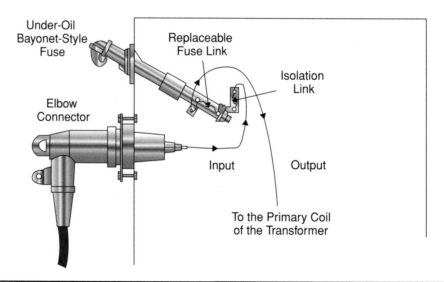

Figure 9–28 An under-oil bayonet-style fuse.

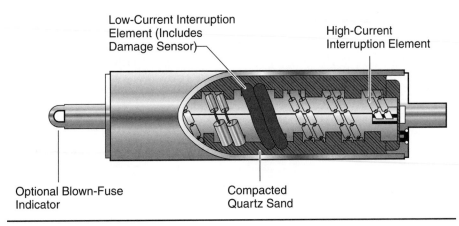

Low-Current Interruption
Element (Includes
Damage Sensor)

High-Current
Interruption Element

Optional Blown-Fuse
Indicator

Compacted
Quartz Sand

Figure 9–29   Current-limiting fuse.

The current-limiting fuse (Figure 9–29) will clear a fault or overload while limiting the let-through fault current to prevent damage to equipment. Ensure that the proper fuse length and adapters are used because they can be different for different voltages. An incorrect length will not make good contact and will lead to arcing and failure.

The fuse is inserted into a dry-well canister, such as the molded one shown in Figure 9–30.

Multipoint Junctions

9.6.6 There are large pad-mount and submersible switching units where underground feeders can be switched from one feeder to another. Figure 9–31 shows a top view of a switching and connection arrangement with four feeders coming in and how each feeder can be connected together or separately to the center bus to

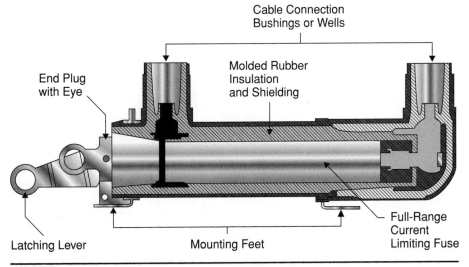

Cable Connection
Bushings or Wells

End Plug
with Eye

Molded Rubber
Insulation
and Shielding

Latching Lever

Mounting Feet

Full-Range
Current
Limiting Fuse

Figure 9–30   A molded dry-well canister.

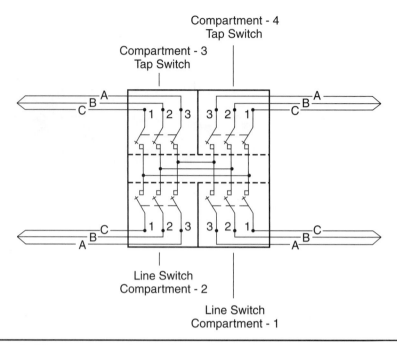

Figure 9–31   A top view of a switching and connection arrangement.

feed elsewhere. The individual switches for each feeder can be live-front or dead-front, fused, or some other kind of breaker.

Figure 9–32 shows the outside of an S&C PME pad-mounted switching cabinet that would have switching arrangements similar to those shown in Figure 9–31.

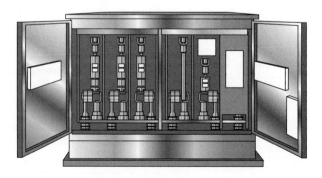

Figure 9–32   A pad-mounted switching cabinet.

Review Questions

1. What two main types of switchgears are used in an electrical system?

2. What is the main potential hazard when opening any type of switchgear?

3. Can a load-interrupter switch interrupt a fault current?

4. When a disconnect switch is operated, a breakage may cause live leads to contact the switch frame. What is the best protection for an operator when standing on the ground, to open a three-phase gang-operated switch with an operating handle?

5. What potential hazard exists when switching from the ground using a telescopic witch stick?

6. Why should a cutout not be opened with a switch stick to interrupt load?

7. May a sectionalizer be used by a line crew to interrupt load?

8. Why is it important to use a phasing tool before closing a switch between two sources?

9. Name four ways to verify a line is isolated when applying a lockout/tagout procedure.

10. What potential hazard exists when operating an electronic recloser from the control box mounted on the same structure?

CHAPTER 10

Circuit Protection

Topics to Be Covered	Section
Introduction	10.1
Transmission System Protection	10.2
Distribution Protection	10.3
Specifying Protection for a Distribution Feeder	10.4
Over-Voltage Protection	10.5
System Grounding for Protection	10.6
Protection from Corrosion	10.7

10.1 Introduction

The Purpose of Circuit Protection

10.1.1 An abnormal voltage or current is an indication of a problem somewhere in the circuit. Protective equipment is installed to detect and clear these abnormal voltages and currents.

- Circuit protection limits the time people are exposed to hazardous voltage and current due to situations such as a fallen conductor.

- Circuit protection limits the time equipment is exposed to damaging voltage and current.

- Circuit protection minimizes the number of customer outages during adverse conditions by automatically isolating and removing a faulted circuit from the system.

- Circuit protection is programmed to open and reenergize a circuit that was subjected to a transient fault.

A common task for a powerline worker is tracing problems due to over-current, abnormal voltage, or poor system grounding. Troubleshooting will be easier with an understanding of how protective equipment is specified to operate.

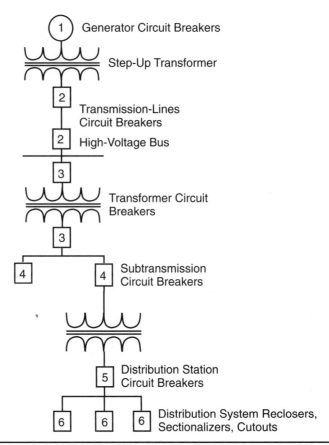

Figure 10–1 Circuit breakers in an electrical system.

10.2 Transmission System Protection

Circuit Protection

10.2.1 When a fault occurs in a transmission system, circuit breakers go into action and automatically separate the fault from the system. Figure 10–1 shows where circuit breakers are used to protect every part of an electrical system.

Other than a lightning surge, there are two main types of faults in an electrical system that cause a circuit breaker to operate: short circuits and open circuits. Relays can detect a fault only if measurable conditions show up at the terminals of the circuit. Three types of faults, or combinations of faults, can show up and are measured at a terminal:

1. The current flow in one or more phases becomes abnormally high.

2. The current in the three phases becomes abnormally unequal.

3. The voltage in one or more phases becomes abnormally low.

Protective Relaying

10.2.2 A relay is a low-voltage switch that is normally in either an open or a closed position. Depending on the design, the relay switch will operate when electrical current passes through it or electrical current stops passing through it. The relay can be electromechanical or solid-state (electronic). Each relay is designed to operate when a certain amount of current is reached.

Potential transformers and current transformers installed on high-voltage circuits send representative low voltage and low current to the relays. Relays are designed to operate when the voltage and/or current is beyond the range of the specified relay settings.

A relay designed to detect over-current would operate if the representative current from the current transformer was beyond the specified setting. The relay switch would operate and send a low-voltage signal to the circuit-breaker control mechanism and cause it to open.

Relays Controlling Circuit-Breaker Operation

10.2.3 An electrical system can become unstable with adverse conditions ranging from a low over-current fault, such as a tree contact, up to and including a *geomagnetically induced current* (GIC) on long transmission lines, due to increased sunburst activity on the sun.

Relays can be designed to detect various conditions on a circuit as long as the voltage and current representing the condition of the circuit can be brought into the relay. Examples of some of the relays that can be installed to protect a circuit are the following:

- An over-current relay detects current when it exceeds predetermined limits.
- An under-current or under-power relay detects current when it has decreased beyond a predetermined limit.
- An over- or under-voltage relay detects voltage change beyond predetermined limits.
- A differential relay detects current entering a protected zone that does not equal the current leaving the zone.
- A current- or voltage-balance relay can detect a predetermined difference between two circuits or between phases on a circuit.
- An under- or over-frequency relay detects frequency when it changes abnormally.
- A thermal relay detects an abnormal rise in the temperature of a generator or transformer.
- A directional-power relay detects a change in the direction the power is flowing on a circuit within the grid.
- A power-factor relay detects changes to the reactance in a circuit beyond predetermined limits.

Circuit Breaker Operation

10.2.4 Relay settings specified by a planning engineer will determine the sequence speed and number of times when a breaker will open and reclose on a fault. A circuit breaker must open within a speed range that will prevent damage to equipment, such as a substation transformer, and still coordinate with other switchgears on the system so that only the faulted section will be isolated.

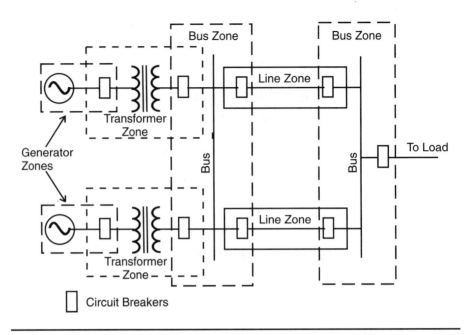

Figure 10–2 Typical protection zones.

The tripping time for a breaker is very fast. The speed is normally expressed in cycles. For example, a breaker can open on as few as three cycles, which means that a circuit breaker on a 60-hertz line can operate in 0.133 seconds after sensing a fault.

Zone Protection

10.2.5 The protection scheme of the high-voltage system is divided into protective zones. When trouble occurs in a zone, relays sense the problem and send a signal to the appropriate circuit breakers to disconnect the zone from the system. The usual protective zones (see Figure 10–2) are generator, transformer, bus, and lines.

Due to its length, the line zone has the greatest exposure to faults and is the most frequent zone to be disconnected from the system.

The Blackout of 2003

10.2.6 The blackout of August 14, 2003, is an example of how a protection system can fail.

The complete cause of this particular blackout is complex. The system was already stressed with a high customer demand, voltage swings, and a need for more reactive power (capacitance) in the grid. Under these unstable conditions, a transmission line tripped out due to a short circuit caused by a brush fire under the line. Hot gases from the fire ionized the air and caused the air under the line to become conductive. Normally within a grid, other lines pick up the load dropped by the fault line. Extra load on another circuit caused the power conductors to warm up and sag into a tree and trip out. A generation plant tripped out when the transmission lines were no longer available. The resultant overload, voltage collapse, and current swings in the rest of the grid caused instability in the power system and circuits tripped out, one after the other.

System operators and the protective relays are supposed to isolate a fault to protect equipment from damage and prevent the fault from cascading into neighboring systems. However, unless there is intervention, the route that power will flow in an electrical grid is controlled by the laws of physics. The flows will go over many different lines, choosing a path of least resistance to get to the load center; meanwhile, relays will sense any overload, a voltage collapse, low frequency, reactive power overload, and other factors and cause signal breakers to open.

System operators in different jurisdictions can reroute power to a different transmission line by turning down the generation in one location and turning up generation at a different location. This assumes that there is reserve generation capacity available and that there is excellent coordination and communication between jurisdictions. Meanwhile, under normal conditions, a system operator (market player, generator, or trader) considers the price of power from different generation sources. A system operator is supposed to ignore economics and markets to relieve a transmission line overload, but these could still be complicating factors when making quick decisions.

10.3 Distribution Protection

Distribution-Protection Requirements

10.3.1 A distribution system is exposed to over-current, over-voltage, and open-circuit conditions. Protective equipment is strategically placed to limit and isolate the faults so that the remainder of the system is not affected.

In many cases, especially in urban areas, a circuit breaker in a substation can detect faults in the full length of the circuit. Sensing problems such as open circuits, abnormal ground current, or abnormal phase imbalance can be obtained by using circuit breakers or electronic reclosers and their associated relays.

Downstream equipment, such as fuses or hydraulic reclosers, will trip out and sectionalize a circuit automatically, without the need for relays or other power sources. Only an over-current condition will trip out these devices.

Protection in a Distribution Substation

10.3.2 At a distribution substation, normally high-voltage fuses or a circuit breaker are on the high-voltage source side of the substation transformer, and circuit breakers or reclosers on each distribution feeder are on the low-voltage load side. Figure 10–3 shows a distribution substation with high-voltage (HV) fuses on the primary side of the transformer. A fault in the substation should trip out the high-voltage fuses before the circuit breakers at the source of the incoming sub-transmission line trip out. The low-voltage (LV) reclosers should trip out a faulted feeder before there is any damaging current through the substation transformer. (Figure 10–4 is a photograph of a similar substation setup.)

Protection Using Home Wiring as an Example

10.3.3 The protection for the electric wiring in a home (Figure 10–5) is not unlike the protection of a distribution system. Home wiring for a 120/240-volt service is fed to a main breaker (or main fuses). Many individual circuits, each with its own breaker (or fuse), go from the panel to various loads in the home.

The breaker (or fuse) on an individual circuit trips out when it is exposed to over-current, such as an overload or a short circuit. The rating of the main breaker is coordinated so that the individual circuit breaker will trip before the main

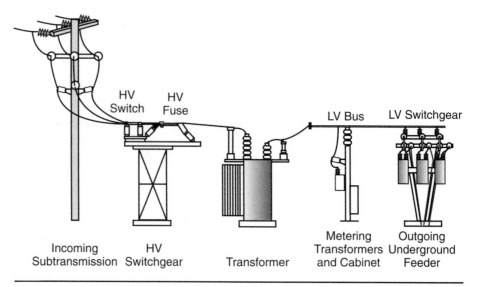

Figure 10–3 Distribution substation protection.

Figure 10–4 Distribution substation.

breaker. This protection scheme is similar to the protective setup with a distribution substation and its feeders.

Circuits feeding a bathroom or the outdoors need more sophisticated protection to protect people in these well-grounded locations. Protection that will open a circuit at a current level below the threshold of a person's sensation is available. A ground-fault circuit interrupter (GFCI or GFI) is used on these circuits where

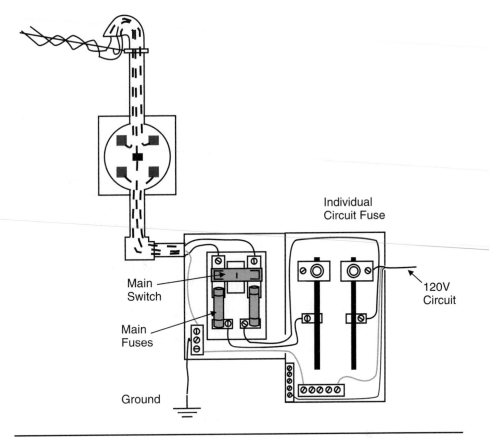

Figure 10–5 Protection in residential wiring.

it is desirable for the circuit to trip out quickly for even a minor fault. The protection of a household circuit using a GFI can be compared to the ground-fault relay protection available on transmission and distribution circuits. A GFI monitors the current flowing to the load and the current returning to the source on the neutral, as shown in Figure 10–6. The live and neutral wires pass through a coil. Under normal conditions, the current through each wire would be equal but would be flowing in opposite directions. No magnetic field would be induced into the coil because of the canceling effect of the two wires of opposite polarity. If some of the current flow returned to the source through ground, there would be more current flowing in the hot wire than in the neutral wire, and there would be a small magnetic field induced in the coil. This primary coil induces a voltage into a secondary coil whose output is amplified by an electronic amplifier. The output from the amplifier is applied to a relay coil, which opens the circuit. A typical GFI will trip out within 30 milliseconds when there is a current imbalance of only 5 milliamperes. Faster and slower GFIs are available. A very low level of current will trip a GFI quick enough to prevent a person from feeling any electrical sensation.

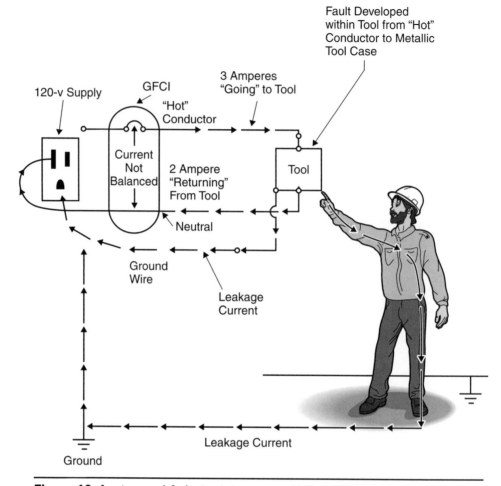

Figure 10–6   A ground fault circuit interrupter (GFI or GFCI).

Consequence of Poor Over-Current Protection

10.3.4 Faults such as phase-to-phase contacts, phase-to-ground shorts, or a follow-through current after a lightning strike show up in a circuit as an over-current condition. *If* the circuit stays in service during an over-current condition, *then* the following will occur:

- Equipment such as transformers, regulators, and conductors will overheat and be damaged.

- An over-current condition will cause the voltage on the system to collapse, which, if not corrected, can damage customer equipment.

- There will be a greater risk to the public when they are involved with a conductor falling to the ground or when they have an accidental powerline contact with a ladder, antenna, or tree.

Just as it is essential to have a fuse or breaker panel to protect household circuits, utility circuits also need protection. Having no protection is similar to a householder putting a coin behind a fuse to bypass the fuse protection.

Transient or Permanent Faults

10.3.5 Depending on the protection scheme and location, about 90 percent of overhead-circuit faults are transient. A transient fault such as a lightning strike or a conductor contact with a tree in a windstorm can cause an initial trip of the circuit, but the circuit is automatically reclosed, and—if the fault is gone—the circuit stays energized. A line crew is needed to repair and reenergize the circuit for the 10 percent of faults that are permanent.

Transient faults are rare on underground circuits. Most underground faults are permanent and require a line crew to make repairs. Underground faults are not as obvious as overhead faults because faults on underground systems tend to be high-resistance faults. The protection opens the circuit before the fault becomes a dead short, thereby making the location of a fault more difficult to find.

Causes of Over-Current

10.3.6 A circuit is faulted anytime a live conductor makes contact with another element that is at a different potential. When the resistance or impedance between a live conductor and another element is low enough, the fault becomes a short circuit.

- Lightning is the most frequent cause of transient faults. At the flashover point, a high-voltage arc establishes a path of ionized air to ground. A high follow-through current is established through the ionized air and causes a fault current to flow in the circuit.

- A phase-to-ground or a phase-to-neutral fault is the cause of about 70 percent of permanent over-current faults. A phase-to-ground fault could be caused by a broken insulator, a contaminated insulator, a tree contact, a broken conductor, an animal contact, a car accident, or an accidental public contact with a crane, sailboat, ladder, or antenna.

- A phase-to-ground fault on an underground cable can occur due to an insulation breakdown, a dig-in, or a driven fence post.

- A phase-to-phase contact is fairly rare. It occurs when conductors slap together in long, slack spans or when ice-covered conductors gallop. Phase-to-phase contact can also occur due to external forces such as a car accident or a falling tree.

- Over-current due to an overload occurs when the customer demand exceeds the specified setting of the circuit protection. Circuit protection does not differentiate between over-current due to an overload or a fault. Protection settings become difficult when the load current approaches the value of the available fault current.

Magnitude of Fault Current

10.3.7 Fault current, like any electrical current, needs a complete circle (circuit) in order to flow. The same current level flows into the fault, returns to the source, and returns through the protective switchgear to the fault. When a fault occurs, the amount of current that flows through the complete circuit depends on the capacity of the electrical system, the conductivity of the circuit, and the type of fault.

The capacity of the electrical system feeding the fault starts with the size of the transformer at the source of the feeder. The larger the transformer feeding the circuit, the greater the ability of the system to supply a high-fault current. A short distance and a large conductor provide a low-resistance (impedance) path for a current to flow. A low-resistance path provides a greater capacity to carry a high-fault current.

A poor return path to the source reduces the current in the complete circuit and reduces the current through the protective switchgear. A neutral or other phase provide the best return path for a fault current. The resistance of a fault affects the amount of fault current flowing in the circuit. A phase-to-phase contact or a phase-to-neutral contact is a dead short and has virtually no resistance to impede current flow. A conductor lying on the ground or contacting a tree has a relatively high resistance and limits the amount of fault current generated. A high-resistance fault is really just another load on the circuit if the current generated in the circuit is not high enough to trip any over-current protection switchgear. Likewise, a customer load is just like a high-resistance fault.

Impedance to Fault Current

10.3.8 A fault can be a dead-short or a partial short circuit, depending on the impedance or resistance between a live conductor and the object causing the short. A fault to ground, such as a dry tree limb or a broken conductor lying on dry or frozen ground, is a high-impedance fault and does not provide a good path for current to flow into earth. A high-voltage feeder is more likely to overcome any impedance and is able to generate a higher current flow back to the source. A phase-to-phase or a phase-to-neutral fault is a low-impedance fault. The circuit conductors provide a good return path to the source. The complete circuit has a high-fault current flowing through it and trips the protective switchgear quickly.

Distribution-Protection Scheme

10.3.9 A protection scheme for a distribution feeder has a protective device at the source and protective devices downstream at junctions, lateral taps, and transformers.

Feeder Protection at the Substation

The source of a feeder can be protected by fuses, reclosers, or circuit breakers. A fuse is a one-shot device and is sometimes used in small, older stations as feeder protection. A recloser and a circuit breaker are multishot devices that provide a number of tripping and reclosing operations to give transient faults time to clear.

Downstream Multishot Protection

A substation recloser or circuit breaker is often able to provide multishot protection to the end of the feeder, especially on the shorter urban feeders or on high-voltage distribution feeders. Long rural feeders require downstream reclosers to maintain multishot protection to the end of the line.

Downstream Sectionalizers

A sectionalizer is a slave device to an upstream multishot device. A fault downstream from a sectionalizer will cause an upstream multishot device to trip out and reclose the circuit for a specified number of times. Depending on how the protection is specified, a sectionalizer will isolate a permanent fault during one of the intervals while the circuit is de-energized by the multishot device. A sectionalizer can interrupt a load current, but it does not have the capacity to interrupt a fault current.

Downstream Fuses

A fuse can be specified to isolate a permanent fault after the upstream multishot device has operated a specified number of times. Generally, the speed of the specified fuse will be set to melt before the third or fourth operation of the multishot device.

10.4 Specifying Protection for a Distribution Feeder

Planning a Protection Scheme

10.4.1 Planning a protection scheme is normally outside the scope of a powerline worker's duties, but it is useful and interesting to have an understanding of the process. While there is more than one way to prepare a protection scheme for a distribution feeder, an example of a common method is described here. There are four major steps in planning a protection scheme for a distribution feeder:

1. Gather the data needed to calculate a feeder profile.
2. Calculate the voltage, load current, and fault current on the feeder.
3. Interpret the results of the study.
4. Specify the protective devices needed on the feeder.

Gather Feeder Data

10.4.2 A planning engineer prepares a map or a schematic drawing of a feeder (see Figure 10–7) and breaks the feeder into segments. Each line segment is assigned a numbered node or point.

- Nodes are assigned to each junction, switch, conductor-size change, and load center.
- The length and conductor size in each line segment are recorded.
- The transformer load from node to node is added up and recorded. Transformers on a feeder are not always loaded to 100 percent capacity, so a diversity factor is used to approximate the actual loading. In the sample feeder shown in Figure 10–7, a balanced load is assumed between three phases. In reality, many utilities would add up the load on each individual phase.
- The available fault current at the source of the feeder is needed to do the feeder calculations. This information is based on the impedance and size of the distribution substation transformer and the voltage, conductor, size, and length of the circuit feeding the substation. In the sample feeder shown in Figure 10–7, the available phase-to-phase fault current at the secondary of the substation transformer will be given as 5,000 amperes.

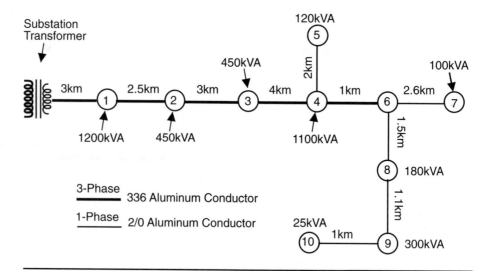

Figure 10–7 Distribution feeder data collection.

Calculating Feeder Information

10.4.3 Converting the field data to fault current, voltage, and peak-load current at each node is not normally done manually. The feeder data is input into a computer program, and the output shows the fault current, the voltage, and the peak-load current at each assigned node.

Calculations for fault current are based on a dead short, such as a phase-to-phase fault or a phase-to-neutral fault at each node. Most faults are, of course, not dead shorts, and this is taken into consideration when protective switchgear is specified. Figure 10–8 shows the results of the calculations.

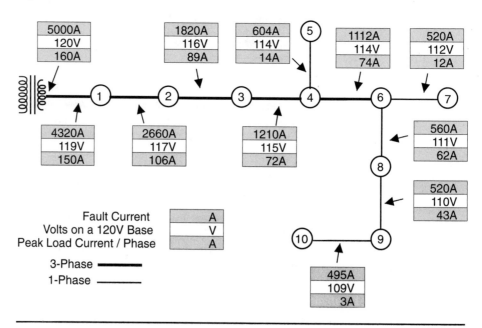

Figure 10–8 Results of calculations for fault current.

To keep the sample-feeder drawing uncomplicated, only the phase-to-phase fault current is shown in the three-phase sections. At node 6, for example, the phase-to-phase fault current is shown as 1,112 amperes, but the phase-to-ground fault current at this location is 960 amperes. Notice how quickly the fault-current values drop off with distance from the source.

The peak-load current shown at each node in the figure was based on the kilovolt-amperes loading in each line segment between nodes. A diversity factor is put into the calculations to change the transformer kilovolt-amperes loading to a more realistic value. A planning engineer would base a diversity factor on field data such as a feeder voltage/current survey and a recording of ammeters at the distribution substation.

The voltage at each node is also calculated by the computer program. The voltage in the sample feeder is shown to drop in proportion to the feeder load and the distance from the source. In this example, the voltage was put on a 120-volt base. The voltage on the single-phase line farthest from the station is shown to be too low, and the planning engineer would probably specify a voltage regulator.

Protection-Scheme Philosophy

10.4.4 Protection schemes will vary depending on utility preferences and whether the feeder is urban, rural, underground, or overhead. A protective coordination scheme provides automatic isolation of faulted circuits from the system while leaving the rest of the system in service. Where two protective switchgear devices are in series with each other, the *protected* switching device is on the source side and the *protecting* switching device is on the load side. If a fault develops downstream from the protecting device, it should trip out before the protected device. For example, a transformer fuse should have a size and speed that will clear a faulted transformer from a circuit before a protected upstream line fuse is damaged.

Most distribution feeders have a recloser or a circuit breaker that provides multishot protection to the feeder. A multishot protective device can be set for a sequence of a specified speed and number of trips and reenergizations. A *fuse-saving* philosophy has the first trip-out operation of a source-multishot device happens so fast that a downstream fuse does not even begin to melt. For lightning and other transient faults, this protection scheme reduces outages and trouble calls. Everyone on the feeder experiences at least one trip-out for each transient, which starts their digital clocks blinking. A permanent fault on a lateral will cause a multishot device to trip out and reenergize the circuit for the complete specified number of times. The downstream fuse will blow on the second or third reenergization, depending on how the protection is set up.

A *time-delayed-instant* philosophy has the first trip-out operation of the source-multishot device delayed long enough for a downstream fuse to blow first. This prevents everyone on the feeder from being exposed to a momentary trip. This philosophy is often used with fuses protecting underground feeders, where most faults are permanent. The time-delayed-instant philosophy keeps a feeder exposed to a fault longer and increases the likelihood of damage, such as a conductor burning down.

Interpreting the Results of a Feeder Study

10.4.5 The results of a feeder study, similar to the sample, give a planning engineer all the information needed to specify, prepare, and justify betterment specifications for the feeder.

- The maximum and minimum fault current available along the feeder gives the necessary information to prepare a protective coordination scheme. For example, the sample feeder study shows that the reclosers in the distribution substation must be big enough to interrupt 5,000 amperes of fault current and carry a load current of approximately 200 amperes continuously.

- Normal data collection and calculations are done for each individual phase. The results show the load current on each phase and whether there is a need for some phase-balancing work.

- The study results show where there is a need for voltage correction. A voltage profile of the feeder is available from node to node. Voltage regulators or capacitors can be located near the node where the equipment will provide maximum benefit.

- Justification for major betterment work is based on a feeder study. The cost of line losses can be worked out and compared to the cost of reconductoring. A feeder study will show whether conversion of a single-phase circuit to three phases will solve phase-balancing, voltage, or protection problems.

Specifying a Hydraulic-Recloser Frame Size

10.4.6 Recloser types vary depending on the voltage rating, the interrupting capacity, and their mode of operation. Table 10–1 shows a variety of recloser frame sizes and the voltage rating, maximum current rating, and maximum interruption rating for each. Each manufacturer would have some kind of catalog designation to identify each type of recloser. In Table 10–1, the designations of recloser types have been made up to avoid using a particular manufacturer's designation. Identifying the types of reclosers as H_1, EL_1, ET_1, etc., simplifies reference back to this table for the protection examples shown later. The table does not give all the needed information about a recloser rating. For example, the interrupting capacity of the H_3 recloser is shown as 6,000 amperes, but its actual interruption rating is 6,000 amperes at 4.8 kilovolts and only 4,000 amperes at 14.4 kilovolts.

When a recloser is chosen for a specific location, it must have a suitable frame size, which means a unit must have its contacts and its trip mechanism big enough to interrupt the highest fault current that could occur at that location. In the sample feeder, a fault immediately in front of the substation recloser could generate 5,000 amperes. The recloser frame must have its contacts and a spring mechanism able to safely carry and interrupt 5,000 amperes.

Table 10–1 shows that the smallest recloser for a 12.5/7.2-kilovolt system that can interrupt 5,000 amperes would be an H_3 recloser. The table shows that this recloser can interrupt 6,000 amperes. However, this interruption rating applies to 8.32/4.8 kilovolts. The interrupting capacity for the H_3 recloser on a 12.5/7.2-kilovolt system is 5,000 amperes.

TABLE 10–1　**Typical Recloser Ratings**

Types of Reclosers	Types	Maximum Rating (kV)	Maximum Current (A)	Interruption Rating (A)
The ratings of five typical sizes	H$_1$	14.4	50	1,250
of *hydraulic* units are shown. The	H$_2$	14.4	100	3,000
contacts on hydraulic reclosers	H$_3$	14.4	280	6,000
open when over-current flows	H$_4$	24.9	100	2,000
through a solenoid coil, which	H$_5$	24.9	280	4,000
creates a magnetic force on a				
plunger and opens the contacts.				
The two typical *electric* reclosers	EL$_1$	14.4	560	12,000
shown require a low-voltage	EL$_2$	34.5	560	8,000
supply to operate their heavy				
contacts.				
The ratings of four typical three-	ET$_1$	14.4	400	6,000
phase relay-controlled *electronic*	ET$_2$	14.4	560	10,000
reclosers are shown. The relays	ET$_3$	34.5	400	6,000
can be set to detect specified	ET$_4$	34.5	560	8,000
over-current and ground-current				
conditions.				

Specifying a Trip-Coil Size

10.4.7 An over-current situation will cause a recloser or circuit breaker to trip out a circuit. Relay-controlled devices, such as a circuit breaker or an electronic recloser, will trip out when a relay senses the over-current and sends a signal to trip out the circuit. A hydraulic recloser opens when over-current flows through its trip coil. A trip coil installed in a recloser must be able to carry the expected peak-load current. For example, the sample feeder shown in Figure 10–8 has a projected peak load of 160 amperes per phase. A 200-ampere trip coil would probably be specified to allow for load growth and unbalanced load. A 200-ampere recloser will carry 200 amperes continuously and will carry some overload without damage.

In general practice, an over-current device will not trip for a small or temporary overload. A trip coil in a hydraulic recloser is normally designed to trip a circuit when the current flowing through it is twice the rating of the coil; therefore, when 400 amperes flow through a 200-ampere coil, the circuit will trip out. An over-current of double the recloser setting would normally be a fault.

A Recloser Protection Zone

10.4.8 A recloser will provide multishot protection downstream to any location where the circuit has the capacity to generate the needed fault current to trip it out. For example, the lowest fault current available in the sample circuit shown in Figure 10–8 is 495 amperes phase to ground at node 10. A dead short between phase and neutral at node 10 could generate 495 amperes, which would be enough to trip a 200-ampere recloser at the substation. A more common higher-impedance fault, such as a broken conductor lying on dry ground or a tree contact, will not generate the 400 amperes needed to trip the circuit.

In the sample feeder, the reclosers at the substation will likely "see" most faults just beyond node 6 where the circuit can generate a phase-to-phase fault current of 1,112 amperes and a phase-to-ground fault current of 960 amperes. At node 6, even a high-impedance fault is likely to generate the minimum 400 amperes needed to trip a 200-ampere recloser. Ideally, a safety factor is needed to provide a greater likelihood of a circuit tripping out for a high-impedance fault. A safety factor of two would require a minimum of an 800-ampere fault current to be available at the end of a zone protected by a 200-ampere recloser.

Specifying Recloser Speed and Operating Sequence

10.4.9 A planning engineer chooses a recloser with a sequence of opening and closing speeds based on coordination with upstream and downstream protective devices. When a fault is beyond a downstream fuse, the planning engineer would choose a fuse size and speed to blow at the desired time—for example, at the second or third closing of the recloser. The timing sequence of a recloser is coded as follows:

A = instantaneous
B = retarded
C = extra retarded
D = steep retarded

A typical speed and sequence may be A1B3, which means the recloser opens instantaneously on sensing a fault and recloses. If the fault persists on the line, the recloser opens and recloses after a retarded delay. For a permanent fault, the recloser will go through the complete sequence of one instantaneous trip and three retarded trips before remaining open. The speed and sequence chosen by the planning engineer depend on the protection scheme philosophy and on the need to solve particular protection problems.

Typical TCC Curve for a Recloser

10.4.10 When specifying a protective device, the speed of operation must be known in order to be able to coordinate the device with other protective equipment in the circuit. A *time current characteristic* (TCC) curve is available for each size of fuse, sectionalizer, recloser, or relay. A TCC curve is plotted on graph paper and shows the response time, minimum damage time, and total clearing time. Note that the TCC for a 200-ampere recloser in Figure 10–9 shows that the minimum fault the recloser will see is 400 amperes. The A curve shows that 400 amperes will trip out the circuit in about 0.5 second. The recloser will clear a permanent fault of 400 amperes in about 15 seconds. A permanent 5,000-ampere fault will clear in about 0.2 second.

Specifying a Downstream Recloser

10.4.11 In the sample feeder shown in Figure 10–8, a downstream recloser is needed to provide multishot protection to the end of the feeder. A higher-impedance fault would not be "seen" by the source recloser. Ideally there is multishot protection to the end of every feeder. For economic reasons, multishot protection may be unavailable for higher-impedance faults near the end of a feeder. The end of the feeder can still be protected by a fuse, but without multishot protection a transient

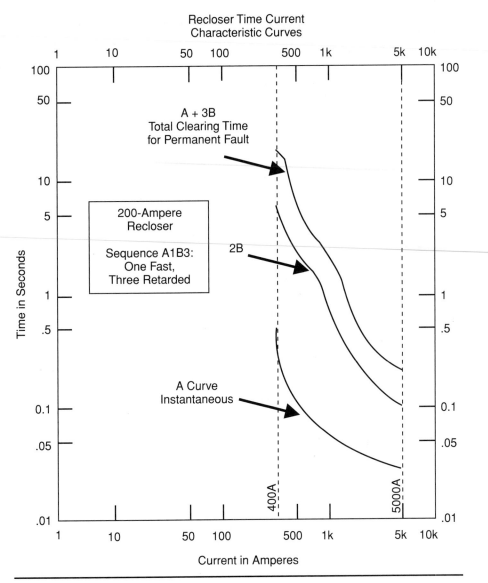

Figure 10–9 TCC for a 200-ampere recloser.

fault will blow a fuse and cause an easy callout for a line crew. To have multishot protection for a higher-impedance fault on the single-phase line past node 6, a downstream recloser should be installed.

As shown in Figure 10–10, a 100-ampere H_2 recloser on the single-phase line at node 6 will carry the 62 amperes of load current and should see most faults at node 10, which has 495 amperes of available fault current. To provide node 7 with multishot protection, another recloser would need to be installed in that line.

Specifying Fuse Size and Speed

10.4.12 A line or a station fuse is chosen based on its current rating and speed. The speed of a fuse is indicated by the letter on the fuse link (e.g., K-link or T-link). In

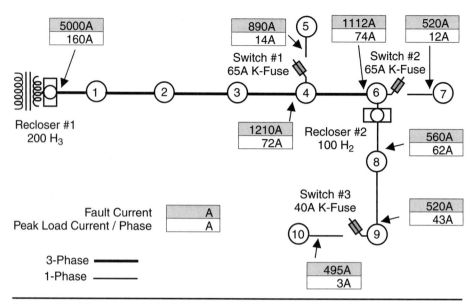

Figure 10–10 A sample feeder with specified protection.

order to coordinate the speed of the fuse with upstream and downstream protective switchgear, the minimum damage time, minimum melting time, and total clearing time must be known.

The TCC curve for a 100-ampere K-link fuse (Figure 10–11) shows how quickly the fuse melts as the current going through it is increased. In this example, 200 amperes will melt the fuse link after about 100 seconds of exposure, and 1,000 amperes will melt the fuse in about 0.2 second.

Specifying Downstream Fuses

10.4.13 A fuse size and speed can be chosen so that the fuse will melt in any of the energized intervals of an upstream multishot device as it goes through its sequence during a permanent fault. In the sample feeder shown in Figure 10–10, the lateral protected by a fuse in switch 1 is specified to coordinate with the 200-ampere substation reclosers. The lateral has a peak-load current of only 14 amperes. A 25-ampere fuse would protect this lateral, but it would melt before the upstream recloser could go through the instantaneous trip. A 65-ampere fuse would stay intact as the substation recloser went through its instantaneous trip for a fault on the lateral. The 200-ampere reclosers can see to the end of the lateral because the available fault current is 890 amperes.

A TCC curve for a 65-ampere fuse superimposed on the TCC curve for a 200-ampere H_3 recloser can show that the two devices coordinate with each other. A quicker method is the use of a recloser-to-fuse coordination table. The data in Table 10–2 can be used with a 100-ampere H_2 recloser. In the sample feeder shown in Figure 10–10, the lateral tap protected by a fuse in switch 3 is specified to coordinate with recloser 2, which is a 100-ampere H_2 recloser. The lateral is lightly loaded with a peak load of 3 amperes, but if the circuit is exposed to transients from

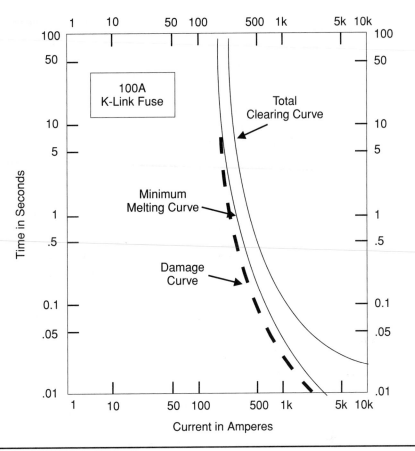

Figure 10–11 TCC curve for 100A K-link fuse.

TABLE 10–2 Recloser-to-Fuse Coordination Table

A 100-ampere H_2 Recloser Set at Sequence: One Fast, Three Retarded (A1B3) Type K Fuse Links

Protecting Fuse Link	Recloser-to-Fuse Coordination Range in Amperes		Protecting Fuse Link	Maximum Fuse-to-Fuse Coordination Current within the Recloser Zone of Protection				
				Protected Link				
	Min.	Max.		50	65	80	100	140
40	200	690	40	600	690	690	690	
50	200	1,020	50		510	1,020	1,020	1,020
65	200	1,400	65			600	1,400	1,400
80	280	1,880	80				1,280	1,880
100	560	2,560	100					2,560
140	1,970	3,000						

lightning or trees, it would save a callout to have the fuse in switch 3 coordinate with recloser 2. The fault current at the end of the lateral is 495 amperes, which means that the 100-ampere recloser should see most faults. Table 10–2 shows that the lateral at switch 3 has a minimum of 495 amperes and a maximum of 520 amperes fault current and needs a 40-ampere fuse to coordinate with a 100-ampere recloser.

In the sample feeder, the lateral protected by the fuse in switch 2 has multishot protection for low-impedance faults from recloser 1. The available fault current of 620 amperes at the end of the line may not generate enough current for a higher-impedance fault such as a tree limb. A judgment has to be made regarding what to do:

1. Install a recloser at switch 2.

2. Install a fuse that coordinates with recloser 1.

3. Install a small fuse that would blow quickly for any fault.

Option 2 is a compromise wherein recloser 1 sees most faults except for higher-impedance faults near the end of the line. A 200-ampere recloser table similar to Table 10–2 shows that a 65-ampere fuse coordinates with recloser 2.

Specifying Sectionalizers

10.4.14 Sectionalizers are specified in a way similar to how fuses are specified. TCC curves or tables determine the most appropriate size and speed sectionalizer to coordinate with an upstream multishot device. A sectionalizer must coordinate with a multishot device because it isolates or opens a faulted circuit in an interval when the multishot device has tripped out the circuit. A sectionalizer is more reliable than a fuse for specifying at which interval of the upstream multishot-device sequence it will open during a permanent fault. A trip coil for a sectionalizer is specified for its current rating and has a two-shot or three-shot sequence.

Over-Current Trouble Calls

10.4.15 During an over-current situation, a line crew is called out after circuit breakers, reclosers, sectionalizers, or fuses have gone through their sequences and have isolated any circuit with a permanent fault.

High-Voltage Distribution Conversion

10.4.16 Many utilities have voltage conversion programs to convert their systems from typical primary voltages such as 8.3/4.8 kilovolts and 12.5/7.2 kilovolts to higher distribution voltages such as 25/14.4 kilovolts and 34.5/19.9 kilovolts. The following are the advantages of a higher-voltage distribution system:

- The substation breaker or recloser can see out much farther because the available fault current level remains high much farther downstream. There is often no need for downstream reclosers or fusing to maintain protection at the end of the line. Sectionalizing devices are still installed for operating purposes.

- There are fewer substations needed and fewer feeders needed from the substation.

- For a given load, a higher-voltage feeder would have less load current and, therefore, there is less voltage drop along the feeder. Downstream voltage regulators are rare, except for a very long or very heavily loaded feeder. There is a rule of thumb that a distribution feeder with an average

TABLE 10–3 Over-Current Trouble Calls

If	Then
There has been wind, ice, wet snow, or lightning.	The problem is often the traditional broken conductors, broken poles, or fallen trees and branches.
Protection tripped out on a nice clear day.	The fault is sometimes due to public contact, such as a car accident, tree cutting, or a boom contact. An outage on a clear day suggests that a patrol should be carried out before energizing the circuit.
An overload is the likely cause of an outage.	The most common fix is phase balancing. The planning engineer often assumes that the load on the feeder is balanced among the three phases. When the load is not balanced, one phase of the three-phase system is carrying more than its share of the load and the protective device will trip out.
The circuit has been out for a while, especially during peak-load periods.	There is a high initial inrush current when the switch is closed, and the line trips out again. A heavily loaded circuit may have to be picked up a section at a time.

customer load can feed about 1 mile (1.6 km) per 1 kilovolt (phase to neutral) before needing voltage regulation. Based on this rule of thumb, an 8.3/4.8-kilovolt feeder would need voltage regulation about 5 miles from the substation, and a 34.5/19.9-kilovolt feeder would need voltage regulation at about 20 miles from the station.

- A higher-voltage feeder can feed much more load. For example, an 8.3/4.8-kilovolt feeder typically can be considered heavily loaded when supplying about 3 megawatts, while a 34.5/19.9-kilovolt feeder is considered heavily loaded when it is supplying about 15 megawatts.

- A utility would normally not be able to feed an individual customer that has a requirement for a 750-kilowatt service on an 8.3/4.8-kilovolt system. A subtransmission feed would be required, along with all the associated costs. Meanwhile, if a 25/14.4-kilovolt or 34.5/19.9-kilovolt feeder were available, a 750-kilowatt load could be supplied on that system with standard distribution transformers without creating a problem for other customers on the feeder.

10.5. Over-Voltage Protection

Causes of Over-Voltage

10.5.1 Other than lightning, not many trouble calls are due to over-voltage. Lightning is the most common source of over-voltage and of the most transient faults on an electrical system. The high voltage and current generated by lightning usually cause a momentary outage to customers because the automatic circuit protections open and reclose after the strike.

Switching operations can cause a transient over-voltage. The magnitude of the surge is much lower than lightning and normally is significant only on circuits of

230 kilovolts and above. An over-voltage situation can occur when a voltage regulator is stuck in a maximum-boost position, a switched capacitor is left in service during an off-peak time period, a higher-voltage wire falls onto or makes contact with a lower-voltage wire, or, in rare cases, a transformer with a partially shorted coil results in a high secondary voltage.

Convection and Frontal Thunderstorms

10.5.2 The two types of thunderstorms are convection storms and frontal storms.

A *convection thunderstorm* is the most common thunderstorm, especially on a hot summer day. It is a localized storm that occurs when the hot air near Earth's surface rises and meets the cold air at a higher altitude. A convection thunderstorm does not last long because it is usually accompanied by rain. The rain cools the earth, which removes the energy source for the storm.

A *frontal thunderstorm* occurs when a cold front meets a front of warm, moist air. The storm can stretch for hundreds of miles and last for hours. It can regenerate itself because air masses continue to move in as the fronts collide. A frontal storm is more severe than a convection storm.

10.5.3 Lightning is part of an overall electrical circuit between earth and atmosphere (Figure 10–12). Electrical charges are created in the atmosphere by the friction between particles of rapidly moving air. The cloud normally associated with a frontal storm or a convection storm is the cumulonimbus cloud, also called thunderhead. During rain or hail, negative charges fall to the bottom of the cloud. When these negative charges travel toward positive charges, the air becomes electrically stressed and breaks down, resulting in high voltage and high-current dis-

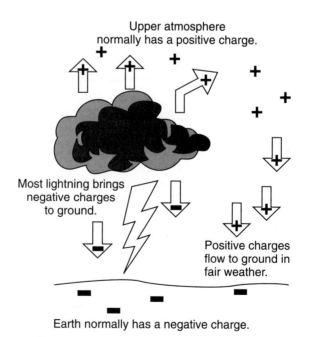

Figure 10–12   Electrical circuit between atmosphere and ground

charge (lightning) between the positive and negative charges. The electrical discharge can be within the same cloud, clouds, or to earth.

The direction or polarity of the current flow due to lightning is not important as far as protection is concerned. Both positively charged and negatively charged lightning strikes earth. Contrary to its appearance, the most common direction for the current flow is from cloud to earth. A rarely visible charged leader from the cloud reaches earth, and, as it starts to neutralize there, it becomes a visible arc from earth to cloud. The following are some characteristics of lightning:

- Lightning can have a charge of up to 100 million volts.
- Lightning establishes an electrical path through which the follow-through current flow can be from 2,000 to 200,000 amperes.
- Lightning can generate heat in a 2.5-cm path of approximately 60,000°F.
- Lightning generates heat, which causes an explosive expansion of air and is heard as thunder.

Estimating Distance from Lightning

10.5.4 The *flash-bang method* is a quick method for estimating the distance to lightning. Count the *number of seconds between seeing the lightning and hearing the thunder:*

Number of seconds divided by 3 = Number of kilometers away
Number of seconds divided by 5 = Number of miles away

Determining the direction in which a storm is moving is important for determining safe working conditions on distribution lines. If the storm is 5 miles away but heading toward a work area, it is time to get clear of the circuit. The next lightning flash will be closer. As soon as lightning is seen or thunder is heard, work on powerlines, especially transmission lines, should be suspended because some part of the line could reach into the storm area.

Effects of a Direct Stroke of Lightning

10.5.5 The effects of a direct stroke of lightning can be very dramatic. When lightning flashes, an electrical circuit is being completed. When lightning strikes earth, an electrical circuit is completed through the closest and lowest-resistance path to ground.

A tall, pointed object is the most attractive object for a lightning strike. A 1,000-foot (300-m) structure may be struck four times a year, while a 100-foot (30-m) structure is struck once every 25 years. Tall towers and buildings with lots of steel in them are struck by lightning but can carry the current to ground without overheating and causing damage.

Concrete footings of transmission-line towers can be damaged because lightning will heat the moisture in the concrete and expand it explosively. Concrete footings are, therefore, usually bypassed with a heavy-gauge conductor to carry the current. Trees and wood poles are more attractive to lightning than Earth is. Although trees and wood poles are higher-resistance paths than steel buildings or towers, they are still lower-resistance paths than air. When lightning strikes these objects, the moisture in the wood is suddenly vaporized and the resultant explosion will cause the wood to splinter.

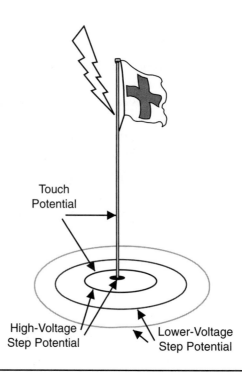

Touch
Potential

High-Voltage
Step Potential

Lower-Voltage
Step Potential

Figure 10–13 Step and touch potentials during a storm.

Ground-Gradient Effect

10.5.6 There are step and touch potentials up to 70 kilovolts per foot (200 kV per m) in the immediate area of a lightning strike. People standing near a tall object that is struck by lightning are injured because of the high step and touch potentials at the base. Figure 10–13 illustrates how people standing on the ground can be hurt by touching an object struck by lightning, as well as by standing near the object struck by lightning.

Even when lightning discharges in the clouds and does not reach earth, voltage-gradient changes are taking place on the ground. Induction from the lightning discharge can cause gradients of 3 kilovolts per foot (10 kV per m) on the ground. The induced gradients cause corona discharge from pointed, grounded objects and can cause hair to stand on end and skin to tingle. Sparks from induced gradients and corona discharge can cause fires around unprotected flammable liquids, even without a lightning strike.

An object isolated from the ground can have an induced potential up to 100 kilovolts. When lightning is seen or thunder is heard, there may already be an induced potential buildup on isolated conductors.

Safety Tips for Working Near Lightning

10.5.7 The following safety tips for working near lightning can apply to on-the-job and off-the-job situations:

- The safest place to be during a thunderstorm is in a vehicle. If a vehicle is struck by lightning, all the metal in the vehicle will be at the same potential and anyone in the vehicle will not be exposed to any potential difference. The vehicle provides an equipotential zone.

- When your hair stands on end and your skin starts to tingle, there is a potential difference building up between the earth you are standing on and the clouds above. Lightning is about to strike. Drop into a fetal position.

- Lightning usually strikes tall objects such as trees. People nearby are injured due to the ground gradients of the lightning dissipating into earth. The ground gradients are like the rings formed when a stone is thrown into water. Each "ring" is a different voltage with the greatest potential differences being near the center. Staying away from tall objects reduces exposure to the highest-voltage gradients. Keeping your feet together reduces exposure to the different potentials of the rings, or to ground gradients. In the outdoors, with no nearby shelter, crouch low with feet together.

- In buildings, stay away from grounded objects. Grounded objects rise in potential when lightning strikes nearby.

Tracking Lightning Storms

10.5.8 Many electrical utilities have access to information from lightning-detection systems, which detect the location and intensity of lightning discharges. This information is valuable for determining which transmission lines are at risk of a lightning strike and, therefore, at risk of being tripped out. When possible, system operators reduce the loads on vulnerable transmission lines and increase the loads on other generators and lines to make up the difference. Putting a storm limit on a key extra-high-voltage (EHV) circuit is critical because an unexpected loss of a large source of power could destabilize an entire electrical system.

Lightning-detection systems can also provide an early warning to line crews working on transmission lines. A voltage surge due to lightning is a hazard when working on a live line, as well as when working on an isolated and grounded line.

Effect of Lightning on a Circuit

10.5.9 A voltage surge from lightning travels like an ocean wave in all directions, except that it travels at the speed of light. The wave is attenuated (diminished) when it encounters a location where it will flash over, preferably at a surge arrestor where a sparkover occurs and some or all of the energy is dissipated. A voltage surge, which causes a coupling effect between the phase conductor and the neutral or shield wire, can be attenuated in other ways. The coupling effect reduces the voltage on the phase conductor while it raises the voltage on the neutral or shield wire. When the neutral and shield wire are well grounded, the voltage is quickly lowered and the coupling effect, in turn, lowers the voltage on the phase conductors.

A high-voltage surge will be attenuated by corona discharge because distribution conductors are too small for such high voltages. The relatively small conductor also limits the current-carrying capacity of a conductor because of skin effect. The current flow is subject to skin effect in the conductor even though the current resulting from lightning is DC. However, it is not a steady-state current; it reaches a peak value and then diminishes. The effect of the change in current means it has a similar effect on conductors as AC. When an ocean wave hits a wall, it is reflected back double in size and then dissipates quickly. A voltage surge acts out similarly when it comes to a dead end. That is why transformers on dead-end poles are more vulnerable to lightning damage.

Underground cables are very sensitive to voltage surges and are exposed to surges when lightning strikes at or near a cable riser pole. While arrestors are installed at a riser pole, the cable shield and arrestor ground are tied together and the discharge voltages from arrestors will travel through the ground and cable sheath. The design of a riser pole and location of arrestors minimize the effect of lightning through factors such as arrestor lead length and location.

Switching Surges

10.5.10 Switching operations cause transient over-voltages. The magnitude of the voltage surge is much lower than lightning and is significant only on circuits 230 kilovolts and higher. If a switch opens and is immediately reclosed, a brief over-voltage occurs when energizing a capacitor. A length of parallel conductors on a transmission line is like a big capacitor and arcing inside a circuit breaker can have the same effect as though the breaker is reclosing and a restrike is occurring. An arc of a restrike on a capacitor causes a switching surge in the line.

When carrying out live-line work, the risk of a restrike or switching surge is reduced if the circuit breaker is put into a nonreclose position.

Effects of a Voltage Surge

10.5.11 A voltage surge can cause a flashover, a sparkover, or a puncture:

- A *flashover* is a disruptive discharge along a solid material such as an insulator string or a live-line tool.

- A *sparkover* is a disruptive discharge through the air.

- A *puncture* is a disruptive discharge through a solid material such as rubber cover-up, rubber gloves, or a fiber conductor cover.

A voltage surge can be compared to the action of a wave of water (see Figure 10–14 and Table 10–4).

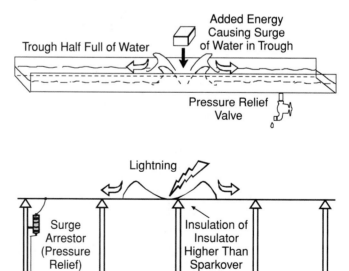

Figure 10–14 Voltage surge/wave action.

TABLE 10–4   **Comparison of Voltage Surge to Water Surge**

Surge Activity	Water System	Electrical System
Initiation of Surge	An outside energy source such as a brick is thrown into the water.	An outside energy source such as lightning strikes a line.
Speed of Energy Wave	The speed of a wave of water can be calculated with a relatively complicated formula. The speed of a wave of water is relatively slow.	The speed of a voltage surge through a powerline is at the speed of light.
Surge or Wave Impeded	A wave of water is impeded by these: • The size and shape of the trough or conduit holding the water • The frictional resistance of material making up the trough	A large conductor offers less impedance than a small conductor.
Surge or Wave Action at a Dead End	The wave is reflected off the dead end and is doubled in magnitude.	The wave is reflected off the dead end and is doubled in magnitude. It diminishes in a relatively short distance.
Uncontrolled Surge Discharge	Water spills over the edge of the trough.	Voltage surge spills over or sparks over at location with least insulation.
Controlled Surge Discharge	A pressure-relief valve reduces the pressure of a surge in a water system. The amount of discharge is dependent on the spring pressure of the pressure-relief valve and the size of the discharge pipe.	A surge arrestor with a voltage rating lower than the system insulation provides a path for a voltage surge to be dissipated into the ground. The amount of discharge depends on the resistance of the path to ground and the resistance of the ground.
Dissipation of Surge	Wave action on the edge of the trough reduces the size of the main wave.	A high-voltage surge on a small conductor causes some dissipation of the curve due to corona and skin effect. A high-voltage surge dissipates when it couples with a nearby phase, neutral, or ground.

Circuit Protection from Over-Voltage

10.5.12 The basics of over-voltage protection are to intercept the over-voltage and conduct it to earth, where it is dissipated. Circuits are protected from over-voltage by the following:

1. Surge arrestors shunt a transient over-voltage to ground and control the resultant follow-through current before insulation, such as porcelain, polymer, air, oil, cable, or wire insulation, flashes over or is punctured.

2. Shield wire, which is an overhead ground wire, protects circuits and stations from direct strokes of lightning. Shield wire is strung high above a circuit or station and is more attractive to lightning than the power conductors and equipment below. Shield wire is grounded at every structure and will discharge a voltage surge to ground.

3. Insulation coordination protects equipment from over-voltage by providing insulation on equipment and lines that can withstand a voltage considerably higher than the voltage rating of the circuit.

4. Good system grounding provides a low-impedance path for a voltage surge that has gone to ground at an arrestor to dissipate into earth.

Surge Arrestors

10.5.13 A surge arrestor is a device that provides a path for a surge current, almost always due to lightning, to discharge to ground. After the voltage surge is diverted to ground, the arrestor chokes off the follow-through current, and the arrestor is restored and ready for the next surge.

A normal voltage will not discharge to ground across a gap or many gaps inside the arrestor. Surge arrestors are designed to operate at a voltage higher than the circuit voltage but lower than the voltage that would cause an insulator to flash over or a transformer to be damaged. The arrestor must operate in time to avoid damage to equipment or, in other words, coordinate with the withstand curves of equipment needing protection.

Surge arrestors can fail violently and, if in a porcelain housing, the shrapnel coming from a violent failure can cause severe injuries. Some utilities require that all arrestors over a certain voltage, such as 15 kilovolts, be tested before being reenergized. A tester applies a voltage across the arrestor. The arrestor conducting at lower voltages than specified indicates that it could fail while the powerline worker is energizing it. A tester is used to test distribution-class arrestors. The tester puts out 0 to 30 kilovolts DC in 1-kV steps, and the current meter will indicate if there is any current leakage while the voltmeter will display the breakover voltage of the arrestor.

Because of the high fault current available, arrestors in a substation should be energized remotely. Polymer housing of an arrestor will reduce the damaging effect of a failure.

Types of Surge Arrestors

10.5.14 An arrestor provides a sparkover location for a voltage surge, provides a path for a high-surge current flow to ground, and then stops the current flow to ground before it becomes a permanent ground fault. The following paragraphs present some types of surge arrestors. Improvements always are being made.

A *spark gap* or *rod gap* is installed between the line and ground to discharge a surge and protect insulators. Figure 10–15 shows 230-kilovolt overhead to underground potheads with a grounded rod between the potheads acting as a spark gap. This type of protection is found mostly on transmission lines. Once an arc is established, however, the ionized air becomes a conductor and the arc continues until the circuit trips out. This continuing arc is a fault current called the *power-follow current*. The spark gap will erode and be damaged by a prolonged arc.

A *valve-type arrestor* is designed to limit a power-follow current after passing the voltage surge to ground. A valve-type arrestor is made of air gaps and a special resistor called a *valve element*. The valve element in the arrestor will pass a lightning surge to ground, but it has a high resistance to 60 hertz and stops any 60-hertz power-follow current.

Figure 10–15   Spark gap surge protection.

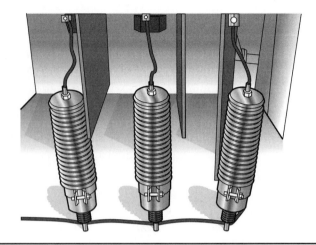

Figure 10–16   A live-front transformer arrestor.

In *metal-oxide varistors* (MOV), the gaps are not air but layers of highly resistive metal-oxide additives. They do not need air gaps to prevent normal voltage from going to ground. This material can pass a voltage surge without damage. The material is nonlinear, meaning that it sets up a reactance that prevents the voltage and current from being at their peak value at the same time, thereby limiting the energy being dissipated through the arrestor. Figure 10–16 shows an MOV installed in a live-front transformer.

A *dead-front arrestor* is an arrestor assembled in a shielded housing, such as an elbow (Figure 10–17), and installed for the protection of underground and pad-mounted distribution equipment and circuits.

Arrestors should be located as close to equipment needing protection as possible, as seen in Figures 10–18 and 10–19.

Classes of Surge Arrestors

Valve-type surge arrestors come in four classes:

1. A *station-class arrestor* provides the highest degree of protection. It is used in transmission substations because it can withstand a very high surge current.

2. An *intermediate-class arrestor* is used in distribution substations and on subtransmission circuits and is available in ratings up to 144 kilovolts. It is used where the higher quality and cost of a station-class arrestor are not justified. The difference between the circuit voltage and the sparkover voltage of the intermediate-class arrestor is narrower than it is with the distribution-class arrestor. This provides better protection for the equipment that the arrestor is protecting.

3. A *distribution-class arrestor* is used on distribution transformers and other line equipment and is available in ratings up to 42 kilovolts. It provides a

Figure 10–17   A dead-front elbow arrestor.

reasonable balance between protection and cost. Distribution-class arrestors are classified according to the following:

- *Heavy-duty class* is used to protect overhead distribution systems exposed to severe lightning currents.
- *Light-duty class* is used to protect underground distribution systems where the major portion of the lightning-strike current is discharged by an arrestor located at the riser pole.
- *Normal-duty class* is used to protect overhead distribution systems exposed to typical lightning currents.

4. *Secondary-class arrestors* are used for the protection of secondary services and are available in ratings up to 650 volts.

Shield Wire   **10.5.15** Most transmission lines, some subtransmission lines, and some substations have a shield wire (ground wire, sky wire) strung in the top position on the structures. Its purpose is to be the most attractive element for a lighting strike.

Shield wire is grounded at each structure. When a line has a history of too many damaging lighting strikes, often the solution is to improve the grounding of the shield wire along the length of the line.

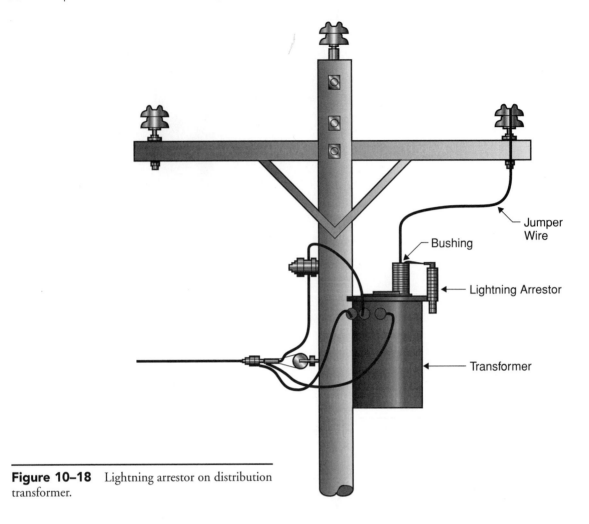

Figure 10–18 Lightning arrestor on distribution transformer.

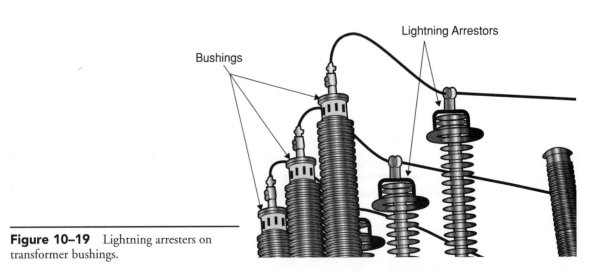

Figure 10–19 Lightning arresters on transformer bushings.

Insulation Coordination

10.5.16 The design of an electrical system includes using insulation that meets the standard insulator *basic-impulse level* (BIL) for the voltage level on the system. The voltage level that can flash over the leakage distance of an insulator is the BIL. A straight-line distance through an insulator is much shorter than the distance over the outside. The longer distance over the outside is the leakage distance.

Over-voltage protection involves ensuring that a voltage surge will not exceed the BIL rating of the equipment or line it is protecting. For example, in a transmission station, the BIL for a 230-kilovolt system could be 900 kilovolts. Every insulator, breaker, and transformer is coordinated to have a BIL of 900 kilovolts. The 230-kilovolt portion of the station can, therefore, withstand up to a 900-kilovolt surge without a flashover. A surge arrestor would have the lowest BIL in the station; therefore, it controls the location where a high-voltage surge would flash over and be dissipated safely to ground.

Insulation and surge arrestors on distribution feeders are specified in the same way. A 25/14.4-kilovolt system with a BIL of 95 kilovolts means that all the insulation and equipment should withstand 95 kilovolts. A surge arrestor would have a voltage rating of less than 95 kilovolts but more than 14.4 kilovolts. On a 25/14.4-kilovolt system, an arrestor would have a voltage rating of 18 kilovolts.

Equipment Voltage–Time Curves

10.5.17 Equipment such as a transformer has a BIL voltage–time curve, which represents the amount of voltage and time a transformer can withstand before it is damaged. Equipment is manufactured to meet a BIL voltage–time curve so that a standard surge arrestor can be used to protect it. Figure 10–20 shows the BIL

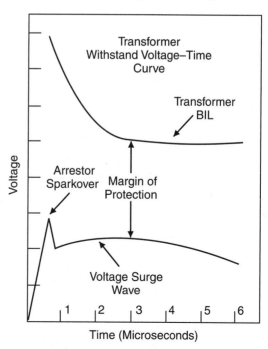

Figure 10–20 A transformer withstand voltage–time curve.

voltage–time curve for a transformer and how the curve of a voltage surge, shunted to ground by a surge arrestor, is well below the level that would damage the transformer.

Shorting Insulators for Live-Line Work

10.5.18 When working on a live transmission line, the BIL level at an insulator string will be reduced by tools, insulated strain links, and live-line rope used by the line crew. On a compact-designed transmission structure with smaller spacing between conductor and ground, live-line tools have an even greater likelihood of lowering the BIL. A location with a lower BIL is more vulnerable to a flashover if a voltage surge occurs. Although a voltage surge due to switching or lightning is extremely unlikely to happen while live-line work is carried out, protection from a possible flashover can be taken.

Prevention of voltage surges at a job site is improved by having a lightning warning system in place. Getting clear of the line when thunderstorms are in the area eliminates exposure to the greatest cause of voltage surges. To avoid a switching surge, the reclose feature of the circuit breaker must be blocked. A blocked recloser avoids the switching surges involved with reenergizing the circuit if it is tripped out for some reason.

To reduce the likelihood of a flashover at a work site, the BIL of an insulator string at an adjacent structure can be lowered. Any voltage surge that occurs while working on the circuit would then flash over at the adjacent structure and not at the work location.

Lowering the BIL of an insulator string at an adjacent structure can be accomplished by shorting out some insulators or by installing a portable protective gap (PPG) device. A PPG can be set to provide a spark gap for a given value of voltage surge and to shunt it to ground.

Protection at Problem Locations

10.5.19 Some circuits and locations are exposed to more lightning than others. Additional steps can be taken to reduce outages to circuits prone to lightning strikes:

- On transmission lines where a shield wire is already in place, improvements to grounding of the shield wire dissipate the effects of lightning more quickly.

- On problem subtransmission and lower-voltage transmission lines, lightweight, polymer, and metal-oxide arrestors can be installed on all three phases at the most vulnerable locations. In some cases, these arrestors are installed on every pole or tower. One arrestor on each of the three phases is better than a single arrestor on the center phase because, when lightning strikes one phase, the three arrestors allow all three phases go to the same voltage, preventing flashing (backflash) from one phase to another. These types of arrestors have a hotline clamp on the top and a grounded isolator on the bottom and can be installed live line.

- Stringing a shield wire in a problem-plagued location will give additional voltage surge protection, although it is more expensive than installing arrestors on each structure and phase.

- Problem distribution circuits can have surge arrestors installed in more locations.

- Improving the grounding of a system neutral reduces a voltage surge more quickly because of the coupling effect that occurs between the neutral and the phase conductors during a surge.

- On individual equipment such as a transformer, surge arrestors should be installed as close as possible to the equipment. The ground wire from the arrestor should go as directly as possible to ground.

- A transformer on a dead-end pole is more vulnerable to lightning damage because of the doubling of voltage when the lightning comes back from the dead end. Stringing the line one span farther is sometimes done in problem locations.

10.6 System Grounding for Protection

Purposes of System Grounding

10.6.1 System grounding a power system means electrically connecting the neutrals of every wye-connected transformer or generator to earth. The importance of grounding an electrical system is not always obvious. Under normal conditions, an electrical system delivers power without good grounding. It is during a voltage surge, an unbalanced-load condition, a short circuit, or an equipment failure that a dangerous voltage rise occurs on the grounding system. The voltage rise occurs on the neutral and everything connected to it. Good grounding is necessary to protect the public and workers from a dangerous voltage rise at places where the system is grounded, such as at a down-ground on a pole.

System Grounding for People Protection

10.6.2 Good grounding provides people protection and circuit protection.

People Protection

Grounding an electrical system limits the rise in potential on the neutral, metal structures, noncurrent-carrying electrical equipment, and everything electrically connected to ground. When equipment is connected to a low-resistance ground, a voltage surge is kept to a lower level and will dissipate more quickly.

Circuit Protection

Good grounding improves the likelihood of a circuit breaker, recloser, or fuse tripping out the circuit for a phase-to-ground fault. Most faults on an electrical power system are line-to-ground faults. A well-grounded electrical system provides a better return path for the fault current to flow back to the source to complete the circuit for the fault current.

Importance of System Grounding

10.6.3 When a line or substation is built, the installation of a grounding and bonding network is essential for safe operation. The design of electrical installations includes system grounding so that a person touching any equipment during a fault condition is not subjected to a dangerous current or potential.

- The installation of a ground-gradient control grid reduces step and touch potentials around such equipment as a pad-mount transformer or a switching kiosk.

- The use of crushed rock around equipment, especially in a substation, increases electrical resistance under the feet of workers.

- Standing on a ground-gradient control mat that is bonded to a switch handle protects the switch operator from electric shock if the handle becomes alive during a switch failure. With the mat bonded to the switch handle, the operator's feet and hands are at the same potential, which means there will be no current flow.

- Grounding the system neutral at frequent intervals provides a good return path for current from a line-to-ground fault. The current from a fault would have a relatively short path back up to the neutral.

- During a fault condition, voltage rises in the ground grid and everything attached to it. To limit the travel of this potential rise, station fences are isolated from the ground grid. Any railway spur that enters a station has one section of rail removed.

- To ground electrical equipment means to connect transformer tanks, metal-clad equipment, and so on, to earth. The main purpose is to reduce shock hazards by limiting the potential difference between the grounded equipment and earth. It is also important to electrically bond together all tanks of electrical equipment to prevent someone from getting in between and becoming a path from one piece of equipment to the other.

Ground versus Neutral Connections

10.6.4 On an equipment installation, ground wires and their connections should not be confused with neutral wires and their connections. A *neutral* is part of the electrical circuit and is a current-carrying conductor that provides a path for current to flow back to the source. If a neutral connection on energized equipment is opened, voltage is equal to the circuit voltage across the open point.

A *ground wire* grounds the equipment tank and surge arrestor lead-to-earth potential. During a fault or a voltage surge, a good ground reduces the potential rise on the equipment and prevents equipment failure or flashover. An equipment installation may appear to have a ground wire and a neutral connection doing the same job, but skipping one of the connections can cause a dangerous potential rise or service problem. Figure 10–21 shows a typical transformer-grounding installation with one major oversight: The primary neutral of the transformer is not connected to the system neutral. A person working on the ground would be electrocuted while trying to repair a damaged ground-rod connection. In this illustration, the down-ground is part of the primary circuit, and, when it is opened, a primary voltage difference appears across the opening.

The Neutral as Part of the Grounded System

10.6.5 For a circuit to be complete, all the current leaving the source must return to the source. In a balanced three-phase circuit, the return flow occurs in the phase conductors. Unbalanced three-phase and single-phase wye-distribution circuits use the neutral for current to find its way back to the source.

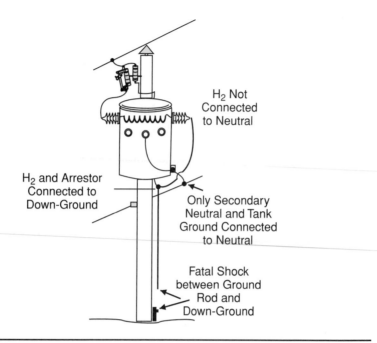

H₂ Not
Connected
to Neutral

H₂ and Arrestor
Connected to
Down-Ground

Only Secondary
Neutral and Tank
Ground Connected
to Neutral

Fatal Shock
between Ground
Rod and
Down-Ground

Figure 10–21 A transformer grounding accident.

The neutral also provides a return path for a fault that goes to ground. On a well-grounded, multigrounded neutral, about two-thirds of the current returns to the source through the neutral and the remaining current returns through ground.

Neutral Potential

10.6.6 From Ohm's law ($E = I \times R$), it can be seen that if there is a current flow, there is a voltage. There is always some current on a distribution neutral. A neutral potential, which is measured between the neutral and a remote ground, should be kept at less than 10 volts.

A neutral potential will be lowered if the current flowing through it can be reduced. A neutral is the return path for any unbalanced current between phases. The current on the neutral can be reduced by converting heavily loaded single-phase circuits to three phases and balancing load between the three phases. A neutral potential can also be lowered by installing more grounds in good earth in many locations along its length.

If the resistance of a neutral is lowered, the potential is lowered. Ohm's law shows that less resistance means less voltage. Neutral resistance can be reduced by stringing a larger conductor and ensuring that all neutral connections are in good condition.

Note: Under a line-to-ground fault condition, the voltage on the neutral can rise to many kilovolts.

Grounding for Over-Current Protection

10.6.7 A line-to-ground fault is by far the most frequent type of fault. When a line-to-ground fault occurs, the protective switchgear trips out the circuit, but only if the current feeding the fault is high enough. To draw a fault current high enough to trip the circuit, a return path to the source must also be able to carry the same amount of current. The return path is the neutral and earth.

Frequent grounding of the neutral in good earth aids the fault current in finding its way back to the neutral and the source. When a conductor falls in a location that is not well grounded, such as rocky ground, sandy soil, or dry snow, insufficient fault current is generated to trip the circuit because the resistance of the return path through the earth is too high. Every powerline worker, however, has seen circuits fail to trip out when they should have. In these cases, the culprit is poor grounding or an outdated protection scheme.

Inserting an Impedance in the Ground Return

10.6.8 At some substation transformers, the neutral point is not grounded directly to earth. A resistor or reactor is placed in series with the connection to earth. The fault-current levels on high-voltage distribution feeders from some substations can be very high and very damaging. Inserting a resistor or reactor into the return circuit from ground has the effect of reducing the fault generated from a line-to-ground fault in the whole circuit.

Surge Protection

10.6.9 The dissipation of a voltage surge is greatly improved through good grounding. Circuits in a location with a poor ground are more vulnerable to outages due to lightning.

When a voltage surge occurs on a phase conductor, the neutral conductor acts as a coupling wire. The voltage on the neutral rises along with the voltage on the phase conductor. This coupling lowers the potential difference across insulators and equipment. The coupling of a well-grounded neutral or shield wire also helps lower the voltage of the surge more quickly. A good grounding design dissipates a voltage surge.

- The ground resistance of a driven ground rod should be low, preferably below 25 ohms.

- A grounding wire should be short because there is a big voltage drop during the high current due to a fault condition. The added resistance of a long lead will add substantially to the voltage drop.

- A ground lead should be as straight and direct as possible because a high-voltage surge will jump across sharp bends.

- A surge arrestor should be well grounded and as close as possible to the equipment being protected.

Choose the Best Ground Available

10.6.10 When you have a choice, use the best ground available. The resistance of earth varies with the type of earth, moisture content, and temperature. The resistivity of earth is measured in ohms per meter, which is equal to the resistance between the opposite faces of a cubic meter of soil. Table 10–5 shows the great variance found in soil resistance.

Soil with no moisture content would be an insulator. The mineral salts of earth, dissolved in water, give the soil low resistance. A ground rod should be driven straight down, where moisture is more likely to be found.

TABLE 10–5 **Typical Soil Resistance**

Earth Type	Resistivity (Ohms per Meter)
Sand Saturated with Seawater	1 to 2
Marsh	2 to 5
Loam	5 to 50
Clay	5 to 100
Sand/Gravel	50 to 1,000
Sandstone	20 to 2,000
Granite	1,000 to 2,000
Limestone	5 to 10,000

The temperature of earth affects its resistivity. When the temperature decreases, the resistivity of the earth increases. When the moisture in the earth freezes, the resistance increases dramatically. A ground rod must be driven below the frost line to be effective in winter. Frozen ground around part of a ground rod can double or triple the resistance.

Measuring Ground-Rod Resistance

10.6.11 Measuring the resistance of a ground rod can confirm that an installation meets design requirements. For example, an acceptable resistance for a ground rod at a transformer installation is typically 25 ohms. Ground-resistance measurements are also carried out when investigating calls such as those regarding tingle voltage, high-neutral voltage, excessive vulnerability to lightning, or failure of protective switchgears to operate.

Two different types of instruments are used to measure ground-rod resistance.

1. The method that has been used for many years is the *fall of potential test*. The fall of potential test is done by applying a fairly high voltage to the ground rod and measuring the voltage at a potential probe and the current at a current probe that is installed far enough away to represent remote ground. This method is for a bare ground rod, with no connections. Figure 10–22 shows the earth resistance tester and how the leads and probes are connected.

2. A simpler test is the *clamp-on tester* (Figure 10–23). It is clamped over a ground rod much like a clamp-on ammeter is put on a conductor. Instead of magnetic induction being imposed on the clamp by a current-carrying conductor, the clamp imposes induction on the ground rod. The unit then measures the current and voltage drop to measure resistance. This instrument tests a grounding system and does not measure the resistance of an unconnected single ground rod. It works best when the ground being measured is a ground rod in a system of many other ground rods.

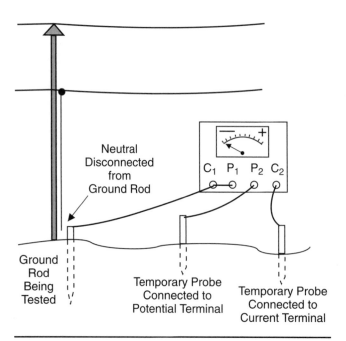

Figure 10–22   Measuring ground-rod resistance.

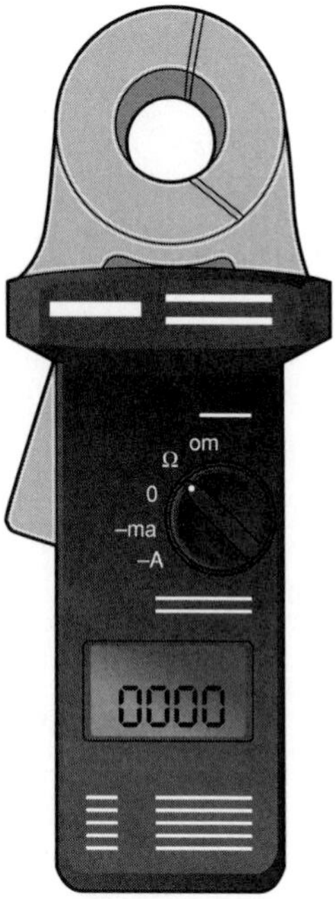

Figure 10–23   A clamp-on tester.

10.7 Protection from Corrosion

Corrosion Hazards

10.7.1 Corrosion reduces the life of metal hardware used in electrical utilities. Corrosion due to road salt, fertilizers, seawater, and damaged paint surfaces is a normal occurrence. There is, however, an electrical component to understanding the cause of premature corrosion of metal hardware. Line materials such as tower footings, anchor rods, electrical connections, and underground/submarine cable sheath normally last a long time, but occasionally these items corrode prematurely and create severe hazards. The most vulnerable locations for premature corrosion are near pipelines and in marshy areas. The corrosion is usually at its worst just below the ground line, so it is reasonably easy to inspect vulnerable locations. When a tower footing or anchor rod corrodes, an unseen hazard results that could cause a structural failure. When the metallic sheath of an underground/submarine cable is also the neutral for the circuit, an electrical hazard exists when the sheath has corroded away and a voltage difference occurs across the open point.

Dissimilar Metals in a Circuit

10.7.2 Two dissimilar metals can generate DC when placed in contact and connected together into a circuit. There is a small, self-generated electric current without any external source. For example, a lead-acid battery consists of two different metals (lead and lead oxide) in an electrolyte (a conductive solution, such as diluted sulfuric acid). The battery becomes part of a circuit when it is connected to a load. One post of the battery gives off ions, eventually deteriorates (corrodes), and disappears. Similarly, two dissimilar metals connected together with some kind of electrical bond and placed in a conductive solution are like a battery. A circuit is created when a self-generated current leaves one metal (an anode), flows through the electrolyte, and enters another metal (the cathode). The self-generated current flows because of a natural difference between the potentials of the metals in the electrolyte. As current leaves the metallic anode and flows into the electrolyte, metal ions separate from the anode and cause the anode to be consumed (corrode).

Galvanic Series of Metals Used in Line Hardware

10.7.3 Metals have a tendency to dissolve into ionic form and lose electrons when they become part of a circuit capable of conducting electricity. Some metals (such as aluminum) have a strong tendency to lose electrons, while other metals (such as copper) have a weaker tendency. An active metal with a strong tendency to lose ions is *anodic* in an electrical circuit and will corrode. A less-active "noble" metal with a weak tendency to lose ions is *cathodic* in an electrical circuit and does not corrode.

Table 10–6 lists metals used in electrical utilities and shows the relative placement of their activity in relation to other metals. The wider apart the metals are on the list, the greater the rate of corrosion.

Galvanic Corrosion

10.7.4 Premature corrosion of metal hardware occurs when the metal becomes part of a corrosion cell. A typical corrosion cell involving line hardware must have certain conditions present:

1. There must be an anode and a cathode. The anode and the cathode must be connected to each other by a wire or some other kind of metallic contact.

2. An electric circuit must be completed between the anode and the cathode through an electrolyte. An electrolyte is a conductive solution, such as the earth in a wet, marshy area.

TABLE 10–6   Galvanic Series of Some Metals

Anodic End (Most Active) **Positive Polarity**
Magnesium
Zinc (Galvanized Metal)
Aluminum
Cadmium
Steel or Iron
Lead
Brass
Copper
Graphite
Silver
Cathodic End (Least Active) **Negative Polarity**

3. There must be a DC potential causing current to flow in the circuit. Dissimilar metals connected in a circuit generate a DC potential. When current leaves the anode, it takes minute particles of metal with it and the anode corrodes. A flow of DC through the ground can cause corrosion to vital components of an electrical system.

Copper-to-Aluminum Connections

10.7.5 It is well-known in the line trade that when copper is connected directly to aluminum, the connection corrodes prematurely and fails. Aluminum is an active metal, while copper is less active. To prevent galvanic corrosion of the electrical connection, normally a spacer with another metal, such as cadmium, is placed between the copper and aluminum. A conductive grease can also be used to slow down any corrosion. With an aluminum-to-copper or aluminum-to-brass connection, the aluminum should always be placed on top to prevent copper salts from leaching and corroding the aluminum.

Cathodic Protection

10.7.6 A tower leg or anchor in wet soil becomes vulnerable to corrosion. Cathodic protection is installed at vulnerable locations. Cathodic protection consists of electrically connecting a sacrificial anode, such as magnesium, to a tower leg and burying it nearby. A circuit is set up between the sacrificial anode and the tower leg through the surrounding soil (electrolyte). The magnesium is a more active metal than the galvanized tower leg. Thus, the magnesium anode corrodes instead of the tower leg. The anodes must be replaced on a regular basis as they corrode away.

Stray-Current Corrosion

10.7.7 Stray-current corrosion is due to a DC of external origin flowing from a metal into an electrolyte. When a DC leaves a metal and enters an electrolyte, some metal leaves and the metal corrodes. Alternating current is not significant in producing corrosion because the reverse flow will build up the anode again. One source of stray DC can be a natural current due to the magnetic fields in earth. Long pipelines can be vulnerable to this current. Human-made DC that can stray into earth can come from a nearby DC transmission line, a mining operation, or a welding operation.

Pipeline Cathodic-Protection Hazard

10.7.8 Buried electrical utility line materials are subject to corrosion when a pipeline is nearby. The cathodic protection used to protect a pipeline from corrosion accelerates the corrosion of nearby utility anchors, cable sheaths, and ground rods. To protect a pipeline from corrosion, a negative potential is applied to the pipeline. This prevents a current from flowing into the surrounding earth (electrolyte) from the pipeline and prevents any metal ions from leaving the metal pipe. Any stray current flows toward the pipeline.

Review Questions

1. Name three reasons why a circuit needs protection.

2. Name four types of faults that relays can be programmed to detect on a transmission-line system.

3. If a recloser is bypassed with a solid jumper or switch, what is the consequence if a conductor falls to the ground somewhere downstream?

4. What are three influences that affect the magnitude of a fault current during a short circuit?

5. Why is a good multigrounded neutral important for circuit protection on a wye system?

6. Why does a dry tree limb or a broken conductor lying on dry or frozen ground not always trip out the circuit protection?

7. What is meant by the frame size of a recloser?

8. Name three advantages for converting to a higher distribution voltage.

9. What is the most common cause of over-voltage on a distribution system?

10. Why is a vehicle the safest place to be during a thunderstorm?

11. What is the difference between connections to a neutral and connections to ground?

12. How does good grounding of the neutral improve over-current protection on a circuit?

13. When making an aluminium-to-copper connection, the aluminium is kept in the higher position. Why?

Installing Personal Protective Grounds

Topics to Be Covered   **Section**

Reasons to Install Personal Protective Grounds   11.1

Applying the Grounding Principle to Control Current   11.2

Applying the Bonding Principle to Control Voltage   11.3

Controlling Induced Voltage and Current from

Electromagnetic Induction   11.4

Procedures for Applying Protective Grounds   11.5

Specific Grounding Hazards   11.6

Protective Grounding of Underground Cable   11.7

11.1 Reasons to Install Personal Protective Grounds

Reasons for Placing Protective Grounds

11.1.1 The main reason to ground a circuit is to make an electrical connection to Mother Earth, where we feel safe. Three more technical reasons to install grounds and bonds on an isolated circuit before work is started are these:

1. *Install protective grounds to prove isolation.* After isolation and testing, the installation of grounds is the final proof that you are about to work on the correct circuit.

2. *Install protective grounds to have protection from accidental reenergization.* When working on a grounded circuit, it is necessary to have protection from accidental reenergization, which can come from operator error, contact with neighboring circuits, lightning, or backfeed.

3. *Install protective grounds to provide protection from induction.* Grounds are needed to provide protection from two kinds of induction hazards. *Electrostatic induction* will induce a voltage on an isolated circuit. *Electromagnetic induction* will induce a current flow in the conductor and grounds of an isolated and grounded circuit.

347

Protective Grounds Control Current and Voltage

11.1.2 Voltage and current on a circuit will likely not be zero after protective grounds are installed. There can be a voltage relative to a remote ground, and there can be a current flow in the conductors. The saying "It is not dead if it isn't grounded" is not entirely correct. "It is not safe to work on a circuit until protective grounds are installed" would be a more accurate saying.

The discussion in this chapter is on line grounding. It does not include grounding for stringing operations or truck grounding because most of the effort there is for touch and step potentials for working around equipment on the ground, and that adds to the complexity of the line grounding discussion.

To be assured that a person will not be exposed to any hazardous current or voltage *after* the protective grounds are installed, adhere to the *grounding principle,* which will control the current around a worker and adhere to the *bonding principle,* which will limit the voltage exposure to a worker.

- *The Grounding Principle:* Protective grounds are installed to reduce any current flow through a worker to an acceptable level by providing a low-resistance *parallel shunt* around the worker. At the same time, if the circuit is or becomes energized, the grounds must be big enough to withstand any *fault current* in the circuit.

- *The Bonding Principle:* Bonds must be installed so that a worker is kept in an *equipotential zone.* A worker must not be able to bridge between a grounded circuit and any unbonded structure, vehicle, boom, wire, or other object not tied into the bonded network.

11.2 Applying the Grounding Principle to Control Current

Sources of Current in Protective Grounds

11.2.1 Applying the grounding principle means controlling the current after the grounds are applied. Even after protective grounds have been installed, a constant current could be due to induction from neighboring circuits, backfeed from a generator, or backfeed from within the electrical utility system. A very high current would occur if the line were to be accidentally reenergized. The protective grounds do not act as a gate that shunts everything to earth.

Using the Proper Size of Protective Grounds to Control the Current

11.2.2 When the size of protective grounds are specified for a circuit, they are sized to carry a fault current for enough time to trip out the circuit. During accidental reenergization, a set of grounds on a circuit provides a major short circuit. The ground wires and clamps will be subject to all the current that the circuit can deliver to that point.

Engineering at each utility will have data on the maximum fault current available on each circuit. Many utilities opt to standardize on one or two sizes of ground cable and clamps to cover all their circuits.

Inspecting and Testing Grounding Sets

11.2.3 Grounding sets must be maintained and tested on a scheduled basis. They are prone to broken strands—especially near the clamps—and loose and corroded cable connections at the clamps. A visual inspection will not necessarily pick up these defects because a lot of them are hidden under the jacket and heat shrink cover over the ferrule.

When dealing with parallel circuits, some current will go down each path. A few extra milliohms of resistance in the grounds means that the other parallel path—for example, a powerline worker—will carry more current. Therefore, use a grounding set tester to verify the condition of the grounds.

Promoting a Fast Trip-Out of Circuit Protection to Control Current

11.2.4 Circuit breakers, reclosers, and fuses open when a current feeding a fault goes through these devices for a specified period of time.

In the case of reenergization, grounds on all three phases will provide an excellent phase-to-phase fault that will activate the protective switchgear. If one phase is energized the protective grounds need to be connected to a good ground electrode. The best ground electrode is a permanent ground network such as a neutral, station ground, or tower steel.

Providing a Parallel Path Around a Worker to Control Current

11.2.5 When a person on a structure is in contact with a circuit that is accidentally reenergized, the protective grounds and the person form two parallel paths to ground. Based on the parallel circuit theory, both paths will carry some current to ground (see Figure 11–1). By far, most of the current will go through the low-resistance grounds. However, because a person working from a structure is a parallel path to earth, some current will go through the worker. To provide a good shunt around the worker, the protective grounds set must be kept in excellent condition. The current that flows through the worker must be kept well below a 10-milliampere threshold and, ideally, below the threshold of sensation.

When discussing controlling current flow, the worst case is where one phase is accidently reenergized. Protective grounds installed on three phases provide a balanced

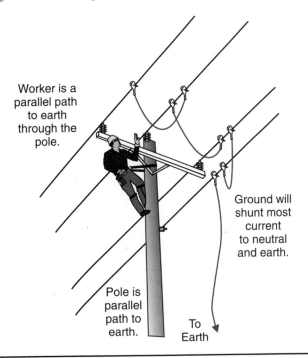

Worker is a parallel path to earth through the pole.

Ground will shunt most current to neutral and earth.

Pole is parallel path to earth.

To Earth

Figure 11–1 Grounds as a parallel shunt around a worker.

three-phase fault if the line should be accidently reenergized from a source three-phase breaker. The fault current would flow back to the source through the other phases and very little would flow back through the earth or neutral. However, grounding procedures, ground cable size, and so on have to address worst-case single-phase reenergization, such as one phase contacting an overbuild or underbuild circuit, backfeed on one phase, single-phase circuits, and so on.

Grounding Differences of Wye and Delta

11.2.6 The phase-to-phase installation of grounds will short out both wye and delta circuits. On single-phase installations, a phase-to-neutral ground on a wye circuit and a phase-to-phase ground on a delta circuit will short out the circuit and trip out the protection.

On a wye system, the protective grounds connect the phases to the neutral. The connection to the neutral is made first, and a live circuit mistakenly left alive will trip out when the first phase is grounded. Grounding the phases to the neutral also lowers the potential of the grounded conductors at the work site.

On a delta system, the protective grounds connect the phase to a ground rod in earth. The connection to earth will trip out a live circuit when the first phase is mistakenly grounded, if the circuit protection has a ground fault relay, otherwise the circuit will not trip out until the second phase is grounded. In order to not be in contact with the grounds while installing the first ground, use a grounding support stud as shown in Figure 11–5.

Protective Grounding Hardware

11.2.7 Protective grounds must carry very high fault current long enough to cause the protection for a circuit to trip out. Grounds also must be in excellent condition to provide a very low-resistance shunt around a worker so that all but a harmless amount of current passes through the parallel path established by a worker.

A typical jumper ground or ground set consists of a flexible copper stranded cable covered with a jacket rated at 600 volts. The jacket is intended mostly for the mechanical protection of the small stranding of the cable. During an accidental reenergization, the jacket may provide protection for anyone near it because the voltage drop along the cable will reduce the voltage in the cable.

The clamp chosen for grounding has to be the right size, have the correct current-carrying capacity, and have the right shape for the object to which it is to be attached. Clamps are classed in different grades based upon maximum fault-current-carrying ability. For example, a grade 5 clamp with 4/0 copper cable withstands 43,000 amperes for 15 cycles without failing.

Figure 11–2 shows a typical protective ground with a conductor clamp at each end used to go from conductor to conductor.

Figure 11–3 shows a typical protective ground with a conductor clamp at one end and a clamp that fits on a ground rod, stud, or flat steel and is typical for grounding on a steel transmission line. Some utilities insist on installing a stud on steel for a ground attachment instead of attaching to flat steel.

The cable terminations are compressed in ferrules and a heat shrink covers part of the ferrule and cable where strands are most vulnerable to corrosion and breakage (see Figure 11–4).

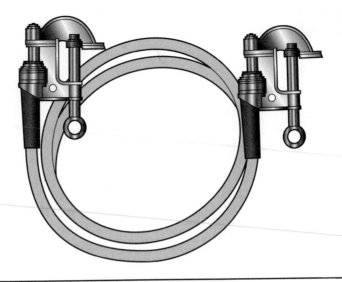

Figure 11–2   A jumper ground.

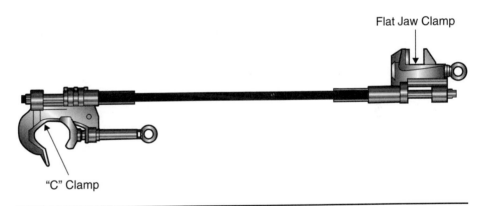

Figure 11–3   Ground cable and clamps.

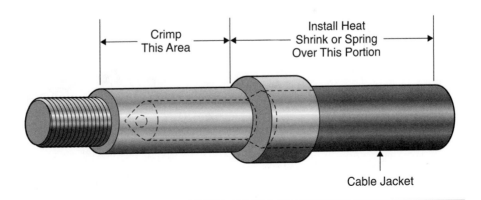

Figure 11–4   A ferrule.

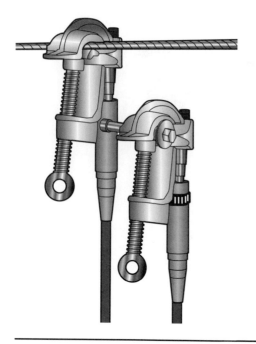

Figure 11–5 A piggyback clamp.

Figure 11–6 A wire brush for a hot stick.

Ground sets used for going from conductor to conductor can have a grounding support stud (piggyback stud), as shown in Figure 11–5, to allow the installation of grounds from the end of the shot gun stick and to maintain clearance.

To make a good low-resistance connection between the protective ground clamp and the conductor, the conductor must be cleaned. There is no really easy way to do this well at the end of a hot stick and is often overlooked. However, a little bit of effort with a brush, as shown in Figure 11–6, can make a big difference.

Ball-and-socket studs and clamps (see Figure 11–7) are used in many locations, especially in substations. The ball-and-socket studs are permanently installed where grounds would typically be installed.

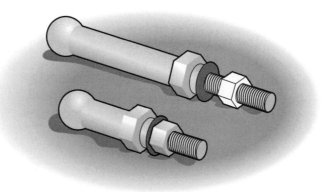

Figure 11–7 Ball-and-socket studs.

11.3 Applying the Bonding Principle to Control Voltage

Sources of Voltage on a Grounded Circuit

11.3.1 Applying the bonding principle means controlling the voltage after the grounds are applied. Even after protective grounds have been installed, voltage may be present on the conductors in relation to a remote ground. Voltage can be from induction from neighboring circuits, backfeed from a generator, or backfeed from within the electrical utility system. Voltage on the line would be very high in relation to a remote ground if the line were to be accidentally reenergized.

Providing Equipotential Bonding to Control Voltage

11.3.2 When protective grounds are installed, ensure that everything a person is likely to touch will be at the same potential while working on the circuit. Protective grounds also act as bonds, keeping all grounded conductors at the same potential. If there is little or no potential difference across a person's body, there can be no current flow.

When working on a pole or steel structure, a powerline worker is a parallel path to ground. When a structure is bonded to the grounded conductors in such a situation, there would be little or no voltage difference for a worker to bridge across.

Attaching the grounds to the pole, as shown in Figure 11–8, keeps the worker in an equipotential zone.

Theoretically, bonds can be very small and still able to keep different objects at the same potential. From a practical point of view, bonds must be rugged enough to be handled in the field. When a lighter cable is used as a bond to keep different objects at the same potential, they must not be used in a position where they would carry fault current.

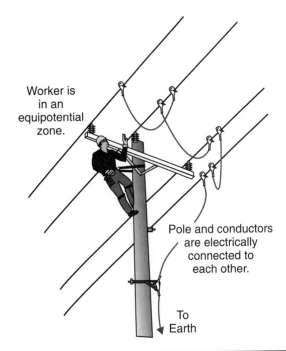

Worker is in an equipotential zone.

Pole and conductors are electrically connected to each other.

To Earth

Figure 11–8 Worker in an equipotential zone.

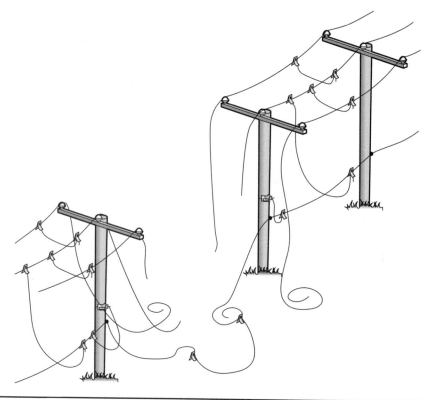

Figure 11–9   Open point between grounds.

A common cause of accidents over time has been a failure to bond (ground) across an open point in a conductor. The assumption had been that once protective grounds were installed on each side of a beak or open point, it was safe to go to work. Consider the following examples:

1. People have received serious and fatal electrical burns while removing or installing loops on a transmission line, even with grounds installed on each side. Installing or removing loops can interrupt or complete a circuit and a lethal current flow.

2. People have been hurt when preparing to make a splice on the first conductor of a three-phase line that was completely separated by a tree or car accident (see Figure 11–9). With grounds on each side of the break, when the first conductor ends were brought together they completed a circuit, probably because the neutral was open between two different substations.

3. A connector on a 44-kilovolt lateral feed to a distribution substation burned off, as shown in Figure 11–10. Protective grounds were placed on the three-wire circuit and down to a temporary ground rod in earth. The lateral was grounded to the substation grid. The second circuit on the

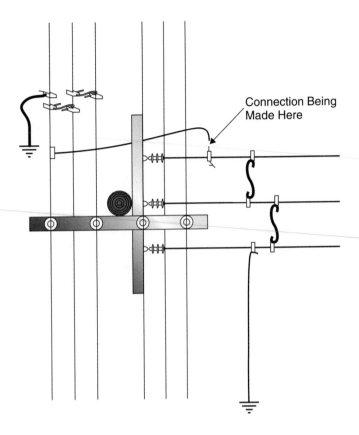

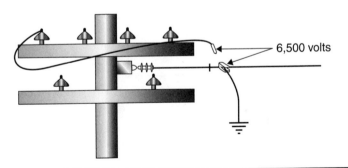

Figure 11–10   Bonding between grounds.

44 kilovolts was left energized. When the powerline worker tried to remake the connection at the tap pole, he received a severe shock. The ground electrode at the substation was much better than the ground rod, and a circuit was completed between the two different electrodes when the worker tried to make the connection.

Bonding to Control Voltage Rise Due to Induction or Reenergization

11.3.3 If a circuit with protective grounds already installed is exposed to induction or accidental reenergization, the voltage will rise in the complete circuit, the grounds, the neutral, and the earth where a ground rod is installed. If a vehicle is connected to the grounding setup, the voltage will rise on it as well.

Any component not connected electrically to the bonded network will be at a different potential, until the circuit trips out or the source of induction is removed. A person working on a pole or structure that is not bonded to the grounds will be a parallel path to ground through that pole or structure.

At the site where a set of protective grounds is installed, the phase and the neutral or the phase and steel structure are tied together and will remain at an equal potential in case of induction or accidental reenergization. When working farther away from the installed set of grounds, the potential on the phase will remain high while the potential on a multigrounded neutral or a remote structure will drop quickly, as illustrated in Figure 11–11. The difference of potential between the phase and a neutral or structure can become dangerous when working more than 300 feet (100 m) from the installed set of grounds.

When working up to 300 feet (100 m) away from the grounds on another structure, the structure must be bonded to the grounded conductor. This can be done as shown in Figure 11–12.

Bonding the Structure for Equipotential Grounding

11.3.4 When an isolated circuit becomes accidently reenergized or is exposed to high induction, the potential at the work site will rise and be at a different potential than any other objects not bonded to the grounded conductors. The structure will be a parallel path to ground. To eliminate the potential difference between the structure and the circuit, the structure is bonded to the circuit.

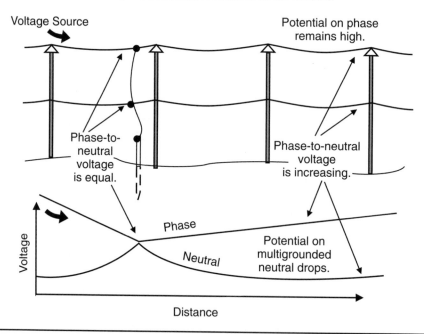

Figure 11–11   Point-of-work grounds.

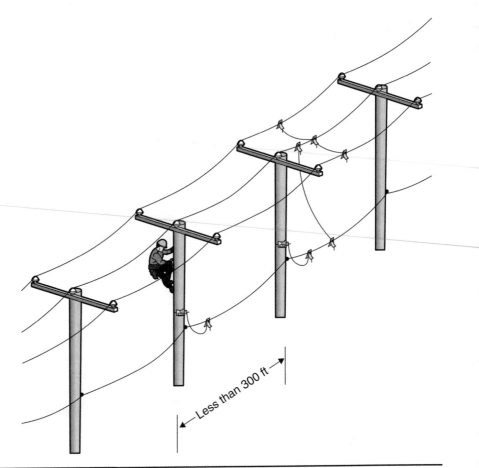

Less than 300 ft

Figure 11–12 Bonding at another pole.

Making a bond between the grounded conductors and a wood pole will not be a typical electrical connection. A common method is to install a pole band below the feet, as shown in Figure 11–13. Attaching a ground clamp to a bolt through the pole, as in Figure 11–14, will also bond the pole to the grounded conductors. The connection made to a bolt through the pole or to a band around the pole lowers the potential difference to acceptable levels when the wood pole is bonded to the grounded conductors. If working on a transformer pole or other equipment pole, the transformer is bonded to the pole, to ground, and to the neutral. The protective ground placed on the neutral, therefore, also bonds the pole and equipment to the power conductors. Even if working from a bucket the protective grounds must be bonded to the structure in case a worker is in contact with both the structure and the conductors.

The more conductive the pole is, the less important it is to have the bond to the pole near the workers' feet. On a steel pole or tower, the connection between the grounded conductors and the structure can be a good electrical connection. The complete steel structure will be electrically uniform. A person working on the structure will not be exposed to a dangerous potential difference between the structure and the conductors.

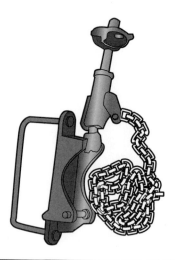

Figure 11–13 Pole band.

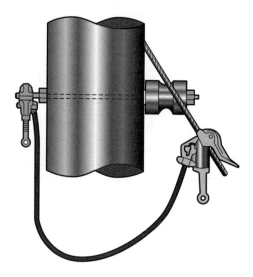

Figure 11–14 Bonding a pole.

11.4 Controlling Induced Voltage and Current from Electromagnetic Induction

Applying Protective Grounds to Control Induction

11.4.1 The electromagnetic field from an AC powerline causes two kinds of induction: an *electric field* (capacitive) induction and *magnetic field* (inductive) induction.

Proper application of protective grounds/bonds will control, but will not eliminate, voltage and current induced on isolated circuits from nearby powerlines.

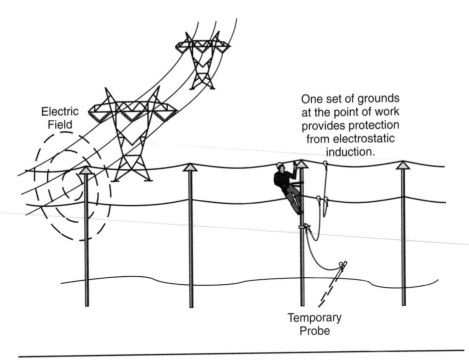

Electric Field

One set of grounds at the point of work provides protection from electrostatic induction.

Temporary Probe

Figure 11–15 Protection from electric-field induction.

Protective grounds/bonding will control voltage and current to a level that is safe to workers.

Reducing Voltage from Electric Field Induction

11.4.2 A powerline will induce a *voltage* on a nearby isolated conductor (Figure 11–15). There is no current flowing in the isolated conductor if the isolated conductor is not part of a circuit (closed loop). One set of protective grounds on an isolated circuit will collapse the voltage due to electric field induction, but there will still be no circuit for current to flow.

If a worker was to get between an isolated conductor and the earth, the exposure would be to a high-induced voltage but not high current. While in relative terms there is very little current, there is likely still enough current available to cause a fatal shock.

Controlling the Current from Magnetic Field Induction

11.4.3 A powerline will induce *current* on a nearby isolated conductor when that conductor forms part of a circuit. Grounding a conductor on each side of a work zone (bracket grounding) will create a circuit through the conductor, down one set of grounds, through the earth, and back up the other set of grounds (Figure 11–16).

The first set of grounds installed on an isolated conductor will collapse the induced voltage from the electric field, and a second set of grounds will create a circuit for an induced current to flow from the magnetic field.

When bracket grounds are removed, the first set of grounds removed will open the circuit and interrupt the current flow. An immediate voltage will appear

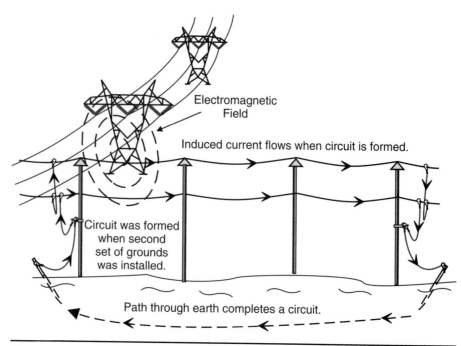

Electromagnetic
Field

Induced current flows when circuit is formed.

Circuit was formed
when second
set of grounds
was installed.

Path through earth completes a circuit.

Figure 11–16   Protection from magnetic-field induction.

(recovery voltage) across the gap between the ground clamp and the conductor. In high-induction areas, a long arc could be drawn. When more sets of grounds are installed along the line, it will be the second-to-last ground removed where a long arc could be drawn.

Sometimes a ground clamp that is in the way of making a splice or other task must be removed, and because other grounds are on the circuit a powerline worker may be tempted to move the clamp by hand or using rubber gloves. However, it can be seen that the second ground can be quite dangerous to handle with anything but a hot-line tool. It is also against grounding principles to install or remove grounds at any time using rubber gloves instead of a hot stick.

Working and Grounding between Bracket Grounds

Once bracket grounds are installed, the conductor between the two sets of grounds will have very little induced voltage but could have a high electrical current flowing through it. When grounds are installed at a work site (between the bracket grounds), the work-site set of grounds will have relatively very little current flowing in it.

The middle set of grounds creates two circuits (Figure 11–17) for the ground current to flow where previously there was only one. The current from one circuit goes up the middle set of grounds, and the current from the other set of grounds goes down the set of grounds. The two currents tend to cancel each other out, and, therefore, very little current flows in these grounds.

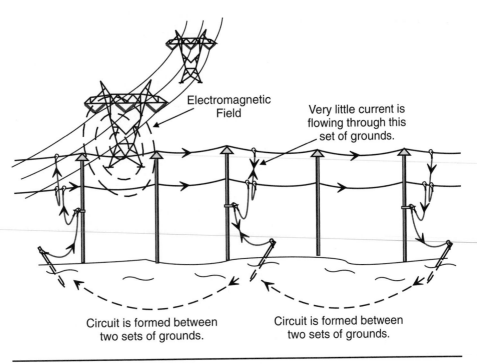

Electromagnetic Field

Very little current is flowing through this set of grounds.

Circuit is formed between two sets of grounds.

Circuit is formed between two sets of grounds.

Figure 11–17 Working between bracket grounds.

11.5 Procedures for Applying Protective Grounds

Distribution Equipotential Grounding/ Bonding Procedure

11.5.1 A grounding procedure is probably the most sacred procedure in line work, and every utility/employer has some very rigid concept about how circuits are to be grounded. The grounding procedures described in this section would be superseded by an employer's procedure.

Equipotential grounding (also called *single-point grounding*) refers to grounding and bonding to a single point at a work site so that everything that will be worked on or touched is tied together. Thus, everything a person is likely to touch will have the same potential and not have any current flow through them, even during an accidental reenergization.

The grounding and bonding procedure in Table 11–1 applies to all distribution overhead circuit applications where grounds can be physically accessed at the point of work.

Distribution Bracket Grounding Procedure

11.5.2 Bracket grounding *does not protect* a worker from accidental reenergization. Bracket grounding *will protect* a worker from induction and backfeed from small portable generators.

Bracket grounding should be used only where it is very impractical to ground at the work site *and* where accidental reenergization is impossible. An example of

TABLE 11–1 Single-Point Grounding and Bonding Procedure

Step	Action	Details
1	Arrange for isolation of the circuit.	Use a lockout/tagout procedure to get a guarantee that the line will be isolated and remain isolated. Apply tags and/or locks on isolation points.
2	Choose suitable grounding location(s).	Ground at the point of work. Grounding on the structure being worked on or grounding within 300 ft. (100 m) of the work location is considered grounding at the point of work. *Note:* When the grounds are not on the structure being worked on, a bond must be installed from the structure to one conductor (neutral).
3	Determine the proper grounding cable size.	The grounding cable and clamp must be large enough to carry the short-circuit current available at the work location to ground and stay intact until the circuit protection opens. The level of short-circuit current available will be dependent on the ability of the system to feed the fault. If the work site is close to a substation and the circuit conductor is large, the circuit can deliver a large amount of current. A utility planning engineer would have the fault current available for the circuits to be worked on. Many utilities merely specify a minimum cable size for the whole utility and, perhaps, designate some specific locations for larger ground cables.
4	Choose the most effective ground electrode.	On a wye system, the system neutral is the best electrode. Some utilities/employers may insist on an additional cable going to a ground rod in earth. On a delta circuit, the ground electrode will be the best electrode found at the earth level—usually an anchor or a ground probe.
5	Establish a bonded work zone at the work site.	Install bonds between the ground electrode and the pole. If the pole is wood, this means making an electrical connection between wood and the ground electrode: • Install a ground support assembly around the pole. *or* • Install a jumper from the neutral to any bolt through the pole. Tightening the bolt first will improve the electrical connection. To keep everything in the work zone bonded, any wires or winch cables brought into the work zone must be bonded to the same ground electrode. Workers on the ground who are handling conductors are outside of the bonded zone and must use rubber gloves or, in more hazardous situations, ground-gradient mats.
6	Test the circuit to be grounded to verify isolation.	Use an approved potential tester to verify that the circuit is isolated. Buzzing or teasing is not a reliable method. The hook of a clamp stick (shotgun) is the only metal in the head of the stick, and on distribution voltages it is not enough metal for a reliable indication. If more metal is used, buzzing still does not adequately distinguish between induction and an actual live circuit.

Step	Action	Details
7	Install the ground clamps on the phase conductors.	Ensure that all personnel are either completely in or out of the bonded work zone before installing the protective grounds.
		Use a live-line tool (shotgun) that is at least 8 ft. (2.5 m) and wear eye protection. Some utilities/employers will insist on rubber gloves also.
		Put one grounding jumper clamp on the neutral. Then, in one firm movement, apply the other end to the closest phase conductor. Install ground sets from the grounded conductor (or neutral) to the other conductors. Using grounding jumpers with a support stud arrangement allows you to keep a distance from the cable while installing the ground.
		Note: If a ground is mistakenly installed on live circuit, *do not remove* the ground clamp. Removing the ground clamp could draw a very long and hazardous arc. Let the circuit protection take out the circuit.
8	Remove grounds in reverse order.	If a ground rod in earth was used as an electrode, do not remove any clamps until all the ground clamps have been removed aloft in order to avoid accidently removing the wrong clamp.
		Use a clamp stick and personal protective equipment when removing ground. In high-induction areas, removing the grounds can interrupt current and drop voltage.

where it is impractical to apply equipotential grounding at a work site are stringing operations where existing wire is being removed and new wire strung along the ground is being put up on structures.

Because bracket grounding does not protect a worker from accidental reenergization, it must be seen as an exception to equipotential grounding and require a supervisor's approval for each application. Every time a bracket grounding procedure is used, a written job plan for grounding, approved by a supervisor, should be created. The grounding plan should identify all potential sources of reenergization and the control barriers that are put in place.

The bracket grounding procedure described in Table 11–2 should be considered as an exception to the single-point grounding/bonding procedure.

Transmission Equipotential Grounding/ Bonding Procedure

11.5.3 The grounding and bonding procedure in Table 11–3 applies to all transmission overhead circuit applications where grounds can be physically accessed at the point of work.

TABLE 11–2   **Distribution Bracket Grounding Procedure**

Step	Action	Details
An Exception to the Single-Point Grounding/Bonding Procedure		
1	Arrange for isolation of the circuit.	Use a lockout/tagout procedure to get a guarantee that the line will be isolated and remain isolated. Apply tags and/or locks on isolation points.
2	Check for additional reenergization hazards.	• Isolation points with suspect insulation; flashed, broken and suspect brands or type. • Suspect switchgear, SCADA operation disabled. • Potential for the work operation to cause contact with overbuild, underbuild, or crossing circuits. • Physical condition of pins, insulators, ties, crossarms, etc., of overbuild and crossing circuits.
3	Choose the suitable grounding locations.	• Grounds must be placed on all sides of the work zone not more than 2 miles (3 km) apart.
4	Determine the proper grounding cable size.	The grounding cable and clamp must be large enough to carry the short-circuit current available at the work location to ground and to stay intact until the circuit protection opens. Technically, bracket grounding is used only where it is virtually impossible for the circuit to be reenergized; however, it is still valid to use the ground cable size meant for the system in that location (see Section 11.5.1: Distribution Equipotential Grounding/Bonding Procedure).
5	Choose the most effective ground electrode.	On a wye system, the system neutral is the best electrode. Some utilities/employers may insist on an additional cable going to a ground rod in earth. On a delta circuit, the ground electrode will be the best electrode found at the earth level, usually an anchor or a ground probe.
6	Test the circuit to be grounded to verify isolation.	Use an approved potential tester to verify that the circuit is isolated. Neither buzzing nor teasing is a reliable method. The hook of a clamp stick (shotgun) is the only metal in the head of the stick, and on distribution voltages it is not enough metal for a reliable indication. If more metal is used, buzzing still does not adequately distinguish between induction and and an actual live line.
7	Install the ground clamps on the phase conductors.	Ensure that all personnel are either completely in or out of the bonded work zone before installing the protective grounds. Use a live-line tool (shotgun) that is at least 8 ft. (2.5 m) and wear eye protection. Some utilities/employers will insist on rubber gloves also. Put one grounding jumper clamp on the neutral and then apply the other end to the closest phase conductor in one firm movement. Install ground sets from the grounded conductor (or neutral) to the other conductors. *Note:* If a ground is mistakenly installed on live circuit, *do not remove* the ground clamp. Removing the ground clamp could draw a very long and hazardous arc. Let the circuit protection take out the circuit.

Step	Action	Details
8	For additional protection, establish a bonded work zone at the work site.	When working between bracket grounds, the grounds will reduce potential on the conductors and trip out a circuit if it should become reenergized. However, in high-induction areas, the grounds are not on the structure being worked on, so a bond must be installed from the structure to one conductor (neutral). • In a high-induction area, the induction on the bracket grounded circuit will be low; the induction on work equipment, and on any wires or winch cables brought into the work zone, could be high and at a different potential than the grounded circuit. • Working in a bonded area will provide additional protection from accidental reenergization.
9	Remove grounds in reverse order.	To avoid accidently removing the wrong clamp from the ground probe, do not remove any clamps until all the ground clamps have been removed aloft. • Use a clamp stick and personal protective equipment when removing grounds.

Transmission Bracket Grounding Procedure

11.5.4 There are times when a transmission-line bracket grounding procedure can be very practical, such as a project involving the setting of poles in a deenergized circuit. However, bracket grounding *does not protect* a worker from accidental reenergization but *will protect* a worker from induction. If bracket grounding is used, it must be considered as an exception to the single-point grounding/bonding that is planned, documented, and approved by a utility/employer.

Bracket grounding should be used only where it is impractical to ground at the work site and where there is no possibility of accidental reenergization. A written job plan for grounding should include any extra steps taken to disable any sources of renergization, including removing a span, removing loops at a switch, and so on.

11.6 Specific Grounding Hazards

Hazards and Procedural Controls

11.6.1 This section discusses specific grounding hazards, along with procedural controls to implement when appropriate.

Grounding a Live Circuit

11.6.2 In addition to getting a work clearance on a circuit, a person must identify the correct circuit, conductor, or cable in the field with a potential tester suitable for the voltage rating of the circuit.

Teasing (buzzing) a conductor with the metal head of a live-line tool is not an effective method of checking for isolation. There is not enough metal on a stick attachment for low voltage to be heard, and it is difficult on high voltage to differentiate between dynamically alive and induction.

TABLE 11–3   Grounding/Bonding Procedure for Overhead Transmission-Circuit Applications

Step	Action	Details
1	Arrange for isolation of the circuit.	Use a lockout/tagout procedure to get a guarantee that the line will be isolated and remain isolated. Verify that the control center has isolated the proper circuit and opened and locked/tagged the correct switchgear on an operating drawing. If there are grounding switches on the circuit, ensure that they are closed.
2	Choose a suitable grounding location.	Ground at the point of work. Grounding on the structure being worked on or grounding within 300 ft. (100 m) of the work location is considered grounding at the point of work.
		Note: When the grounds are not on the structure being worked on, a bond must be installed from the structure to one conductor or to the same ground electrode.
3	Determine the proper grounding cable size.	The grounding cable and clamp must be large enough to carry the short-circuit current available at the work location to ground and stay intact until the circuit protection opens. The level of short-circuit current available will be dependent on the ability of the system to feed the fault. If the work site is close to a substation and the circuit conductor is large, the circuit can deliver a large amount of current. The utility is responsible for specifying the fault-current availability for the circuits to be worked on.
		Note: If parallel grounds are needed, the first set of grounds installed on a circuit is supposedly not able to carry the fault current and will fail if the circuit being grounded is still hot.
4	Choose the most effective ground electrode.	On steel poles and steel-lattice structures, install a ground stud on the structure. With the shield wire properly bonded to the steel structure, the structure becomes a good ground electrode. The structure is also well bonded to the conductor after the ground is installed.
		• On wood poles, use an anchor or a ground probe and install a ground clamp on the shield wire. If all the work is aloft and nothing on the ground must be bonded to the bonded network, only the shield wire must be used as a ground electrode.
5	Establish a bonded work zone at the work site.	On wood poles, install a ground support assembly on the pole and bond it to the down leads, guys, and ground probes.
		• Steel structures provide a bonded area to workers aloft.
		• Install bonds on any wires, booms, or winch cables brought into the work zone for both wood pole and steel work.
		• Ensure that workers on the ground are protected by using ground-gradient mats or rubber gloves, as applicable.
6	Test the circuit to be grounded to verify isolation.	Use an approved potential tester.
		• Teasing is not a reliable method to test for isolation because it does not adequately distinguish between induction and an actual live line.

Step	Action	Details
7	In addition to installing single-point grounds at the work site, install bracket grounds where necessary.	Install bracket grounds on each side of the work site under the following conditions: • The work site is in a high-induction area. • Poor soil conditions at the work site reduce the effectiveness of the installed ground probe. Bracket grounds will reduce the voltage of the bonded work zone in relation to remote ground and will reduce the current in the on-site protective grounds.
8	Install the ground clamps on the phase conductors.	• Ensure that all personnel are either completely in or out of the bonded work zone. • Use rubber gloves, live-line tools, and eye protection. • Ground the closest phase conductor first. • On wood poles, install grounds on all three phases. On steel structures, only the phase being worked on must be grounded. *Note:* If the ground is installed on a live circuit, *do not remove* the ground clamp. See Figure 11–18 for an illustration of equipotential grounding on an H-frame transmission line.

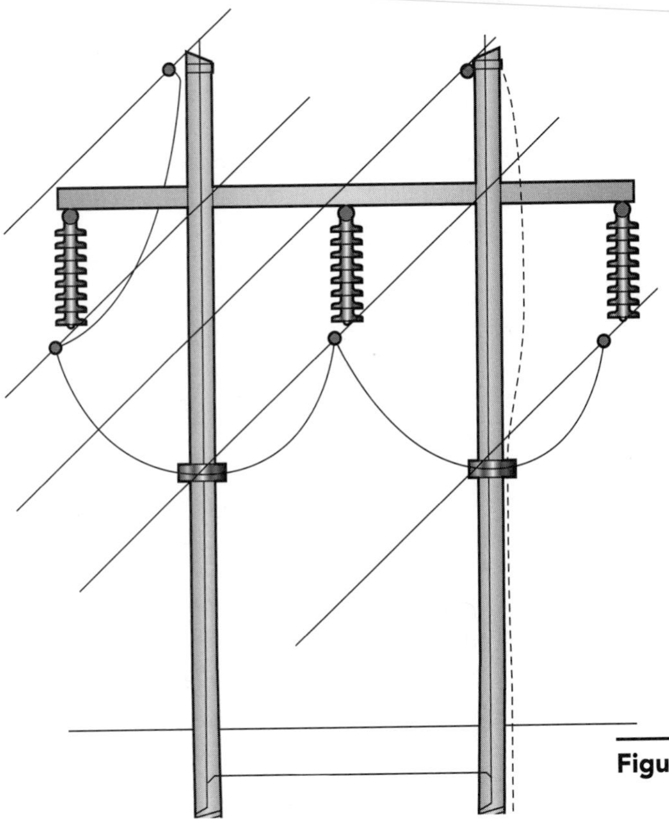

Figure 11–18 Typical transmission-line grounding.

Step	Action	Details
9	Remove grounds in reverse order.	• Remove the clamp from the shield wire after the phase clamps are removed. There could be a high-potential difference between the grounded phases and the shield wire. • To avoid accidently removing the wrong clamp from the ground probe, do not remove any clamps until all the ground clamps have been removed aloft. • Use a clamp stick and personal protective equipment when removing grounds.

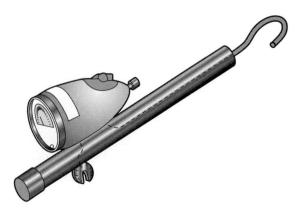

Figure 11–19 A voltage detector.

Applying protective grounds is the ultimate test for isolation. Figure 11–19 shows one of the three or four potential testers available to test for potential on a high-voltage circuit.

Cutting or Joining a Grounded Conductor

11.6.3 If a current flow is interrupted by a break in a circuit, an immediate high voltage appears across the break. Even if a set of protective grounds is installed on each side of a break in the conductor, it is still likely a potential difference might occur across the break, unless the two grounds are connected together electrically.

Use a live-line tool to install a jumper across an open point in a circuit. When planning the location of the protective grounds, any switchgear or fuse in the work zone that could operate during reenergization should be treated as a potential break or open point.

Electrical Hazards to Workers on the Ground

11.6.4 Accidental reenergization or induction will create touch and step potentials around any ground probes, vehicles, wire, etc., that is bonded to the protective grounds. Workers on the ground are very vulnerable unless they are in the bonded zone.

A worker on the ground must continuously apply the bonding principle for protection from electrical shock. Applications of the bonding principle while working on the ground include, but are not limited to, the following:
- Stay clear of everything attached to the bonded network.
- When operating a boom, stay on the truck platform.
- If tools are required from a bonded vehicle, use rubber gloves.
- If a ground wire must be sent aloft, use a ground-gradient mat.

In a station yard, the station ground network and the graveled yard provide some protection from ground gradients.

Wood Pole Work in Poor Soil or in High-Induction Areas

11.6.5 When working on a three-wire system, especially on transmission lines, protective grounds will not necessarily reduce the voltage of the grounded conductors to acceptable levels in relation to a remote ground. A truck boom or unbonded down guy being sent aloft could become a source of a remote ground if they are not bonded to the protective grounding set up.

When available, grounding to the shield wire (static wire, ground wire, or counterpoise) will lower the voltage on the bonded system. The shield wire can be the best ground electrode available at the work site because it is multigrounded and a direct path to the station ground.

In addition to installing grounds at the work site, installing bracket grounds (grounds somewhere on each side of the work site) will lower the voltage at the work site. The bracket grounds can be installed in any convenient location that has a good ground electrode.

Grounding Gradients when Only One Phase Has a Protective Ground Installed

11.6.6 Grounding all three phases results in fast clearing in the case of reenergization. When the three phases are tied together there is less current flow through the ground cable and there are less ground currents flowing to earth. An additional benefit is that there will be a reduced level of touch and step potentials for the workers on the ground.

On steel transmission lines, some utilities will allow the grounding of only the phase being worked on. The steel provides a good ground electrode, and grounding only one phase will trip the three-phase circuit breaker during an accidental reenergization. The workers on the steel structure will be working in a bonded area, but workers on the ground should stay clear of the tower.

Protective Grounds Whipping during a Fault

11.6.7 During a high-fault current condition, the portable ground cable can whip violently. The ground cable can also burn off if it is wrapped around a steel structure or is left coiled. The huge magnetic field around the ground cable when it is carrying a high-fault current results in major mechanical forces exerted on the cable.

Use a rope to tie off grounds where workers could be exposed to the whipping action. Keep grounds as short as practical and lay out the ground so it is not coiled or wrapped around steel.

Protective Grounding for Backfeed from a Portable Generator

11.6.8 Backfeed from a generator that was improperly connected at the customer can feed back through the secondary of the transformer and create a high potential on the primary side.

When working on an isolated circuit, protective grounds on the circuit will reduce the voltage due to backfeed from a portable generator to an acceptable level. The transformer impedance and the resistance of the conductor between the grounds and the generator will probably not create a fault current large enough to cause the generator to overload.

As long as the generator keeps running, the voltage on a conductor with protective grounds installed will be a current flow in the conductor. Because there is always a chance of current flow in a conductor, the conductor should not be cut or joined without first installing a jumper.

The magnitude of the voltage and current from a large industrial or commercial generator would cause a higher voltage and current to appear on grounded conductors at the work site, but because these generators are more likely to be installed and inspected properly, backfeed is very unlikely. The hazard from backfeed is from the unknown portable generator.

Working from a Transformer Pole or Lateral Tap Pole

11.6.9 If is to be done on a transformer pole, and there is a source of unknown secondary backfeed, the protective grounds will protect a powerline worker as long as the transformer fuse is intact. However, it is against protective grounding principles to rely on a fuse for continuity of grounds. The fuse could blow or the cutout could fall open, leaving the high-voltage transformer bushing at full line voltage. The secondary transformer leads should be removed or should be shorted out with some heavy battery-boosting cables before working on the power conductors.

11.7 Protective Grounding of Underground Cable

Reasons to Ground Underground Cable

11.7.1 The reasons to apply protective grounds on underground cable include the following:

1. *Install protective grounds to prove isolation.* Underground cable is difficult to trace physically, so it is critical to test the cable at a riser, to test at the capacitive test point at an elbow, or to spike the cable before placing grounds.

2. *Install protective grounds to have protection from accidental reenergization.* When working on a grounded cable, a set of protective grounds must always be in place to have protection from accidental reenergization.

3. *Install protective grounds to provide protection from induction.* Underground cable is a capacitor that can maintain a charge for a long time. A protective ground must be installed and maintained to drain these charges.

Applying the Grounding Principle

11.7.2 A protective ground, sized for the available fault current, is needed to trip out the protective switchgear in case of accidently grounding a live circuit or in case of reenergization.

Apply grounds to the cable wherever it is possible to get access—for example, at risers, at switching cabinets, at transformers, and at live-front switchgear cabinets.

Grounding at a Riser

Conventional protective ground sets can be applied at a riser pole (also called a *dip pole* or *transition pole*), as long as enough conductor is exposed somewhere on the structure. A method that allows a protective ground to be connected to the bottom of a cutout is to use a clamp similar to the device shown in Figure 11–20.

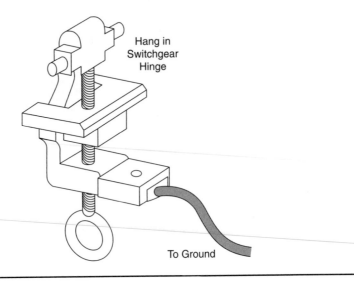

Hang in
Switchgear
Hinge

To Ground

Figure 11–20   A ground clamp attachment.

Grounding at a Dead-Front Transformer or Switchgear

A cable terminal that is a load-break elbow plugged into a transformer or other dead-front equipment can be grounded by removing the elbow from the transformer bushing and inserting it into a grounded bushing. A portable feed-through (as seen in Figure 11–21) can serve as the grounded bushing.

Using a hot stick, a feed-through is placed on a parking stand in the transformer cabinet. Using an elbow puller, remove the elbow of the cable to be grounded and insert into one-half of the feed-through. If the other end of the cable terminates as

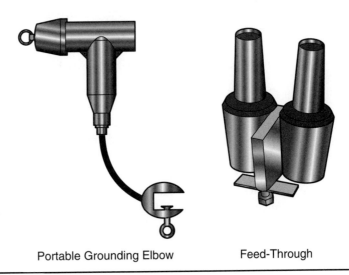

Portable Grounding Elbow   Feed-Through

Figure 11–21   A grounding elbow and a feed-through.

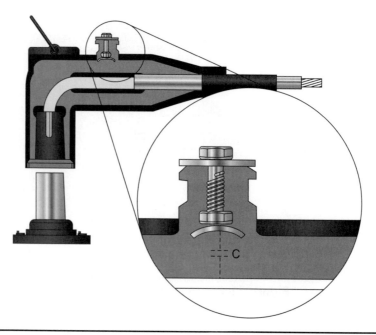

Figure 11–22   Capacitive test point.

a load-break elbow, the same actions are performed there. The cable is now in an isolated state but is not grounded.

Verify that the cable is isolated by using a stick-mounted potential tester and testing at the capacitive test point (Figure 11–22). On confirmation that the cable is isolated, a portable grounding elbow, as shown in Figure 11–21, is fastened to the grounding bus in the cabinet and the elbow end is inserted into the other half of the feed-through. When this is carried out at both ends of the cable, it effectively grounds the cable.

The protective ground set shown in Figure 11–23 is typically used to ground a three-phase feeder at a dead-front switching kiosk.

Grounding at a Live-Front Transformer or Switchgear

On live-front equipment, the load side of switchgear is exposed and somewhat accessible to protective grounds that have clamps suited to the equipment to be grounded. Isolating the cable to be grounded requires opening the appropriate switches at both cable terminals. One way to ground is to remove the fuse tube (door) and place a ground at the load side of the switch using the proper clamp, such as that shown in Figure 11–20. Ball-and-socket connections also are available for grounding at a switch.

The Cable between Terminals

To work on a cable between terminals, each end of the cable must first have grounds installed. At the work location, the cable is then spiked to positively iden-

Figure 11–23   Dead-front grounding set.

tify the cable as isolated and jumper the sheath before cutting through the cable. The spiking tool shown in Figure 11–24 can be driven into the cable which will short it out. If the cable does not have a grounded concentric neutral, there is a "ground lug" on the tool that has to be connected to a driven ground rod or any other good ground electrode.

Applying the Bonding Principle

11.7.3 If a protective grounded cable is accidently reenergized, the protective grounds will trip out the circuit. However, the grounds are not like a gate where all the current is shunted to ground. There will be a momentary rise in potential on the core conductor, the sheath, the grounding network in a cabinet, and everything bonded to the protective grounds. Anyone touching or near the cable, transformer, or switching cabinet (kiosk) will be a parallel path to a remote ground and subject to a lethal electrical burn.

An equipotential zone must be created so that a worker is totally bonded to the protective grounds. A ground-gradient mat bonded to the protective grounds will keep a worker within an equipotential zone. The mat serves the same function as bonding a structure to the protective grounds in an overhead lines situation. When working on a cable in a trench, work from a ground-gradient mat bonded to the sheath/concentric neutral.

If a cable is being cut in two, there could be a high potential between the two ends of the cable, even with protective grounds installed at each end. A jumper should be installed to bond the two ends before cutting to keep continuity between the grounds.

Figure 11–24   A spiking tool.

Review Questions

1. What are the three reasons to place protective grounds before working on an isolated circuit?

2. When using protective grounds, does the application of the grounding principle control current or voltage?

3. Does all the current in a grounded conductor take the easiest path to earth?

4. How does a powerline maintainer determine the size of grounds needed in a given location?

5. Why is it important to test grounding sets?

6. What is the best ground electrode on a wye circuit?

7. What is the bonding principle?

8. How does bonding a grounding set to a structure provide an equipotential zone for a powerline worker?

9. When removing protective grounds on an isolated circuit, which set of grounds is more likely to create an arc: the first set or the second set?

10. At what locations is an underground cable exposed enough to be able to apply grounds?

Connecting and Troubleshooting Transformers

Topics to Be Covered	Section
Introduction	12.1
Transformer Basics	12.2
Transformation Effect on Current	12.3
Transformer Losses and Impedance	12.4
Transformer Protection	12.5
Single-Phase Transformer Connections	12.6
Three-Phase Transformer Connections	12.7
Three-Phase, Secondary-Voltage Arrangements	12.8
Troubleshooting Transformers	12.9
Working on a Voltage Conversion	12.10
Specific Hazards Working with Transformers	12.11

12.1 Introduction

The Purpose of a Transformer

12.1.1 Transformers are used throughout an electrical system, first to raise voltage for efficient transmission of electrical power, then to reduce voltage to a manageable level for local distribution along roadways and streets, and eventually to reduce the voltage to a utilization level.

The power carried in a circuit is equal to volts × amperes. To transmit a large block of energy would require an extremely large conductor if the voltage were not stepped up. Likewise, it would be extremely costly to distribute power to customers along residential streets at high transmission voltages. The transformer is the link between the different voltage systems.

This chapter discusses the distribution transformer, which is used to reduce the voltage on local distribution lines to a utilization voltage. It is the most common piece of line equipment that the line trade installs and maintains.

Large transformers found in substations work on the same principle as distribution transformers. Substation transformers often have under-load tap changers, additional cooling radiators, and fans. Transformer reliability affects many customers; therefore, most transformers are monitored for temperature and voltage output by control-room operators.

Other Transformer Applications

12.1.2 In addition to transformers that are used for stepping up or stepping down voltage, some transformers in an electrical system are used for other purposes, including the following:

- A *neutralizing transformer* is one that is used where telecommunications (telephone) cable enters a substation. The grounded network in a substation is subject to a voltage rise when a fault occurs in the electrical system. Any communications cable coming in from outside the station would be seen as a remote ground, and there would be a dangerous potential difference between the communications cable and anything attached to the grounded network in the substation. The neutralizing transformer is a 1-to-1-ratio transformer that removes the direct connection between the cables in the substation from the cables leaving the substation. Fiber-optic communications cable will eliminate the need for these specialty transformers because fiber-optic cable does not transmit electricity and will not propagate voltage and current from a station.

- A *grounding transformer* is used as an indirect way to ground one phase of a delta circuit. The grounding transformer provides the means for a phase-to-ground fault to get back to the source. A ground-fault relay senses this ground current and trips out the circuit.

- *Instrument transformers* are potential transformers and current transformers that reduce voltage and current to lower, manageable levels. The lower voltage and current represent the primary voltage and current at a given ratio for use in relays and metering.

- A *constant-current transformer* is used for applications such as series street lighting where the current must be kept constant and the voltage is allowed to fluctuate.

- A *voltage regulator* is a tapped autotransformer that can regulate voltage under loaded conditions.

- A *compensator starter* is a tapped autotransformer that is used to soft-start large induction motors. Soft-starting a large motor will prevent a voltage flicker for other customers on the circuit.

12.2 Transformer Basics

Components of a Transformer

12.2.1 A transformer is an electromagnetic device that provides a magnetic linkage between two electrical circuits. Energy is transferred from one circuit to another by the magnetic field.

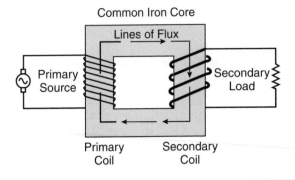

Figure 12–1 A basic transformer.

A transformer consists of a tank, a steel or iron core, and two or more separate coils or windings of wire (Figure 12–1). The windings are placed in a common magnetic path. On a single-phase transformer, two separate coils of wire are mounted on a common iron core. When a voltage and current are applied to one coil of wire, a strong electromagnetic field is created in the iron core. The electromagnetic field in the iron core induces a voltage and current into the second wire coil. Therefore, even though the two coils are not electrically connected to one another, voltage and current in one coil induce voltage and current into the second coil.

Two Types of Steel Core Configurations

12.2.2 The actual configuration of the steel core and the windings are of two main types. The steel cores are either shell type or core type. The primary and secondary coils are not necessarily wound around separate legs of the steel core (as shown in Figure 12–1) but are wound separately around the same core (as shown in Figure 12–2). The shell-type design is more economical for low voltage and for a high kilovolt-ampere (kVA) rating, and the core-type design is more economical for high voltage and a low kilovolt-ampere rating.

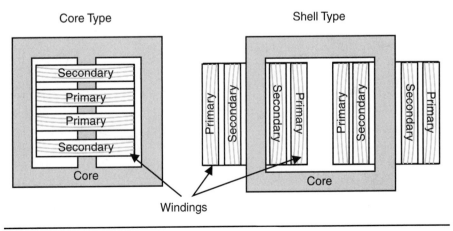

Figure 12–2 Steel core configurations.

Turns Ratio

12.2.3 The same electromagnetic field that is in the iron core cuts through both the primary (connected to the source) and the secondary (connected to the load) coils. The same voltage, therefore, is induced in each turn of both coils. The total voltage induced in each coil is proportional to the number of turns in the coil. When the secondary coil has fewer turns than the primary coil, the voltage output is reduced at the same ratio as the ratio of the number of turns of wire on the primary coil to the number of turns of wire on the secondary coil.

For example, a transformer selected to step down 4,800 volts primary to 240 volts secondary must have 20 times more turns on the primary or a 20-to-1 ratio, because 4,800 divided by 20 is 240.

Input Equals Output in a Transformer

12.2.4 Regardless of the turns ratio, and ignoring some transformer losses, the energy input into the transformer is equal to the energy output.

Input Voltage × Input Current = Output Voltage × Output Current

When the voltage is stepped down, the secondary current is increased. On a step-down transformer, the secondary coil and leads carry more current and are larger than the primary coil and leads.

Transformer Test for Turns Ratio

12.2.5 Every transformer has a nameplate showing the rated primary voltage and the expected secondary voltage. A field test can confirm that the actual turns ratio is equal to the ratio shown on the nameplate. A ratio test will ensure that there are no shorts between turns in the windings.

To conduct a turns-ratio field test on a transformer (Figure 12–3), energize the *high-voltage* coil with a low voltage, such as 120 volts. Measure the input voltage and the output voltage with a voltmeter. The ratio is calculated with this equation:

Input ÷ Output = Transformer Ratio

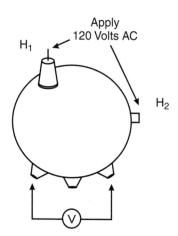

Figure 12–3 Turns-ratio field test.

Caution: Transformers work both ways! For this test, the low-input voltage must be connected to the *high*-voltage winding. If the input voltage was connected to the low-voltage winding, the transformer would be a step-up transformer and a lethal voltage would appear at the high-voltage terminal.

Transformer Backfeed

12.2.6 A powerline worker must always be alert to a transformer that is accidentally fed backward and to the fact that a secondary voltage can be stepped up to a full primary voltage at the transformer primary terminal.

Portable generators available at hardware stores are likely sources of transformer backfeed because unqualified people often connect the generators to the service. When grounds are applied to a primary circuit that is backfed from a portable generator, the generator keeps running and does not short out. The resistance of the circuit between the generator and the grounds is too high to short out the generator.

It can still be safe to work on the grounded conductors because the voltage at the grounded location has been lowered to an acceptable level. However, current will be flowing in the conductor, and the conductor must be jumpered before cutting or opening the circuit.

Large, permanently installed generators do not normally create a hazard because they are more likely to be properly installed with double-throw switches so that the generators cannot feed back into the electrical system.

Sources of secondary backfeed are not always obvious. Removal of the transformer secondary leads, when working on a transformer, will ensure that there is no possibility of backfeed.

Consider the following examples:

- A recreational vehicle (RV) with a generator is sometimes connected into nearby home wiring.

- An extension cord from a neighboring house can be a source of backfeed.

- When working on a transformer that is networked with other transformers to a common secondary bus, the primary bushing remains alive after the transformer is disconnected from the primary. The secondary bus continues to feed into the secondary of the isolated transformer.

Transformer Taps

12.2.7 Some distribution transformers have off-load tap changers. By changing the position of the tap changer, additional or fewer turns are applied to the primary winding. The nameplate of the transformer will show the various positions and the percentage change for each tap (Figure 12–4). Depending on the manufacturer, each tap raises or lowers the secondary voltage by 4.5 percent or 2.5 percent. The nameplate shown in Figure 12–4 has 2.5 percent taps.

An external switch knob can be turned to the various positions to change the taps. *The transformer must be isolated before turning the knob.* On some older transformers, the cover has to be removed to have access to the tap-changer switch knob. Feeder voltage changes during the day and at different seasons. Therefore,

Taps	
%	
105	A
102.5	B
100	C
97.5	D
95	E

Figure 12–4   A nameplate showing tap settings.

changing the taps at the transformer could produce extreme voltages when the primary voltage returns to its normal level in off-peak periods.

Example: A customer is continuously receiving about 210 volts instead of the rated 240 volts. The transformer, bus, service, or upstream regulators are not the cause of the problem. The 4,800/240-volt transformer at this location has a 20-to-1 ratio. The primary voltage at this location must be very low and can be calculated:

$$20 \times 210 = 4,200 \text{ V}$$

The transformer has taps that will adjust the voltage in 4.5 percent increments. Raising the voltage by three tap settings would change the secondary voltage:

$$3 \times 4.5\% = 13.5\%$$

Therefore, 210 volts can be boosted to:

$$210 \times 13.5\% = 238.4 \text{ V}$$

Caution: If the primary voltage returns to 4,800 volts during off-peak periods, this will be the secondary voltage:

$$240 \times 13.5\% = 272.4 \text{ V}$$

Transformer Polarity

12.2.8 There is no fixed polarity with AC as there is with DC. The polarity of AC changes 120 times a second on a 60-hertz system. However, the coil terminals always have a relative polarity in relation to other terminals. In other words, when the voltage at one end of a coil is positive, the voltage at the opposite end of the coil is negative.

Confirming the actual transformer polarity is important when installing transformers on a secondary network or when banking the transformer together with any additional transformer(s). By convention, the high-voltage terminals are H_1, H_2, and so on, and the secondary terminals are X_1, X_2, and so on.

Additive and Subtractive Polarity

12.2.9 The polarity of a single-phase transformer is considered to be either *additive* or *subtractive* (Figure 12–5). Whether the transformer is additive or subtractive is based on the direction the coils are wound. The direction of the coil winding

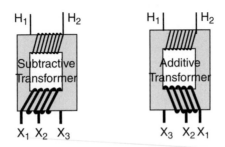

Figure 12–5 Subtractive and additive transformers.

determines the direction of the current flow at the primary terminals with respect to the direction of the current flow at the secondary terminals. From a powerline worker's perspective, it is based on how the secondary leads are brought out of the transformer; or, in simpler terms, the X^l is either on the left side or the right side of the transformer.

The nameplate on the subtractive transformer shows the H_1 and the X_1 terminals directly opposite one another on the same side of the transformer. Usually, transformers larger than 200 kilovolt-amperes or more than 8,600 volts are subtractive.

The nameplate on an additive transformer shows the H_1 and the X_1 terminals diagonally opposite one another. Distribution transformers less than 8.6 kilovolts tend to have additive polarity.

Test for Transformer Polarity

12.2.10 A field test can determine which secondary terminal is the same polarity as the H_1 terminal or whether a transformer is additive or subtractive. Figure 12–6 shows a test on a 10-to-1 ratio additive transformer.

Testing a Transformer for Additive or Subtractive Polarity

1. When facing the transformer (Figure 12–6), install a jumper between the high-voltage neutral (or the right-side high-voltage terminal) and the low-voltage terminal on the right-hand side.

2. Apply 120 volts across the *primary* of the transformer.

3. Measure the voltage between the left-side high-voltage terminal and the left-side low-voltage terminal.

If the voltage is lower than 120 volts, *then* the transformer polarity is subtractive and the X_1 terminal is on the left.

If the voltage is higher than 120 volts, *then* the transformer polarity is additive and the X_1 terminal is on the right.

Connections for Transformers with Different Polarities

12.2.11 It is possible to use transformers with different polarities by ensuring that the X_1 of one transformer is connected to the X_1 of the other transformer (similarly with X_2 and X_3), regardless of the position of the terminals on the transformer tank.

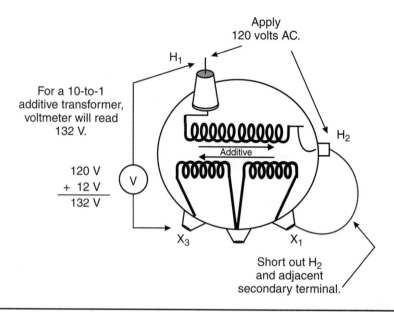

Figure 12–6 A test for transformer polarity.

When installing a transformer on a secondary network or when banking the transformer together with other transformer(s), ensure that the transformers are connected at the same polarity. When single-phase transformers are to be connected in parallel or connected into a three-phase bank, it is normal to select transformers with the same polarity. However, an additive and a subtractive transformer can be banked together by ensuring the X_1 of one transformer is connected to the X_1 of the other transformer (similarly with X_2 and X_3), regardless of the position of the terminals on the transformer tank.

Insulation Resistance and Continuity Testing

12.2.12 Testing a transformer for damaged insulation or coil continuity can be carried out using a 1,000-volt insulation tester (megger). Remove any ground from the X_2 terminal for these tests.

Insulation Test

The readings between the high-voltage terminal and the low-voltage (X_1, X_2, or X_3) terminals should be infinite. Readings between the low-voltage terminals and the transformer tank should be infinite. The insulation test readings with a three-phase transformer should be as shown in Table 12–1.

Continuity Test

Readings between each of the primary terminals and each of the secondary terminals should be 0 as shown in Table 12–2.

TABLE 12–1   Insulation Resistance Tests on a Three-Phase Transformer

HV to LV Insulation Resistance		LV Insulation Resistance to Tank	
Test Connections	*Readings*	*Test Connections*	*Readings*
H_1 to X_1, X_2 or X_3	Infinite (∞)	X_1 to Tank	Infinite (∞)
H_2 to X_1, X_2, or X_3	Infinite (∞)	X_2 to Tank	Infinite (∞)
H_3 to X_1, X_2 or X_3	Infinite (∞)	X_3 to Tank	Infinite (∞)

TABLE 12–2   Continuity Tests on Three-Phase Transformer Windings

Continuity Tests of HV Windings		Continuity Tests of LV Windings	
Test Connections	*Readings*	*Test Connections*	*Readings*
H_1 to H_2	0	X_1 to X_2	0
H_2 to H_3	0	X_2 to X_3	0
H_3 to H_1	0	X_3 to X_1	0

TABLE 12–3   Voltage Standards

Service Voltage	Range A Minimum (V)	Range A Maximum (V)	Range B Minimum (V)	Range B Maximum (V)
% of Nominal	*95%*	*105%*	*91.7%*	*105.8%*
120/240 3 wire	114/228	126/252	110/220	127/254
240/120 4 wire	228/114	252/126	220/110	254/127
208Y/120 4 wire	197/114	218/126	191/110	220/127
480Y/277 4 wire	456/263	504/291	440/254	508/293

Always Check the Voltage

12.2.13 After the installation of a transformer, it is essential to do a secondary voltage check as a final test to ensure that the customer is supplied with a voltage that falls within Range A, as shown in Table 12–3. Many embarrassed powerline workers have skipped this step.

12.3 Transformation Effect on Current

Load Current

12.3.1 When the voltage from one coil is being induced into a second coil, current is also induced into the second coil. The current, however, is transformed in the *inverse* ratio to the voltage transformation. For example, if the turns ratio of the transformer is 20 to 1, the current transformation is 1 to 20. The voltage is stepped down, but the current is stepped up. In a transformer:

$$Input: Volts \times Amperes = Output: Volts \times Amperes$$

Example: A 4,800-volt transformer with a turns ratio of 20 to 1 has a 200-ampere load on the 240-volt secondary. What current does the transformer draw on the primary side of the transformer?

$$Input: 4,800\ V \times xA = output: 240\ V \times 200\ A$$
$$4,800\ V \times 10\ A = 240\ V \times 200\ A$$

The primary coil on a 20-to-1 ratio transformer draws 10 amperes to produce 200 amperes on the secondary coil.

Calculating Load Current

The actual load on a transformer can be measured and calculated in the field by measuring V_1 and V_2 and I_1 and I_2, as shown in Figure 12–7, and applying it to the following formula.

$$\frac{(I_1 \times V_1)+(I_2 \times V_2)}{1,000} = total\ kVA\ load$$

If there is a need for a fairly high degree of accuracy, *then* the current and voltage on each leg should be taken at the same time to reduce the effects of a load shift from one side to the other.

Load on Secondary Is Reflected Back into the Primary

When one end of a transformer coil is connected to a live primary source and the other end is connected to a neutral, why is the coil not a dead short? The resistance or impedance of a transformer coil is low and a DC would, in fact, short out between the positive and negative ends of the coil. When AC is applied to the pri-

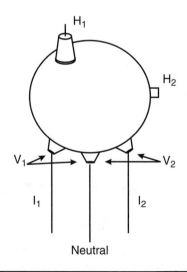

Figure 12–7 Calculating the actual transformer load.

mary coil, there is an induced counter-electromotive force (cemf) from the secondary into the primary to prevent a short circuit.

Lenz's law states that *"An induced electromotive force (emf) always tends to oppose the force that causes the* induction." In a transformer, the magnetic field of the primary coil induces a magnetic field on the secondary coil. The secondary coil induces a cemf back into the primary coil. In a transformer, the load on the secondary is reflected back magnetically into the primary. The amount of secondary current that is transferred to the primary is governed by the turns ratio.

Secondary Fault Current

12.3.2 A step-down transformer can generate a very high current on the secondary side if the secondary wires are accidentally shorted. The magnitude of the fault current available on a secondary transformer is mostly dependent on the size of the transformer. The larger the transformer, the greater the capability to generate a large fault current.

If the secondary wires are shorted, the transformer can briefly carry a load more than ten times its rating and supply a high fault current to the faulted location. Depending on the impedance of the transformer, a short at the secondary terminals of a 100-kilovolt-ampere transformer can be as high as 18,000 amperes. The level of fault current at the location of the short depends on the distance from the transformer and the conductor size, as shown in Figure 12–8. The level of fault current available on secondary wires drops quickly with distance away from the transformer.

Secondary services are not always recognized as high-energy circuits by powerline workers. However, the magnitude of a fault on the secondary is very explosive when a short circuit is close to the transformer. Safety glasses should be worn when working on a live secondary because an eye can be permanently damaged by a large flash.

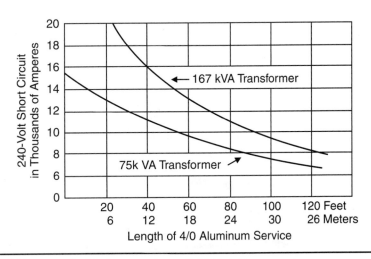

Figure 12–8 Level of fault current at various distances on service.

12.4 Transformer Losses and Impedance

12.4.1 It would appear from the following equation that there are no losses in a transformer:

$$Input \ V \times A = Output \ V \times A$$

This is essentially true because power transformers are more than 97 percent efficient. However, transformers do account for the largest proportion of energy loss in a distribution system.

For example, a typical 25-kilovolt-ampere transformer could have losses of about 150 to 350 watts, which would add up, considering the number of transformers in an electrical system. The losses in a transformer are due to core loss and conductor loss.

Core Loss

Energy is consumed when the iron core is magnetized and demagnetized by AC power at 120 times a second. This energy loss is referred to as *hysteresis loss*. To reduce hysteresis loss, the core is made of more permeable iron, which means the core is made with various steel alloys that are easier to magnetize and demagnetize.

When voltage is induced into a transformer coil, voltage is also induced into the iron core. Induced voltage causes current, known as *eddy current*, to flow in the iron core. Eddy currents cause heating and are a waste of energy. Eddy-current flow is reduced by the use of a laminated steel core that has thin strips of steel core material insulated from each other. Eddy currents are, therefore, kept smaller within each separate lamination.

Hysteresis loss and eddy-current loss together make up *core loss* or *iron loss*. The core loss of a transformer is constant and is not affected by the load on the transformer. Core loss can be referred to as *no-load loss*.

Relatively excessive core losses occur when a larger-than-necessary transformer is installed for the load to be served. If a 25-kilowatt load were fed from a 100-kilovolt-ampere transformer, there would be considerably more core loss than if the load were fed from a 25-kilovolt-ampere transformer.

A high-permeability material called *amorphous* (having no regular form) steel offers 70 percent less power loss than the conventional iron core. It is also called *metallic glass* because it has an atomic structure similar to glass. It is made when hot liquid iron is forced through supercooled rollers. The steel solidifies so fast that it forms a crystalline structure. The result is an amorphous or irregular structure that is more permeable.

Conductor Loss

There is a resistance to current flow in any wire. A transformer coil is made from a long length of wire, and it offers resistance to current flow. Current flow is also impeded when it flows in a coil because the induced counter-electromotive force in the coil causes a reactance. The resultant resistance and reactance are an impedance to current flow and are called *conductor loss, copper loss,* or *I²R loss* (where I = current in amperes and R = impedance in ohms). Conductor loss is dependent on the cross-sectional area of the wire in the coils. A lower resistance results in a lower *I²R* loss. Conductor loss can also be called *load loss* because the loss varies with the amount of load on the transformer. Load losses vary by the square of the current (*I²R*). That means that a fully loaded transformer has four times the copper loss as one loaded to 50 percent.

Transformer Efficiency

12.4.2 The efficiency of a transformer is calculated with the following formula:

$$\frac{Output}{Output + conductor\ loss \times pf + core\ loss} = percent$$

For example, a fully loaded 100-kilovolt-ampere transformer could have a 2,000-watt conductor loss at full load, and a 500-watt core loss at a 90 percent power factor.

Thus, the efficiency of this 100-kilovolt-ampere transformer is equal to the following:

$$\frac{100,000}{100,000 + 2,000 \times 0.9 + 500} = 97.75\%$$

When the output or load decreases during the day, the iron losses remain constant; therefore, the percent efficiency of the transformer is lower.

Transformer Impedance

12.4.3 The turns ratio of a transformer determines the ratio between the primary voltage and the secondary voltage. When load is applied, the load current is impeded by the resistance and reactance in the windings. When under load, the voltage at the secondary terminals is lower than the voltage indicated by the turns ratio. The impedance of a transformer is expressed as the percentage of the voltage drop at a full load compared to the voltage drop at no load. For example, if a transformer with a 2.2 percent impedance delivers 240 volts at no load, it will deliver 2.2 percent less than 240 volts (234.7 volts) at a full load.

There are practical limits to designing a transformer with lower impedance. And there is an advantage for a transformer to have some impedance because the impedance limits current going through the transformer during a fault.

Voltage-Survey Accuracy

12.4.4 When a planning engineer carries out a voltage survey, recording voltmeters are installed at the end of a feeder where a problem low voltage is likely to first show up. This voltage is used by the planning engineers to verify and update their computed feeder calculations.

To get an accurate line voltage, a recording voltmeter is installed on the secondary of an unloaded transformer. An unloaded transformer is used because with a loaded transformer the internal impedance will cause a voltage drop and the actual feeder voltage would still be unknown.

12.5 Transformer Protection

Sources of Transformer Damage

12.5.1 Transformer problems are usually due to an internal insulation breakdown. Insulation in a transformer usually breaks down because of heat or a voltage surge.

Transformer Overheating

Overheating of a transformer is usually due to overload, a short-circuited secondary, or the follow-through current initiated by lightning. The transformer is designed to be fairly tolerant to an overload for short duration. An oil-filled transformer, for example, may withstand an overload of 25 times the rated current for 2 seconds or two times the rated current for 30 seconds.

The kilovolt-ampere rating of a transformer is based on it being at 30°C. When the average temperature is higher or lower than the standard 30°C, the transformer rating can be changed. The kilovolt-ampere rating of a transformer can increase 1 percent for a decrease of each degree below 30°C and is decreased 1.5 percent for an increase of each degree above 30°C.

Larger transformers found in stations normally have a permissible rating that is calculated based on ambient temperature, load factor, and the existence of external cooling, such as by fans. Figure 12–9 is an example of a transformer rating sheet for a distribution station transformer with no external cooling in a mid-northern climate.

Transformer Loading

The heating effect of current flowing in a transformer coil determines the amount of energy a transformer can supply without causing damage to the insulation. The heat developed in the transformer winding is based on the following formula:

$$\textit{Heating effect in watts} = I^2R$$

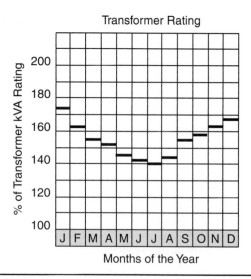

Figure 12–9   Temperature-dependent transformer rating.

If a transformer were allowed to carry three times more than its rated load current, the heating effect would be nine times as great as with full-load current. The full-load current in the windings of a transformer can be calculated for either the primary or secondary coil.

$$Full\text{-}load\ current = \frac{kVA \times 1,000}{voltage\ across\ coil}$$

Example: The following is the full-load current for a 25-kilovolt-ampere, 14,400/240-volt transformer:

$$Primary\ full\text{-}load\ current = \frac{25 \times 1,000}{14,400} = 1.74A$$

Secondary full-load current:

$$Secondary\ full\text{-}load\ current = \frac{25 \times 1,000}{240} = 104A$$

Overhead Transformer Fuse Protection

12.5.2 The fuse in a transformer cutout melts when exposed to over-current. The fuse melts before the transformer is damaged from the heat generated by an overload or a secondary short circuit. The fuse is also coordinated so that it isolates a faulted transformer before any upstream protection opens the primary circuit.

A link fuse speed and size are specified according to the preferences of the utility. The speed of a transformer fuse is generally specified as a K-link (fast) or a T-link (slow) fuse. The slower T-link fuse reduces nuisance fuse blowing due to transients, such as lightning.

The kilovolt-ampere rating of the transformer and the primary voltage are two factors that govern fuse size. For example, a transformer on a 2.4-kilovolt system has a fuse size of approximately 1 ampere per transformer kilovolt-ampere and a transformer on a 14.4-kilovolt system has a fuse size of approximately 0.2 ampere per transformer kilovolt-ampere.

Always install the specified fuse, current-limiting fuse, and surge arrestor at a transformer.

Underground Transformer Fuse Protection

12.5.3 Protection for transformers on underground systems varies depending on whether the transformer is in a vault, is submersible, or is a pad mount. Transformers in a vault often have standard overhead protective switchgear. Live leads, terminals, and switchgears are exposed and must be in locked enclosures to prevent accidental contact.

Pad-mount transformers are used on underground systems and sit on a concrete pad above the surface of the ground. A pad-mount transformer can be live front or dead front. A live-front transformer has exposed live switchgears when the metal enclosure is opened. The switchgear in a dead-front transformer is insulated. Figure 12–10 shows a dead-front transformer that has a draw-out load-break, bayonet-style, expulsion fuse holder.

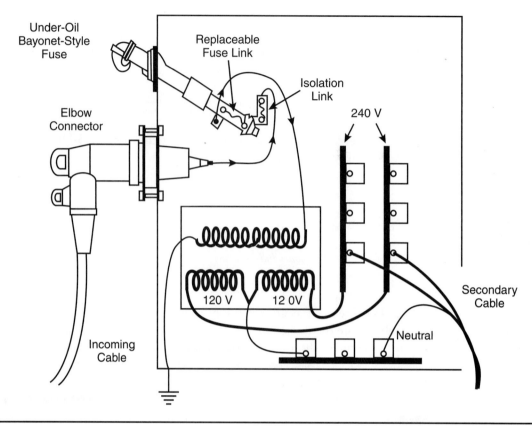

Figure 12–10   Pad-mount transformer fusing.

A bayonet-style fuse is an under-oil expulsion fuse cutout that has a stab-sheath arrangement to hold the fuse and is field replaceable by a line crew.

An isolation link or a current-limiting fuse is used in series with a bayonet-style fuse. During a transformer failure, the isolation link or current-limiting fuse opens the primary lead to the faulted transformer. This safety feature prevents a line crew from reenergizing a faulted transformer. The isolation link or the current-limiting fuse is not replaceable in field conditions.

Current-Limiting Fuse Protection

12.5.4 On overhead transformers, a current-limiting fuse is sometimes installed in series with a fuse cutout to limit the amount of current that can rush into a transformer during a fault. A current-limiting fuse protects a powerline worker from a catastrophic transformer failure that could occur when a worker is trying to energize a defective transformer in a high-fault-current location. A transformer on an underground system often uses a current-limiting fuse to limit arcing, because an arc could easily spill over to a nearby grounded object.

Voltage Surge Protection

12.5.5 A surge arrestor is installed to channel any voltage surge and its associated current away from the transformer. On distribution circuits, the source of a voltage surge is almost always lightning. Occasionally, an accidental contact with a higher-voltage overbuilt circuit results in a surge.

The surge arrestor is installed ahead of the primary transformer terminal; however, utilities differ on whether to install the arrestor ahead of or after a fuse cutout. An arrestor protects best when it is installed as close as possible to the equipment it is protecting, but there is a concern about nuisance fuse blowing when the arrestor is installed after the fuse cutout. There is usually a high follow-through current associated with a voltage surge, and a surge arrestor causes the current to bypass the cutout when it is installed before the fuse.

The rating of an arrestor is specified at a slightly higher voltage than the circuit. If the rating is too low, continuous exposure to small surges will cause the arrestor to deteriorate prematurely. If the voltage rating of the arrestor is too high, a damaging voltage and current may not be bypassed. The ground wire leading away from the arrestor must be as short as possible and at least the same size as the primary lead.

Neutral Connections and Ground Connections

12.5.6 The neutral and ground connections on a transformer may appear to be interchangeable because the two are interconnected. For all transformer installations, the neutral connections have one purpose and the ground connections have another.

A neutral is a *grounded* conductor. Neutral connections are part of the electrical circuit and during normal operation carry the current back to the source.

A ground wire is a *grounding* conductor. Ground-wire connections provide a path for current under abnormal conditions, such as during a lightning storm when an arrestor or an insulator sparks over. The ground connections also bond the transformer tank and related equipment to keep them all at the same potential.

12.6 Single-Phase Transformer Connections

Single-Phase Transformers

12.6.1 Single-phase transformers have one high-voltage primary coil with two high-voltage terminals. Only one high-voltage terminal needs to be insulated when the coil is connected between a phase and a neutral. Both high-voltage terminals must be insulated when the coil is to be connected phase to phase.

In North America, 90 percent of all transformers are installed as single-phase transformers connected to supply a standard 120/240-volt service. A customer receives a three-wire service consisting of two 120-volt hot wires and a neutral. One 120-volt leg is the polarity opposite the other. In other words, the current on one leg is moving in one direction while the current on the other leg is moving in the other direction. The voltage between the two legs is 240 volts. Because the two legs are not always equally loaded, the neutral carries the current difference of the two legs.

This type of service is referred to as a *single-phase service* by electrical-utility personnel because of the primary connection. The secondary, consisting of two 120-volt hot wires, is really two-phase power with each phase being 180 degrees out of phase with the other.

The two low-voltage coils can be wired up in parallel or in series. Figure 12–11 shows a standard 120/240-volt service; the positive end of one coil is connected

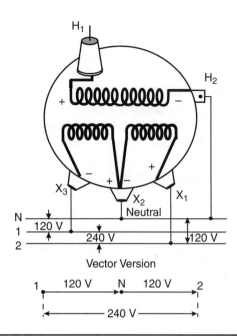

Figure 12–11 Single-phase transformer connections.

to the negative end of the other coil, which means the two secondary coils are connected in series. The coils are connected in parallel when only 120 volts are needed.

Note that the vector representation of the secondary helps to show how the secondary is 180 degrees out of phase with each other. One arrow represents the current flowing towards the neutral while the other arrow represents current leaving the neutral 180 degrees out of phase.

In some other places in the world, where a standard 240 (or 220) volts are used, the service is fed from a bus supplied by a 240/415-volt, three-phase transformer or from a single-phase, 240/480-volt transformer. A residential customer would have a three-wire service with one active (hot) wire, one neutral wire, and one safety ground wire. Higher voltage would be available with a four-wire service.

Typical Nameplate for a Single-Phase Transformer

12.6.2 The nameplate shown in Figure 12–12 is for a standard single-phase transformer. A nameplate would also show whether the transformer had dual primary voltage or had voltage taps. An overhead transformer is the same as an underground transformer except underground transformers are constructed for installation either in a vault, as a pad mount, as a submersible, or direct buried.

Figure 12–13 shows a typical single-phase overhead transformer, and Figure 12–14 shows a typical single-phase, pad-mount transformer.

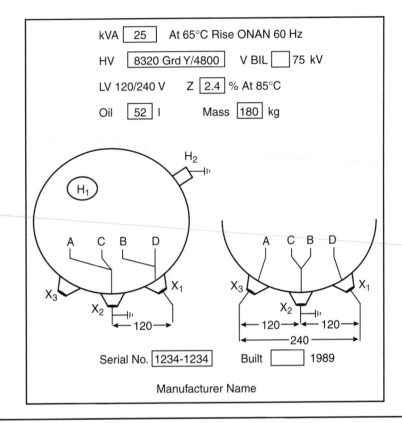

Figure 12–12 A typical nameplate for single-phase transformer.

Connections to Delta or Wye Primary Systems

12.6.3 The primary of a single-phase transformer can be connected in two ways to create a high-voltage potential between the H_1 and H_2 terminals.

Phase-to-Phase (Delta) Systems

For a single-phase connection to a delta circuit, connect one high-voltage terminal to one phase and the other high-voltage terminal to another phase. The transformer must have two insulated high-voltage terminals for a delta connection. To protect the transformer, a fused cutout and a surge arrestor are installed on both of the high-voltage primary leads.

Phase-to-Neutral (Wye) Systems

For a single-phase connection to a wye system, one high-voltage terminal is connected to the phase and the other is connected to the system neutral. Transformers intended for connection to wye systems can be constructed with only one insulated high-voltage terminal. The neutral connection to the high-voltage terminal of a *cover bushing transformer* is not insulated.

Figure 12–13 A typical single-phase overhead transformer.

Figure 12–14 A typical single-phase, pad-mount transformer.

It is possible to connect a transformer with two high-voltage terminals phase to phase on a wye system, but the voltage rating of the transformer would have to be suitable. On an 8.3/4.8-kilovolt wye system, a transformer connected phase to phase (delta) must be rated as an 8.3-kilovolt system, and a transformer connected phase to neutral (wye) must be rated as a 4.8-kilovolt system.

Transformers Connected in Parallel

12.6.4 Two smaller transformers are sometimes connected in parallel to give the equivalent capacity of one large single-phase transformer. In Figure 12–15, the two secondary coils in each transformer are connected in parallel. One transformer feeds one leg at a positive polarity while the other transformer feeds the other leg at a negative polarity.

It is also possible to interconnect two transformers with the secondaries left connected in series. The positive terminals are connected to one leg of the bus, and the negative terminals are connected to the other.

The impedance of the individual transformers must be very close to each other because the transformer with the lowest impedance will draw the most current and can become overloaded. The difference in impedance should be within a range of plus or minus 0.2 percent of each other. In other words, if one transformer has an impedance of 2 percent, then the impedance of the other transformer should be between 1.8 percent and 2.2 percent.

Secondary Network (Banked Secondaries)

12.6.5 Many utilities feed their secondary bus radially from one transformer. The secondary bus will have bus breaks installed to prevent any interconnection with other transformers. In a network system, a secondary bus can also be fed from many transformers connected in parallel to the same secondary bus

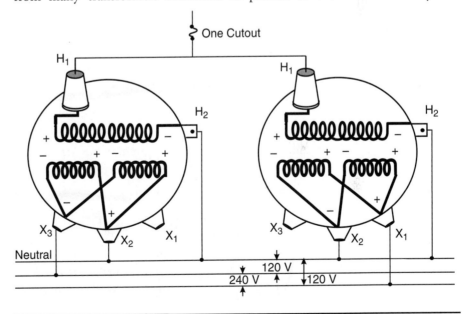

Figure 12–15 Single-phase transformers connected in parallel.

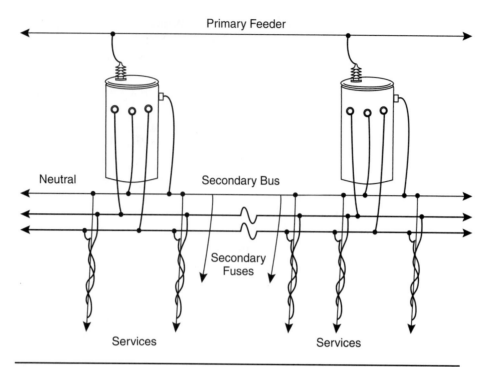

Figure 12–16 A secondary network.

(Figure 12–16). The most likely application would be an underground system in a city. Some cities have very large secondary networks with very large transformers and secondary bus.

- The load is divided among all the transformers connected to the bus.
- Individual customers with peak loads are supplied by the greater available reserve capacity of the multiple transformers.
- Fuses on the secondary bus (network protectors) between transformers isolate faulted transformers and interrupt only the customers near the defective transformer.
- All of the transformers on a common bus are connected to the same phase and connected with the same polarity.
- Ideally, the secondary bus should form a complete loop.
- Because of the multiple transformers feeding into the same bus, a secondary fault is extremely explosive.
- *When the primary of the transformer is opened, the primary terminal will remain alive because of backfeed from the live secondary. Open the network protectors or remove secondary leads to isolate a transformer completely.*

12.7 Three-Phase Transformer Connections

Three-Phase Transformers

12.7.1 A three-phase service can be supplied by one three-phase transformer unit or by interconnecting three single-phase transformer units. One three-phase unit (Figure 12–17) is smaller than an equivalent-size bank consisting of three single-phase units. One three-phase transformer tends to be used in underground vaults or as a pad-mount transformer (Figure 12–18).

An illustration of a three-phase transformer is shown in Figure 12–19. One three-phase unit is easier to install because the polarity and interconnections between the phases are fixed.

The use of three single-phase units is common in overhead distribution. When single-phase transformers are banked together, they can be interconnected to supply more than one type of service. For example, three transformers with 120/240-volt secondaries can supply a 120/208, 240/416, or a 240-volt three-wire service. Fewer specialized spare emergency transformers are needed when single-phase transformers are used.

Figure 12–17   A single-unit, three-phrase transformer.

Figure 12–18 A single-unit, three-phase, pad-mount transformer.

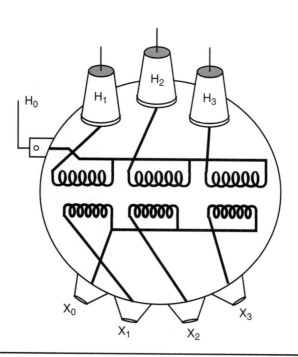

Figure 12–19 A three-phase, wye–wye transformer.

Choosing the Correct Transformers

1. The voltage rating of the transformer primary coil must be compatible with the applicable circuit. The voltage impressed across the primary coil will depend on whether the coil is connected in a wye (phase-to-neutral) or a delta (phase-to-phase) configuration.

2. The transformer must be able to deliver the needed secondary voltage. The supplied secondary voltage will be dependent on the following:

   - The voltage rating of the secondary coil.
   - Whether the transformer secondaries are interconnected in a wye or delta configuration.
   - Whether the secondary coils inside the transformer are connected together in series or in parallel.

3. If equipped with tap changers, the transformers must be on the same voltage tap. Dual-voltage transformers must be set on the proper voltage.

4. The impedance of the transformers in the bank should be within 0.2 percent of each other to avoid having the transformer with the lowest impedance taking a greater share of the load. In other words, if one transformer has an impedance of 2 percent, then the impedance of the other transformer should be between 1.8 percent and 2.2 percent.

Typical Nameplate for Three-Phase Unit

12.7.2 A transformer nameplate (Figure 12–20) should be checked to determine which three-phase configuration and voltage the transformer is able to supply.

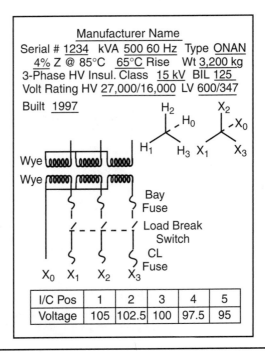

I/C Pos	1	2	3	4	5
Voltage	105	102.5	100	97.5	95

Figure 12–20   Nameplate for a three-phase unit.

The name plate shows that the transformer is an oil-filled, three-phase unit to be fed from a 27.6/16-kilovolt primary. The secondary will feed a three-phase 600/347-volt service. Both the primary and the secondary are wye connected. The transformer has a tap changer with 2.5 percent increments.

Using Vectors as an Aid in Banking Three Single-Phase Units

12.7.3 When interconnecting three single-phase transformers into a three-phase transformer bank, as in Figure 12–21, the interconnections between the transformers can get confusing, even when following a specifications drawing.

The relationship between phases, series connections, parallel connections, and polarity can all be represented on paper as a vector drawing.

For electrical drawings, the proper term is *phasor* instead of vector, but in line work, *vector* continues to be used. A vector representation of a wye–delta transformer (as in Figure 12–22) shows the three arrows, each representing a phase that will always be 120 degrees apart from the other. The pointed end of the arrow will always have a positive polarity, while the tail will be negative.

When the arrows are in a wye or parallel configuration, the tails will be tied together as a common neutral. If a plus comes in contact with a negative, it will be a dead short. When the arrows are in a delta or series configuration, the pointed plus end of one arrow makes contact with the negative tail of the next arrow. If a plus–minus combination comes in contact with another plus–minus combination, there will be a dead short.

Figure 12–21 A three-phase transformer bank with single-phase transformers.

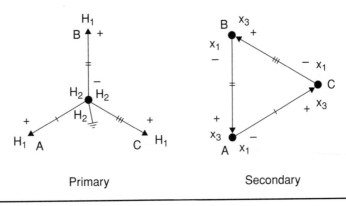

Primary   Secondary

Figure 12–22 Vector representation of wye–delta.

Note in Figure 12–22 that the three phases on the wye–connected primary are at the same angle as the delta–connected secondary but in the opposite direction. The slash (slashes) at the midpoints of the arrows indicate the A, B, and C phases. Note that the arrows with one slash representing the A phase is at the same angle in both the primary and the secondary. The secondary must always be at the same angle as the primary.

Putting in the polarity markings puts logic into the drawing. When a plus and a negative are connected together, the connection is in series; when the negatives are together and the pluses are going out separately, the connection is parallel.

Completing a vector drawing before connecting up a three-phase bank makes it more likely that the work will be done in a more logical fashion, rather than by rote.

Wye or Delta Connections

12.7.4 A transformer coil must have a potential difference across it to operate. To have a potential difference across a transformer coil, the polarity of the terminal at one end of a coil is positive and the polarity of the terminal at the other end of the coil is negative. There are two ways to get a voltage across a transformer coil:

1. One way is to connect a coil between a phase and another phase. When each of the three transformers have their coils connected between the phases AB, BC, and CA, the transformers are interconnected in a delta configuration.

2. The second way is to connect a coil between a phase and the neutral. When each of the three transformers has its coils connected between a phase and a common neutral, the transformers are interconnected in a wye configuration.

Primary Delta Transformer Connections

The three ways to connect a transformer primary into a delta (phase-to-phase) configuration are shown in Figure 12–23. Note how labeling the polarity of the transformers on a drawing reduces confusion when making connections. Each transformer coil in a delta primary or delta secondary is connected phase to phase. When two or more transformers are interconnected in a delta configuration, the

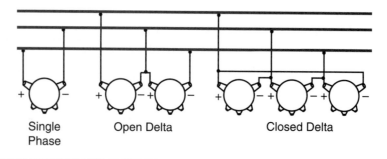

Figure 12–23   Three types of delta connections.

coils are connected in series with each other. To connect a coil in series, each positive terminal of one coil is connected to a negative terminal of another coil. If a transformer primary is to be delta connected on a wye circuit, the voltage rating of the primary coil must be equal to the phase-to-phase voltage of the circuit.

Primary Wye Transformer Connections

The three ways to connect a transformer primary into a wye (phase-to-neutral) configuration are shown in Figure 12–24. Note how labeling the polarity of the transformers on a drawing reduces confusion when making connections. Each transformer coil in a wye primary or wye secondary is connected phase to neutral. When two or more transformers are interconnected in a wye configuration, the coils are connected in parallel with each other. To connect a coil in parallel, each positive terminal is connected to a phase and each negative terminal is connected to a neutral.

Wye–Wye Transformer Bank

Figure 12–25 shows the connections for a typical three-phase, wye–wye transformer bank. A wye–primary–wye–secondary transformer bank can supply 120/208-volt, 240/416-volt, 277/480-volt, or 347/600-volt services. The phase-

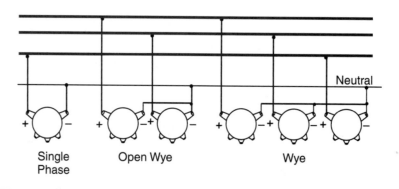

Figure 12–24   Three types of wye connections.

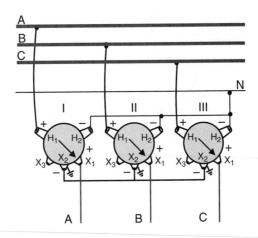

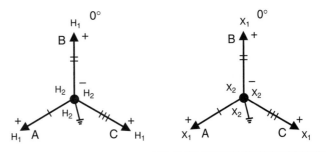

Figure 12–25 A wye–wye transformer bank.

to-phase voltage is or 1.73 times the phase-to-neutral voltage. The voltage across each transformer coil is equivalent to the phase-to-neutral voltage.

The primary neutral must be connected to the secondary neutral in a wye–wye transformer bank. This neutral connection provides a path for any fault current or current from an unbalanced load to get back to the source. There is a potentially lethal voltage between the primary and secondary neutrals if they are not connected together.

Delta–Delta Transformer Banks

Figure 12–26 shows the connections for a typical delta–delta transformer bank. A delta–primary–delta–secondary transformer bank supplies three-phase power at 120 volts, 240 volts, 480 volts, or 600 volts. The voltage across each transformer secondary coil is equivalent to the voltage supplied to the customer, which is the phase-to-phase voltage. The load on a delta–delta transformer bank must be well balanced. Any imbalance will result in circulating currents within the service as the unbalanced current tries to find its way back to the source. To ensure that the utility is supplying a balanced voltage to the customer, the three transformers must have similar impedance and be on the same voltage tap.

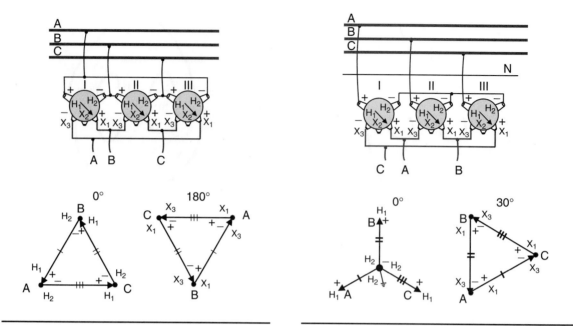

Figure 12–26   A delta–delta transformer bank.

Figure 12–27   A wye–delta transformer bank.

Wye–Delta Transformer Banks

Figure 12–27 shows the connections for a typical wye–delta transformer bank. A wye–delta transformer bank supplies three-phase delta services at 120 volts, 240 volts, 480 volts, or 600 volts.

A wye–delta bank must have transformers with insulated H_2 bushings. The H_2 bushings are interconnected but not connected to system neutral or grounded. The neutral connection is left floating (ungrounded) and, therefore, can have a high potential on it. It must not be treated like a grounded neutral by anyone working on the transformer bank. If the H_2 bushings were connected to the system neutral, the transformer bank would carry extra current not related to the current needed to supply the normal service load. If the primary wye circuit is unbalanced, extra current flows through the delta secondary as it tries to balance itself through the secondary of the transformer bank. If one phase on the primary circuit is faulted to ground, the high unbalanced current flows through the delta secondary.

When the H_2 is connected to the system neutral, the transformer bank automatically becomes a wye–open-delta transformer bank if one of the primary phases is opened. The two energized transformers continue to provide three-phase power but are subject to burnout because of overload. Two transformers now carry the load normally supplied by three transformers. This arrangement has a capacity of 57.7 percent of the capacity of three transformers.

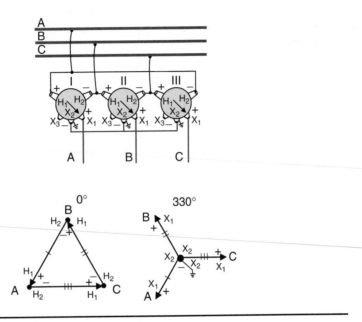

Figure 12–28 A delta–wye transformer bank.

Delta–Wye Transformer Banks

Figure 12–28 shows the connections for a typical delta–wye transformer bank. A delta–primary–wye–secondary transformer bank can supply standard wye services. The secondary neutral should be well grounded because a primary system neutral is unavailable.

Open-Delta Transformer Banks

A three-phase delta service can be supplied with two single-phase transformers. This type of service is called an open delta because the delta configuration is missing one side, preventing it from being a closed loop. Figure 12–29 shows the open-delta loop with three phases available. To feed an open-delta, three-phase secondary service, three primary wires are needed. A wye primary would need two

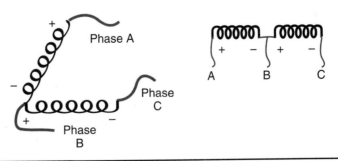

Figure 12–29 An open-delta transformer bank.

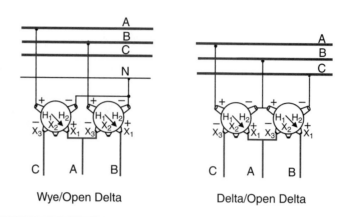

Figure 12–30 Open-delta transformer connections.

phases and a neutral, and a delta primary would need three phases. This hookup is sometimes used as an economical way to feed a small three-phase delta load. One of the two transformers is often called the *lighting transformer* and is sized larger to feed the single-phase portion of the load. The smaller transformer is often called the *power transformer* and is there to help provide the three-phase load, typically a motor. A three-phase, wye-secondary service cannot be fed from two transformers.

An open-delta secondary provides three-phase power. The capacity of the two transformers is reduced to 86.6 percent of the nameplate rating. For example, two 100-kilovolt-ampere transformers are 100 percent loaded when they supply $0.866 \times 100 \times 2 = 173$ kilovolt-amperes.

When one transformer of a normal three-phase delta–delta or wye–delta transformer bank is found to be defective, the connections can be changed to the configurations shown in Figure 12–30, which restores the service as an open delta. The customer should be told to reduce demand on service until the transformer is replaced because the two good transformers will now only have the capacity to supply 57.7 percent of the capacity of three transformers.

Scott Connections

12.7.5 Scott-connected transformers provide two-phase power from a three-phase system. They can also be used to supply three phases from a two-phase system. Two special single-phase transformers are used. Each single-phase transformer has three primary bushings and special taps on the primary coil where the three-phase primary connections are made. The transformers can also feed a four-wire, two-phase service.

Connecting Three-Phase Transformer Banks in Parallel

12.7.6 Three-phase transformer banks are sometimes networked together to a common secondary to add extra capacity and security to the service. Each transformer bank on the common secondary network must be similar:

- Each bank must have a similar impedance.
- Each bank must be on the same voltage tap setting.
- Each bank must have the same angular displacement or phase shift.

Angular Displacement of Wye–Delta and Delta–Wye Transformer Banks

12.7.7 Occasionally, it is necessary to know if there is an angular displacement or phase shift between the primary and secondary of a transformer. An example of an angular displacement is the difference between the X_1 and X_3 of a single-phase transformer. Even though each leg will read 120 volts from phase to neutral, the two legs would produce a dead short if they contacted each other. The X_1 is 180 degrees out of phase with the X_3. Similarly, depending on the type of three-phase transformer bank and the way the secondary connections are made, there is an angular displacement or phase shift between the primary and the secondary. There is always an angular displacement or phase shift with a wye–delta or a delta–wye transformer bank. The secondary will be 30 degrees out of phase with the primary. This means that a wye secondary of a wye–wye bank, which has a 0-degree angular displacement, cannot be connected in parallel with a wye secondary of a delta–wye bank, which has a 330-degree angular displacement (Figure 12–31). There is no way a line crew can switch secondary connections to allow these two transformer banks to be connected in parallel. Similarly, a delta secondary of a delta–delta bank, which has a 0-degree angular displacement, cannot be connected in parallel with a delta secondary of a wye–delta bank, which has a 30-degree angular displacement (Figure 12–32). There is no way a line crew can switch secondary connections to allow these two transformer banks to be connected in parallel.

Angular Displacement of Substation Transformers

12.7.8 Control-room operators have to be aware of the existence of a phase shift between different feeders. A line fed from a substation, where the substation transformer is delta–wye, cannot be connected in parallel with a line fed from a substa-

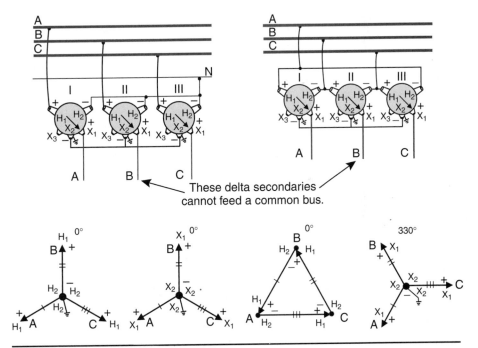

Figure 12–31 Angular displacement of a wye secondary.

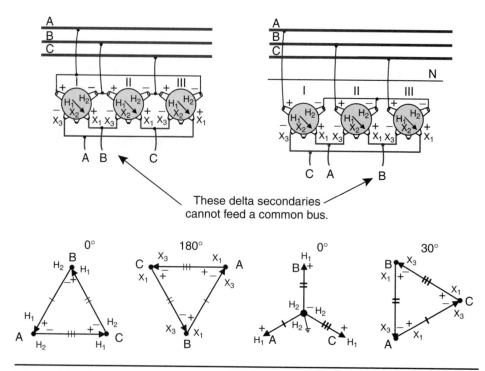

Figure 12–32 Angular displacement of a delta secondary.

tion where the substation transformer is wye–wye. Similarly, lines from a delta–delta substation transformer cannot be connected in parallel with a line from a wye–delta substation transformer.

To add further to the confusion, a wye–delta or delta–wye transformer bank can also be connected so that there is a 180-degree phase shift in addition to the 30-degree phase shift. A line crew, therefore, should always check with operating control before closing a tie switch between two feeders fed from different stations. Phasing sticks can be used for a field test to determine if there is a voltage difference across an open-tie switch.

Voltage Imbalance on a Three-Phase Service

12.7.9 A three-phase service supplied to a customer should not have a voltage imbalance exceeding 1 percent.

$$\% \ Voltage \ unbalance = \frac{max \ V \div min \ V - average \ V}{average \ V} \times 100$$

Where the *average V* is the average of the three voltages and the *maximum* or *minimum V* are the voltages that have the greatest difference from the average, an unbalanced secondary voltage can be caused by any of the following:
- An unbalanced customer load.
- An unbalanced primary voltage.
- Banked single-phase units with different kilovolt-ampere ratings.

- Banked single-phase units with different voltage tap settings.
- Banked single-phase units with different impedances.

12.8 Three-Phase, Secondary-Voltage Arrangements

Various Voltages Available from a Transformer Bank

12.8.1 The secondary voltage from a three-phase transformer bank depends on more than just the transformer ratio. Three transformers with a given ratio can be interconnected to provide up to four different types of services. The secondary voltage is based on whether the transformer secondary is interconnected as wye or delta. The secondary phase-to-phase voltage is:

- Equal to the actual voltage across the transformer coil *with a delta connection.*
- Equal to 1.73 times the voltage across the transformer coil *with a wye connection.*

The secondary voltage is also dependent on whether a transformer with a center-tapped secondary coil has the two parts of the coil inside the tank arranged in parallel or in series. The output voltage of series-connected coils is double the output of two parallel-connected coils.

Secondary Coil Arrangements Inside the Tank

12.8.2 The turns ratio of a selected transformer is based on the desired output voltage. Transformers with a center-tapped secondary coil have a certain voltage induced across the full length of the coil and half of that voltage on each side of the center tap. When the two secondary coils are interconnected in series inside the tank, the secondary voltage is double the voltage of the two coils connected in parallel. For example, on a 120/240-volt transformer (see Figure 12–33), the secondary provides 240 volts when the two coils are connected in series. Placing the two secondary coils in parallel allows the complete coil to be used to provide 120 volts.

Services Available

12.8.3 Table 12–4 shows three-phase voltages available from common distribution transformer secondaries in North America. In much of the world, the three-phase voltage available to the customer is equal to the standard voltage in that country $\times \sqrt{3}$ or 1.732.

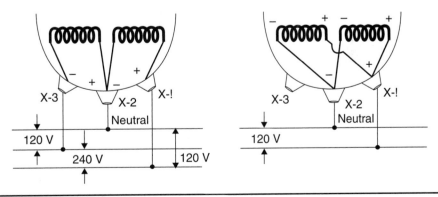

Figure 12–33   *Series and parallel secondary connections.*

TABLE 12–4   Standard North American Three-Phase Voltages

Transformer Secondary	Type of Three-Phase Service	Coil Arrangements Inside the Tank	External Configuration
120/240	120/208	Parallel	Wye
	240/416	Series	Wye
	120	Parallel	Delta
	240	Series	Delta
240/480	240/416	Parallel	Wye
	240	Parallel	Delta
	480	Series	Delta
277	277/480	NA	Wye
347	347/600	NA	Wye
600	600	NA	Delta

For example, the following are common three-phase voltages:

North America, 120 × 1.732 = 208 V.
Europe, 220 × 1.732 = 380 V.
Other countries, 240 × 1.732 = 416 V.

Three-Phase Voltages from a 120/240-Volt Secondary

Three single-phase transformers with a 120/240 secondary can supply a 120/208-, a 240/416-, a 240-, or a 120-volt, three-phase service.

A *three-phase, 120/208-volt service* (Figure 12–34) has the secondary coils in each transformer internally connected in parallel to provide 120-volt output. The external secondary leads of the three transformers are interconnected as wye. Each phase-to-neutral voltage is 120 volts, and the phase-to-phase voltage is 120 × 1.732 = 208 volts.

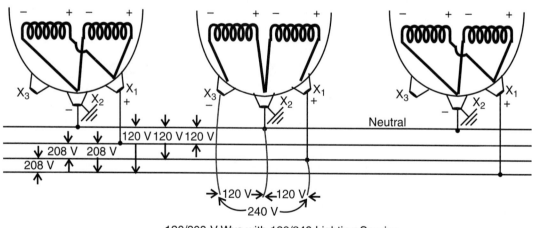

120/208-V Wye with 120/240 Lighting Service

Figure 12–34   A three-phase 120-208V service.

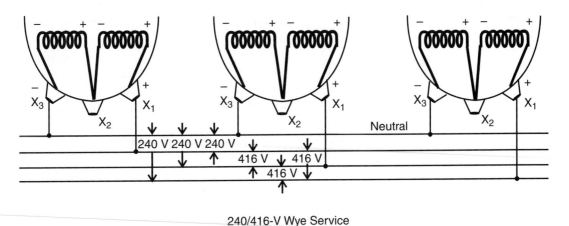

240/416-V Wye Service

Figure 12–35 A three-phase, 240/416-volt service.

A *standard single-phase, 120/240-volt lighting service* can be provided from a three-phase, 120/208-volt service. In Figure 12–34, the internal secondary coils in the center transformer are left in series to provide a 120/240-volt supply. The kilovolt-ampere rating of the center transformer is usually increased to provide the capacity for the extra load.

A *three-phase, 240/416-volt service* (Figure 12–35) has the internal secondary coils of each transformer connected in series to provide 240 volts. The external secondary leads of the three transformers are connected wye. Each phase-to-neutral voltage is 240 volts, and the phase-to-phase voltage is 240 × 1.732 = 416 volts.

The ground strap is removed from the X_2 terminal, and the terminal will be alive at 120 volts to ground.

A *three-phase, 240-volt* service (Figure 12–3) has the internal secondary coils of each transformer connected in series to provide 240 volts. The center tap is left ungrounded. The external secondary leads of the three transformers are connected in delta, and 240 volts are available from phase to phase. A phase-to-ground voltage reading is 0 volts because there is no path or circuit back to the ungrounded delta. If there was a voltage from phase to ground, it would mean that there was a phase-to-ground fault somewhere or that there was a lighting service from one of the transformers.

A phase-to-ground fault would mean that the earth was at 240 volts in relation to each of the two other phases. One phase-to-ground fault would not normally blow a fuse because there is no path for current to flow through earth back to the source.

To get a 120/240-volt lighting load, the center tap of one secondary coil must be grounded. There are 120 volts phase-to-neutral available from each of the two phases connected to the grounded transformer.

The remaining phase is sometimes called a *wild phase* and has a phase-to-neutral voltage of about 210 volts. This does not happen with a wye connection because the distances through the coil from each phase to the neutral center point are equal. A delta connection has one of the windings tapped in the middle, which leaves one phase of the transformer farther away from the neutral than the other two. This results in two phases with 120 volts to the neutral and one phase (the wild phase or *high leg*) at 87 percent of 240 volts.

The transformer with the grounded center tap will carry its full one-third share of the 240-volt, three-phase load and two-thirds of the single-phase, 120/240-volt load. A larger transformer is usually installed for the center-tapped transformer to handle the extra duty of the *power leg*. A lighting service from one of the transformers introduces a ground in the delta. One ground in a delta is not a short circuit, but if any other secondary phase becomes faulted to ground, the delta is shorted and a fuse should blow.

A *three-phase, 120-volt transformer bank* has the secondary coils in each transformer internally connected in parallel to provide 120-volt output. The secondary leads are connected in a delta configuration similar to the 240 delta bank shown in Figure 12–36.

Three-Phase Voltages from 240/480-Volt Secondary

Three interconnected single-phase transformers with 240/480-volt secondaries can supply a 240/416-, a 480-, or a 240-volt, three-phase service.

A *three-phase, 240/416-volt service* (Figure 12–37) can be supplied from three 240/480-volt transformers using the same secondary connections as the 120/208-

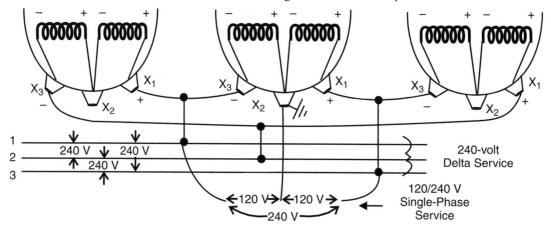

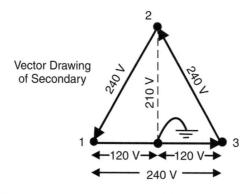

Figure 12–36 A three-phrase, 240-volt service.

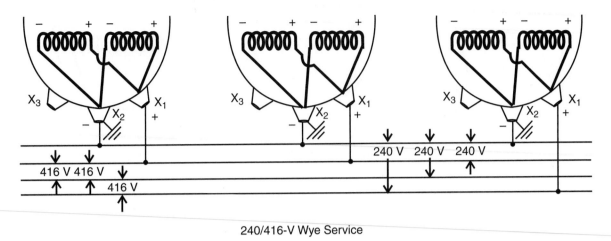

240/416-V Wye Service

Figure 12–37 A three-phase, 240/416-volt series.

volt transformer bank. The internal secondary coils are connected together in parallel, and the external leads are interconnected as wye.

A *three-phase, 480-volt service* (Figure 12–38) is supplied from a 480-volt secondary. The secondary coils are connected in series inside the tank, and the external leads are connected in a delta configuration. The phase-to-phase voltage is 480 volts. A 240-volt supply could be made available by grounding the center point on one transformer.

A *three-phase, 240-volt service* can be fed from a transformer bank with a 480/240-volt secondary. The secondary coils in each transformer are internally connected in parallel to provide a 240-volt output. The secondary leads are connected in a delta configuration similar to the 480-volt delta bank shown in Figure 12–38.

Three-Phase Voltages from a 347-Volt or 277-Volt Secondary

Three single-phase transformers with a 347- or 277-volt secondary coil can supply 347/600 volts and 277/480 volts, respectively. The connections shown in

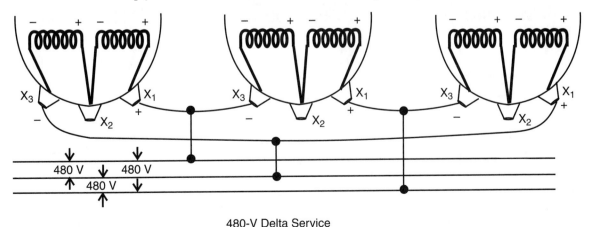

480-V Delta Service

Figure 12–38 A three-phase, 480-volt service.

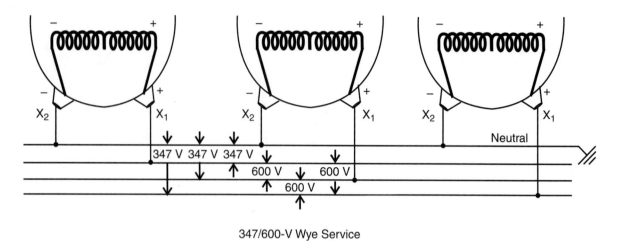

347/600-V Wye Service

Figure 12–39 A three-phase, 347/600-volt service.

Figure 12–39 apply to both the 277/480-volt and 347/600-volt transformer banks.

A *three-phase, 277/480-volt transformer bank* has the secondary connections in a wye configuration. Each phase-to-neutral voltage is 277 volts, and each phase-to phase voltage is $277 \times 1.73 = 480$ volts.

A *three-phase, 347/600-volt transformer bank* has the secondary connections in a wye configuration. Each phase-to-neutral voltage is 347 volts, and the phase-to phase voltage is $347 \times 1.732 = 600$ volts.

A *three-phase 600-volt or 277 volt Delta transformer bank*

Three single-phase transformers with 600-volt secondary coils can supply a three-phase, 600-volt delta service (Figure 12–40). The transformers are

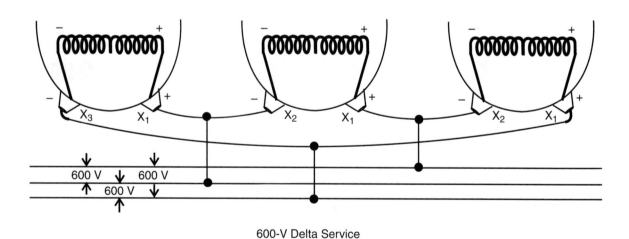

600-V Delta Service

Figure 12–40 A three-phase, 600-volt service.

interconnected in a delta configuration and the phase-to-phase voltage is 600 volts.

Similarly, three single-phase transformers with 277-volt secondary coils can supply a three-phase, 277-volt secondary service.

12.9 Troubleshooting Transformers

Investigating the Secondary for Transformer Problems

12.9.1 Troubleshooting transformers (see Tables 12–5, 12–6, and 12–7) mainly involves checking for problems on secondary services. Many *no-power* or *partial power* calls are due to internal customer problems. A utility responsibility normally ends at the service entrance. Opening the main switch and taking a voltage reading will determine whether the utility is the cause of the problem.

TABLE 12–5   **Troubleshooting a Single-Phase, 120/240-Volt Service**

If	Then
A customer has intermittent power and flickering lights.	Check for a voltage imbalance in the two 120-volt legs. If one 120-volt leg is two or more volts different from the other 120-volt leg, turn on a large 120-volt load. If the voltage increases on one leg and decreases on the other, there is a poor neutral connection.
	A loose connection on either leg can increase resistance to current flow and result in arcing and intermittent power.
The lights in part of the customer's premises are very bright, and in another part the lights are very dim.	A poor or open neutral connection blocks the normal return path from 120-volt appliances. The current travels back to the source through the other 120-volt leg or through 240-volt equipment. The 240-volt equipment operates normally.
A customer is receiving half power. Some of the lights work and some do not. None of the 240-volt appliances work.	One of the main fuses at the service entrance is likely blown. A voltage reading of about 120 volts between the top and the bottom of the fuse indicates that there is a voltage difference and, therefore, that the fuse is blown. If the power is off, a continuity tester or ohmmeter can also be used to check the fuse.
	If the fuses are good, check the connections back to the transformer.
A customer complains about erratic or low voltage.	A poor connection could cause low voltage at various times. Heavy-duty equipment used by a neighbor on the same bus can cause voltage problems for others on the bus.

TABLE 12–6   Troubleshooting a Wye Secondary (120/208-, 240/416-, or 347/600-Volt) Service

If	Then
A customer has an abnormal voltage.	Open the customer's switch and check the voltage. If the voltage on a phase to neutral reads 0, then check for a defective transformer or an open phase on the primary feeder.
	If the voltages on all three phases are balanced, close the customer switch and check the voltage. An unbalanced voltage indicates the customer's load is unbalanced.
Three-phase motors are overheating, and the thermal overload protection trips out the motor.	The usual cause of trouble on one phase is an unbalanced load. This type of service has single-phase loads. Unbalance beyond 3 percent can cause the low-voltage leg to draw more current and create heating of equipment.
	A faulty winding in a three-phase motor can cause a high current on a phase.
The load is balanced at the service entrance, but there is still a problem.	Open the customer's main switch and verify that the utility-supply voltage is correct.
	Close the customer's circuit breakers one circuit at a time and take voltage and current readings. A suspect circuit will have an unbalanced voltage or abnormal current readings for the equipment being fed.
All three-phase equipment and some single-phase equipment will not operate.	One phase is probably out. A phase-out can be due to a feeder problem, a transformer problem, or a blown fuse at the service entrance.
The single-phase equipment has intermittent power. The three-phase load is operating normally.	A poor or broken neutral connection will cause problems with single-phase loads.
	A customer-owned secondary (dry) transformer that steps down the higher 600- or 416-volt supply to 120/208 can be the cause of problems.

12.10 Working on a Voltage Conversion

Preparing the Circuit for Voltage Conversion

12.10.1 Conversion of distribution systems to higher primary voltages, such as 25 kilovolts, 27.6 kilovolts, and 34.5 kilovolts, makes it possible to serve a lot more customers on existing lines. One substation with 34.5-kilovolt feeders can make it possible *not* to have to build six or more substations with lower-voltage feeders. The higher-voltage distribution also saves on restringing, voltage regulators, capacitors, and downstream reclosers.

TABLE 12–7   **Troubleshooting a Delta Secondary (600-, 480-, or 240-Volt) Service**

If	Then
The customer has abnormal voltage. With the customer's switch open, the voltage on the supply side shows one or more of the phase-to-phase voltages at 0 volts.	One or more phases feeding the customer is out of service. Check the transformers and the primary feeder. The customer's switch must be open for this voltage check because the backfeed in a delta service can show a voltage at the service entrance.
At the main panel, the phase-to-phase voltage readings are lower than normal and one phase-to-phase voltage reading is 0 volts. For example, on a 240-volt service, the readings are 210 volts, 210-volts, and 0-volts.	When one phase of a primary feeder loses power, the voltage at a wye–delta transformer bank will have a reduced voltage on two of the phase-to-phase readings and 0 volts on the third phase-to-phase reading. On a wye–delta transformer bank, the primary neutral is not connected to the system neutral or the secondary neutral, but it is left ungrounded or floating. If the transformer neutral was grounded and one primary phase is opened, the transformer bank would become an open-delta bank and continue to supply three-phase power at a 57 percent reduced capacity, exposing the bank to a burnout because of an overload.
At the main panel, all three phase-to-phase voltage readings are normal, but one phase to ground is reading very low or 0 voltage.	A ground fault exists on a phase. When one phase of a delta circuit is faulted to ground, it does not blow a fuse because there is no path for a return current to the source. Both the phase and the ground are alive; therefore, a faulted phase-to-ground voltage reading will show a very low or 0-voltage difference. Both the faulted phase and earth are alive in relation to the other two phases. A customer with a delta service often has a ground-fault-indicating light connected between each phase and ground. The light will go out when there is a ground fault and the ground becomes alive.

Work that can be done on the circuit *prior to the day of the voltage conversion* includes the following:

1. If going to a higher voltage, change out all insulators on the circuit where that has not been done previously during prebuilding projects.

2. Change out any switchgear to the type that can handle the duties for both voltages.

3. If going to a higher voltage, change out any surge arrestors that are on the circuit. The utility will have to decide if the risk of having the

higher-voltage arrestors on the circuit for a period of time is acceptable.

4. Primary underground cable that cannot accommodate the new voltage must be replaced or fed at the original voltage using a primary step-down transformer.

Work to be done *on the day of the voltage conversion* includes the following:

1. If going to a higher voltage, existing voltage regulators will likely not be needed, especially in the same location and they can be removed from service.

2. If going to a higher voltage, existing capacitors will likely not be needed, especially at the same location and can be removed from service.

Working at Transformer Installations

12.10.2 Work that can be done at transformer installations *before the day of the voltage conversion* includes the following:

1. Install dual-voltage transformers. There may not be any dual voltage transformers for 277/480- or 347/600-volt three-phase banks.

2. Install surge arrestors for the new voltage.

3. Install cutouts and fuses for the new voltage.

4. If needed, install current-limiting fuses for a higher-voltage distribution system.

5. Make preparations if existing wye–delta transformer banks have to be changed to wye–wye on conversion day to accommodate single primary bushing transformers. The customer service entrance must be upgraded to accept a neutral.

Work to be done *on voltage conversion day:*

1. Isolate all transformers from the circuit and energize the circuit at the new voltage.

2. Change out transformers that are not dual voltage.

3. Change the tap setting on the dual-voltage transformers to the new voltage.

4. If the circuit has been energized at the new voltage, energize the transformer and take voltage checks and phase rotation checks before the customer applies load (remove meter or open customer breaker).

5. If, however, it is preferred to energize the new higher-voltage surge arrestors from a remote location, continue to work under the general outage and attach the riser and arrestor to the circuit. Leave the customers disconnected and do voltage checks at each transformer after the circuit is energized.

6. If, a transformer is to be fed from a primary step-down transformer, ensure there is proper voltage and phase rotation before connecting customers.

7. Using a checklist for these operations will reduce the risk of forgetting to change the tap on a transformer and leaving a customer with a very high and damaging voltage.

Working at Underground Installations

12.10.3 Work that can be done at underground installations *before the day of the voltage conversion* includes the following:

1. If using existing cable at the new voltage, cable size may not match the bushing inserts of new switching cabinets or transformers. Nonstandard equipment may be needed.

2. If a new higher-voltage cable is installed, larger elbows (separable connectors) before conversion day may not match existing equipment. Nonstandard equipment may be needed.

3. Install dual-voltage transformers or plan a change-out during the outage.

4. A higher-voltage distribution system may need current-limiting fuses.

5. Replace switchgear and fusing to accommodate the new voltage.

6. Change out surge arrestors at riser poles and any elbow arrestors installed at dual-voltage transformers.

Work to be done *on voltage conversion day* includes the following:

1. Change the tap setting on the dual-voltage transformers to the new voltage.

2. If the circuit has been energized at the new voltage, energize the transformer and take voltage checks and phase rotation checks before the customer applies load.

3. If the transformer is to be fed from a primary step-down transformer, ensure that there is proper voltage and phase rotation before connecting customers.

Working at Primary Step-Down Transformer Installations

12.10.4 During a voltage-conversion project, primary step-down transformers are often installed in line locations to delay the conversion of some line sections, especially underground. Work that can be done at underground installations *before the day of the voltage conversion* includes the following:

1. Do a turns-ratio test on the primary step-down transformer because setting the external switch or tap does not always make the proper internal connection.

Work to be done *on voltage conversion day* includes the following:

1. Reduce the risk of causing damage to a customer's appliance by isolating all the transformers on the load side of the primary step-down transformer and doing a voltage test and phase rotation tests on an individual basis as the transformers are energized.

2. Make a clear separation at tie points between the two primary voltage levels.

12.11 Specific Hazards Working with Transformers

Energizing an Overhead Transformer

12.11.1 The most common indicator of transformer trouble is an open fuse cutout. Often, the cause is transient and the usual process is to look things over and reenergize the transformer. If the transformer is not tested before reenergizing, then energize the transformer from a safe distance because a permanent fault can result in a violent expulsion of molten products from the fuse chamber or, in rare cases, a transformer explosion.

If the transformer is defective, the fuse can blow back violently with hot particles blowing back at the powerline worker. Precautions include staying out from under the cutout, using a stick with an attached shield, and/or using an extra length of hot stick.

A current-limiting fuse in series with the cutout fuse will reduce the risk of a violent transformer failure in locations where there is a high fault current capability.

A proper size and speed of fuse must be installed to protect the transformer, as well as to protect the system. Fusing protects the transformer from overload, short circuits, and any follow-through current from a lightning surge. The fuse size and speed (type of fuse) are specified by the utility and influenced by its business philosophy. Table 12–8 is a sample of how a utility might specify fuses for the voltages in its system. The manufacturer and speed of the fuse chosen by the utility influences the size of the fuse. The utility using Table 12–8 decided on a K-link fuse (a manufacturer's speed designation) and on a minimum of a 10-ampere fuse.

Energizing an Underground Transformer

12.11.2 There are very few transient faults on an underground transformer. A pad-mount or submersible transformer is likely to have a bayonet-style fuse. A bayonet-style fuse is an under-oil expulsion fuse with a stab-sheath arrangement to hold the fuse. Bayonet-style fuses and current-limiting fuses in a dry-well canister have been known to fail explosively when using them to energize a faulted transformer. Energizing the transformer with a load-break elbow or from a remote location can reduce this risk.

TABLE 12–8   **Typical Transformer Fuses**

Transformer Size	Delta Primary (kV)		Wye Primary (kV)		
	8,320	*4,160*	*4.8/8.32*	*8/13.8*	*14.4/25*
10 kVA or 3% 10 kVA	10 K	15 K	10 K	10 K	10 K
25 kVA or 3% 25 kVA	25 K	25 K	15 K	10 K	10 K
50 kVA or 3% 50 kVA	40 K	40 K	25 K	15 K	10 K
75 kVA or 3% 75 kVA	65 K	65 K	30 K	20 K	15 K
100 kVA or 3% 100 kVA	65 K	80 K	40 K	30 K	20 K
167 kVA or 3% 167 kVA	100 K	140 K	80 K	50 K	25 K

Review Questions

1. A transformer with a 240-volt secondary has a 60-to-1 turns ratio. What is the primary voltage feeding this transformer?

2. To conduct a turns-ratio test on a transformer, why is it necessary to energize the high-voltage coil with a low voltage such as 120 volts?

3. What two kinds of tests can be carried out on a transformer using a 1,000-volt megger?

4. Why is there a greater hazard working on a ive secondary close to a transformer rather than farther away?

5. Can a single-bushing transformer be installed on a delta circuit?

6. A transformer coil must have a potential difference across it to operate. What two types of connections are possible to get a voltage across a transformer coil?

7. What would be the expected full-load current (100 percent loaded) on the 240-volt secondary of a 100-kilovolt-ampere, 7,200/240-volt transformer?

8. When a secondary bus is fed from many transformers connected in parallel, what kind of secondary system is it?

9. When two or more transformers are interconnected with the positive terminal of one transformer connected to the negative terminal of another transformer, what kind of interconnection is it?

10. When two or more transformers are interconnected with the positive terminal of each transformer connected to a phase and all the negative terminals connected together, what kind of interconnection is it?

11. Why should the primary neutral of a wye–delta transformer bank be left floating (ungrounded)?

12. Can two phases of a delta primary supply a three-phase, open-delta service?

13. Can the wye secondary of a wye–wye bank be connected to the same bus as the wye secondary of a delta–wye bank of the same secondary voltage?

14. A center-tapped 120/240-volt secondary coil has the two parts of the coil inside the tank arranged in parallel. What would be the voltage between the X1 and the X3 terminals?

15. Name three types of three-phase services that three single-phase units with a 120/240-volt secondary can serve.

16. The lights in part of a customer's premises are very bright, and in another part the lights are very dim. What is the likely cause?

17. At the main panel, the phase-to-phase voltage readings of a delta 240-volt service are lower than normal and one phase-to-phase voltage reading is 0 volts. For example, the readings are 210 volts, 210 volts, and 0 volts. What is the likely cause?

CHAPTER

13

Supplying Quality Power

Topics to Be Covered	**Section**
Introduction	13.1
What Is Power Quality?	13.2
Factors Affecting Voltage in a Circuit	13.3
Voltage on the Transmission-Lines System	13.4
Distribution Substation Voltage	13.5
Distribution Feeder Voltage	13.6
Feeder Voltage Regulators	13.7
Capacitors	13.8
Troubleshooting No Power, High Voltage, or Low Voltage	13.9
Harmonic Interference	13.10
Voltage Flicker	13.11
Ferroresonance	13.12
Tingle Voltage	13.13
Investigating a Radio and Television Interference (TVI) Complaint	13.14

13.1 Introduction

More Sensitivity to Power Quality

13.1.1 Electrical disturbances in powerlines and on customer premises appear to be increasing. This is due to a greater amount of disturbance-producing electrical equipment and to an increased sensitivity of certain customer loads. Other than power outages, a variation in voltage is the most noticeable and obvious power-quality problem. Some power-quality problems are not picked up by a voltmeter. It is worthwhile for powerline workers to recognize the signs of poor power quality when checking customer complaints of erratic power problems.

13.2 What Is Power Quality?

Definition of Power Quality

13.2.1 A quality power supply is one where the AC and voltage rise and fall at a rate that can be represented by a sine wave. Any deviation in the magnitude or frequency of the 60-hertz sine wave is considered a power-quality disturbance. Poor power quality affects the performance of electrical equipment adversely.

Power Supply Disturbances

13.2.2 Electrical disturbances have always occurred in the supply of power. The increased sensitivity of certain loads causes these disturbances to be unacceptable to the customer. Momentary disturbances that affect the quality of power can be due to any of the following:

- Switching surges, fault clearing, and capacitor switching
- Voltage flicker from starting large motors or arc welders
- Transient faults and operation of surge arrestors

Continuous disturbances that affect the quality of power can be due to any of the following:

- An unacceptable range of voltage rise and fall
- Intentional voltage reductions (brownouts) during periods of peak load
- Unbalanced voltages between phases
- Harmonic distortion
- Tingle voltage
- Electrical noise (radio and television interference)

Modes from Where Disturbances Are Measured

13.2.3 There are two modes, or means, where the voltage can be erratic. These modes refer to the points where the unwanted voltage is measured. The *differential mode* (also called the *normal mode*) refers to disturbances between phases or between the phase and the neutral. Most voltage problems on the supply system would be differential mode and the source of trouble calls looked into by the line trade.

The *common mode* refers to disturbances between the neutral and the ground. This is also called *noisy ground.* Most common-mode problems would be on a customer's premises. For example, tingle voltage involves a voltage between the neutral and the ground. Trouble in this mode would normally involve engineering staff.

Corrective Measures Available

13.2.4 Customers understand that a utility cannot completely eliminate power outages, but some types of customers are becoming less tolerant to momentary outages and other disturbances. Often, a power-quality problem suffered by a customer comes from equipment on the customer's own service, such as large motors or arc-welding equipment.

A utility can improve power quality on a feeder by installing voltage regulators, capacitors, and surge arrestors. It can even build a dedicated substation or dedicated feeder to a customer who would be willing to pay more for a quality power supply with fewer disturbances.

Some customers own an uninterruptible power supply (UPS), which is a backup power supply to maintain service from batteries or some kind of generator during a power failure. A UPS will not protect the customer from voltage surges. Surge arrestors can be installed on customer equipment for extra protection from voltage surges. Filters are available for installation on customer equipment to limit harmonic interference.

A Frequent Fix for Power-Quality Problems

13.2.5 Poor grounding is often a cause of power-quality problems. In most cases, poor or improper grounding is within the customer's premises. Good grounding is important to the customer because grounding balances the electrical system by bleeding off over-voltage or over-current.

There is a difference between a neutral and a safety ground. The neutral is intended to carry current. A safety ground is usually a small wire intended to drain away voltage that occurs during a failure of equipment, such as appliances and tools.

The neutral and the safety ground are normally tied together both at the transformer supplying the service and at the service panel. The neutral and the ground should not be tied together anywhere else on the load side of the main service disconnect because a circuit will be formed through the ground and the neutral. The safety ground wire will then share with the neutral the job of carrying current back to the source. The resulting ground currents can cause tingle voltage as well as disturbances to the normal operation of electronic equipment in the customer's premises.

Supplying "Custom Power"

13.2.6 *Custom power* is the ultimate solution to power-quality problems. Instantaneous voltage regulation, voltage flicker control, reduced harmonics, and no momentary outages are possible with specialized equipment installed on the utility system. The equipment uses the technology developed for high-voltage DC (HVDC) transmission and flexible AC transmission systems (FACTS). An electronic controller can convert DC from a backup source to AC with any wave shape needed.

Modern electronic rectifiers and inverters convert AC to DC and vice versa. High-speed switching (less than 10 milliseconds) is possible with solid-state breakers (SSB), which are practically instantaneous. A backup DC source provides power to an electronic controller, which can counter voltage dips, momentary outages, voltage flicker, and changes in reactive power.

For example, a dynamic voltage restorer (DVR) is an injection-transformer device that is installed in series with a circuit. Capacitors in the DVR maintain an internal bus, which is a DC power source that an electronic controller can draw on to supply AC power. During a disturbance, the electronic controller reshapes the power wave back to a proper sine wave by injecting real or reactive power as needed.

Similar technology is used in a distribution static compensator (DSTATCOM), which is connected into the system like a shunt capacitor. An electronic controller will put in and take out real power and reactive power as needed from a rechargeable energy-storage system.

Other devices are static VAR compensators (SVC) and adaptive VAR compensators (AVC), which are electronic devices that instantaneously input reactive power to counter changes in a supply system.

13.3 Factors Affecting Voltage in a Circuit

Voltage as a Measure of Power Quality

13.3.1 There is a voltage drop along every circuit and through every transformer. The extent of the voltage drop depends on how much the current flow is impeded by the device through which the current flows. For example, more current flow is impeded in a long length of a conductor than in a short length of a conductor, and more current flow is impeded by a small-diameter conductor than by a large-diameter conductor.

Voltage fluctuates throughout the day and throughout the seasons in proportion to fluctuation of the electrical load (current flow). Almost all circuits need some kind of additional voltage regulation and control. Some loads are very sensitive to voltage variations. It is important to keep the voltage to a customer within an acceptable range. High or low voltage is noticed by a customer, and both high and low voltage can damage customer equipment.

Customers and their motors, lights, and computers require a voltage that falls within a standard range. A standard would apply to steady-state voltages, not to a fluctuation caused by switching, motor starting, and so on.

A utility has to meet a voltage standard when supplying power to a service. Table 13–1 shows the voltage ranges that must be met and are measured at the point of delivery, usually at the meter base. Standard Range A refers to a favorable voltage level, and the utility planning engineer designs the distribution system to supply to this voltage standard. Standard Range B refers to voltages outside of this range and, while tolerable for awhile, corrective action to fix the situation should be carried out. Once voltage falls outside of Standard Range B, the customer equipment will not operate properly.

Voltage Control and Voltage Regulation

13.3.2 The terms *voltage regulation* and *voltage control* tend to be used interchangeably.

Voltage control refers to the direct method of voltage change, such as changing a transformer output with transformer taps or changing the feeder voltage with line-voltage regulators.

TABLE 13–1 **Voltage Standards**

Service Voltage	Range A Minimum	Range A Maximum	Range B Minimum	Range B Maximum
% of Nominal	95%	105%	91.7%	105.8%
120/240 3-wire	114/228	126/252	110/220	127/254
240/120 4-wire	228/114	252/126	220/110	254/127
208Y/120 4-wire	197/114	218/126	191/110	220/127
480Y/277 4-wire	456/263	504/291	440/254	508/293

Voltage regulation refers to the indirect method of keeping voltage at a proper level. Voltage is regulated by ensuring that the conductor size and distance and the power factor of a circuit are adequate. Improving the power factor in a circuit reduces the amount of apparent power or current needed to supply the load. Less current in the circuit reduces the voltage drop.

Voltage Drop

13.3.3 When the load in an electrical system increases, the voltage at the load decreases. The amount of current flow affects the voltage drop. The following equations show that line loss and voltage drop are related to current flow.

$$Power\ loss = I^2R$$
$$Voltage\ drop = IR$$

Current flow varies according to the amount of customer load and the impedance offered by the powerlines and transformers feeding the load. Resistance is the largest component of the total impedance of current flow in a circuit. The design of the electrical-power system includes keeping losses as low as practical because line loss in a powerline or transformer is wasted energy.

Voltage Regulation

13.3.4 *Voltage regulation* is the difference between no-load voltage and full-load voltage, expressed as the percentage of full-load voltage.

$$\%V\ regulation = \frac{(no\text{-}load\ V) - (full\text{-}load\ V)}{no\text{-}load\ V} \times 100$$

For example, if a station transformer delivers 4,900 volts at no load and 4,800 volts at full load, the voltage regulation on the transformer is this:

$$\frac{4,900 - 4,800}{4,900} \times 100 = 2\%$$

If there is no load on a transformer, it would have a near-perfect voltage regulation of 0 percent. However, because load changes constantly, an electrical system should be designed so that the voltage regulation does not exceed a range of 2 to 3 percent.

Conductor Size and Length

13.3.5 Conductor size and circuit length affect the magnitude of the voltage drop in a circuit. A large-diameter conductor offers less resistance to current flow than a small-diameter conductor. Less resistance reduces line loss and, therefore, reduces voltage drop. The distance to a customer affects the voltage, because a longer conductor imposes more resistance to current flow than a shorter conductor.

Daily Changes

13.3.6 Because a load increase can result in increased voltage drop, voltage-control equipment must adjust the voltage to reflect the load changes during the day. A load profile of a customer at the end of a residential feeder is displayed on the graph in Figure 13–1.

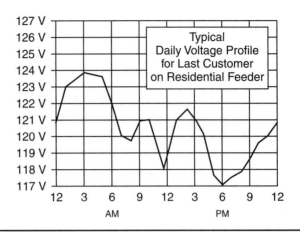

Figure 13–1 Daily voltage profile.

Seasonal Changes

13.3.7 The heat in summer and the cold in winter produce the peak-load periods for an electrical system. Voltage-regulation studies by a planning engineer consider these peak loads as the benchmarks for worst-case, low-voltage conditions.

Peak-load statistics are used to determine where an upgrade is needed to sub-station transformers, the conductor size of feeders, or the number of feeders, voltage regulators, and capacitors.

Reactance in a Circuit

13.3.8 The amount of reactance in a circuit adds to the total impedance of the circuit. If the current was kept in phase with the voltage, very little voltage drop would be due to reactance. Transformers, motors, and fluorescent lighting have an inductive component in their energy demand, and, therefore, an inductive reactance is set up in the distribution feeder. Additional impedance caused by reactance in a circuit results in the need for additional current to feed the load. A higher current will cause a greater voltage drop.

13.4 Voltage on the Transmission-Lines System

Voltage Control of Transmission Lines

13.4.1 Transmission-line voltage is regulated and controlled by equipment at substations. The voltage at the source of a transmission line can be boosted so that the voltage at the load end of the line is at the required level. This method would not work on a distribution line because customers are usually spread out along the whole circuit. Voltage can be boosted by changing the transformer voltage taps to alter the transformer ratio. Most of these taps are designed to be changed under load. Transformer taps must change position regularly to keep the voltage constant as the load changes.

At the end of the line, voltage can be regulated by installing capacitors. Capacitors improve the power factor on a circuit. An improved power factor results in a lower current and, therefore, a boost in voltage. Relays control the amount of capacitance needed to maintain a relatively constant voltage.

Parallel conductors on very long transmission lines increase capacitance on a circuit to a level where the capacitive reactance causes a high impedance to current flow. At transmission substations, reactors are installed for input of inductive reactance, balancing the capacitive reactance of the long line.

13.5 Distribution Substation Voltage

Voltage at the Distribution Substation

13.5.1 A distribution substation is the source for distribution feeders. The voltage at the source of the feeder must be high enough to provide an adequate input voltage to transformers and voltage regulators feeding customers downstream. The voltage at a substation can be corrected by the following:

- Adjusting the subtransmission line voltage.
- The automatic operation of a load tap changer (LTC) at the substation transformer, if equipped.
- The changing of the no-load tap changer at the substation transformer, if equipped.
- The automatic operation of a feeder voltage regulator in the distribution substation, if equipped.

Subtransmission-Line Voltage

13.5.2 The voltage of a subtransmission line can be controlled at the source substation. If a subtransmission line is short and does not feed many distribution substations, the voltage stays fairly constant along the full length of the line. The voltage on a long subtransmission line that feeds multiple distribution substations cannot be controlled to suit the needs of each substation. Each distribution substation will need its own voltage control to supply the distribution feeders. Voltage regulators can be installed along a subtransmission line to ensure that the distribution substation receives an acceptable voltage.

Voltage Control at a Distribution Substation

13.5.3 Tap changers at a distribution substation transformer can adjust the voltage by changing the ratio between the primary and the secondary coils of the transformer. Similar to a line voltage regulator, a transformer LTC can boost or buck voltage as needed while the transformer is in service.

A no-load tap changer requires all the load to be dropped from the transformer while the tap change is made. A transformer with a no-load tap changer cannot make regular adjustments during the day and would depend on the subtransmission-line source or line step-voltage regulators to regulate the voltage for daily adjustments.

Feeder Voltage Regulator in a Substation

13.5.4 A feeder voltage regulator is sometimes used in small or lightly loaded substations where the substation transformer is not equipped with an LTC. A feeder voltage regulator is more commonly installed downstream from the substation on long, individual feeders. The voltage is boosted or bucked as needed to ensure that the customers receive a voltage within the standard range.

13.6 Distribution Feeder Voltage

Voltage Profile of a Feeder

13.6.1 The design of a distribution feeder facilitates keeping the voltage drop along every element of the circuit to a minimum. To provide an acceptable voltage to the customer, each part of the distribution system (Figure 13–2) must also have an acceptable voltage.

Conductor Size

13.6.2 The amount of current in a circuit is a prominent factor affecting voltage drop. The less resistance there is to the current flow, the less line loss or voltage drop there will be. A large conductor over a short length offers the least resistance.

An ampacity chart to determine conductor size for a utility circuit is not very useful. For example, the ampacity chart for conductors may show that a 3/0 aluminum conductor has a capacity to carry 255 amperes. However, at 255 amperes, the voltage would drop about 1 percent every 40 feet (10 meters), which means it can carry a 120-volt service at that current for about 200 feet (60 meters) before the voltage is below standard.

Distribution circuits have larger conductors than are needed for ampacity. A larger conductor is used to reduce the voltage drop and line loss on a circuit. Less line loss also keeps the available fault current higher for a longer distance and allows circuit breakers or fuses to "see" a short circuit farther downstream. For example, a short lead in and out of a set of voltage regulators would need to be sized to carry the current but does not need to be the same size as the main line conductors. The use of a smaller conductor for the short distance involved in and out of the voltage regulator would not reduce the voltage significantly.

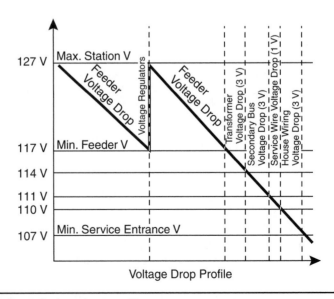

Figure 13–2 A feeder voltage profile.

The cost of conductors affects the size of a conductor chosen for distribution feeders. Usually, a utility decides on a few standard sizes for their feeders and selects conductors large enough to keep the voltage drop within practical and economical limits.

Locating Feeder Voltage Regulators

13.6.3 To improve the voltage on a feeder, it is usually more economical to install voltage regulators than to carry out a major improvement—such as stringing larger conductors, converting single phase to three phase, or installing additional feeders. Feeder voltage regulators should be installed in a location where the voltage is still high enough that the voltage is boosted from an adequate base. Voltage regulators step up voltage in percentages. For example, boosting 2 percent of 117 volts boosts the voltage to about 119.3 volts, which stays at a higher level for a longer distance than boosting 2 percent of 110 volts to about 112.2 volts.

As a point of interest, a rule of thumb states that it requires 1,000 volts to feed 1 mile of a normally loaded circuit before the voltage needs boosting. A 4,800-volt circuit should be able to feed about 5 miles before needing a boost.

Locating Capacitors

13.6.4 Installing a capacitor is the most economical way to improve the voltage on a feeder and also benefit the whole electrical system. When the power factor of the circuit improves, there is less apparent power needed to feed the load and, therefore, less current and less voltage drop. Capacitors can be in a substation or downstream on a distribution circuit.

A capacitor is a capacitive load on the system used to offset the inductive load put on the system by motors, transformers, and fluorescent lights. Improving the power factor of the circuit affects the amount of current and the power factor of the circuit upstream. On a distribution feeder, capacitors are located near load centers to reduce the need for apparent power on the circuit. The capacitor reduces the current flow and reduces the voltage drop in the circuit.

Transformers

13.6.5 Transformer losses can add to the total line loss in a circuit. The loss presented by a transformer can be unnecessarily excessive when larger-than-needed transformers are installed. The current required to excite the iron core is constant regardless of load. The greater the load on the circuit, the greater the voltage drop.

A transformer with a tap changer can be a quick solution to a voltage problem for an individual customer. Individual distribution transformers with tap changers alter the output voltage by changing the number of turns on the primary coil. Depending on the manufacturer, each tap change raises or lowers the secondary voltage by 4.5 percent or 2.5 percent. Tap changers on distribution transformers are *no-load* tap changers. The transformer must be de-energized before turning the tap-changer handle.

13.7 Feeder Voltage Regulators

Voltage Regulator Operating Principle

13.7.1 The most common feeder voltage regulator used on a distribution feeder is a step-voltage regulator. A step-voltage regulator corrects excessive voltage variation and raises or lowers the voltage during low- or high-voltage conditions. Step-voltage regulators are normally used on long rural feeders or at small, older distribution substations where the transformer is not equipped with an automatic under-load tap changer.

A step-voltage regulator works on the same principle as an autotransformer. On an ordinary distribution transformer, the primary and secondary coils are coupled magnetically; on an autotransformer, the primary and secondary coils are connected magnetically and electrically, as shown in Figure 13–3. The secondary coil is connected in series with the primary. If the transformer ratio was 10 to 1, then the voltage on the load side would be 10 percent higher than the source voltage.

Step-Voltage Regulator

13.7.2 A voltage regulator is an autotransformer with an under-load tap changer on the secondary coil. It has the ability to step the voltage up or down in small, incremental steps by moving a contact along the series-connected secondary coil sections. If the ratio of the primary to the secondary is 10 to 1, the secondary voltage at the highest tap would be 110 percent. In Figure 13–4, the 10-to-1 ratio regulator has the secondary coil divided into eight equal sections. Each tap change would change the voltage by $10 \div 8 = 1.25$ percent. A reversing switch allows the regulator to either boost or buck the voltage eight steps each way to make this a 16-step regulator.

Typical Step-Voltage Regulator Name Plate

13.7.3 A typical step-voltage-regulator nameplate is shown in Figure 13–5. It shows the voltage settings of the regulator and the types of connections available.

Regulator Controls

13.7.4 A potential transformer (PT) is installed on the output of the regulator. It sends a representative voltage to the control box. For example, on a 7,200-volt primary system, a 60-to-1 PT is installed. If the voltmeter at the control box reads 120 volts, it is known that the primary voltage is 7,200 volts. This meter, therefore, tells what the *actual* voltage level is on the regulator output. The voltage-level control knob is set to the *desired* output voltage, and the regulator raises or lowers the actual output to the desired level.

The settings of a control panel (Figure 13–6) indicate the desired operation of the regulator. The *voltage-level* setting is the desired voltage output of the regulator. If the voltage level drops below the voltage shown on the voltage-level setting, the regulator automatically moves up one tap to boost the voltage.

Bandwidth Setting

13.7.5 A voltage regulator changes taps in steps that do not result in the exact desired voltage. For example, on a typical voltage regulator, each step changes the voltage 0.625 percent, which brings the voltage close to the desired voltage but is probably not exact. The regulator would keep boosting and bucking, trying to reach the desired voltage if some tolerance for an inaccuracy were not available.

The *bandwidth* setting allows some variation from the actual desired voltage setting. A voltage setting of 125 volts and a bandwidth setting of 2 volts will cause the regulator to maintain a voltage between 124 and 126 volts. The difference between the minimum and maximum voltages allowed is the bandwidth. The

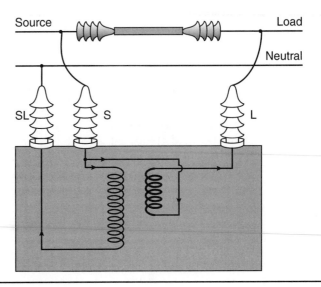

Figure 13–3 An autotransformer.

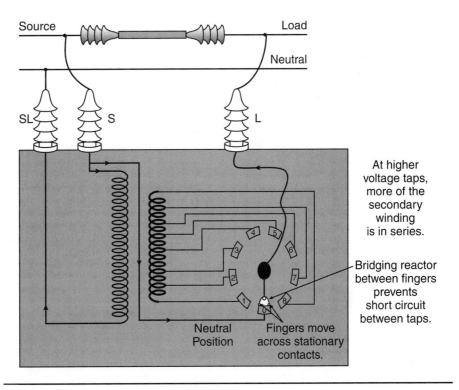

At higher
voltage taps,
more of the
secondary
winding
is in series.

Bridging reactor
between fingers
prevents
short circuit
between taps.

Neutral
Position

Fingers move
across stationary
contacts.

Figure 13–4 A step-voltage regulator.

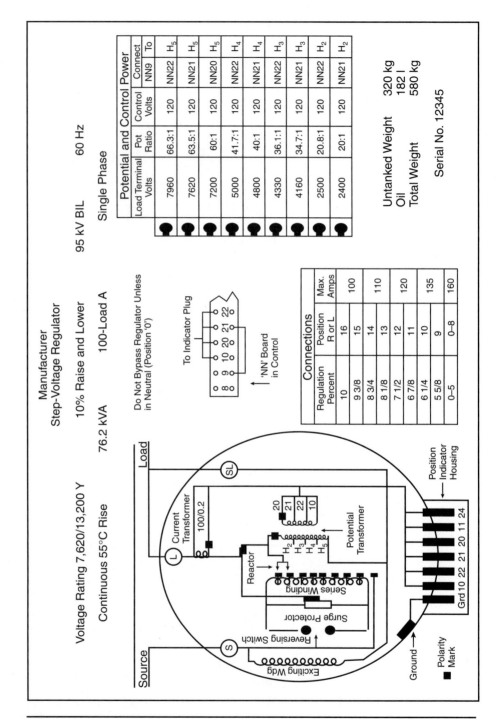

Figure 13–5 A regulator nameplate.

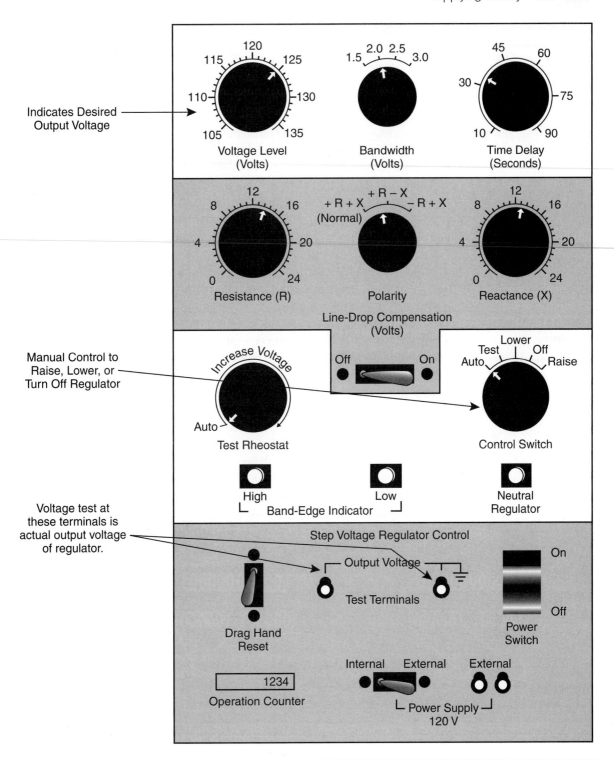

Figure 13–6 Regulator control.

bandwidth indicator lights on the control panel indicate when the output voltage is outside the bandwidth.

Time-Delay Setting

13.7.6 The voltage on a circuit can dip temporarily, such as when a customer's large motor is started. To save the regulator from reacting to every voltage change and to reduce unnecessary operations, a *time-delay switch,* found in the control box, is set to delay the operation of the regulator. The *time-delay setting* delays the operation of the regulator long enough to avoid needless operations. A time delay of 30 seconds is common and prevents the regulator from starting to adjust the voltage each time the output voltage is outside the bandwidth setting.

When a downstream voltage regulator makes a voltage adjustment, it does not affect the upstream regulator. However, each time an upstream regulator makes a voltage change, the downstream regulator also senses a need for a voltage change and starts an unnecessary operation. Therefore, the time delay on a regulator downstream from another regulator should be set at least 10 seconds longer so that it does not react immediately to the upstream regulator.

Compensation Settings

13.7.7 The line-drop compensation settings are an option used to supply a constant voltage at a point downstream, remote from the regulator. A voltage regulator *without compensation* keeps the voltage constant at the output terminal. As the load current changes, the voltage at the output terminal stays constant, while the voltage drops at the end of the line. Figure 13–7 shows what happens when the voltage starts to drop and continues to drop as the distance from the source regulator increases. To supply the end of the line with an adequate voltage, the voltage setting at the regulator must be increased. Customers close to the regulator would then have a constant high voltage.

A regulator with *line-drop compensation* keeps the voltage swings on the circuit to a minimum when the load current changes. Instead of keeping a constant voltage at the output terminal, the compensation settings give the regulator the ability to keep a constant voltage at some point downstream, as shown in Figure 13–8. The resistance and reactance between the regulator and a point downstream are calculated. These values become the compensation settings in the control panel. The projected voltage drop for that distance is automatically added to the voltage output by the compensator circuit in the regulator. When the load current increases, the voltage at the regulator terminal increases so that the load center

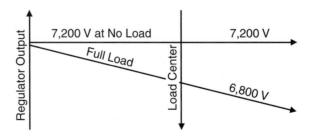

Figure 13–7   A voltage profile *without* line-drop compensation.

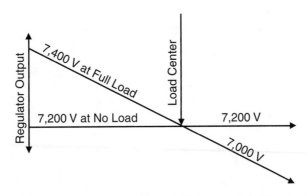

Figure 13–8 A voltage profile *with* line-drop compensation.

downstream continues to have a relatively constant voltage. The planning engineer must choose settings that will not cause the customer near the regulator to get a voltage that is too high.

Operating a Regulator

13.7.8 Operating a regulator normally involves putting the regulator into service or taking it out of service. The operation involves a bypass, a source (S) switch, and a load (L) switch (Figure 13–9).

The most critical operation involving a regulator is ensuring that the source and load voltages are equal when the bypass is about to be closed. If the source and load voltages are not equal when the bypass is closed, the regulator will be subjected to a short circuit.

Note: A bypassed regulator is damaged more quickly when it is one step up or down from the neutral tap (shorting 45 volts) than when it is at full boost or buck (shorting 720 volts). When the series winding of the regulator is shorted out, there is more impedance to the current flow when it travels through all of the windings. With the regulator at the number-one tap, there is not enough impedance to reduce the current and prevent the series winding from burning out. The *control switch* is used to manually raise or lower the regulator to the neutral position. The *neutral indicator* light should come on when the regulator is in neutral position. To equalize the voltage, the auto–manual switch in the control box is turned to manual operation. The voltage then can be raised or lowered until it reaches the 0 or neutral tap. When the neutral tap is reached, the switch is turned to the off position. The bypass switch (as shown in Figure 13–10) can then be closed, and the input and output cutouts can be opened to isolate the regulator. Some utilities require that a test be made to prove that the electric neutral of the regulator coincides with the neutral-position indicator before carrying out any switching.

Troubleshooting a Regulator

13.7.9 The troubleshooting guide shown in Table 13–2 assumes that the trouble crew does not actually maintain the regulator or calculate the required setting for bandwidth, time delay, or compensation. A temporary fix means that the regulator problem will be reported to have the unit fixed as soon as practical.

Figure 13–9   A single-phase voltage regulator.

TABLE 13–2   **Guide for Troubleshooting a Regulator**

If	Then
There are excessive regulator operations.	The regulator could be overloaded. Phase balancing may unload the affected regulator.
There is a voltage complaint on a circuit where there is a regulator.	Often, the tap-changing mechanism gets stuck on a tap. Raise and lower the voltage using the auto–manual switch, and then return the switch to automatic to see if the tap changer will move of its own accord.
The voltage problem was not due to a sticking tap changer.	The compensation settings may be out of date due to changes to the circuit, such as the installation of a capacitor, an upstream regulator, new conductors, or an increase in load.
	As a *temporary* measure, adjust the voltage using the auto–manual switch and then turn the switch off. Test the voltage at the customer and at the voltage test studs in the regulator control box. Now customers close to the regulator and/or at the end of the line will be exposed to more extreme voltages when the load current changes.

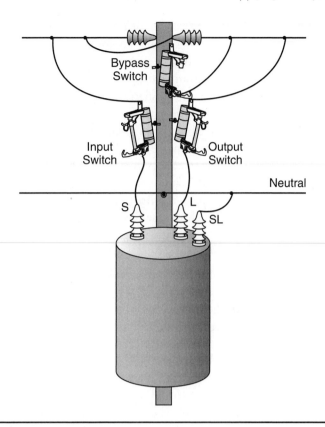

Bypass
Switch

Input
Switch

Output
Switch

Neutral

S

L

SL

Figure 13–10 Typical regulator switching arrangement.

If	Then
The regulator is chattering or hunting. The regulator is changing taps continuously.	The bandwidth or time-delay settings are incorrect. As a *temporary* measure, adjust the voltage using the auto–manual switch as before. This fix is temporary because customers may be exposed to extreme voltages when the load current changes.
The regulator does not respond to the previous solutions.	The regulator may be damaged. Take the regulator out of service. If the tap changer cannot be put in the 0 or neutral position, arrange to take the circuit out of service by opening the source switch with a load-break tool, then open load switches and close the bypass.
The regulator is at the maximum boost position but is not able to supply an acceptable voltage.	1. An increased load in the circuit may have reduced the input voltage to the regulator. 2. Phase balancing could unload the affected phase. 3. An upstream or downstream regulator may be needed.
The actual position of the 0 or neutral tap is not certain.	The pointer on the tap position indicator can be broken and/or the neutral indicating light is not working. Sometimes the specifications for the control settings do not have the 0 tap at the center. If in doubt, take the regulator out of service by opening the source switch with a load-break tool, as before.

Reverse Feed through a Voltage Regulator

13.7.10 When a circuit is temporarily fed in reverse through a regulator, the regulator continues trying to adjust the voltage on its load side, which is now the source. The voltage sensor measures the input instead of the output voltage. The regulator tries to change the input voltage, though it is not able to do so.

Typically, the regulator goes to the maximum boost or to the maximum buck position. To avoid these problems, the regulator should be bypassed and removed from service before the circuit is fed in reverse.

The S terminal must always be connected to the source and the L terminal always connected to the load. It is possible to set up a *reverse-power-flow* switching arrangement, which swings the input and output around so that the new source goes into the S terminal. This fairly complex switching arrangement is useful in cases in which reverse feeding is a common requirement.

13.8 Capacitors

The Purpose of Capacitors

13.8.1 Most capacitors are installed to provide power-factor correction on an electrical system, which in turn boosts the voltage. An electrical-power system must supply the apparent power needed to meet customer needs. Customers tend to have motors that cause inductive reactance in the circuit, which increases the overall impedance of the circuit.

When capacitors are installed, a capacitive reactance is introduced into the circuit, which neutralizes the inductive reactance. Therefore, the overall impedance of the circuit is reduced. Figure 13–11 shows that with less impedance, less current is needed to supply the load. Less current results in less voltage drop. To improve the voltage on an electrical system, installing capacitors is more economical than installing voltage regulators, stringing larger conductors, or adding more feeders.

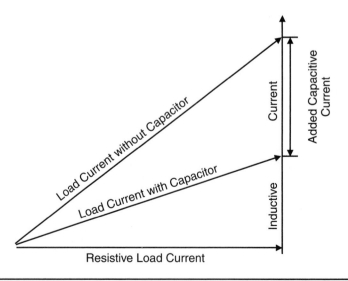

Figure 13–11 Capacitor effect on load current.

Power Factor Improvement or Voltage Booster?

13.8.2 Sometimes capacitors are installed on a distribution system to help improve the power factor on the transmission system right back to the generator. There is little need for system capacitors today because most utilities have capacitors on their high-voltage systems within the transmission substation yards. There is more control over station capacitors because operators can install a variable amount of capacitance as required by the system.

From a system point of view, there is very little control over capacitors on distribution circuits. Most capacitors on distribution circuits are installed to boost distribution voltage and to reduce line loss. The location of the capacitors on a feeder is important because the voltage boost is upstream toward the source. While the best location can be calculated, a typical rule for placement of distribution lines is to place the capacitor bank about two-thirds of the distance from where the voltage has dropped by two-thirds (the "2/3–2/3 location rule"). The rule is intended to prevent the customers closest to the source from exposure to over-voltage and to improve the voltage at the end of the line.

Construction of Capacitors

13.8.3 Capacitors consist of two plates with insulation between them. The larger the plates, the more capacitance there is. The closer the two plates are to each other, the more capacitance there is.

A typical distribution capacitor consists of two plates (Figure 13–12) made up of two long sheets of aluminum. The long sheets of aluminum are rolled up with insulation, such as oiled paper or polyethylene film, between them. Each aluminum sheet or plate is connected electrically to a terminal. The rolls are made up flat so that they are more compact and can be stacked with other rolls in the capacitor tank. Multiple rolls within a unit can be interconnected in series or parallel

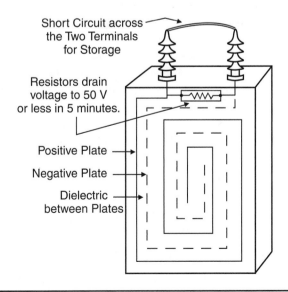

Figure 13–12   Capacitor construction with discharge resistor.

depending on the capacitor kilovolt-ampere reactive rating and voltage rating. The capacitor case is filled with an insulating oil.

Capacitors store a charge. Inside the capacitor unit, between the two terminals, are discharge resistors designed to drain the electric charge from the capacitor after a capacitor is isolated. It is normal to wait about 5 minutes after isolating a capacitor to let the resistors drain the charge before a powerline worker applies grounds to the capacitor. The terminals of a capacitor should always be left shorted out when the unit is exposed to contact by people.

How a Capacitor Works

13.8.4 The plates of a capacitor are charged and discharged 60 times a second in a 60-hertz circuit. During the first half of a cycle, one plate is positively charged, which causes a negative charge of equal voltage to be electrostatically attracted to the other plate.

Current flows into the capacitor only while the voltage is rising. When the voltage approaches peak value, the counter-electromotive force is also approaching peak value, which causes the current flow to decrease. There is no current flow when the voltage is at its peak (90 degrees). In a capacitor, the current reaches its peak before the voltage reaches its peak. A capacitor opposes the *change* in voltage, which in an AC circuit is constantly changing.

Because change to the voltage across the capacitor plates is delayed, this capacitive reaction causes the voltage wave to lag behind the current wave. In a circuit where the current lags behind the voltage, the capacitor effect of the current leading the voltage helps to cancel the two effects and to bring the circuit closer to a unity power factor.

Shunt Capacitors versus Series Capacitors

13.8.5 In an electrical-power system, most capacitors are connected in parallel (shunt), which has the full-line voltage applied between the two capacitor plates. On a distribution system, shunt capacitors are connected near the load center to help reduce voltage drop. The voltage drop is reduced because the capacitors reduce the line loss in the complete circuit back to the source.

Series-connected capacitors are used to reduce a severe voltage flicker on radial circuits where frequent motor starting, electric welders, or electrical arc furnaces affect other customers on the circuit. Construction-wise, shunt and series capacitors are the same. Series capacitors are connected in series and, therefore, conduct the full-line current through them. The voltage drop across a series capacitor changes instantly when the load changes, and, therefore, reduces the effect of a voltage flicker.

Switched Capacitors

13.8.6 On distribution lines, shunt capacitors are installed downstream closer to the load center. During peak-load periods, the capacitors are needed to reduce line loss and keep the voltage at the proper level. During light-load periods, the capacitors can improve the power factor to the point where the voltage will be too high.

Capacitors must be switched off before damaging high voltage occurs. Capacitors can be switched on or off with electrically operated oil switches. Control of the oil switches can be by a time control, a radio control, a voltage control, a power-factor control, or a kilovolt-ampere reactive-power (VAR) control.

Daily switching of capacitors in and out of service, especially large capacitor banks in substations, causes a transient overvoltage in the circuit. Sensitive customers, such as those with variable-speed-drive motors, may find these fairly large voltage fluctuations unacceptable.

System Capacitors in Substations

13.8.7 Capacitors on a distribution system affect the transmission system, and utilities have specified the installation of "system" capacitors on distribution. The "system" capacitors usually did not switch in and out, and they could be a problem to distribution workers trying to solve voltage problems on a feeder.

System control operators have more control of the power factor of the transmission system when capacitor banks are installed in substations. On distribution substations, a capacitor is either all in service or all out of service. Capacitor banks in substations are more sophisticated, and there are choices as to how many VARs an operator wants to put into the system.

High-voltage capacitors would have operating problems, so lower-voltage capacitors are put in series and connected between the transmission line and neutral, like two 12-volt batteries are put in series to produce 24 volts. Figure 13–13 shows a small three-phase capacitor bank. In a substation, such capacitor banks are set up on insulators and surrounded with danger signs.

Figure 13–13   Small three-phase capacitor bank.

**Operating
Capacitors**

13.8.8 Unlike transformers, shunt capacitors (Figure 13–13) draw a constant current regardless of the customer load. The current drawn by the capacitor is due to the energization of the relatively large amount of "metal" of the capacitor plates. Large capacitors have oil switches to allow safe energization or de-energization. Large capacitors should not be energized or de-energized with a cutout unless a load-break tool can be used.

The current a capacitor bank draws can be measured or calculated. The following are some typical current readings for a 25-kilovolt system:

600 kVAR bank 13.9A
450 kVAR bank 10.4A
300 kVAR bank 7.0A
225 kVAR bank 5.2A

Use the following equation to calculate the expected current for other voltages on wye systems:

$$I = \frac{kVAR \text{ of capacitor bank}}{3 \times phase\text{-}to\text{-}ground\ kV}$$

where

$$
\begin{aligned}
I &= \text{current in one phase} \\
kVAR &= \text{rating (of capacitor bank)} \\
kV &= \text{phase-to-ground voltage}
\end{aligned}
$$

For example, how much current can be expected in the leads feeding a 600-kVAR capacitor bank on a 12.5/7.2-kilovolt system?

$$I = \frac{600}{3 \times 7.2} = 27.8\ amperes$$

**Operation of
the Discharge
Resistors**

13.8.9 The discharge resistors in a capacitor drain the voltage of an isolated capacitor to a level below 50 volts in about 5 minutes. Draining the voltage allows for safer installation of portable grounds.

When a capacitor is isolated with the intent to reenergize it, it is important to wait 5 minutes to allow the voltage on the capacitor to drain before reenergizing. If a *charged* capacitor is returned to service, the line voltage builds up well above normal.

There is a danger when energizing capacitors with a fuse cutout because, if proper contact is not made the first time, any immediate second strike to retry closing the cutout results in double the line voltage across the cutout. Wait 5 minutes before trying to reclose a capacitor.

13.9 Troubleshooting No Power, High Voltage, or Low Voltage

**Troubleshooting
an Individual
Customer's
Service**

13.9.1 Usually the first thing a powerline worker does is check for voltage somewhere at the service. The following are typical items to check when troubleshooting an individual service:

- *At the customer's breaker.* If there is normal voltage at the top of the breaker, look for an open or faulty breaker or for blown fuses (breakers) in the panel. Some utilities will not check beyond the meter.

- *At the meter base.* If there is power to the top of the meter base, check for a faulty meter or bad connections in the meter base.

- *At the transformer.* If the primary circuit is supplying normal power to the transformer, check for a blown primary fuse, loose connections, bad neutral connections, a blown surge arrestor, an open current-limiting fuse, or a faulty transformer.

Using an Ammeter/ Voltmeter

13.9.2 Checking or testing voltage is a task that is carried out often. Testing for the existence of any voltage can be carried out on transmission and distribution lines with a potential tester, and for circuits under 750 volts with a voltmeter. Phasing sticks can be used on subtransmission and distribution circuits to measure voltage, but the most accurate voltage readings are made at the customer service entrance (meter base).

Typically, the voltmeters used by powerline workers are clamp-on ammeters with a voltage testing function.

Literature for the safe use of a voltmeter and ammeter will state that to read current with an ammeter the leads must be connected in series and that the leads must be connected in parallel to read voltage with a voltmeter. However, the clamp-on feature is much safer than having to break into a circuit to connect the meter in series to measure current while maintaining service to the customer and ensuring that the ammeter is rated for the current to be measured. The clamp-on ammeter can be used on primary voltage within the rating of the rubber gloves, and clamp-on (although they actually stay open) ammeters are available that can be attached to a hot-line tool to take ammeter readings.

Voltage measurements are actually in parallel or in series. For example, powerline workers sometimes test for voltage between the source side and load side of a meter base, and they test between any two terminals, objects, or wires within the voltage rating of the voltmeter. A voltmeter has a high resistance compared to the circuit being tested because there should be very little current flow through the meter. An extra safety measure is to use fused leads or probes with high rupturing capacity (HRC) fuses that will operate quickly under high fault current conditions.

If voltage tests are needed to investigate tingle voltage, a more accurate voltmeter with a capability to read very low voltage will be needed.

If there is an ohmmeter feature on the multimeter, make sure that the circuit is de-energized before taking resistance readings. Also make sure that the multimeter settings are not in the ohmmeter setting when taking a voltage reading. (The multimeter will blow up unless the fused leads protect it.)

Figure 13–14 Clamp-on ammeter/voltmeter.

Troubleshooting a No-Power Call on an Overhead System

13.9.3 From a power-quality perspective, having no power is the ultimate in poor-quality power. A no-power call is always a priority call. Table 13–3 outlines some common causes of outages.

Troubleshooting a No-Power Call on an Underground System

13.9.4 Troubleshooting power outages on underground systems—whether duct bank/vault systems or direct bury/pad-mount/submersible systems—relies much more on testing and technology. An initial patrol can determine if there is an obvious dig-in, failed or charred elbows, dead animals, a burnt smell, and so on. Locals may be aware of cables in specific locations that are vulnerable due to aging, overloading, improper backfill, stresses from settling soil, and so on.

The outage will be either with the system at large, with the transformer, or with the individual customer.

A no-power call from an individual customer starts with a voltmeter check at the meter base. For no voltage, check out other customers fed from the same trans-

TABLE 13–3   Troubleshooting a No-Power Call on Overhead Distribution

Common Problems	Restoration
Lightning is the most frequent cause of a transient fault. At the flashover point, a high-voltage arc establishes a path of ionized air to ground. A high follow-through current is established through the ionized air and causes an over-current fault.	In an urban area, a patrol on the circuit is always wise before closing in the circuit. In a rural setting, lightning without high winds should allow reenergization without a patrol.
When *wind, ice, or wet snow* have been present, the cause of an outage is often a phase-to-ground fault. A phase-to-ground fault is the cause of about 70 percent of permanent faults. Probable causes are a bad insulator, tree contact, broken conductor, or animal contact. Accidental contact by the public includes car accident, crane contact, sailboat contact, ladder contact, or antenna contact.	In a populated area, patrol the line before reenergization. In a rural setting, patrol the line unless special circumstances indicate that local knowledge would allow reenergization.
On *very cold or very hot days,* suspect an overload problem. Over-current due to an overload occurs when the customer demand exceeds the specified setting of the circuit protection. Circuit protection does not differentiate between over-current due to an overload or a fault.	The most common fix to an overload problem is phase balancing. When the load is not balanced between phases, one phase of the three-phase system is carrying more than its share of the load and the protective device will trip out. A low-resistance tree contact on a tap protected by a fuse can be seen as an additional load by the upstream three-phase device.
On an underground cable, a phase-to-ground fault can occur due to an *insulation breakdown, dig in, or a driven fence post.*	Other than an overload, a blown fuse on an underground cable normally calls for checking out the cable before reenergizing.
The *circuit has been out for awhile,* especially during peak-load periods. There is a high initial in-rush current when the switch is closed and the line trips out again.	A heavily loaded circuit may have to be picked up one section at a time. On an electronic recloser, the handle can be held closed momentarily until the in-rush current drops. On a hydraulic recloser, holding the handle closed will not prevent a trip-out.
After patrolling, there is *no apparent cause* for a permanent line outage, but the protective device trips out each time the line is reenergized.	• The cause may be a faulty surge arrestor. • There may be a fault downstream past the section that was patrolled. When the downstream protective devices do not trip out in proper sequence, it could be that incorrect fuses were installed during previous work. • A punctured dead-end insulator could also be the cause.

former. The voltage checks will show if the problems are a faulted service cable or a transformer problem.

If a larger section of the underground system is out, it is not a good idea to use an approach common in overhead lines—that is, close in on the circuit and see if the fault is still there. Very few transient faults are found on an underground system. Energizing the circuit for testing or sectionalizing will stress the cable, elbows, and so on each time the high fault current generated by the fault goes through it. Using a smaller fuse does not change the fact that the cable is subjected to the full fault current generated by the fault.

If fault indicators have been installed on the system, the faulted section can be found by observing the fault indicators. In the relatively simple system shown in Figure 13–15, the line crew would find the switch at the riser pole open, check the fault indicators at each transformer, and find the fault indicators at the first three transformers showing that the fault passed through there and that the fault did not go through the indicator at transformer 126. The conclusion would be that the fault lies somewhere between transformers 125 and 126.

Without fault indicators, sectionalize the system and test the cable sections with instrumentation and a voltage that will not damage the cable. (Cable testing was introduced in Chapter 8.)

If the riser pole is in the section that has faulted, the cable there should be the first suspect. The cable is more vulnerable because the cable on the pole is not able to dissipate heat as well, so as the cable enters the ground it is vulnerable to frost and settling.

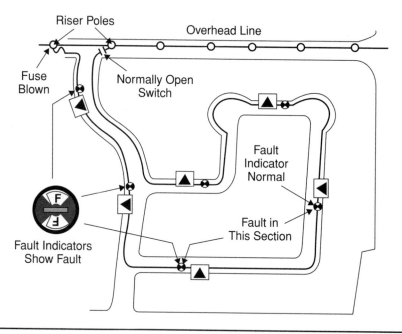

Figure 13–15 Fault indicators in an underground system.

Troubleshooting Low-Voltage Problems

13.9.5 Low-voltage problems usually show up during peak-demand times, such as during cold and hot weather and at dinnertime. A customer may notice low voltage when an electric motor is running hotter than it should. During low voltage, the motor draws more amperes and the torque that the motor produces is reduced. The torque is inversely proportional to the square of the voltage. For example, even though most motors are designed to run at 90 percent of their voltage ratings, a motor running at 90 percent of voltage produces 81 percent torque and runs hotter.

Low voltage has many causes. Finding the precise cause is a step-by-step process that starts at the customer and works toward upstream equipment (see Table 13–4).

Troubleshooting a High-Voltage Problem

13.9.6 A high-voltage problem becomes noticeable to a customer when lights seem brighter and light bulbs, motors, and electronic equipment burn out prematurely. High voltage has many causes. Finding the cause is a step-by-step process that starts at the customer and works toward upstream equipment (see Table 13–5).

13.10 Harmonic Interference

What Are Harmonics?

13.10.1 With AC power, the magnitude and rate of current and voltage rise and fall are represented graphically by a sine wave. *Harmonics* are AC and voltage disturbances that can also be represented by sine waves but are at different frequencies than the fundamental 60 hertz.

The harmonic frequency is a multiple of the fundamental 60-hertz frequency. Harmonic frequencies can be 30 hertz, 120 hertz, 180 hertz, and so on. A 120-hertz harmonic is twice the fundamental frequency and is called the *second harmonic*. Similarly, 180 hertz is the *third harmonic*.

Many of the various harmonic waveforms exist in the power supply at one time. These waveforms are out of phase with each other. The many differing waveforms tend to sum and cancel each other to form a distorted, but a predominantly 60-hertz sine wave.

Figure 13–16 shows only one harmonic. There are generally many more. The 60-hertz power wave stays predominant in a normal distribution system. The resultant 60-hertz wave becomes distorted, and, when it becomes severely distorted, it affects sensitive electronic equipment.

Sources of Harmonics

13.10.2 Electric loads that are nonlinear propagate harmonics back into the electrical-supply system. Nonlinear loads are not purely resistive but have a capacitive or inductive component in them.

There are many kinds of nonlinear loads, and all distort the "pure" 60-hertz waveform to the same degree. Examples of nonlinear loads are transformers, arc furnaces, arc welders, adjustable-speed and variable-frequency motor drives, electronic lighting ballasts, converters, rectifiers, and large computer systems.

Harmonics are a steady-state disturbance that exists in the system as long as the equipment generating the harmonics is in operation.

TABLE 13–4   **Finding the Cause of Low Voltage**

Step	Action	Details
1	Check the voltage at the customer meter base.	If the voltage is low, check for any recent increase in the load a customer is drawing. An increase in load could make the length or size of secondary conductors inadequate for the additional load. The planning engineer or engineering standards books have voltage-regulation charts for secondary bus and services.
2	Remove all load from the transformer and take a voltage reading at the transformer.	If the voltage reading is normal at the unloaded transformer, the low-voltage problem must be due to the length and/or size of the secondary or possibly an overloaded transformer. A recording voltmeter may need to be installed if the problem is intermittent. If the voltage reading is low at the unloaded transformer, the primary voltage is low and the cause of the problem is upstream. Other customers should be affected by upstream problems. A quick fix to an individual customer is to make a change to the transformer tap if equipped.
3	Check out any upstream voltage regulator or transformer with a load tap changer (LTC).	A voltage regulator could be stuck in a low position. Put the regulator in "manual" position and raise the voltage. Similarly, the LTC at the substation transformer could be malfunctioning.
4	Check out any capacitors on the line.	Switched capacitors should be in service during daily peak-load times and switched out of service during lightly loaded times. Check to ensure that the time clock or other control is working. Check that the motor-operated oil switches are closed during peak-load periods.
5	On a heavily loaded circuit, check the phase balance.	The planning engineer may show that the circuit is able to carry the load, but if one phase is carrying more than its share, it could be overloaded and cause an excessive voltage drop on that phase.

TABLE 13–5   **Finding the Cause of High Voltage**

Step	Action	Details
1	Check the voltage at the customer's meter base.	If the voltage is high and the customer is close to a distribution substation or close to a voltage regulator, the voltage is often relatively high at these locations to provide good voltage farther downstream. Check the voltage of a neighbor fed from a different transformer to find out if the high voltage is unique to the one customer that is complaining.
2	If the neighbors have normal voltage, do a ratio test on the transformer causing the high voltage.	A transformer can occasionally suffer some shorted-out turns in the coil and cause high voltage to customers.
3	Check out the substation load tap changer (LTC) or upstream regulator.	A voltage regulator could be stuck in a high position. Put the regulator in "manual" position and lower the voltage. Similarly, the LTC at the substation transformer could be malfunctioning.
4	Check out any nearby capacitors.	Capacitors that have not automatically switched out of service when the circuit is lightly loaded can raise the voltage during off-peak times.
		Check to ensure that the controller (load controller, VAR controller, time clock, and etc.) of the capacitor switch is working. In other words, check that the motor-operated oil switches are open during off-peak load periods.
5	If all other conditions are normal, change the voltage taps only on the transformers feeding customers with the high voltage.	Depending on the manufacturer, each tap will raise or lower the secondary voltage by 4.5 percent or 2.5 percent. The nameplate on the transformer must be consulted. *The transformer must be isolated before changing the voltage tap.*
		The feeder voltage will change during the day and at different seasons. Therefore, changing the taps at the transformer could produce extreme voltages if the primary voltage returns to a normal level.

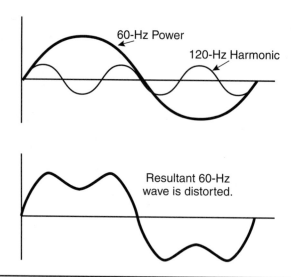

Figure 13–16   Harmonic illustrated as waves.

Conductive Harmonic Interference

13.10.3 Harmonic interference can be conducted back into the power supply from the direct connection to the harmonic-producing customer load. The harmonic currents conducted back into the power source add additional current to conductors, transformers, and switchgears. Harmonic currents can also interfere with protective relays, meters, and induction motors.

Capacitors are exposed to overloading because they act as a sink for the higher-frequency harmonics. When capacitors are on the system, there is also a possibility for resonance to occur at one of the other frequencies.

Inductive Harmonic Interference

13.10.4 Just as voltage and current can be induced on adjacent circuits, harmonic voltage and current can be induced on a neighboring power supply or telephone circuit. Unshielded telephone cable running parallel to power circuits is especially vulnerable to induced harmonics from the powerline.

Signs of Harmonic Problems

13.10.5 One of the first signs of a problem due to harmonics is from customers with sensitive electronic equipment. Harmonics distort the needed voltage and current magnitude, which can show up when a computer acts erratically or loses data.

Conductors, transformers, and motors are subject to heating because the high-frequency component of a harmonic disturbance causes an increase to the skin effect of conductors. A larger proportion of current is carried on the outer edge of a conductor, which limits its current-carrying capacity. Harmonics reduce the reliability of electric signals that activate meters, relays, powerline carriers, and equipment such as robots.

Testing for Harmonics

13.10.6 Before remedial action is taken for harmonic interference, tests should be carried out to confirm its presence. A specialist uses a power harmonic analyzer to make tests, interpret the waveform, and predict the most likely cause of the disturbance.

Harmonic Interference Solutions

13.10.7 Once a problem has been diagnosed as a harmonic problem, filters can be installed at the customer to limit the effect on their sensitive loads. The filter consists of an inductor, a capacitor, and a resistor, which are tuned to provide a low impedance to ground for specific harmonic frequencies. For large customers with big power-quality problems, arrangements can be made to supply "custom" power.

13.11 Voltage Flicker

The Voltage Flicker Problem

13.11.1 Erratic fluctuation in voltage shows up as blinking lights or intermittent shrinking of a television screen. For a customer with sensitive electronic equipment, such as a computer or an electronic cash register, the problem becomes unacceptable. Normally, calculations for potential voltage-flicker problems are carried out by the planning engineer when a customer with large motors or welders applies for service.

Sources of Voltage Flicker

13.11.2 A loose neutral or other bad connections are possible sources of flickering lights, especially during windy or heavy-load conditions. When a customer has a very noticeable dip in voltage on a regular basis, other sources must be investigated. Large motors, arc welders, X-ray machines, and electrical arc furnaces have loads that have a varying demand, are mostly unbalanced, and have a poor power factor. Under starting conditions, these loads draw considerably more current than when operating. A voltage flicker is noticed by other customers served by the same feeder as the offending motors, welders, and so on. The extent of the voltage flicker depends on the capacity of the feeder supplying the load to the customer.

When Does a Voltage Flicker Become Objectionable?

13.11.3 There are standards for an acceptable or unacceptable voltage dip. These standards may change as more sensitive electronic devices come on the market. The standards combine the percentage of voltage dip with the frequency of its occurrence. A typical standard looks like the graph in Figure 13–17. For example, it can be seen from the graph that a 3 percent voltage dip five times per minute would be objectionable.

Factors Affecting Voltage Flicker

13.11.4 The size of voltage flicker is dependent on the type of load and the capacity of the feeder supplying the load. The load itself can have equipment that reduces the start-up in-rush current. In-rush current information for motors, arc welders, and so on is normally found on the equipment nameplate. An electric motor has an in-rush current of about six times its load current. This can be reduced by using motors with soft-start capability.

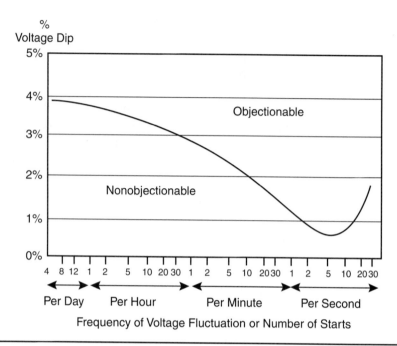

Figure 13–17   Threshold of objectionable voltage.

The greater the capacity of the feeder supplying the load, the less the feeder is affected by voltage flicker. Voltage flicker is reduced in these circumstances:

- The source transformer is large and able to carry a high peak load for a short period of time.
- The distribution feeder conductor is large.
- The distribution feeder distance to the offending load is short.

Calculating Predicted Voltage Dip

13.11.5 To predict a voltage dip, detailed calculations can be made. However, the planning engineer normally enters the needed information into a computer program or uses an estimating chart. The information needed is the in-rush current for the load to be fed, the capacity of the power-supply system (which is the phase-to-phase fault-current availability of the feeder at the source substation transformer), and the length and size of the conductor from the station to the load.

13.12 Ferroresonance

What Is Resonance?

13.12.1 Objects have their own natural frequencies. For example, a rattle in the dashboard of a car can vibrate annoyingly when a car travels at a certain speed. The frequency of the engine matches the frequency of the dashboard and sets up a sympathetic vibration in the dashboard. Soldiers are told to march out of step when they cross a bridge because when they march in step they sometimes match the natural frequency of the bridge; the sympathetic vibration set up in the bridge can cause severe damage. When the vibration in one object matches the natural frequency of another object, the two objects vibrate together in resonance.

Resonance in an Electrical Circuit

13.12.2 In any series-RLC circuit (circuits that have resistance, inductive reactance, and capacitive reactance), resonance occurs at some frequency. When the frequency rises, the inductive reactance increases and capacitive reactance decreases. As the frequency rises, the increasing inductive reactance will at some point be equal to the decreasing capacitive reactance and vice versa. When this happens, the inductive reactance cancels out the capacitive reactance, which means there is no reactive load impeding the current flow in the circuit.

If the resistance in the circuit happens to be low, there is very little to impede current flow and the current increases. As the current increases, the voltage also increases and rises above the source voltage.

The tuner on a radio varies the capacitance in a circuit to match the inductance at a desired frequency. The signal is amplified when it resonates at the desired frequency. Of course, the frequency on an electrical-power system is constant. Resonance only occurs by coincidence when the capacitive reactance is in series with and happens to match the inductive reactance at the standard 50 or 60 hertz. When resonance occurs, the voltage can build up from two to nine times the normal phase-to-ground voltage. The increase in voltage damages equipment, which is evidenced by rumbling and whining noises at transformers, arcing at insulators, and sparkover at arrestors.

Resonance with Harmonic Frequencies

13.12.3 The frequency of an electrical-power system may be a constant 50 or 60 hertz; however, there are frequencies superimposed into the system from certain loads. The power at these "harmonic" frequency waves sometimes resonates.

Causes of Ferroresonance

13.12.4 Resonance is a rare occurrence in a circuit because *all* of the following factors must be in place:

- The inductive reactance X_L is equal to the capacitive reactance X_C.
- The inductive load and the capacitive load must be in series with each other.
- There must be virtually no resistive load on the circuit.

When these factors are in place, there is practically no impedance to current flow in the circuit. Ferroresonance usually occurs when one or two phases are disconnected from the source by a fault; or, by switching a single-pole device, the transformer windings connected to the open phases are excited through the capacitance to ground in the cables and between phases.

The Source for Inductive Reactance in Series

13.12.5 Most electrical-system circuits have loads that are a source of inductive reactance, but these loads are normally connected in parallel. The most common and possibly the only way to get an inductive load in series with a circuit is to open one or two phases feeding a three-phase transformer bank.

As seen in Figure 13–18, the windings in the transformer with a delta primary are in a series configuration when one phase is open. The windings in a transformer with a wye primary do not become a series load when one switch is open. This only applies when the wye point is grounded. However, the wye point on a wye–delta transformer is left ungrounded or floating.

The inductive reactance of a transformer changes as the magnetic field from the coil magnetizes and eventually saturates the iron core. This gives a range of inductive-reactance values, which increases the possibility of matching the capacitive reactance in the circuit. The process of saturating the iron (ferrous) core is where the term *ferroresonance* originates.

The Source of Capacitive Reactance in Series

13.12.6 There is some capacitance on any circuit because a live conductor acts as one plate; the air or cable insulation is the dielectric between the plates, and any conductive material near the conductor acts as the second plate. Paralleling overhead conductors causes a capacitive reactance in a circuit. The capacitive reactance from long transmission lines is often countered by the installation of reactors at stations. Underground cable is a natural capacitor with the live conductor separated from another conductor, the grounded sheath, by relatively thin insulation. Long lengths of underground cable need reactors to cancel some of the capacitive reactance.

Field Examples of Ferroresonance

13.12.7 The most common occurrence of ferroresonance involves a three-phase transformer bank fed with a length of underground cable, as illustrated in Figure 13–19. A certain critical length of underground cable provides the crit-

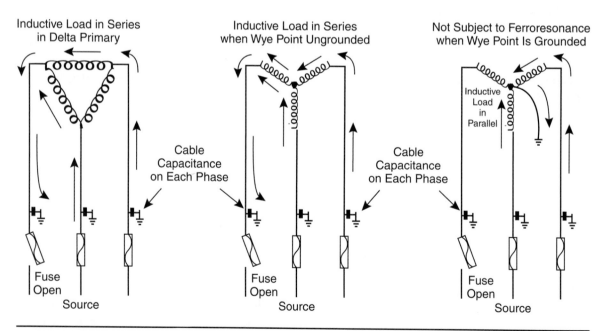

Figure 13–18 Sources of inductive reactance in series.

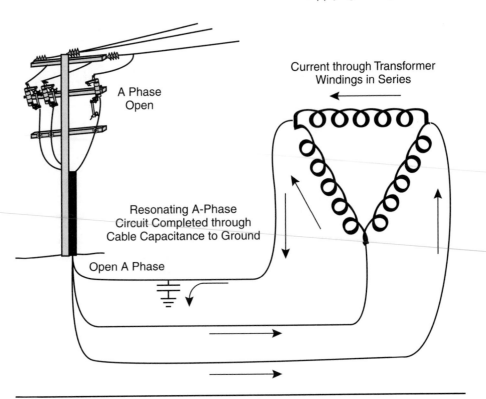

A Phase
Open

Current through Transformer
Windings in Series

Resonating A-Phase
Circuit Completed through
Cable Capacitance to Ground

Open A Phase

Figure 13–19   An example of ferroresonance.

ical amount of capacitative reactance in the circuit. A transformer bank can provide the inductive reactance matching the capacitive reactance of the cable. The inductive load and the capacitive load must be in series with each other, and this occurs when only one or two phases are energized. Resonance is most likely to occur when switching single-pole devices on a high-voltage distribution underground cable feeding a transformer with a delta primary.

One example of ferroresonance on an overhead 115-kilovolt line occurred when one of the blades of a gang-operated air-break switch failed to open during the isolation of a substation transformer. With one phase closed, the unloaded transformer became an inductive load connected in series with the 115-kilovolt line. The paralleling 115-kilovolt conductors supplied the capacitive load. A corona discharge was seen on the 115-kilovolt conductors, and surge arrestors operated as the voltage climbed higher.

Prevention of Ferroresonance

13.12.8 Ferroresonance can be avoided by removing one of the causes of the phenomenon (see Table 13–6). By changing the design of the installation or changing the switching procedure, the capacitance, inductance, series connection, or loading can be changed.

TABLE 13–6   **Prevention of Ferroresonance**

Causal Factor	Action
Operating single-pole switches to energize or de-energize an underground cable feeding a three-phase transformer allows the transformer coils to be an inductive load in series with the circuit.	Install a three-phase gang-operated switch.
If there is no load on the transformers when they are energized, the low resistance in the circuit causes a higher voltage when resonance occurs.	Keep a load on the transformer when it is being energized or de-energized. The increased resistance in the circuit will lower the effects of resonance.
A three-phase bank with a grounded wye primary shorts out the two windings that are part of the series circuit, causing induction.	At the planning stage, where possible, use a transformer with a wye primary and the wye point connected to the neutral.
Changing the length of the underground cable feeding the three-phase transformer will change the amount of capacitive reactance in the circuit.	Changing the length of the cable as a retrofit is probably an expensive option. Calculating the length needed to avoid ferroresonance is complex.
	The changing inductive reactance that occurs before the transformer core becomes saturated means that there is also a range of capacitive reactance that will at some point be equal to the inductive reactance.
A wye primary with a floating (ungrounded) neutral is susceptible to ferroresonance.	Temporarily ground the floating neutral of the wye primary, which will short out the series circuit.
	A three-phase bank with a grounded wye primary shorts out the two windings that are part of the series circuit causing induction.

13.13 Tingle Voltage

What Is Tingle Voltage?

13.13.1 The term *tingle voltage* (also called *stray voltage*) refers to a small voltage that is noticed by people or animals while contacting certain equipment or hardware. This occurs when there is an unacceptable voltage between the neutral and earth.

A system neutral on a utility distribution circuit will have some voltage on it in relation to a remote ground. This voltage is kept very low, normally below 10 volts, by grounding at each transformer and at other locations. At a transformer, the primary neutral is bonded to the secondary neutral. This connection takes advantage of the customer-service grounds to lower the voltage on the neutral even more and to prevent a potentially dangerous open circuit in the grounding network. However, depending on the quality of grounds and other factors, there will still be some voltage left on the neutral.

With the ground bonded to the neutral at the service entrance, the safety ground will have some voltage on it because it is connected to appliances, equipment, and fixtures by the many electrical circuits coming out of the customer panel. Tingle voltage occurs between a grounded object and a remote ground. There will always be some current flow back to the circuit's source through earth. Where there is current flow, there has to be some voltage. Figure 13–20 shows how a circuit can be established through a person between a shower control and a main drain.

Examples of Tingle Voltage Problems

13.13.2 The voltage between the neutral and earth is normally well below the threshold of sensation for the vast majority of customers. Very vulnerable cus-

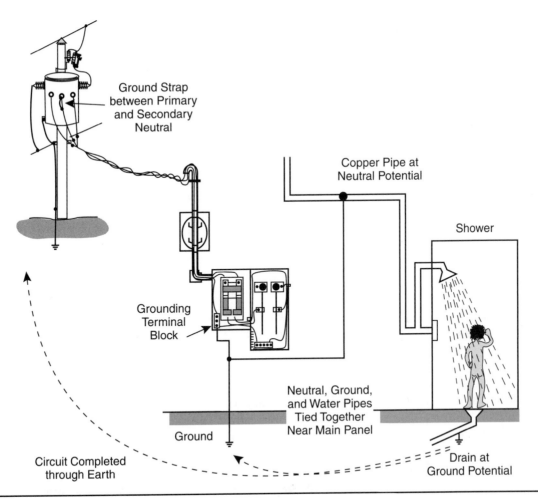

Figure 13–20 Tingle voltage in a shower.

tomers, such as dairy farms, require additional efforts to reduce tingle voltage. Milk cows have been the most vulnerable to tingle voltage. A small voltage between the stanchions, water bowl, or milking machine in relation to the floor that the cow is standing on results in a current flow that turns the animal into a "dancing cow." In these conditions, a cow can feel a potential difference as low as 0.5 volt.

Normally, people would not feel tingle voltage because 10 volts or less is not enough to overcome a person's skin resistance. However, skin resistance is reduced when it gets wet. People have noticed tingle voltage in a shower, kitchen, wet basement, or barn. In a shower, a person can feel a potential difference as low as 2 volts.

Investigating a Tingle Voltage Problem

13.3.3 Although it is not usually part of a line worker's job to investigate a service past the meter, some typical customer-generated tingle voltage is listed here for information.

- There should be only one electrical connection between the neutral and earth: at the service entrance. A connection between the neutral and the safety ground wire at an appliance some distance from the main panel will mean that the neutral and safety ground will be parallel paths. This will encourage more current flow through the safety ground wire. More current in the safety ground wire will mean more voltage in the safety ground network.

- There could be a poor neutral or ground connection at the service entrance or at junctions.

- There could be ineffective grounding due to poor earth, insufficient number of ground rods, or poor ground rod connections.

- There could be too much load on one leg of the 120-volt service, which will result in more current returning to the source through the neutral and ground.

- There could be a voltage on an electrical appliance because there is no safety ground connection.

- There could be worn or poor insulation in wiring or equipment. Leakage to ground will flow back to the source.

Measuring Tingle Voltage

13.13.4 To find the existence of tingle voltage, connect an AC/DC voltmeter between the neutral and remote earth (a temporary ground rod about 50 feet [15 meters] away). The voltmeter should be able to measure as low as 0.1 volt.

Table 13–7 shows how a voltmeter is used to find the source of tingle voltage.

The Utility as a Source of Tingle Voltage

13.13.5 Single-phase circuits have current flowing back to the source through the neutral, and a portion of this current flows through the parallel path in earth. When there is a current flow, there is some voltage. A heavily loaded single-phase circuit will have an unacceptable voltage buildup on the neutral if the neutral is poorly grounded. Normally, the voltage on the neutral should not exceed 10 volts.

Delta circuits and three-phase circuits have considerably less current flowing back to the source through earth because the phase conductors carry current back

TABLE 13–7   **Finding the Source for Tingle Voltage**

If	Then
A DC voltage is found between the neutral and earth.	The likely cause is communications circuits or cathodic protection on a nearby pipeline.
An AC voltage is found between the neutral and earth.	Disconnect the customer at the transformer but leave the neutral connected. If the voltage drops to 0, the problem originates with customer equipment. If the voltage remains the same, it is a neutral-to-earth voltage problem. Ensure that the neutral is intact all the way back to the substation.
The common neutral is intact back to the substation.	Start sectionalizing the primary feeder, starting with the primary circuit downstream from the customer. Continue to sectionalize until there is a drop in neutral-to-earth voltage at the complaining customer. A drop in voltage will mean the section of line causing the problem has been found.
The section causing the neutral-to-earth voltage is found.	Check for a defective neutral. Check for the existence of a large customer on the same circuit. Check for defective equipment causing a ground current by disconnecting the customer and looking for a drop in neutral-to-earth voltage at the complaining customer. If the customer is on a heavily loaded single-phase circuit, there may be an unacceptable voltage buildup on the neutral if the neutral is poorly grounded.
The source of the complaint is a high system neutral voltage and there is a need for an engineering solution.	Engineering solutions include the following: • Additional ground rods are driven to lower the voltage on the neutral. • A larger neutral conductor can be strung to promote more current flow through the neutral and less through earth. • A conversion to three phase will promote more current returning to the source in the other phases and less current flow in the neutral.
An immediate solution is required.	Have the customer install a tingle voltage filter. In an emergency, with concurrence from the supervisor, split the secondary neutral from the primary at the transformer. Install a warning sign on the pole to warn others about the split neutral.

to the source. The more evenly the load is balanced on the three phases, the less current there is in the neutral.

If the voltage on the neutral has to be lowered, *then* the following actions are taken:

• Neutral connections are checked.

• Additional ground rods are driven to lower the voltage on the neutral.

- A larger neutral conductor can be strung to promote more current flow through the neutral and less through earth.

- Conversion to a three-phase circuit is done to promote more current returning to the source in the other phases and less current flow in the neutral.

Neutral Separation at the Transformer

13.13.6 In extreme cases, a high neutral voltage on the utility supply system will be isolated from the customer's neutral by removing the connection between the primary neutral and the secondary neutral at the transformer. The separation of the neutral, as shown in Figure 13–21, is a hazard to utility personnel because there could be a potential difference across the open circuit between the primary and secondary neutral. Under fault conditions, the voltage on the transformer tank or on the down-ground could be lethal.

A gas-tube type of surge protector can be installed between the secondary neutral and the transformer tank. During a voltage surge, the protector sparks over internally and temporarily connects the secondary neutral to the transformer tank. With the transformer tank connected to the down-ground and primary neutral, the primary and secondary neutrals are temporarily connected together, thereby

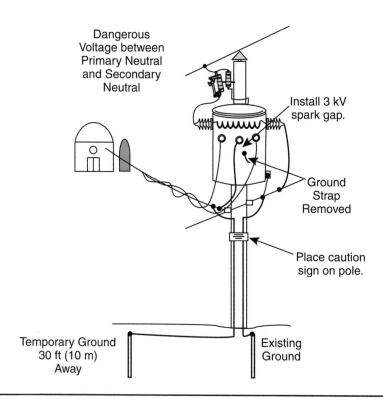

Figure 13–21 Neutral separation at transformer.

preventing a secondary insulation failure in the transformer. A caution sign is normally placed on the pole to alert powerline workers to the hazard of the separated neutrals.

Customer Remedial Action

13.13.7 The usual first step to reduce the voltage on the neutral is to improve the grounding of the neutral at the service entrance. An inspection of the insulation of the wiring, neutral connections, and safety ground connections is also carried out.

The neutral-to-earth voltage can be reduced to acceptable levels by installing a tingle-voltage filter, which is designed for this purpose. It is possible to install a grid bonded to the source of the tingle voltage, using the same principle as the grid attached to tension machines when stringing near live circuits. A grid on the stable floor bonded to the stanchion and water bowl would ensure that there is no exposure to any difference of potential. This is not always practical as a retrofit.

13.14 Investigating a Radio and Television Interference (TVI) Complaint

TVI Trouble Calls

13.14.1 Trouble calls involving finding and fixing the source of radio and television interference (TVI) can be a frustrating experience for the lines trade. Customers that have interference with their reception are quite often on the fringe of being too far from the radio or television transmitter. The source of the interference is not always obvious and is not always due to the electrical-utility facilities. Having a technician who uses specialized instrumentation is the best way to find difficult TVI sources. While checking the instrument or listening to an AM radio, the source pole of TVI can often be found by giving a pole a bump with a sledge hammer.

Three Main Sources of TVI on Utility Facilities

13.14.2 The three main sources of TVI on utility-owned electrical circuits are these:

- Loose hardware
- Defective insulators
- Corona discharge

Table 13–8 provides some assistance in finding the source of TVI.

Loose Hardware

Loose hardware is the most common and the most intense source of TVI. Sparking occurs between loose pieces of metal that are not electrically bonded to each other. For example, a washer does not make a good electric connection to a bolt unless the bolt is tight.

When the wood on a wood pole or crossarm dries and shrinks, the hardware loosens. Dielectric gaps build up where metal pieces are not forming a tight bond with each other, and sparking occurs across the gap. The sparking occurs in repetitive bursts, which results in a radiated noise that interferes with radio and television reception.

TABLE 13–8   **Finding the Source of TVI**

If	Then
The interference is intermittent.	The probable cause of intermittent noise is loose hardware.
The interference is continuous.	The probable cause of continuous noise is from a stable source such as a defective insulator.
The interference appears to be weather dependent.	The noise is most likely from the powerline and not from within the customer's home if the interference occurs during dry weather but disappears during a rain.
The interference is prevalent throughout the neighborhood.	The TVI has a strong source, and the powerline is a probable cause when the noise is prevalent throughout the neighborhood.
The interference affects only one customer.	The noise probably comes from equipment in the building when a weak source only affects one customer.
The interference occurs at similar specific times.	When the noise occurs during specific times, such as during working hours, the TVI could be from industrial equipment such as an arc welder. This type of source should also produce a noise throughout the neighborhood.
The interference on the customer's television occurs on both the video and the audio.	The source is strong when both the audio and the video are affected. The audio signal of a television is an FM signal and is not as vulnerable to interference. If only the audio is affected, the problem is probably within the customer's equipment.
The interference is from devices in the customer's premises.	Devices in the home that have been known to cause noise are an electric motor, a fluorescent light, electronic equipment, a doorbell transformer, flashing decorative lighting, an aquarium pump, heating pad, dimmer switch, or refrigerator butter conditioner.
The interference is from an outdoor source other than a powerline.	Check for potential sources such as radio and television transmitters or two-way radio transmitters used by police, utilities, and other businesses.
The noise is the same across all television channels.	Depending on the strength of the noise, channels 2 to 6 are affected first, channels 7 to 13 are affected next, and UHF is almost never affected. Suspect the television itself if the noise is constant for all channels.

Defective Insulators

Pin-type insulators on subtransmission lines have been a common source of TVI. The problems typically occurred with older insulators or poor conductor ties. Newer pin-type insulators have a semiconducting glaze (Q glaze) on the top surface of the insulator. The semiconducting glaze provides an equipotential area that prevents sparking between the conductor, the conductor ties, and the insulator.

Corona Discharge

Corona discharge as a source of TVI is most likely from higher-voltage circuits. The discharge emanates from sharp points on live hardware. It is most likely to show up when a new line is first put into service or after maintenance work is carried out on the line. The design of the live hardware on a high-voltage circuit requires everything to be smooth or rounded off. The usual cause of a corona discharge is a connection that is not properly smoothed off. Radio noise because of corona discharge should be a rare occurrence.

Review Questions

1. What does quality power look like?

2. Name four types of disturbances to power quality that can be continuous.

3. What is a common fix for poor-quality power?

4. The neutral and the safety ground are normally tied together at the transformer supplying the service and also at the service panel. What happens when the safety ground is tied together downstream on the customer's premises?

5. What influences the amount of voltage drop in a circuit?

6. Why do distribution circuits have larger conductors than what is needed for ampacity?

7. The leads going in and out of a set of voltage regulators are very small compared to the main line conductors. Will the relatively small leads affect the capacity of the feeder to supply the load?

8. Why would a time delay of 10 seconds on a voltage regulator not be considered a good practice?

9. When a circuit is temporarily fed in reverse through a regulator, what adjustments should be made at the regulator?

10. How does a set of capacitors installed on a distribution feeder benefit the electrical system?

11. How much current can be expected in the leads feeding a 450-kVAR capacitor bank on a 25/14.4-kilovolt system?

12. When a capacitor is isolated with the intent to reenergize, why is it necessary to wait 5 minutes before reenergizing?

13. Name three possible causes of a low-voltage trouble call.

14. Name three possible sources for flickering lights.

15. How can ferroresonance be prevented when energizing a three-phase transformer bank?

16. What can a utility do to reduce the risk of being the cause of tingle voltage at a customer?

17. Why is separating the primary neutral from the secondary neutral a hazard for powerline workers?

Working with Aerial Devices and Digger Derricks

Topics to Be Covered	Section
Checking Out the Truck	14.1
Monitoring a Hydraulic System	14.2
Stabilizing a Boom-Equipped Vehicle	14.3
Electrical Protection for Working with Noninsulated Booms	14.4
Electrical Protection for Working with Insulated Booms	14.5
Operating a Digger Derrick	14.6
Operating an Aerial Device	14.7

14.1 Checking Out the Truck

Typical Daily Pretrip Inspection

14.1.1 A daily pretrip inspection is required by law for large trucks. Most utilities/employers require a pretrip inspection for other fleet vehicles. Under the law, the driver is totally responsible for the vehicle. If a truck has poor brakes, is overloaded, or has defective tires, any charges laid will be to the driver, not the mechanic or the utility/employer. Most utilities have a list or illustration showing the items to be checked in some logical order and a requirement to record the results in a logbook. When a different truck is introduced to your crew, make sure you have been shown the inspection points unique to that truck.

To reduce the possibility of a high-risk failure, prioritize on specific items that can lead to a catastrophic failure:

- Check for signs that indicate lug nuts are loose. An off-center valve stem in a truck wheel opening is an indicator of a loose wheel. Visual indicators can also be installed, such as those shown in Figure 14–1.

Figure 14–1 Loose lug nut indicators.

- Too much travel (should be less than 2.5 inches/6 cm) in the slack adjusters of an air brake is a common fault leading to poor braking performance. The angle between the push rod and the adjuster arm should not be more than 90 degrees when the brakes are applied. (See Figure 14–2.)

- Check for a leaking hub or axle seal. If equipped with a sight glass on the wheel, check the oil level.

- Adjust trailer brakes so that they will not lock up when a brake pedal is applied. A trailer with locked-up brakes can slide sideways and strike other vehicles.

Summary of Pretrip Air-Brake Inspection

14.1.2 The following summary of a pretrip air-brake inspection is a memory jogger only and assumes that the driver has checked under the hood and will inspect the physical condition of the braking system and slack adjusters.

1. Drain air tanks to zero pressure, then do the following:

   1.1. Build up pressure; low-air warning signal cuts out at 60 psi (415 kPa) minimum.

   1.2. Pressure buildup between 85 to 100 psi (590 to 690 kPa) must be less than 2 minutes.

   1.3. Governor cuts out between 100 and 135 psi (690 to 930 kPa).

2. At full pressure, fan the brake pedal, then check the following:

   2.1. After a drop of about 25 psi (170 kPa) from the maximum pressure, the governor should cut in.

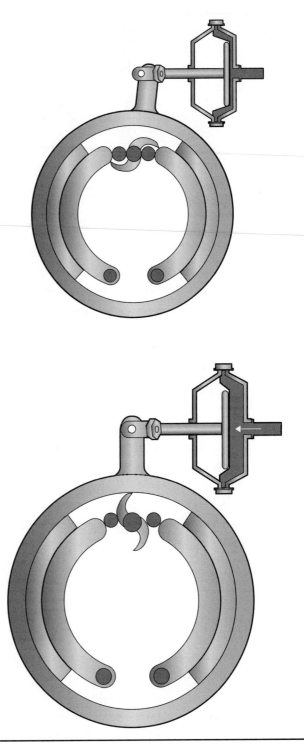

Figure 14–2 Slack adjusters.

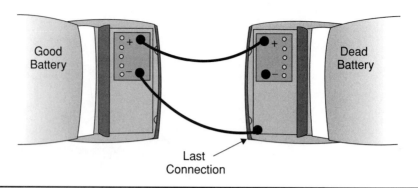

Figure 14–3   Jump-starting a vehicle.

    2.2. At about 60 psi (415 kPa) minimum, the low-air warning cuts in.

    2.3. Between 45 and 20 psi (300 to 140 kPa), the parking brakes (spring brakes) should come on automatically.

3. Build back to full pressure, then do the following:

    3.1. With engine stopped, fully apply the foot brake and hold for 1 minute. Pressure drop must be less than 2 psi (15 kPa). With a trailer, the drop must be less than 4 psi (30 kPa).

    3.2. With the engine at idle speed and the transmission in first gear, check the parking brake adjustment by trying to move forward.

    3.3. With the parking brakes off, drive ahead and apply the service brake as a check for response.

With the truck in motion, activate the trailer brakes (spike) as a check for response.

Jump-Starting

14.1.3 A battery gives off explosive hydrogen gas. A spark near a battery can trigger an explosion.

1. Before jump-starting, check that the fluid level is normal and that the battery is not frozen. A maintenance-free battery should not be jump-started if the indicator is red.

2. Only the last connection will cause a spark that could ignite the hydrogen gas. The last connection should, therefore, be a negative (ground) connection (Figure 14–3) at a location remote from the battery to the truck frame.

Studs are often installed on large trucks to facilitate jump-starting. Look under the hood or near the driver's side step for a remote positive jump-starting stud, and look for a negative grounding stud on the truck frame.

Turning on the headlights or some other load on the truck with the good battery truck will reduce the risk of a damaging voltage surge to electronic equipment.

Ways to Reduce High-Risk Driving Hazards

14.1.4 Driving a truck is part of a lineworker's job. Below are some tips that will reduce the risk of some typical utility truck accidents.

- Never use the hand valve to apply brakes only to the trailer. Locked brakes on a trailer can cause the trailer to slide sideways into other traffic.

- Do not jam on the brakes in an emergency. When the wheels lock up, the truck will go into an uncontrolled skid and steering will be impossible. For a truck without antilock brakes use "stab" braking in an emergency stop. Emergency braking for a truck with antilock brakes requires steady and increasing pressure on the brake pedal. There may be variations for the most effective braking for trucks with antilock braking; check the owner's manual.

- Watch for restricted roadway height or width. Many derrick diggers and aerial devices are close to the maximum dimensions of 13 feet, 6 inches (4.15 m) in height and 8 feet, 6 inches (2.6 m) in width. A jib left out at an angle or a protruding outrigger can cause a vehicle to be over the height or width limits.

- Be in the correct lower gear before starting down a steep hill. Overreliance on brakes to slow down a truck will cause the brakes to overheat and become ineffective.

- When extra space is needed to make a turn with a truck and trailer, take the extra space from the street you are entering, not from the street you are leaving.

- To save confusion when backing a trailer, leave your hands on the bottom of the steering wheel. The trailer will go in the direction of your hands. Use an observer when backing. If there is no observer, walk around the vehicle before backing up.

14.2 Monitoring a Hydraulic System

Inspecting Hydraulic Equipment

14.2.1 The inspection of any hydraulic equipment should be treated as a separate inspection from the vehicle it is mounted on and recorded separately in a log book. An operator must be trained on the inspection, stability, and capacity of each type of hydraulic unit being used.

Hydraulic Fluid Hazard

14.2.2 Hydraulic fluid coming from a pinhole in a hydraulic hose under pressure can pierce the skin. A leak from a pinhole is not normally visible. Fluid under the skin is a serious injury/infection and needs medical treatment.

Never investigate hydraulic leaks with the system under pressure. Insulated hose without steel reinforcement is especially susceptible to this type of leak. Look for kinks in the hose and oil gathering in places near the hose.

A Conductive Vacuum in a Hydraulic Hose

14.2.3 The weight of fluid in a hydraulic line having a separation distance of more than 35 feet (11 m) between the oil reservoir and the upper end of the hydraulic line will drop in the line somewhat and drain into the reservoir. The partial vacuum formed at the top of the hydraulic line has a lower resistance to an electrical flashover than hydraulic fluid or air at atmospheric pressure.

Check valves installed in the hydraulic line prevents the fluid level in the line from dropping and creating an electrically conductive vacuum. Vent valves are installed, as a backup, to allow air to enter the hydraulic line and to keep it at atmospheric pressure. The filter in the valve keeps dirt out. These valves need cleaning. These valves are critical for barehand work where the insulation of the boom and hydraulics provide primary protection.

Troubleshooting a Hydraulic System

14.2.4 Only insulated hydraulic fluids are used in insulated aerial devices. The fluid must be kept clean to prevent an electrical failure.

The touch, sound, look, and smell of hydraulic oil can give clues about impending problems that need correction.

Touch

1. *Caution:* If there is any suspicion of a hydraulic fluid leak and its location is unknown, *do not* try to find the leak by touching any hydraulic lines while the system is under pressure.

2. If the hydraulic pump or a hose is too hot to touch, oxidation in the fluid will cause sludge to form and create more heat and an eventual breakdown. The maximum temperature of hydraulic oil is 135°F (57°C).

3. If a high frequency vibration can be felt when touching steel fittings, it is a sign of a damaging condition that needs correction.

Sound

1. A loud shotlike sound (*water hammer*) is caused by a sudden stoppage of the fluid in the system. A resulting pressure surge can be as high as four times the normal pressure. Feathering the controls (easing the valve open slowly) or some corrective plumbing may be needed to prevent this potentially damaging fault. Valves controlled by radio or by fiber optics are designed to prevent shock loading.

2. A sound like the hydraulic pump is pumping marbles indicates that the pump is pumping more fluid than the system can supply to it. This causes a partial vacuum in the fluid at the pump (*cavitation*).

3. A high-pitched whine indicates back pressure at the pump. This often happens when the fluid is not properly warmed up and too thick to pump at the normal rated speed.

Look and Smell

1. Check the fluid level in the hydraulic oil reservoir.

2. Check the appearance of the oil. A milky appearance means the oil is saturated with air or water.

3. If any of the cylinders have jerky or erratic movement, air may be in the system or a cylinder rod may be bent.

4. A burnt fluid smell indicates that the system is being subjected to high temperatures caused by air bubbles in the oil cavitating at the pump.

Causes of Hydraulic Pump Failure

14.2.5 A partial vacuum in the fluid at the pump is the most common cause of cavitation and hydraulic pump failure.

- Cavitation occurs when the pump is over-revved or brought up to speed before the fluid has warmed up enough to flow adequately.
- Cavitation occurs when the fluid level is low in the reservoir.
- Cavitation occurs when the fluid filter or a suction line is restricted.
- Cavitation occurs when the shut-off valve fails to open after repairs.

Proper Warm-Up for Hydraulic Systems

14.2.6 When the temperature is below freezing, the hydraulic pump can be damaged by running it at the rated rpm while the oil is cold.

A typical warm-up would be to set the engine speed at 600 rpm, (1,000 rpm for diesel engines), to engage the hydraulic pump, to let it run for about 10 minutes, and then to increase the engine speed gradually until it reaches the specified rpm. *Caution:* The rpms may increase to damaging levels as the unit warms up.

High-Pressure Hoses

14.2.7 Compression tools, wrenches, hot-line tools, and tree-trimming tools being operated from the tool outlet at the bucket level must use hydraulic hoses rated for 10,000 psi and must be nonconducting (generally, orange).

A metal-reinforced hydraulic hose, used by mistake, has caused an electric short that resulted in a ruptured hose and a hydraulic fluid fire in the bucket.

Checking Holding Valves

14.2.8 A holding valve will keep a boom up in the air even if a hydraulic hose fails. The following describes how to do a drift check on the holding valves:

1. Extend the outriggers.
2. Put the boom into the positions shown in Figures 14–4 and 14–5.
3. Shut off the vehicle.
4. Activate the valves to lower outriggers and booms in the various positions shown in Figures 14–4 and 14–5. Hold the positions for 15 seconds.

Any movement downward indicates that the holding valve needs maintenance or that air is in the system. A formal drift test can be done in the same

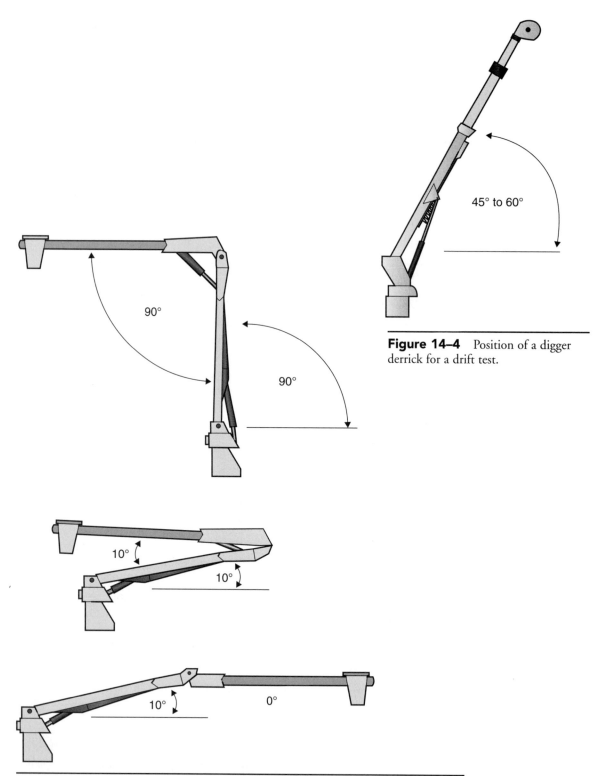

Figure 14–4 Position of a digger derrick for a drift test.

Figure 14–5 Position of an aerial device boom for a drift test.

way, except that the boom is loaded with its rated load and held for a given period of time.

Emergency Lowering of an Aerial-Device Boom

14.2.9 The lower controls are used to bring down the boom in an emergency. The lower controls must be well marked to lessen confusion during an emergency. The lower controls override the upper controls.

It is a given that the crew member on the ground has been trained and has practiced bringing down the boom using the lower controls, removing a casualty from the bucket, and performing necessary CPR and first aid.

Lowering a Boom without Hydraulic Power

14.2.10 When there is a loss of hydraulic power and the boom has to be lowered by manipulating the holding valves, any worker(s) in the bucket(s) should first lower themselves from the bucket to the ground using an approved, and practiced, method and equipment.

It is a given that anyone working from a bucket has been trained and has practiced escaping from the bucket while it is aloft.

Once no one is in the bucket, there remains no urgency to lower the boom and store the outriggers. Generally, no-power lowering is best left to a mechanic or specialist because it is very easy to lose control of the process.

Some units have an auxiliary battery-operated pump to lower the boom in case of a loss of hydraulic power. Some units have hydraulic couplers that allow the hydraulic system of another truck (preferably a truck with clean insulating fluid to prevent contamination) to connect and operate the disabled system.

14.3 Stabilizing a Boom-Equipped Vehicle

Procedure for Stabilizing a Boom-Equipped Vehicle

14.3.1 To reduce the risk of a tip over a truck needs to be set up on a firm level foundation as described in Table 14–1, before using the boom.

Stability on a Slope

14.3.2 Boom-type equipment is designed to work at a slope of 5 degrees or less. The danger of rotation gear failure or tipping over increases with the slope.

Working over the uphill side or the end of a truck improves stability, but rotating a load uphill or downhill will overstress the rotation gears. If work is planned for the uphill side of the unit, plan all lifting so that very little load is on the rotation gears.

The stability of some corner-mount digger derricks can be derated by as much as 40 percent over the downhill side, even if the unit is on a slope of less than 5 degrees. Training and introduction of any unit to a new operator would include any unique stability features.

TABLE 14–1   Stabilizing a Boom-Equipped Vehicle

Step	Action	Details
1	Ensure that the mechanical and hydraulic systems of the unit have been maintained.	Ensure that normal maintenance has been carried out.
		1. Learn the location and check critical welds for surface cracks and lines of rust.
		2. Check pin retainers at pivot points.
		After any repair or hydraulic oil leak, put the boom through its full cycle to ensure that all hoses are full of oil and that there will be no sudden collapse of the boom because of an air pocket. On a scheduled basis, do a drift test on the holding valves. Keep a log book on the hydraulic unit.
2	Apply the parking brake and chock blocks.	Hydraulic-braked trucks with boom equipment have both a mechanical parking brake and a hydraulic locking brake (*accumulock*). Both must be on.
		Caution: Hydraulic parking brakes can bleed off. Should this happen when the job is finished and the outriggers are raised, the truck will be free to roll down a slope unless chock blocks and the mechanical parking brake are applied.
		If they are properly adjusted, the parking brakes on air-braked trucks are very reliable.
		With the vehicle on an incline, extending the outriggers reduces the holding power of the tires. Use wheel chocks to help prevent the vehicle from sliding downhill.
		Actions of the boom sometimes cause the truck to shift on the outrigger planks, especially if the wheels are off the ground. Stability can be increased by anchoring the truck to another truck and/or installing chock blocks, front and back.
3	Use outrigger pads and other means to provide a solid surface for outriggers.	Loss of stability can occur because the outriggers penetrate into the earth, asphalt, or concrete or because the vehicle slips off the outrigger pads. Each outrigger should be on pads (Figure 14–6) to offer a greater surface-for-weight distribution.

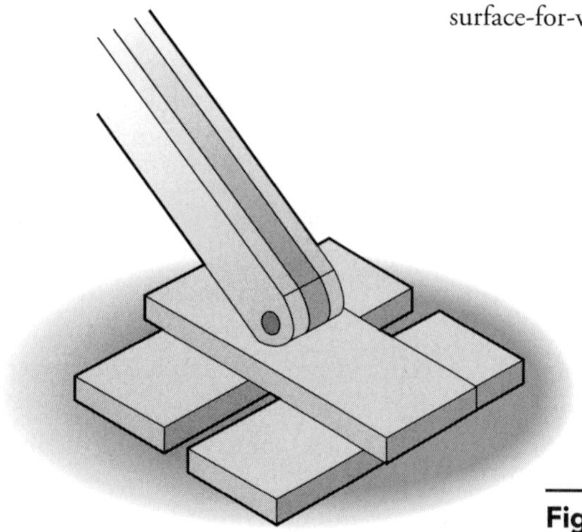

Figure 14–6   An outrigger on pads.

Step	Action	Details
4	Extend outriggers (stabilizers).	The outriggers should lift all the weight normally supported by the springs. Some telescoping outriggers will have a mark indicating the minimum extension needed to provide stability.
		Units with only two outriggers (trucks with the turret mounted just behind the cab) will sometimes have the front wheels lifted from the ground. Planking or support under the front wheels is needed to prevent a sudden shock-loading drop when the boom is rotated toward the front of the truck.
		Keep the outrigger in sight, or make sure that all people are clear while lowering the outrigger.
5	Level the vehicle to less than 5° on a slope.	On sloping ground, extend the low-side outrigger first, then extend the other outrigger(s) until the unit is level. It may be necessary to build up the low side with extra timbers or to dig out the high side or to use the pads specifically made for slopes. If a telescoping-type outrigger cannot be extended far enough, it creates a stability hazard (Figure 14–7). A radial-type outrigger has an advantage over the telescoping-type outrigger for this problem.

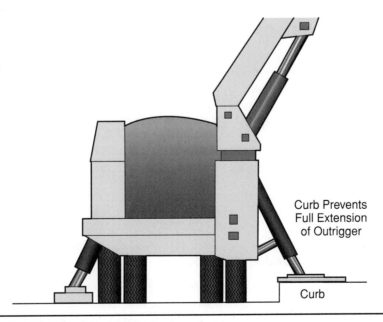

Figure 14–7 An outrigger extension hazard.

(continued)

TABLE 14–1   Continued

Step	Action	Details
6	Trucks without Outriggers	The truck must be set up as level as possible. A boom over the side can put a truck without outriggers on a 3-degree tilt. If the truck is set up initially on a 5-degree slope, the unit could be operating on an 8-degree tilt.
		The low side can be built up by driving up on pads (Figure 14–8) or similar material.
		It is critical to the stability of the truck to maintain proper tire pressure and to learn the inspection points for the stability features of the vehicle.

Figure 14–8   Buildup on the low side of a truck.

14.4 Electrical Protection for Working with Noninsulated Booms

Types of Contact Hazards with Noninsulated Booms

14.4.1   Table 14–2 gives examples as to how a vehicle with a noninsulated boom can become an electrical hazard on a job site to people on the ground.

Protection from Shock around Noninsulated Booms

14.4.2   The only real protections available when a boom makes contact with a live conductor are as follow:

1. *Staying on the vehicle or on a ground-gradient mat* bonded to the vehicle will keep a person at the same potential as the vehicle. As long as a person avoids contact with anything not connected to the vehicle, no current will flow through that person to another object.

2. *Keeping a safe distance away from a vehicle* will keep a person from making inadvertent contact and will keep a person away from any high ground

TABLE 14–2 When a Noninsulated Boom Is Hazardous

If	Then
A person, on the ground, is *in contact* with a utility vehicle, winch line, or power-installed anchor while the noninsulated portion of a boom contacts a live circuit.	The person is a parallel path to ground and will take *some* share of the current flowing to ground.
A person on the ground is *near* a utility vehicle while the noninsulated portion of a boom accidentally contacts a live circuit.	The person is exposed to ground gradients at each location where current is entering the earth.

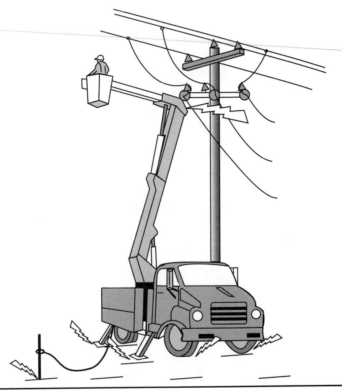

Figure 14–9 Ground-gradient hazard around a truck.

In a high-induction area, a noninsulated boom is used to lift or handle an *isolated and grounded* conductor.	Unless the boom is bonded to the grounded conductors, the boom can be at a different potential than the conductors being handled.

gradients. A wireless remote-control operating system and/or truck barricading promotes the ability to stay away from the vehicle.

3. *Electrical shock-resistant footwear* is a last-resort safety barrier. The increased resistance offered to a worker will provide some additional protection from being in a parallel path to ground and from ground gradients.

Barricading a Vehicle	**14.4.3** The best protection when working near a vehicle with a noninsulated boom (if not on the vehicle) is staying away from the vehicle, the trailer, and any attachments. Barricading promotes keeping a distance from the vehicle.

If the barricades are put in place before they are needed, workers tend to routinely violate the barricades as they prepare a transformer or frame a pole. The operator of a boom should ensure that everyone stays away from the vehicle when the boom is to be moved near a live circuit.

Reducing the Risk of Accidental Contact with a Conductor

14.4.4 Take steps to reduce the risk of a boom contact with a live conductor.

1. Use a signal person, other than the equipment operator, to watch the approach distance to exposed lines and equipment and to give timely warnings before the minimum approach distance is reached.

2. A noninsulated boom, with a utility-trained operator, should not get closer than the allowed minimum approach distance unless the truck is grounded, a signal person is available, and protective cover-up is installed.

Communicating with the Derrick Operator

14.4.5 Use hand signals or a two-way radio to communicate with a derrick or crane operator.

- Have only one signal person.

- Be sure that the signal person and the operator are using the same signals. Figure 14–10 shows eight standard hand signals.

- The signal person watches the load, and the crane operator watches the signal person.

- Make sure the load does not pass above workers.

- Watch for the minimum approach distance to the powerline.

- Watch for anyone who is not a safe distance from the vehicle or load.

Grounding the Vehicle

14.4.6 Grounding the truck promotes a fast trip-out of the circuit if the truck should become alive. A fast trip-out reduces risk by lowering the exposure time to the hazard; it does not eliminate a potentially fatal shock hazard for anyone touching the vehicle.

Note: Anyone touching a vehicle that has become alive will be a parallel path to ground and will, therefore, have some share of current going through their body. Even when the vehicle is grounded to an excellent ground, like a neutral, the amount of current going through the body could still be fatal.

The following are typical ground electrodes, listed in priority:

1. A permanent ground network such as a station ground, a neutral, or a tower ground.

2. An existing ground rod or an anchor rod in earth. (*Note:* A truck ground attached to the guy steel could cause the guy to burn off during a fault.)

3. A temporary driven ground rod. (*Note:* The down-ground on a pole is often too small to carry the available fault current on the circuit.)

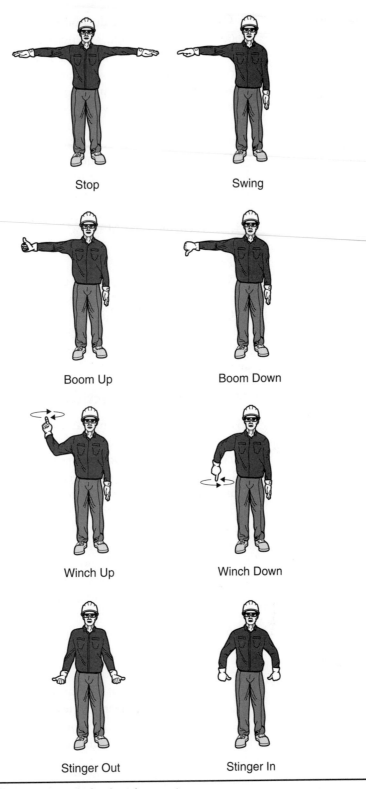

Figure 14–10   Hand signals for derrick operations.

On lower-voltage wye distribution systems, the vehicle must be grounded to a neutral to trip the circuit. The resistance of an existing ground rod or anchor rod will not normally be low enough to generate enough fault current to trip out the circuit. A ground rod may suffice on a circuit protected by a circuit breaker or electronic recloser with a ground trip relay.

On a delta circuit, the vehicle should be grounded to a ground rod. Many delta circuits will be protected by a ground fault relay, which will trip out a circuit when there is a line-to-ground fault.

On higher-voltage distribution and subtransmission circuits, the voltage will be high enough to overcome the resistance of a well-driven ground rod and will cause the circuit to trip out.

Boom Contact with an Isolated and Grounded Conductor

14.4.7 A circuit is not "dead" when it has been isolated and grounded. Current is often flowing in the grounds; a voltage difference often exists between the circuit and a remote ground.

When a noninsulated boom is used to handle conductors on a job where a circuit is isolated and grounded, the boom should be bonded to the protective line grounds.

On a transmission right-of-way that has high induction from live neighboring circuits, or in the rare case of accidental reenergization, bonding ensures that there will be no potential difference between the vehicle, boom or its wire rope winch, and conductors.

14.5 Electrical Protection for Working with Insulated Booms

Minimum Approach Distance with Insulated Booms

14.5.1 When a qualified operator is in the bucket of an electrically tested bucket truck, that bucket and boom should maintain the same minimum approach distance as a qualified worker must maintain when working on a hot line. Maintaining this distance will reduce the risk of inadvertent contact with other phases or objects at different potentials while working with rubber gloves or bare-handed. After protective cover-up is installed, a visible air space should be kept between the insulated portion of the boom and covered conductors.

An unqualified operator in a bucket should maintain a distance of 10 feet (3 m) from a distribution circuit and an additional 4 inches (10 cm) for every 10 kilovolts over that, which works out to 14 feet (4.3 m) for 169 kilovolts, 16 feet (4.9 m) for 230 kilovolts, and 25 feet (7.6 m) for 500 kilovolts.

Maintaining the Insulation Value of the Boom, Bucket, and Jib

14.5.2 To maintain the insulation value of a boom requires continuing care and maintenance.

- Keep the insulated section of the boom, bucket, and jib clean and dry. Maintain a waxed or silicone surface to repel water. Use specified cleaners only; abrasive cleaners can leave tiny scratches, and solvents can soften the surface coatings. A dry boom with a chalky or nonwater-repelling surface may pass the dry dielectric test and still fail electrically after a brief shower.

- Keep the boom interior clean and dry. Wash it out with a low-pressure washer (clean water only), rinse thoroughly, and dry it by leaving the boom in a vertical position or by pouring isopropanol down the boom as a drying agent. High-pressure water can cause water to diffuse through the fiberglass, which will require a very long time to dry out.

- Ensure that insulated booms, buckets, liners, and jibs get their scheduled electrical retests. A boom dielectrically tested while it is still wet can cause permanent damage.

- Boom and bucket covers prevent road salt and road wash from contaminating the insulated portions of a unit. They can also prolong the life of a boom by protecting it from the ultraviolet rays of the sun, causing the boom to look fuzzy when the fibers become exposed.

- Cover the jib or store it in a canvas bag or secured on padded holders in a truck bin.

- Boom leakage over 1 milliampere (1,000 microamperes) can leave track burns, typically inside the boom. If—when checking out the boom for barehand work or carrying out a formal electric test—the reading on the meter shows a return current approaching 1,000 microamperes, stop, clean, or dry the boom.

- Strap down the boom during travel. A boom subjected to vibration and shock loading will shorten the life of fiberglass, and the boom will be damaged where it sits on the boom rest.

Monitoring Boom Contamination

14.5.3 Barehand work and high-voltage rubber-glove work typically require that the aerial device have a boom-contamination monitoring circuit that will measure and monitor the actual leakage current of the insulated boom.

The initial certifying electrical proof test should be used as a reference point for future contamination monitoring. Keeping a log of every test will show trends that may develop.

The monitoring circuit of the aerial device (Figure 14–11) is checked before doing the boom-contamination test. The circuit can be tested for an open or short circuit using the "test" position on the same meter used to measure the leakage current.

A current test is made daily before starting work and before working on a higher voltage. A metal part of the boom or bucket grid is put in contact with the energized circuit to be worked on at intervals of 1 minute.

The microampere meter shows the amount of current between the upper electrode, which consists of all the metal components bonded together, and the lower electrode, which is the collector band mounted inside and outside of the boom, isolated from the metal lower boom. The leakage current should not exceed 1 microampere per kilovolt of the phase-to-phase voltage of the circuit. Many units will be well below this standard. See Table 14–3 for typical action required for poor contamination meter readings.

Caution: Intentionally letting a boom with high leakage current stay in contact with the circuit as a means to dry the boom will leave carbon tracking inside the boom, which will eventually lead to permanent damage and an electrical failure.

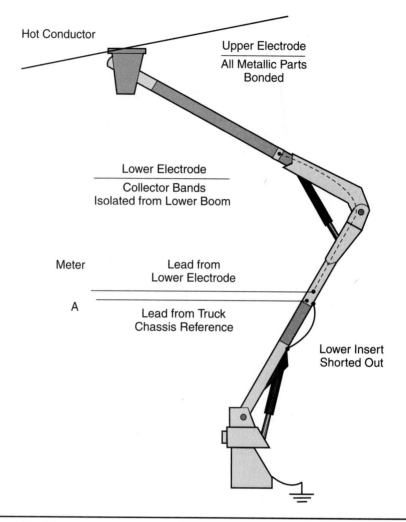

Figure 14–11 A boom-contamination monitoring circuit.

Grounding Vehicles with Insulated Booms

14.5.4 There have been instances of the noninsulated lower boom of an aerial device contacting a live underbuild or a lateral tap. These vehicles must be grounded to protect workers on the ground.

The need to ground an aerial device with an insulated lower boom insert is based on individual utility preference.

Caution: Some lower-boom inserts may have had their insulation short circuited to use the contamination monitoring system.

Caution: If a unit with an insulated lower-boom insert (which has not been shorted out) is used for work on a transmission line, a high voltage can be induced on the section of boom above the insert.

TABLE 14–3   **Contamination Meter Readings**

If	Then
The contamination meter reading is *high* (over 90) or there is a *sudden increase* in the contamination meter reading.	1. Try retesting with the lower-boom position farther away from the conductor (lessen induction). 2. If not successful, clean, dry, and retest the boom. 3. If not successful, remove truck from service and get it checked by specialists.
The contamination meter reading is *fluctuating* up and down.	1. Moisture is probably present. Wipe down the boom and remove the moisture inside of the boom by pouring isopropanol into it. 2. If not successful, there may be a fault in the boom insulation. Remove the truck from service and get it checked by specialists.
The contamination meter reading is showing a *gradual increase* from day to day.	1. There may be dirt contamination on the inside and outside surfaces of the boom. Clean the boom inside and out, let the boom dry out, and then retest. 2. The hydraulic oil may have become contaminated. Shut down the unit for about 15 minutes, drain the water from the reservoir, and then retest. If not successful, change the hydraulic oil and retest. 3. If not successful, there may be a fault in the boom insulation. Remove the truck from service and get it checked by specialists.

14.6 Operating a Digger Derrick

Lifting with a Digger Derrick

14.6.1 Reduce the risk of damaging a digger derrick boom by using the lifting charts and boom features available.

1. The lifting capacity chart for each type of digger derrick must be available to the vehicle operator. A lifting chart similar to the one shown in Figure 14–12 should be visible from the boom operator's position.

2. There is decreased lifting capacity as the boom is extended away from the turret location (see Table 14–4).

3. The winch and stinger can lift loads in a position that will overload the boom.

4. The lifting capacity changes with the direction of the boom in relation to the truck, outriggers, and slope of the ground. Figure 14–13 provides a sample of the derated lifting capacity of a corner-mount two-outrigger unit on an uphill slope.

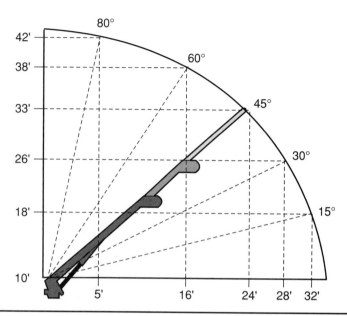

Figure 14–12 A typical digger derrick lifting-capacity chart.

TABLE 14–4 **Lifting Capacities for Digger Derricks**

All Booms Retracted	Boom Angle	80°	75°	60°	45°	30°	15°	0°
	Lbs. Load	9,500	7,900	5,500	4,300	3,700	3,350	2,950
Intermediate Boom Extended	Elevation	80°	75°	60°	45°	30°	15°	0°
	Lbs. Load	7,000	5,900	3,600	2,800	2,500	2,100	1,850
3rd Section Capacity	Elevation	80°	75°	60°	45°	30°	15°	0°
	Lbs. Load	4,000	3,400	2,000	1,450	1,200	1,100	1,000

Rotation Gear Failure Hazard

14.6.2 A rotation gear failure allows the boom and load to rotate freely into objects and people. The rotation gears are often the weakest link when pulling an object from a ditch, operating a heavy load with the truck set up on a slope, or installing a power anchor.

For example, the side-pull capacity of the boom in Figure 14–14 is only 750 pounds at a 23-foot radius.

- Do not pull a load as shown in Figure 14–14. Rather, rotate the boom toward the load to make the lift.

- Set up so that a power-installed screw anchor can be installed with the need for very little rotation. If rotation is necessary, make sure the boom is moved to follow the anchor as it is installed.

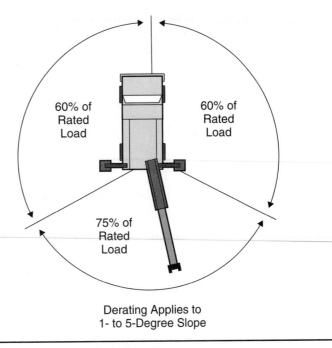

Derating Applies to
1- to 5-Degree Slope

Figure 14–13   Load capacity derated on slope.

- Do not try to loosen a pole setting for removal by rotating the boom side to side.
- Derate the lifting capacity of the boom when set up on a slope.

Lifting with a Digger Derrick Winch

14.6.3 The lifting capacity of a boom tip or turret winch and the strength of the winch cable or winch rope can be greater or less than the capability of the boom or load.

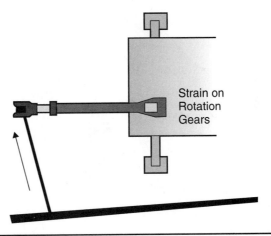

Figure 14–14   Rotating a load.

When the Winch Is Too Strong

A 1/2-inch wire rope winch cable (Table 14–5) with a 4,200-pound maximum working load is strong enough to break a boom or tip over a truck while lifting with the boom in one of many weak positions (seen in Figure 14–13 where a truck lifting capacity is derated on a slope). Make all lifts by booming up first, when the load is suspended, then lift with the winch.

When the Winch Is Too Weak

A digger derrick, with the boom in a vertical or strong position, will lift beyond the maximum working load of a 1/2-inch winch cable. A two-part line must be used to lift heavier weights than the maximum working load of the winch. Figure 14–15 shows the decreased tension on the cable when using a two-part pull.

Winching Failures

- If the winch creeps down under load, the winch brake needs maintenance.
- A rotating load on a winch will damage the winch cable and cause a premature failure. Use a tag line and/or a swivel-type load hook.

Checking a Unit's Overload Protection

14.6.4 If the unit is equipped with overload protection, certain boom functions will not operate when the unit is overloaded.

To check the overload protection, raise the boom to its maximum height until the system bypasses and try to extend the stinger. The stinger will not extend if the overload protection is working.

Lowering the boom to the bottom will reset the overload protection.

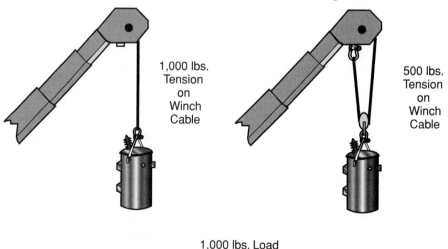

1,000 lbs. Tension on Winch Cable

500 lbs. Tension on Winch Cable

1,000 lbs. Load

Figure 14–15 A boom-tip winch.

TABLE 14–5   **Typical Digger Derrick Winch Cable Capacities**

Maximum Working Load for Winch Cable/Rope	
0.5-inch double-braided polyester rope	2,000 lbs./910 kg
0.75-inch double-braided polyester rope	3,500 lbs./1,590 kg
1-inch double-braided polyester rope	6,000 lbs./2,700 kg
1.25-inch double-braided polyester rope	10,000 lbs./4,500 kg
0.5-inch wire rope	4,200 lbs./1,900 kg

Pulling a Pole

14.6.5 To remove a pole out of the ground, use the hydraulic pole jack (butt puller) to pull a pole out of the ground. If necessary, use the auger to loosen a pole setting, then lift with the boom only.

Do not use the winch, the stinger, or the boom rotation to loosen the pole in the ground.

Do not use the auger as a stiff leg.

Installing a Screw Anchor

14.6.6 The torque needed to install a screw anchor varies with soil conditions, and it is, therefore, not difficult to apply more torque than the anchor can withstand. A unit with a "torque limiter" control can be set to limit the torque generated by the auger motor. Screw anchors have a torque rating stamped on them.

When installing a screw anchor, the anchor will draw the boom into the direction the anchor is going into the ground. This has been the cause of boom and rotation gear failures. Operate the boom so that it follows the anchor as it is screwed into the ground. Reduce the complexity of following the anchor by setting up the unit so that it is not necessary to rotate the boom, as well as by booming down. The risk of boom failure is reduced when the overload protection is working properly.

14.7 Operating an Aerial Device

Aerial-Device Boom Capacity

14.7.1 The lifting capacity of a boom is dependent on many variables.

Stability

The stability of the truck set-up affects the ability to lift the total weight shown on the lifting charts. Lifting charts assume a level, stable set-up. Some vehicles will have a derating factor for vehicles not parked on the level.

Boom Angles

Figure 14–16 provides *a sample only* of the information about lifting capacity that must be taken into account when operating an aerial device. Always use a lifting chart or table for the specific boom being used.

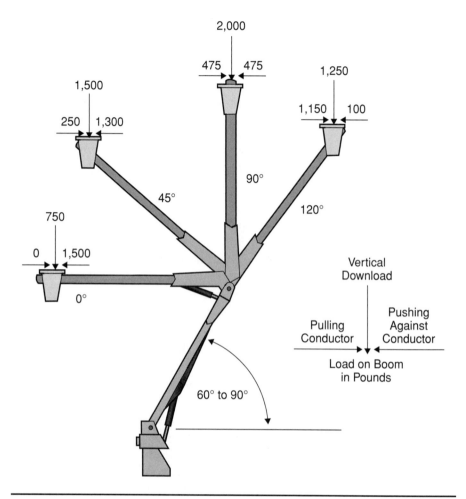

Figure 14–16 A sample lifting-capacity chart.

Caution: Determine whether or not the capacity chart you are using refers to "bare shaft capacity." If so, the total weight of the buckets, jib, and workers must be subtracted from the capacities shown on the chart.

Horizontal Loads

An aerial device is often used to lift conductors into and out of corner structures. Many manufacturers will state that no horizontal load is to be placed on their unit. Horizontal loading-capacity charts are not available for many units.

Moving conductors into a corner is a high-risk operation because the magnitude of the load is usually unknown and the load increases quickly as the conductor is moved into the bisect.

The horizontal loads shown in Figure 14–16 are sample numbers only. *Note:* Some boom configurations have virtually *no* horizontal load capacity. There is virtually no capacity to pull a conductor at a corner.

Jib Capacity

14.7.2 The loading of a jib is also dependent on the angle and length of extension (Figure 14–17). While the boom may be at a good angle to make a maximum lift, the jib angle and extension may very well be the weakest link.

Caution: The winch and hydraulic jib used on material-handling units are for vertical loads only.

Working with a Material-Handling Aerial Device

14.7.3 The risks involved with operating a material-handling aerial device must be reduced, so pay attention to the following:

1. Keep the load low, and raise or lower it only after reaching the position where the load is to be installed or removed.

2. Remember that the *three lifting variables* are known only after reaching the position where the load is to be installed or removed (Figure 14–18):
   - Upper-boom angle (Check the angle indicator on the boom.)
   - Lower-boom angle (Check the angle indicator on the boom.)
   - Load-line radius (How far is the jib extended out from its mounting?)

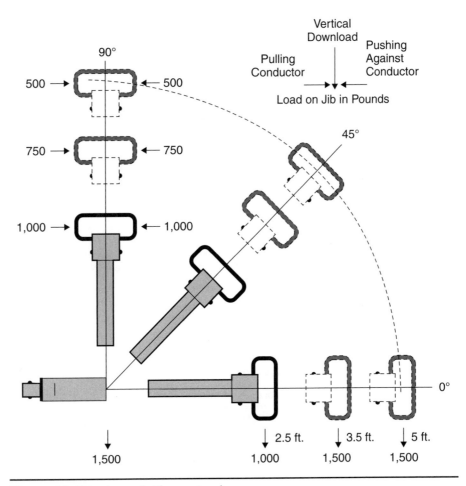

Figure 14–17 A sample jib-capacity chart.

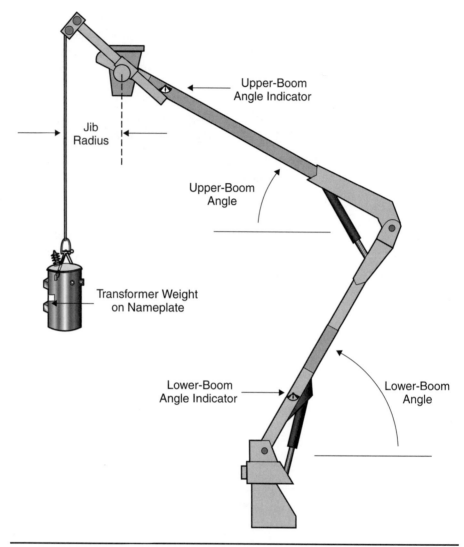

Jib Radius

Upper-Boom Angle Indicator

Upper-Boom Angle

Transformer Weight on Nameplate

Lower-Boom Angle Indicator

Lower-Boom Angle

Figure 14–18 A material-handling aerial device.

3. Check the capacity chart (Table 14–6 provides a sample) for the net load the unit is able to lift in the position. The chart should be easily visible to the operator.

4. Side loading is hazardous. Make vertical lifts only.

5. Maintain your minimum approach distance to live conductors when the winch is in contact with the ground, the pole, etc. A rope winch line eventually becomes conductive because of moisture and contamination.

TABLE 14–6 Sample Jib Boom Net Load

Jib Boom Net Load in Pounds

Lower-Boom Angles		Upper-Boom Angles									Jib R. Ft.
		0°	30°	45°	60°	90°	120°	135°	150°	180°	
81°–100°		15	225	550	1,275	3,000	1,275	550	225	15	1
		0	35	280	800	1,000	800	280	35	0	3
		0	0	80	470	600	470	80	0	0	5
61°–80°		15	225	550	1,275	3,000	1,275	550	225	15	1
		0	35	280	800	1,000	800	280	35	0	3
		0	0	80	470	600	470	80	0	0	5
46°–60°		15	225	550	1,275	2,630	815	475	225	15	1
		0	35	280	800	1,000	690	280	35	0	3
		0	0	80	470	600	470	80	0	0	5
30°–45°		15	225	550	1,275	1,870	575	290	135	15	1
		0	35	280	800	1,000	475	220	35	0	3
		0	0	80	470	600	385	80	0	0	5

6. Use a dynamometer to determine the weight of an unknown load.

7. Watch for "winch pileup." When the rope falls off the buildup on one edge of a winch, a shock load can be severe enough to cause a rope to fail, a transformer to unload, or an outrigger to sink into the ground and cause a truck to tip over.

8. The capacity of a winch is specified at its first layer of rope. A buildup of rope will derate the winch capacity significantly.

Review Questions

1. Who is responsible for doing the pretrip air-brake inspection: the fleet mechanic or the driver?

2. When jump-starting a vehicle, why should the last connection not be at the battery?

3. Why is a small hydraulic oil leak a hazard?

4. When should outrigger pads be used?

5. How does working on more than a 5-degree slope affect an aerial device?

6. There are two fundamental ways a person can be protected working around a vehicle when a boom makes contact with a live conductor. What are they?

7. What is the purpose of grounding a truck?

8. Why does a truck ground not prevent a person from getting an electric shock when touching a truck in contact with a circuit?

9. How can a boom-tip winch break the boom of a digger derrick?

10. Name three ways an operator can reduce the risk involved with operating a material-handling aerial device.

Rigging in Powerline Work

Topics to Be Covered	**Section**
Introduction	15.1
Using Rigging Hardware	15.2
Lifting a Load	15.3
Working with Tensioned Conductors	15.4

15.1 Introduction

Rigging in Line Work

15.1.1 One of the more important skills when doing transmission-line work is the use of proper rigging. Dead-end tensions are very high, and the loads being lifted are very heavy. A rigging failure while dead-ending aloft would have grave consequences. Much of the heavy rigging done on transmission lines is engineered.

Although a lot of rigging on distribution-line work has been done by instinct, good rigging skills are becoming essential as distribution conductors are getting bigger and heavier.

Working Load Limits

15.1.2 The term *working load limit* (WLL) is used for rigging in this text because a term like "*safety factor*" can be misleading. The WLL for individual pieces of equipment does not necessarily mean that a rigging setup configuration is a safe working load. All rigging equipment and rigging setups have a *working-load-limit rating*. A safety factor (design factor) is applied to rigging hardware because, along with wear and tear, whenever a load is picked up, stopped, or moved, increased force results due to dynamic loading. Therefore, do not use rigging hardware at more than the rated WLL. The WLL rating is based on the breaking strength of the equipment plus a safety factor. For example, if the breaking strength of a rope is 5,000 pounds, the WLL is 1,000 pounds with a safety factor of five.

The safety factor is different for different types of equipment. The WLL for a sling, rope, or winch cable may have a 5-to-1 safety factor, but a transformer gin, a scaffold, stability of an aerial device, or a live-line tool may have different safety factors. There is a higher safety factor assigned to rigging used to suspend people.

The term *design factor* is also used when identifying rigging components. A design factor refers to the theoretical reserve capability of a component calculated by dividing the breaking strength by the WLL. The following table lists the sample design factors assigned to rigging components:

Rigging Component	Design Factor
Nylon rope	9
Polyester rope	9
Polypropylene rope	6
Alloy-steel chain	4
Chain fittings	4
Wire rope	5
Synthetic web sling	5
Wire rope fittings	5

Rigging Equipment

15.1.3 A powerline worker should not be making calculations for design factors or WLLs. The WLL of each piece of rigging hardware must be labeled or identified by size (diameter) and checked against working-load-limit tables. When using rigging equipment such as rope blocks, hand line, fiber rope, wire rope, nylon slings, blocks, transformer davits (gins), snatch blocks, anchor pulling eyes, conductor grips, and chain hoists, the WLL must be known. Powerline workers should not depend on the WLL shown in tables in this book without checking against the equipment they use.

15.2 Using Rigging Hardware

Using Fiber Rope

15.2.1 *Fiber ropes* refer to ropes that are made from natural or synthetic versus wire rope. Sailors use the term *line* instead of rope.

Types of Construction

Two general categories of rope construction are used in utilities: *twisted* and *braided.* Twisted rope is formed by coiling three strands together in the same direction and is the type of rope that has been used for the longest time. Three-strand rope has some natural torque that tends to unravel and kink the rope if one end is free. For example, when new and used for a hand line, it must be run through a hand-line pulley quite a few times before the hand line stops twisting.

Three general categories of braided construction exist: solid braid, double braid, and hollow braid.

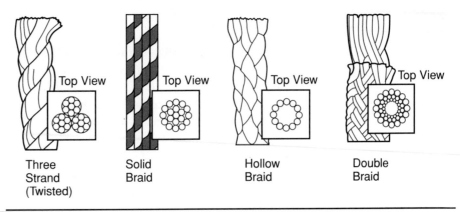

Top View — Top View — Top View — Top View

Three Strand (Twisted) — Solid Braid — Hollow Braid — Double Braid

Figure 15–1 Types of rope construction.

A *solid braid* is firm and stands up well to chafing of stringing blocks. A single, solid-braid rope cannot be spliced, but when used as part of a double-braid rope it can be spliced.

Double braid, also known as *braid-on-braid,* is two braided ropes combined into one rope. A braided rope core is covered with a braided rope sheath to produce a strong and spliceable rope that is abrasion resistant. This rope has less stretch than most ropes and is often used as a pull rope for stringing. The most common type of rope for a digger derrick winch or a material-handling aerial device winch is a double-braided rope. A common error is often made when the end of a rope winch is used to form a sling to hang a transformer, such that the sling angle and choker overloads the rope.

A hollow braid rope is a braided core with a hollow center that is very quick and easy to splice. It is used in smaller ropes, up to about 0.5-inch diameter. It is very flexible but can flatten and is not always easy to grip well when used as a hand line.

Types of Fibers

Rope with natural fibers—Manila, sisal, and hemp—are probably not used in the line trade anymore because they tend to be heavy, soak up water, mildew, and decay. Synthetic ropes are lighter and easier to keep dry and clean and are, therefore, better for use around live lines. Sunlight will deteriorate synthetic rope over time, but by then the rope is probably due for replacement because it has been used and abused. Stringing ropes stored on reels should be covered to protect from sunlight and to keep it dry.

There are so many kinds of synthetic ropes that it is hard to distinguish the different types, although there are some important differences between nylon, polypropylene, dacron, polyethylene, and so on. The differences are found mostly in the strength characteristics of stranded, braided, and double-braided rope. For critical work involving a capstan hoist, live-line work, and pulling conductor near live circuits, it is important to recognize the type of rope being used and its suitability for the application.

Nylon rope has a tensile strength that is nearly three times that of Manila rope, and it also has a lot of stretch. If something breaks or lets go when a rope is under tension, the snapback—especially if the rope is nylon—can cause serious injury. Stay out of the direct line of the rope, or even 45 degrees away from a pull, and also stay out of a bight at a snatch block. The high degree of stretch and the slightly heavier weight make nylon less attractive for use as a long hand line on transmission-line work.

Polyester rope is almost as strong as nylon and is more resistant to abrasion, but it stretches less and cannot absorb shock loads as well. Both polyester and nylon rope are recognized by their very fine hairlike fibers.

Polypropylene can take more shock load and has less stretch, but it is weaker than nylon and polyester. It is the only rope that floats. It is more susceptible to high temperatures and should not be used with a friction hitch—such as a taut line—and should not be used on a capstan hoist. It is used as hot-line rope because water on the surface can be removed by shaking and wiping with a cloth. When used as a hot-line rope, it must be used exclusively for that purpose and stored in clean, dry containers with moisture absorbers.

Polyethylene can be as much as three times as strong as nylon and very flexible. Polyethylene and polypropylene rope can be recognized by their bristlelike fibers.

Polydacron rope has good dielectric properties and heat resistance. It can be used on a capstan hoist and with sliding friction hitches, such as a taut-line hitch. It is a favored rope for hand lines.

Ropes used for stringing come in many forms, though some are called simply *poly ropes.* The ropes come on reels that should identify the working load limit.

Rule of Thumb for Fiber Rope Strength

For accurate ratings, consult tables for the WLL of the fiber rope you will be using. If the tables only show breaking strength, that number should be divided by 5 for the WLL, or 10 if it is to support people.

When accuracy is not critical, the use of the following rule of thumb will be a good indicator of the WLL:

Rule of thumb for WLL

1. Change the rope diameter to eighths.

2. Square the numerator.

3. Multiply by:
   - 40 for three-strand polypropylene rope
   - 50 for hollow-braid polypropylene
   - 50 poly-dacron rope
   - 70 for three-strand nylon rope
   - 90 for double-braid nylon rope

For example, to find the WLL of 1/2-inch polypropylene rope, perform the following calculation:

1. Translate 1/2-inch diameter to eighths of an inch which is 4/8.

2. Square the numerator 4: =16.

3. Multiply 16 by the rule-of-thumb factor of 40.

4. WLL is, therefore, 40 × 16 = 640 pounds.

When deciding which rope to use to let down a shield wire dead end, for example, the tables that give the WLL for the rope provide just the start. When the rope contains an eye splice or a knot, deratings factors also have to be considered.

Common Knots Used in Line Work

The following knots are some of the more common ones used in line work. Others will be learned informally on the job. This book does not try to describe how to tie the knots (probably because I have never been able to learn how to tie a knot from reading and pictures). There is really no substitute for learning these knots from an instructor.

The *bowline* is used to make a fixed-size loop in a rope and is the king of knots for line work. It is the most used knot and can be easily undone if not overstressed. A little ditty that may make it easier to learn or teach is this: *The rabbit comes out of the hole around the tree and then back down his hole.*

The only way a bowline can become undone is if the loose end of the bowline drops back into the hole. Leave the loose end sticking out at least 12 times the diameter of the rope. A bowline cannot be untied while it is under tension. In certain applications, such as tying a bowline in both ends of the rope that later is tightened, it cannot be released and it can be very inconvenient, as well as embarrassing.

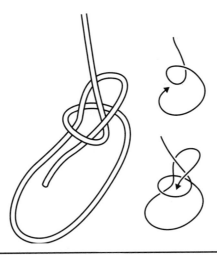

Figure 15–2 A bowline.

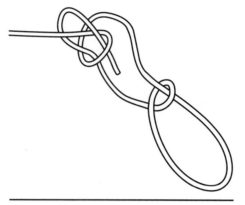

Figure 15–3 A water bowline.

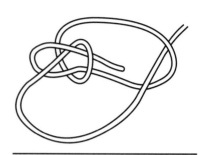

Figure 15–4 A running bowline.

The *water bowline* is a bowline with an extra loop that is especially useful with natural-fiber ropes such as Manila that could swell up and be difficult to untie. Although a bowline is a good knot to untie, when a big rope is being used on a heavy load, a water bowline may sometimes be much easier to untie. The front loop takes much of the strain.

A *running bowline* is a knot that can be used to make a lasso or noose, but because it stays in position it is also useful for jobs such as tying a rope to a pole when rope guying. A running bowline can be tied loose to the bottom of a pole, slid up the pole with a switch stick, and—when in the desired position—tightened by giving it a pull.

A *bowline on a bight* is a useful knot when a good, secure knot is needed somewhere between the ends of a rope (on the bight). It also can be used as a suspension seat and has been used by arborists for years before tree saddles were manufactured. This is one of the more difficult knots to learn.

A *bowline bend* consists of two bowlines tied back to back. It is a very secure way of tying together any two ropes, especially if there is a big difference in the diameters of the ropes. While other knots and bends are available to tie two ropes together, the bowline bend is the most secure and the easiest to untie.

Using *two half hitches* to tie a rope to an object (also called a *snubbing hitch*) is one of the more common and easy knots to learn. A heavy load can come apart with only one half hitch. ("One will hold a block, two will hold a person, three will hold the world.") If the rope is hitched to something with a small diameter, go around the object twice and use two half hitches. Go around a cable or conductor six or seven times, then tie two half hitches, and you will have a substitute for a conductor grip. A typical application for two half hitches is to temporarily hold tension on a conductor at a pole. When using two or three wraps around the pole and two half hitches, the hitch can be released when the wire is under tension.

A *clove hitch* can be tied very quickly and slipped over a bull pin without bending over. Unless a half hitch is added to the tail, the clove hitch should not be used when only one side is loaded. The clove hitch can jam under heavy tension, mak-

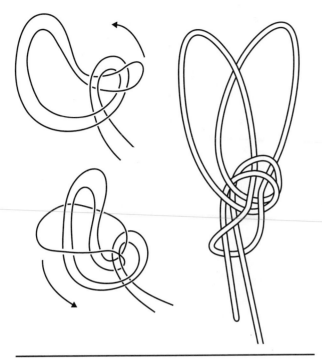

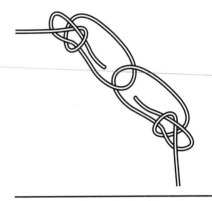

Figure 15–5 A bowline on a bight.

Figure 15–6 A bowline bend.

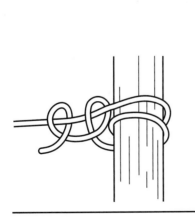

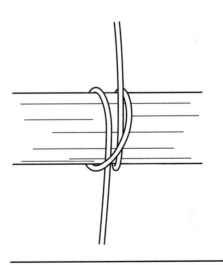

Figure 15–7 Two half hitches.

Figure 15–8 A clove hitch.

ing it difficult to untie. Two half hitches will do anything a clove hitch will do and can always be used as an alternative.

The *square knot* (*reef knot*) is easy to tie and will not jam unless loaded very heavily. In applications, such as hanging a stringing block or snatch block after wrapping the rope around an object such as a pole five or six times, the square knot

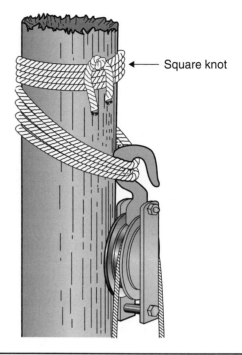

Figure 15–10   An application of a square knot.

Figure 15–9   A square knot.

is used to tie together the two ends of a rope. A square knot should not be used to tie together two ropes that will be under high tension; it will fail. In such cases, use the bowline bend. A square knot is easy to tie incorrectly into a *granny knot,* where the ends of the rope come out in opposite directions. The granny knot looks like a square knot but will fail and will never be used intentionally.

Figure 15–10 shows use of a square knot to hang a snatch block on a pole in such a way that it will not slide down.

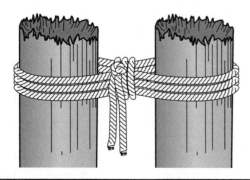

Figure 15–11   Snubbing two poles together.

Figure 15–12   A surgeon's knot.

1

Figure 15–13 A sheet bend.

Figure 15–11 shows how a square knot or tow half hitches finishes the lashing or snubbing together of two poles.

A *surgeon's knot* is a square-knot variation that has an extra turn at the start to help prevent the knot from loosening before the second turn is made. It is used when a little tension or weight is on the rope.

A *sheet bend* is used instead of a square knot to tie together two ropes, typically when the two ropes are different sizes. It is tied incorrectly (like the granny knot, also called a *left-hand sheet bend*) when the two ends are not on the same side of the knot. The bowline bend is a good alternative when tension is going to be applied to the ropes.

A *taut-line hitch* is a friction hitch used to tie on to another rope to hold it from moving or running. It has been used by arborists for years as a hitch to hold them in a working position in a tree and to make possible a controlled descent. A little pressure on the hitch will cause it to slide. It can be tied to a conductor or cable to act as a grip. The more turns around the wire, the better the grip.

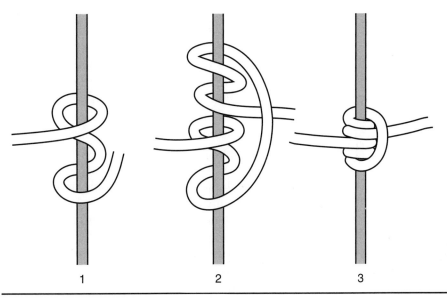

1   2   3

Figure 15–14 A taut-line hitch.

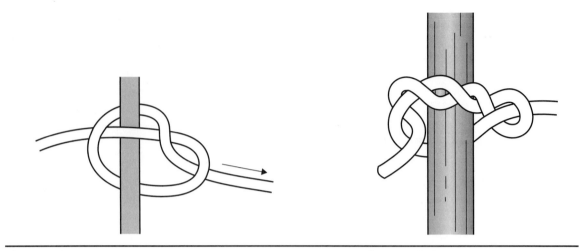

Figure 15–15 A marline hitch. **Figure 15–16** A timber hitch.

A *marline* is a useful knot for tying a bolt or live-line tool to a hand line.

A *timber hitch* is easy to tie, but when it is tied incorrectly it does not form a loop and it goes back on itself. A running bowline is an alternative to a timber hitch, but if tied around a pole that is dragged through the mud or snow, a timber hitch is much easier to untie.

Splicing Fiber Rope

A splice is more permanent and more efficient than a knot. Splices in rope are uncommon because nylon web slings have taken over many of the reasons splices were made. The most common splices are the eye splice, back splice, short splice, and long splice.

Splicing a three-strand rope requires more instruction and skill than splicing a braided rope. For a three-strand rope, inserting the first three strands in the right spot determines if the splice will look good when it is done but does not necessarily affect strength. Three complete tucks are standard for natural-fiber ropes, but four is the recommended number for the slipperier synthetic ropes.

Splicing a braided rope can actually be learned from the book that comes with the splicing kit. Follow the step-by-step instructions and use a very sharp knife.

Figure 15–17 shows finished splices using three-strand ropes. The long splice is not illustrated because if made properly it looks exactly like the rope. A long splice is like a short splice that is longer and tapered near the ends. Made properly, it will pass through a sheave or block. A short splice is a more permanent and more efficient method of tying together two ropes. The back splice or crown splice is more useful with natural-fiber rope because it cannot be taped and the end fibers cannot be melted as is commonly done with synthetic-fiber rope. The eye splice is probably the only splice still seen in line work.

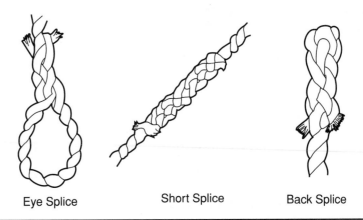

Eye Splice   Short Splice   Back Splice

Figure 15–17 Some finished splices in fiber rope.

Derating factors for the WWL of fiber ropes when using knots and splices

- 10 percent for an eye splice
- 45 percent for a bowline knot
- 35 percent for a running bowline knot
- 60 percent for a square (reef) knot
- 50 percent for a round turn and two half hitches

Using Wire Rope

15.2.2 It is just as important to recognize the type of wire rope as it is to recognize the type of fiber rope. More than a hundred types of wire rope are manufactured. Wire rope comes with different cores such as Manila, polypropylene, and wire rope. It comes with different types of steel such as galvanized, stainless and, ungalvanized. It comes with different lays such as regular lay, lang lay, and cable laid. Because of this extensive variation, it is improbable that any powerline worker can identify a wire-rope type without a label. When used in a sling configuration, the WLL of the sling must be identified with a label attached to the sling. If the wire rope is a winch, the type and size of winch must be identified and WLL tables consulted.

Rule of Thumb for Wire Rope Strength

Tables must be consulted if you want to obtain an accurate rating of the WLL of the wire rope you are going to use. When accuracy is not critical, the following rule of thumb will be a good indicator of the WLL:

Rule of thumb for WLL

1. Change the rope diameter to eighths.
2. Square the numerator.

3. Multiply by 250 for regular-laid wire rope (6 × 19 and 6 × 25) and 150 for cable-laid wire rope (3 × 3 × 19).

For example, to find the WLL of 5/8-inch regular-laid wire rope, perform the following calculation:

1. 5/8 diameter, already has a denominator of 8.

2. Square the numerator 5: 25.

3. Multiply by the rule-of-thumb factor: 250.

4. WLL is, therefore, 250 × 25 = 6,250 pounds.

Types of Wire-Rope Terminations

Note the different characteristics of wire-rope terminations as shown in Figure 15–18.

Making a Temporary Eye

Figure 15–19 shows the correct way to use U-bolts to put a temporary eye in a wire rope. The clips are spaced at a distance equal to six times the diameter of the wire. The clips should be tightened again after strain is put on the rope and also should be checked regularly. The clip farthest away from the eye gets most of the vibration and is usually the first to loosen.

Specific Hazards when Working with Wire Rope

1. Provide padding, such as wood blocking, when a sling is used around sharp edges.

2. Sharp bends in a wire rope sling will derate the strength of the sling. As a rule of thumb, the diameter (D) of the rope bend in relation to the diameter (d) of the rope itself is as follows:

- $D/d = 10$. No reduction in strength: for example, a 1-inch cable bent around a 10-inch object.

- $D/d = 2$. The sling is derated to 65 percent of its original strength: for example, a 1-inch cable bent around a 5-inch object.

- $D/d = 1$. The sling is derated to 50 percent of its original strength: for example, a 1-inch cable bent around a 1-inch object.

3. Wire-rope strength is reduced 20 percent for a U-bolt-clipped eye.

4. Wire-rope strength is reduced 10 percent for a Flemish eye.

5. Never substitute guy steel for wire rope. Guy steel used as a winch will twist to release a wire-form grip (preform), and it will break if used through a snatch block.

6. Wire rope used for stringing is made of harder steel and must not be made into slings. This steel is not meant for the sharp bends typical for slings.

Open Type | Closed Type

Swaged Socket _ 100%

Wire-Rope Socket — Spelter Attachment _ _ _ _ _ _ _ _ _ _ _ _ _ _ 100%

Pressed Sleeve Loop Back Thimble Attachment
25 mm (1 in.) diameter and smaller _ _ _ _ _ _ _ _ _ _ _ _ _ _ _ 90%
29 mm (1¼ in.) diameter and larger _ _ _ _ _ _ _ _ _ _ _ _ _ _ 95%

Flemish Loop with Mechanical Sleeve Attachment
25 mm (1 in.) diameter and smaller _ _ _ _ _ _ _ _ _ _ _ _ _ _ _ 95%
29 mm (1¼ in.) diameter and larger _ _ _ _ _ _ _ _ _ _ _ _ _ _ 92.5%

Wedge Sockets (depending on design) _ _ _ _ _ _ _ _ _ _ _ _ _ _ 75–90%

Clips (number of clips varies with size of rope) _ _ _ _ _ _ _ _ _ _ _ _ 80%

Thimble Splice — Hand Tucked

6 mm (¼ in.)	90%		13 mm (½ in.)	86%
8 mm (⁵⁄₁₆ in.)	89%		16 mm (⅝ in.)	84%
10 mm (⅜ in.)	88%		19 mm (¾ in.)	82%
11 mm (⁷⁄₁₆ in.)	87%		22 mm (⅞ in.)	80%

Loop Splice — Hand Tucked
Efficiencies of loop splice are the same as those given
for thimble splice.

Figure 15–18 Some wire-rope terminations.

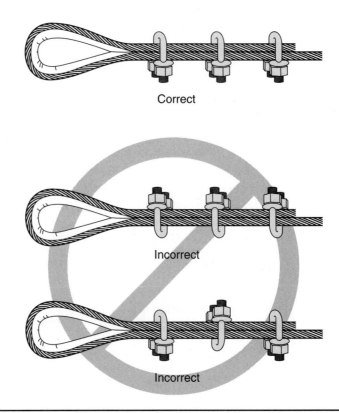

Correct

Incorrect

Incorrect

Figure 15–19 Using U-bolts to put a temporary eye in a wire rope.

7. Conductor grips (Chicago style) should not be used on wire rope.

8. Always stay out of the bight of a wire rope under tension as it is changing direction through a block.

Using Chains

15.2.3 A common perception in the field is that a chain is the strongest piece of rigging for towing a truck out of mud or lifting something very heavy. Regardless, some serious injuries have occurred when a chain has broken and snapped back. The safety rule of staying out of the direct line of the pull does not work well when the windshield and the driver of the stuck vehicle are in direct line.

When used in a sling configuration, the WLL of the sling must be identified with a label attached to the sling. If a length of chain is used, the type of steel and size must be identified and WLL tables must be consulted.

Rule of Thumb for Chain Strength

Tables should be consulted for an accurate rating of the WLL of the chain to be used. When accuracy is not critical, the use of the following rule of thumb will be a good indicator of the WLL:

Rule of thumb for WLL

1. Convert the chain diameter to eighths.

2. Square the numerator.

3. Multiply by 600 for alloy steel chain.

For example, to find the WLL of a 3/8-inch alloy steel chain, perform the following calculation:

1. The 3/8-inch diameter already has a denominator expressed in eighths.

2. Square the numerator 3: 9.

3. Multiply by the rule-of-thumb factor of 600.

4. The WLL is, therefore, is 600 × 9 = 5,400 pounds.

Specific Hazards when Working with Chain

1. Chain slings used for hoisting must not be used for any other purpose. For example, a chain used to bind a load can be subject to severe shock loading.

2. Padding must be used when using chain slings on steel towers.

3. A chain should be used only if the load is known. Avoid using a chain for towing a stuck vehicle. In case of a chain failure, the chain ends can recoil with lethal force.

4. Never use a knot in a chain. Use the proper end fittings.

Using a Ratchet Chain Hoist

15.2.4 Manually operated lever hoists (Figure 15–20) in line work are commonly 3/4, 1/2, 3, and 6 ton, depending on the manufacturer. Like all hoisting devices, these chain hoists require scheduled maintenance and testing by a competent mechanic. A malfunctioning chain hoist can lead to a rigging failure, as well as a temper tantrum, and they malfunction because they are abused by using them to bind poles on a trailer, by tying the chain into a half hitch behind the head of an anchor rod, by overloading, by using a cheater to lengthen the handle, and by leaving the hoist under tension for prolonged periods.

Chain hoists are constructed with the lower hook being the weakest part. The lower hook will start to spread under overload before the chain hoist is overloaded. A chain hoist with a bent hook or binding clutch should be removed from the field and repaired.

Using a Web Hoist

15.2.5 A web hoist is lighter in weight than a chain hoist and has become the hoist of choice, as well as the hoist that is most abused. Web hoists were originally intended and reserved for work on or near live circuits.

The nylon material is vulnerable to contamination and must not be connected directly between a live conductor and a structure without an insulated link. If a web hoist is being used for general duty such as pulling a guy, it should be identified so that it will not be used on a live circuit.

Figure 15–20 A chain hoist.

Working with Blocks

15.2.6 Snatch blocks are used to change the direction of a winch cable, rope, or conductor with no gain in mechanical advantage. Anyone standing in the bight of a winch cable or rope under tension can be severely injured if the snatch block or its anchoring point should fail. It is necessary to know the bisect tension that a snatch block will be holding, the WLL of the block, and the WLL of the anchor point.

The bisect tension on a block at its anchor point depends on tension on the winch or rope and the angle at which the winch travels through the block. When calculating or using a rule of thumb to determine a bisect tension on a block, ensure that the correct angle is measured. Figure 15–21 shows the two typical ways an angle can be measured.

A Rule of Thumb for Bisect Tension

The rule of thumb for determining the bisect tension of a conductor at a corner structure uses the deflection angle illustrated in Figure 15–21 and Figure 15–22.

The Strain on a Block and Anchor Point

0.76 × rope tension for 135°
1.0 × rope tension for 120°
1.41 × rope tension for 90°
1.73 × rope tension for 60°
1.84 × rope tension for 45°
2.0 × rope tension for 0°

Matching Rope Blocks and Rope Size

An improperly sized block can derate the WLL of a wire or fiber rope. A rule of thumb for determining the proper size of a block is that the snatch block should have 1 inch of shell diameter for every 1/8 inch of fiber-rope diameter and 1 inch of shell diameter for every 1/16 inch of wire-rope diameter.

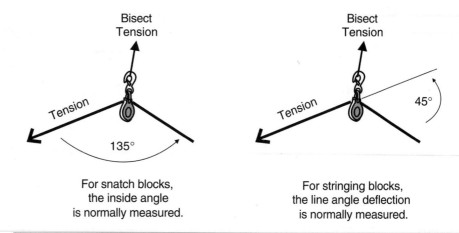

Figure 15–21   Two ways to measure an angle at a block.

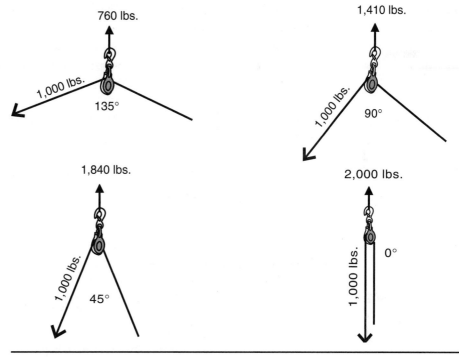

Figure 15–22   Load on a snatch block.

Dealing with Friction

15.2.7 There is a loss due to friction any time a rope, wire, chain, and such goes through a block. This friction adds to the force needed on a fall line, a winch, and a conductor puller. When more than one block is used, such as the sheaves in a set of tackle blocks or the stringing blocks over many spans, the friction loss can become significant.

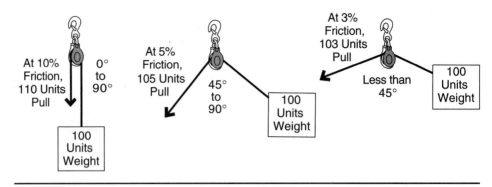

Figure 15–23 Friction on a block.

In addition to the physical condition of a block, the greater the length of rope or winch in contact with a block, the greater the friction loss will be. Figure 15–23 shows some typical values that can be used when calculating friction.

Using Web Slings

15.2.8 Web slings are preferred for distribution work such as lifting transformers, regulators, and such because they are more resistant to cutting and abrasion than fiber rope and easier to work with than wire rope or chains (see Figure 15–24).

The sling size and rated load are identified on a label, which is usually a sewn-on leather tag. The WLL is based on the configuration that is used. Slings should be discarded if any of the following is true:

1. The label showing the load rating is not visible or missing.

2. There are holes, tears, cuts, or snags; the wear indicator (red strand) is visible; or there is excessive abrasion.

3. Knots are present in any part of the sling.

4. Excessive color has been lost, which indicates ultraviolet light damage.

Using an Anchor Pulling Eye

15.2.9 When pulling a down guy, the limiting factor could be the anchor pulling eye being used. The two types of anchor pulling eyes shown in Figure 15–25 each have safe working loads of 3,000 pounds (1,400 kg).

It is very easy to overload the pulling eye, grip, or chain hoist when pulling on a down guy that is in service. Use a derrick boom to help hold or adjust the pole rake.

Working with a Collapsible Bull Wheel

15.2.10 The WLL for a typical collapsible bull wheel (as shown in Figure 15–26) is 4,000 pounds (1,800 kg). When used on the extension shaft of a typical digger-derrick boom-tip winch, the WLL is reduced to 800 pounds (360 kg).

When taking up a rope under tension, the compressive force of a stretched rope can collapse the bull wheel. The number of turns around the bull wheel should be limited to four. Workers should keep a safe distance and not stand in direct line with a bull wheel.

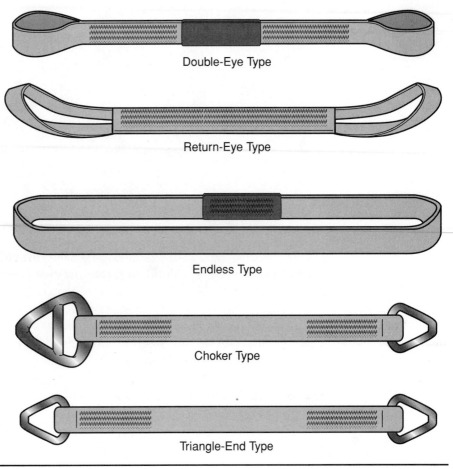

Double-Eye Type

Return-Eye Type

Endless Type

Choker Type

Triangle-End Type

Figure 15–24 Web slings.

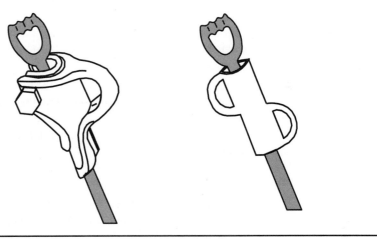

Figure 15–25 Anchor pulling eyes.

Figure 15–26 A collapsible bull wheel.

15.3 Lifting a Load

General Lifting Precautions

15.3.1 Sudden starts or stops place much heavier loads on rigging. A load could be increased by 2 to 50 times its actual weight. When lifting a load, the lift should be started very slowly until the sling becomes taut. Then lifting should continue slowly until the load is suspended. The load must be prevented from rotating. Use a tag line to prevent any rotation and to reduce swinging.

Using a Hand Line

15.3.2 A hand line is a hoisting device that is also used by many utilities as a pole-top/tower-top rescue device. For use as a rescue device, it should be made with hardware and rope capable of withstanding a person's weight plus a safety factor. Because of its rugged use, it should have at least a 10-to-1 safety factor.

The following are some precautions to take with hand lines:

- Keep the hand line away from traffic.
- Do not tie the hand line to a truck unless the worker aloft has the keys.
- While climbing, attach a hand line to a worker's belt so that it breaks away if it gets snagged by passing vehicles or other equipment. Belt hooks that open and release their load when under too much weight are available.

Figure 15–27 is a vector representation of a hand line (not a true vector because the length of the lines do not represent the strength of the rope). Note that there are two lines (ropes), each with 300 pounds, and that both lines are pulling on the pulley and anchor; therefore, there is a 600-pound weight on the pulley and support.

The same principle applies when using a rope and transformer gin to hang a transformer. Powerline workers should check the WLL of the type of transformer gin they are using. The load on a gin can be much higher than the load being hoisted. Note in Figure 15–29 that the load on the gin is double the weight of the transformer, ignoring that the rope through the block at the top of the pole is at a 0-degree angle and that therefore the friction adds 10 percent to the load. The tension on the snatch block and gin will be twice the weight of the transformer. In Figure 15–28, a gin with a WLL of 2,000 pounds (900 kg) can lift a maximum load of 900 pounds (400 kg) when using a single sheave in the gin and adding about 10 percent friction. *Note:* Gins are designed for vertical loads only, so any side pulls and tagging out of a load will derate the WLL of the gin.

An incident caused by not being alert to the doubling of the weight at the anchor point is illustrated in Figure 15–29. The dead-end assembly at the tower failed and the conductor dropped on live underbuild a few spans away.

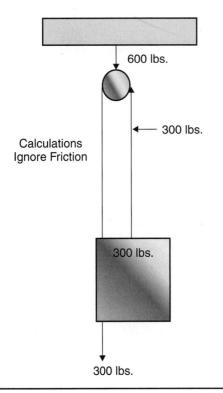

Figure 15–27 A vector representation of a hand line.

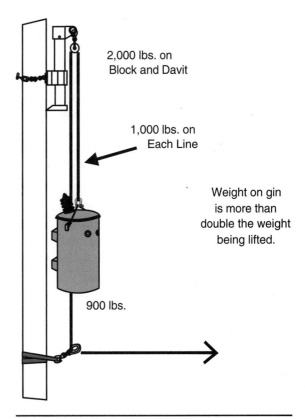

Figure 15–28 A transformer gin.

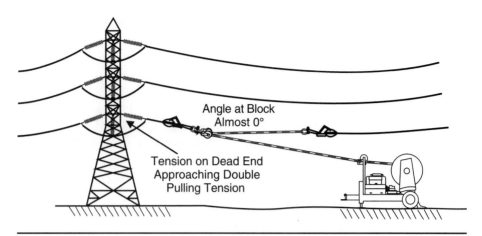

Figure 15–29 Dead-end failure with misuse of block.

Hoisting with a Capstan Hoist

15.3.3 To control the weight to be lifted by a capstan hoist (Figure 15–30), the number of wraps around the capstan hoist should be kept so that about 20 to 40 pounds (9 to 18 kg) of pull are on the fall line. More turns will mean a loss of control to stop the load.

Trying to add or remove turns during a lift could cause a loss of control. To determine the number of wraps needed for the load to be lifted, use data specific to the hoist being used, as shown in Table 15–1. Letting the capstan hoist turn without advancing the rope can cause the rope to melt or weld to the drum, where it will start to wrap up the rope like a winch.

Any hoist used to raise workers up to a conductor for specialized barehand work must be kept exclusively for that work, and the worker should use a backup fall arrest system.

Hoisting with Rope Blocks

15.3.4 Rope blocks (Figure 15–31) are often the only choice for work in back lots, islands, and at wide ditches.

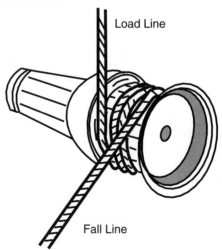

Load Line

Fall Line

Figure 15–30 A capstan hoist.

TABLE 15–1   **Rope Turns on the Drum for Weight to Be Lifted**

Rope Turns on Drum	Ratio of Load Line to Fall Line	Weight on Load Line to Be Lifted Pounds (kg) Pull on Fall Line		
		20 lbs. (9 kg)	30 lbs. (14 kg)	40 lbs. (18 kg)
3	1:15	400 (180)	600 (270)	800 (360)
3.5	1:30	600 (270)	900 (400)	1,200 (540)
4	1:40	1,000 (450)	1,500 (680)	2,000 (900)
4.5	1:70	1,400 (630)	2,000 (900)	2,800 (1,270)
5	1:100	2,000 (900)	3,000 (1,360)	4,000 (1,800)

Figure 15–32 is a vector representation of rope blocks but not a true vector because the lengths of the lines do not represent the magnitude. The figure does show how a 1,000-pound weight is pulled up with only 500 pounds on the fall line. It also shows that the anchor point is 1,500 pounds instead of the 2,000 pounds it would have been without the extra line and block. More lines and block sharing the weight will reduce the weight on the anchor and the pull more on the fall line.

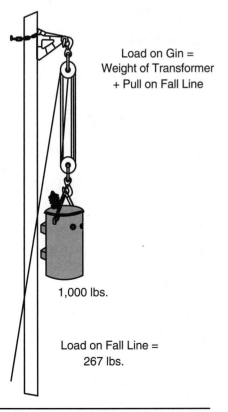

Load on Gin =
Weight of Transformer
+ Pull on Fall Line

1,000 lbs.

Load on Fall Line =
267 lbs.

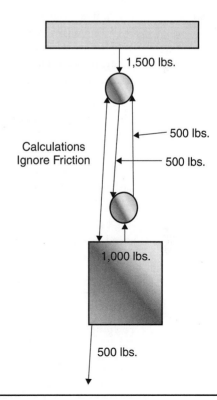

1,500 lbs.

500 lbs.

Calculations
Ignore Friction

500 lbs.

1,000 lbs.

500 lbs.

Figure 15–31   Rope blocks.

Figure 15–32   A vector representation of rope blocks.

The mechanical advantage of rope blocks is shown in the following formula:

$$\text{Fall Line Load} = \frac{\text{Load} + (\text{Number of Sheaves} \times 10\% \text{ of Load for Friction Loss})}{\text{Number of Lines from Moving Block}}$$

For example, the 1,000-pound transformer being raised with a set of three sheave blocks in Figure 15–31 has six lines moving from the moving (bottom) block.

$$\text{Load on the Fall Line} = \frac{1,000 + (6 \times 0.1 \times 1,000)}{6} = 267 \text{ pounds}$$

The friction through the blocks will vary with maintenance and type of bearings.

Matching Rope Blocks and Rope Size

The shell of the block should be eight times the diameter of the rope. For example, a 1/2-inch (1.3-centimeter) rope requires 8×0.5-inch = 4-inch (10-centimeter) blocks.

WLL of Rope Blocks

The WLL of a set of blocks will depend on the WLL of the blocks and the size and type of rope. Table 15–2 shows the WLL of rope blocks for polypropylene rope.

Connecting to a Load with a Sling

15.3.5 The strength of a sling depends on the material strength, the manner in which it is hitched to the load (Figure 15–33), and the sling angle. A single-leg vertical sling with proper end fittings is rated at the strength of the rope and the type of end fittings. A tag line is needed when lifting with a single vertical sling because of the tendency for the load to rotate and swing. Allowing the load to rotate can untwist a sling and weaken any hand-tucked eyes.

A single-wrap choker hitch is the weakest form of a hitch. When it is not under a load, the hitch can open and release its load. Forcing the choker end down places a sharp bend in the sling and reduces the sling angle. Figure 15–34 shows pitfalls and some of the complexities when using a choker.

A *basket hitch* should only be used on straight lifts. Moving the load within the basket hitch can damage and weaken the sling.

A *bridle sling* is intended to be a two-leg sling with two legs carrying the load. If a single sling is used through a clevis and the two ends are attached to a load, an unbalanced load can cause the heavy end to drop and the sling to slide through the clevis.

TABLE 15–2 WLL of Rope Blocks

Typical WLL of Blocks at a 9-to-1 Safety Factor		
Polypropylene Rope	Set of 2-Sheave Blocks	Set of 3-Sheave Blocks
1/2 in. (1.3 cm)	1,500 lbs. (700 kg)	2,000 lbs. (900 kg)
1/2 in. (1.9 cm)	2,400 lbs. (1,000 kg)	3,000 lbs. (1,400 kg)

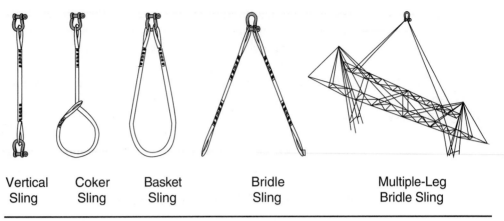

| Vertical Sling | Coker Sling | Basket Sling | Bridle Sling | Multiple-Leg Bridle Sling |

Figure 15–33 Connecting to a load with a sling.

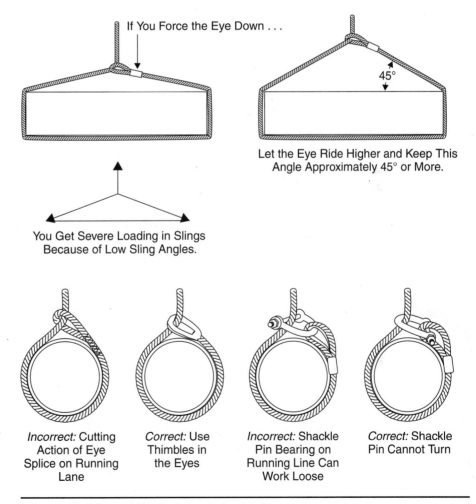

If You Force the Eye Down . . .

You Get Severe Loading in Slings Because of Low Sling Angles.

45°

Let the Eye Ride Higher and Keep This Angle Approximately 45° or More.

Incorrect: Cutting Action of Eye Splice on Running Lane

Correct: Use Thimbles in the Eyes

Incorrect: Shackle Pin Bearing on Running Line Can Work Loose

Correct: Shackle Pin Cannot Turn

Figure 15–34 Pitfalls of using a choker hitch.

When lifting objects with *multiple-leg slings* (three or four legs), two of the legs should be capable of supporting the total load. Multiple-leg slings must be selected to suit the most heavily loaded leg instead of the total weight.

Effect of Sling Angle on Lifting Capacity

15.3.6 A key factor in determining sling stress is chosen angles. Note how the sling angles (Figure 15–35) affect the stress on the sling. For most distribution-line work, if a sling is chosen with a WLL of double the weight to be lifted, it will not be unwieldy and the sling angle can be ignored.

Always use a sling. Using only the end of a tip boom winch could overstress the rope winch and definitely shorten its life.

15.4 Working with Tensioned Conductors

Calculating Conductor Weight in a Span

15.4.1 Conductors are so often lifted or moved in line work that experience usually picks the rigging needed to lift a conductor. However, an aerial lift or rigging can be overloaded when consideration is not given to lifting a conductor from a structure on a hill or lifting a conductor to a higher position. On level terrain, the weight of a conductor is calculated as follows:

Conductor Weight in lbs./ft. (kg/m) $\times$ (1/2 Span A + 1/2 Span B)

When the bottom of the sag is not midspan, the weight of a conductor is calculated as follows:

Conductor Weight in lbs./ft. (kg/m) $\times$ (Lowest Sag Point in Span A + Lowest Sag Point in Span B)

A conductor's maximum lift height occurs when the lowest point of sag reaches an adjacent structure. At this point, the conductor weight has doubled. When planning to lift a conductor with an aerial device or live-line tools, multiply the weight to be lifted by a factor of 2. Figure 15–36 shows the effect of a hill on the weight of a conductor. Similarly, as a conductor is lifted to a higher location, the weight increases as the lowest sag point moves farther away.

Calculating Conductor Tension

15.4.2 The tension on a conductor (Figure 15–37) is generally the heaviest weight dealt with by powerline workers.

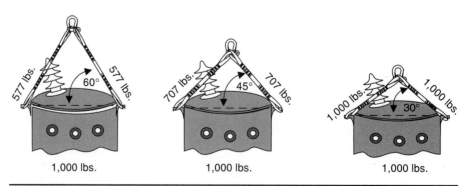

Figure 15–35 Sling angles.

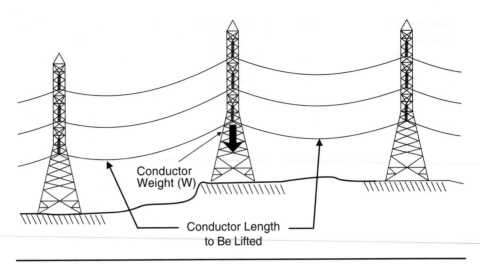

Figure 15–36 The effect of a hill on conductor weight on a structure.

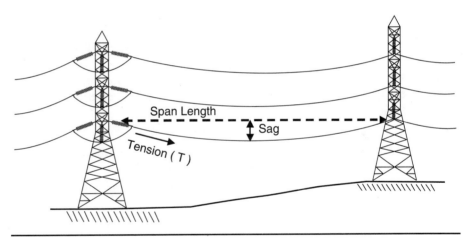

Figure 15–37 Calculating conductor tension.

$$\text{Conductor Tension} = \frac{\text{Conductor Weight in lbs./ft. (kg/m)} \times \text{Span Length}^2 \text{ in ft. (m)}}{8 \times \text{Sag in f.t (m)}}$$

Some rules of thumb for conductor tension

1. On distribution lines:
   - Line tension will be less than 500 pounds (225 kg) for 3/0 or smaller and less than 750 pounds (340 kg) for 3/0 and larger aluminum conductor.
   - Line tension will be less than 750 pounds (340 kg) for 3/0 or smaller and less than 1,000 pounds (450 kg) for 3/0 and larger copper conductor.

2. At temperatures below freezing, the conductor tension increases 20 percent for each 20°F (10°C) drop in temperature.

3. At temperatures above freezing, the conductor tension increases 10 percent for each 20°F (10°C) drop in temperature.

4. When pulling up on a conductor, the tension increases as the sag decreases. Line tension is doubled when one-half of the sag is removed. Line tension is tripled when two-thirds of the sag is removed.

Calculating Conductor Length in a Span

15.4.3 Knowing the arc length of a conductor in a span can improve the planning of certain types of jobs. If a job requires stringing a conductor between two dead ends during an outage, a great deal of outage time is prevented by laying out the proper length of conductor with the dead ends already installed before the outage begins.

The calculated conductor length in a span is from the suspension points. As shown in Figure 15–38, the actual conductor length must have the insulators and dead-end hardware subtracted from the total length.

$$\text{Conductor Length in Span} = \frac{\text{Span Length} + 8 \times (\text{Sag})^2}{3 \times \text{Span Length}}$$

When a conductor is pulled up fairly tightly, a small change in conductor length can make a large change in sag and an even larger change in tension. Rigging equipment can be overloaded when pulling up a conductor tighter than planned.

Calculating Tension on a Loaded Down Guy

15.4.4 The tension on a down guy multiplies fairly quickly as the guy lead decreases and the conductor tension increases.

$$\text{Guy Tension} = T \times \sqrt{\frac{L^2 + H^2}{L}}$$

where   H = height of the guy attachment
        L = length of the guy lead
        T = tension of the conductors held by the down guy

$$\text{Guy Tension} = 1,000 \times \sqrt{\frac{30^2 + 50^2}{30}} = 1,944 \text{ lb.}$$

Calculating the tension on the guy is shown in Figure 15–39.

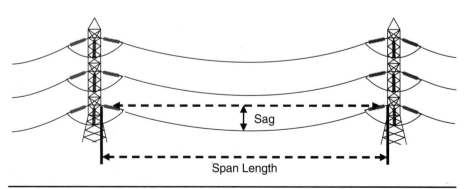

Figure 15–38   Calculating conductor length in a span.

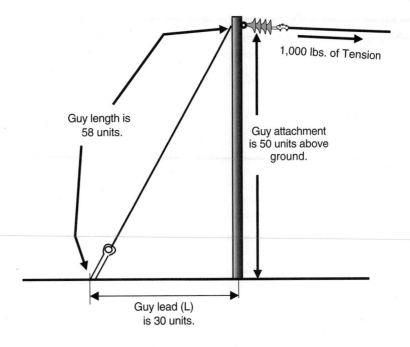

Guy length is
58 units.

Guy attachment
is 50 units above
ground.

1,000 lbs. of Tension

Guy lead (L)
is 30 units.

Figure 15–39   Calculating guy tension.

The tension on a down guy can also be calculated using a scaled vector diagram (Figure 15–40) of the pole, guy, and guy lead. In Figure 15–40, the length of the guy lead is made to represent the conductor tension.

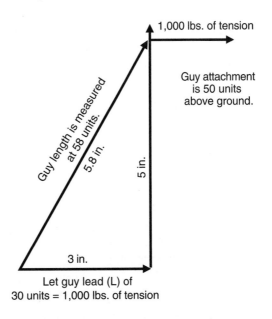

1,000 lbs. of tension

Guy attachment
is 50 units
above ground.

Guy length is measured
at 58 units.

5.8 in.

5 in.

3 in.

Let guy lead (L) of
30 units = 1,000 lbs. of tension

Figure 15–40   Vector drawing method.

Vertical Load Applied by a Down-Pull

15.4.5 The vertical load applied to a crossarm, snatch block, or traveler by a down-pull (Figure 15–41) can be excessive when stringing conductor or temporarily dead-ending conductor to the ground. A short lead will exert a high vertical weight, which could overload a structure or its components.

$$\text{Vertical Weight on a Structure} = \frac{T \times H}{L}$$

where: T = line tension
H = height of the attachment above ground
L = distance from the structure to the anchor

In the example shown in Figure 15–41, T = 1,000 pounds, H = 50 feet, and L = 100 feet. Therefore, the vertical weight on the crossarm = (1,000 × 50)/100 = 500 pounds

It is best to keep the length (L) as long as practical during stringing in the preceding example because the vertical weight would be only 100 pounds if the length (L) were increased to 500 feet.

Measuring a Line Angle in the Field

15.4.6 A line angle must be known to confirm the proper framing for the structure, as well as capable of calculating the bisect tension involved in handling a conductor. To measure an actual line angle in the field, measure out 57 feet in the two directions (as shown in Figure 15–42). The length of Line X represents the line angle. This method is reasonably accurate up to 45 degrees.

For example, if Line X is 30 feet, the line angle is 30 degrees. (For metrics, measure 6 meters in each direction. The line angle is the length of Line X in meters X 10. For example, if Line X is 3 meters, the line angle is 10 × 3 = 30 degrees.)

Calculating the Bisect Tension of a Conductor at a Corner

15.4.7 The approximate bisect tension (shown in Figure 15–43) of a conductor should be known when a conductor is lifted or relocated on a corner structure. A more accurate calculation of the bisect tension is needed as the capacity of the rig-

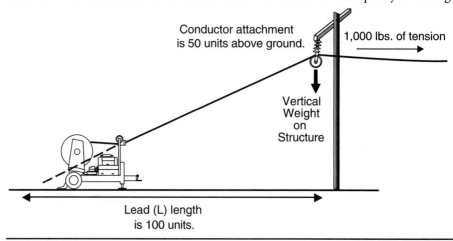

Figure 15–41   Vertical load on a structure.

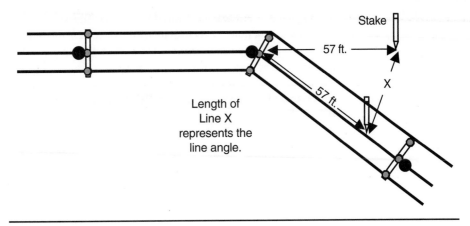

Figure 15–42 Measuring a line angle.

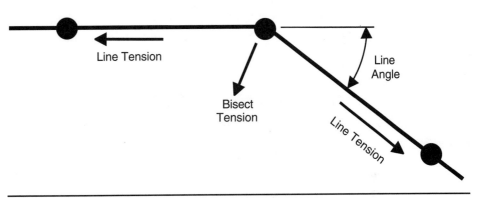

Figure 15–43 Calculating bisect tension on conductor.

ging components approaches the bisect tension of the conductor. The bisect tension can be calculated as follows:

$$\text{Bisect Tension} = \frac{\text{Line Angle}}{60} \times \text{Line Tension}$$

For example, the line tension for a 336-circular mil A1 conductor is 600 pounds (272 kg). The line angle is measured as 43 degrees. What is the bisect tension of one conductor on the corner structure?

$$\text{Bisect Tension} = \frac{43}{60} \times 600 = 430 \text{ lbs. (195 kg)}$$

From the formula, it can be seen that the bisect tension of a conductor with a line angle of 60 degrees would be equal to the line tension. Prorating this fact allows an approximation of bisect tensions when the line tension and the line angle are known. Table 15–3 shows the factors used to determine an approximate bisect

TABLE 15–3   Factors to Calculate Bisect Tension
The table shows how the factors are used to calculate the bisect tensions various angles given a 1,000-pounds line tension. Using the table, an actual line tension can be inserted in the proper row to calculate a bisect tension.

Line Angle (degrees),	Bisect Tension (lbs. or kg)	= Line Tension	× Factor
90	1,500	1,000	1.5
75	1,250	1,000	1.25
60	1,000	1,000	1.0
45	750	1,000	0.75
30	500	1,000	0.5
15	250	1,000	0.25

tension. *Note:* The bisect tensions on the snatch blocks in Section 15.2.6 ("Working with Blocks") may appear different; however, the angle of the rope is measured inside the block while line angles tend to be measured as shown in Figure 15–43.

Moving a Conductor into a Corner

15.4.8 The sag and tension of a conductor can change very quickly when moving conductor into a corner. The tension and sag increase can cause a midspan contact with live overbuilt conductors, a broken jib, or bucket truck instability. Calculating the bisect tension ahead of time is complex. Keeping a close watch on the sag as the conductor is moved in and out of a corner is the most practical way to prevent excess tensions.

Typical Conductor Data

15.4.9 The data in Table 15–4 can be used to calculate weight and tension for some conductor sizes. If an estimate is required and the conductor size is not in one of the tables, use the data for a larger conductor. Otherwise, for accurate calculations, consult conductor data tables.

Table 15–5 shows typical WLL of Jaw Grips and Woven grips for the same size conductors as Table 15–4. This table should be a guide to alert a powerline worker to the limitations of the grips being used.

Compression Sleeves

Typical data stamped on a compression sleeve are manufacturer's name; conductor size, type, and stranding; and the proper die to be used with the sleeve. There is no standard designation for die sizes. Each manufacturer stamps its own die size on the sleeve.

Conductor Sagging Facts

A *ruling span* represents the behavior of all the spans in the line section, and using it determines which sag data to use. Sagging to the proper ruling-span data keeps

TABLE 15–4 **Conductor Data**

Conductor Type	Stranding (g)	Weight (lb./ft.)	Weight (kg/m)	Diameter (in./mm)
1/0 copper	7	0.33	0.49	0.368/9.35
2/0 copper	7	0.41	0.61	0.414/10.52
3/0 ACSR*	6/1	0.23	0.34	0.502/12.75
3/0 AACSR**	6/1	0.26	0.39	0.535/13.60
336.4 kcmil AAC***	19	0.31	0.47	0.665/16.89
336.4 kcmil ACSR	26/7	0.46	0.63	0.720/18.3
477.0 kcmil ACSR	26/7	0.66	0.89	0.858/21.8
556.5 kcmil AAC	19	0.52	0.77	0.856/21.74
795.0 kcmil ACSR	26/7	1.1	1.6	1.108/28.14
1,192.5 kcmil ACSR	45/7	1.34	2.0	1.302/33.07
Alumoweld	7 # 8	0.32	0.48	0.375/9.78
Alumoweld	19 # 8	0.88	1.31	0.642/16.3
3/8 160-Grade Steel	7	0.27		0.36/

*ACSR—Aluminum conductor steel reinforced
**AACSR—Aluminum alloy conductor steel reinforced
***AAC—All aluminum conductor

the tension of the conductor in each span relatively equal, regardless of span-length temperature or loading.

Ruling Span = Average Span + 2/3 of Maximum Span − Average Span

- *Stringing sag* refers to the sag applied by a line crew after stringing the conductor.
- *Final sag* refers to the sag after the conductor has settled and stretched.
- *Maximum sag* refers to the sag under ice loading, wind, and temperature. A conductor under heavy electrical load is typically considered to be at maximum sag when the conductor is at 212°F (100°C).

Aluminum strand conductor may have a die grease coating that can deposit on grip jaws. Conductor and grip jaws should be wiped clean of all grease before use.

Check all parts for distortion or misalignment. Grips should operate smoothly. Spring-loaded "Chicago" grips should lock open with the loop handle in the down position and close automatically with the loop handle in the up position.

TABLE 15–5   Typical WLL for Jaw Grips and Woven Grips for Conductor

Conductor Type		Jaw Grip Manuf. #	WLL lb./kg	Woven Grip (in.)	WLL lb./kg
1/0 copper	7	1656–30	2,000/900	0.19–0.37	1,300/590
2/0 copper	7	1656–30	2,000/900	0.38–0.62	2,800/1,270
3/0 ACSR*	6/1	1656–30	2,000/900	0.38–0.62	2,800/1,270
3/0 AACSR***	6/1	1656–40	4,000/1,800	0.38–0.62	2,800/1,270
336.4 kcmil AAC	19	1656–40	4,000/1,800	0.63–0.87	4,000/1,820
336.4 kcmil ACSR	26/7	1656–40	4,000/1,800	0.63–0.87	4,000/1,820
477.0 kcmil ACSR	26/7	1628–30	7,000/3,170	0.63–0.87	4,000/1,820
556.5 kcmil AAC	19	1628–30	7,000/3,170	0.88–1.12	6,120/2,780
795.0 kcmil ACSR	26/7	1628–30	11,000/5,000	0.88–1.12	6,120/2,780
1,192.5 kcmil ACSR	45/7	1628–40	13,000/5,900	1.13–1.37	9,360/4,250
Alumoweld	7 # 8	1656–30 1628–16	2,600/1,200 4,000/1,800	0.38–0.62	2,800/1,270
Alumoweld	19 # 8	1656–40 1628–16	6,000/2,799 11,000/5,000	0.63–0.87	4,000/1,820
3/8 160-Grade Steel	7	1628-5F	6,000/2,500	0.19–0.37	1,300/590

*ACSR—Aluminum conductor steel reinforced
**AACSR—Aluminum alloy conductor steel reinforced
***AAC—All aluminum conductor
Note: Jaw grip data refers to Klien Grips™. Woven grip data refers to Kellem Dua-Pull™.

The manufacturer's load rating shall not be exceeded for stringing lines, pulling lines, sock connections, and all load-bearing hardware and accessories.

Conductor grips shall not be used on wire rope unless designed for this application.

Grips are to be used for temporary installation, not for permanent anchorage.

Review Questions

1. What does the term *working load limit* (WLL) mean when referring to a rigging component?

2. Which knot is considered the king of knots and the one used most frequently in line work?

3. How much is the strength of a rope derated for an eye splice?

4. Is it an acceptable practice to use a Chicago-type grip to hold tension temporarily on a wire rope?

5. What is an indicator that a chain hoist is or has been overloaded?

6. If the label that identifies a nylon web sling size and rated load is missing, is it still acceptable to use the sling after a careful inspection?

7. If a 100-pound (50-kg) weight is being pulled up on a hand line, what is the weight supported by the hand-line pulley and anchor point?

8. What is the tension in a 1,000-foot (300-meter) span, with a 795 ACSR (26/7 stranding) that weighs 1.1 pounds/foot (1.6 kilograms/meter) and sagged at 15 feet (5 meters)?

9. What is the tension on a down guy where the anchor is 50 feet (15 meters) from the pole, the weight to be held is 2,000 pounds (1,000 kilograms) at 70 feet (20 meters) above the ground?

10. The line tension for a 336-circular mil AL conductor is 800 pounds (400 kilograms). The line angle is measured as 50 degrees. What is the bisect tension on the corner structure with three 336-circular mil AL conductors?

Working It Hot

Topics to Be Covered	Section
Safety Strategy for Hot-Line Work	16.1
Working on a Hot Secondary	16.2
Rubber-Glove Work	16.3
Hot-Line Tool Work	16.4
Barehand Work	16.5

16.1 Safety Strategy for Hot-Line Work

Defining Hot-Line Work

16.1.1 Installing a pole, hanging a transformer, stringing conductor, switching, operating a hot-line clamp, and fuse replacement are examples of work in the *vicinity* of hot circuits, but this work is not normally considered "hot-line work."

Hot-line work generally involves work where a conductor more than 750 volts is unclamped (untied), moved, cut, or spliced or where solid connections are made or removed.

There are a lot of good written procedures for doing hot work, especially on transmission lines. On distribution lines, it is much more difficult to write a procedure for each job because the procedure would be different, depending on access with a bucket truck, the use of rubber gloves or hot sticks, or a combination of both, as well as a multitude of different framings on the pole. Because written procedures do not cover the details of a lot of the hot work done on distribution, preparing a job safety analysis for any jobs other than routine would demonstrate due diligence.

This chapter provides information and discusses some of the preparations for live-line work. It is not a replacement for live-line work procedures.

Choosing the Hot-Line Work Option

16.1.2 Do not approach a circuit closer than the minimum approach distance unless you are insulated, the facility is insulated, or the facility has a clearance in place based on a formal lockout/tagging procedure.

There is an increased risk when a complex job is carried out "hot." A lot of jobs are carried out with the line in service without even considering alternatives. The option of doing a job, with the circuit isolated and grounded, should at least be considered. However, some jobs are better done "hot" when balanced against the complexity of switching, grounding, and notifying customers. Customer impact and the job complexity should be decision factors when planning a job.

If any of the following are true, arrange for an outage:

1. Customer Impact
   - There are no critical customers.
   - There will be no unnecessary economic hardship on commercial customers (hospitals, gasoline stations, restaurants, manufacturing plants, dairy farms).
   - The duration of the outage will not adversely affect the customer (manufacturing plant, shopping mall, ventilation in chicken and pig farms, furnaces or air conditioning on extremely cold or hot days, sump pumps when groundwater is high).

2. Complexity of Work
   - There is no approved work method.
   - The weather or lighting conditions are not favorable for hot-line work.
   - The complexity of doing the job hot does not match the needs of the customer.

Protecting from a Second Point of Contact

16.1.3 A second point of contact is where current would leave a person's body if contact were made with a hot circuit. There can be no current flow (electrical burns) if contact is made with a hot circuit and no other part of a person's body is in contact with another object at a different potential.

At distribution voltages, it is always possible to cover, remove, or maintain a minimum approach distance from a second point of contact. This is a fundamental rule for working on or near hot distribution circuits. An insulated boom and bucket provide protection from earth as a second point of contact, but unless the structure, down guys, and other conductors are covered the protection from a second point of contact is inadequate.

When working hot line from transmission-line structures, the removal of the second point of contact is not always an option. However, the greater approach distances available reduce the risk of inadvertent contact.

Barehand work is an ultimate example of depending on the second point of contact being removed.

Minimum Approach Distance (MAD) Doing Hot-Line Work

16.1.4 When using hot-line tools, the minimum approach distances listed in Table 16–1 apply to the length of clear insulating section of the tool. The flashover voltage for a live-line tool is the same as it is for air. A fiberglass live-line tool may be better insulation than air, but the distance needed on a tool is an air gap between the hands on a live-line tool and the live conductor.

TABLE 16–1   **Typical Minimum Approach Distances
Phase-to-Ground Distances**

Maximum Phase-to-Phase Voltage (Max. Phase-to-Ground Voltage)	Minimum Approach Distance Phase-to-Ground Exposure	Minimum Approach Distance Phase-to-Phase Exposure
0.05 to 1.0 kV	Avoid Contact	Avoid Contact
Up to 15 kV (8.7 kV)	2 ft., 1 in. (64 cm)	2 ft., 2 in. (66 cm)
Up to 36.0 kV (20.8 kV)	2 ft., 4 in. (72 cm)	2 ft., 7 in. (77 cm)
Up to 46.0 kV (26.6 kV)	2 ft., 7 in. (77 cm)	2 ft., 10 in. (85 cm)
Up to 121 kV	3 ft., 2 in. (95 cm)	4 ft., 3 in. (1.29 m)
Up to 145 kV	3 ft., 7 in. (1.09 m)	4 ft., 11 in. (1.50 m)
Up to 169 kV	4 ft. (1.22 m)	5 ft., 8 in. (1.71 m)
Up to 362 kV	8 ft., 6 in. (2.59 m)	12 ft., 6 in. (3.8 m)
Up to 550 kV	11 ft., 3 in. (3.42 m)	18 ft., 1 in. (5.50 m)
Up to 800 kV	14 ft., 11 in. (4.53 m)	26 ft. (7.91 m)

The minimum approach distances are often specified by government safety regulations.

Rubber-glove work and barehand work should not be considered exceptions to the minimum approach distances found in Table 16–1. When in contact with a live conductor using rubber gloves or barehand techniques the minimum approach distance still applies but, to the distance between a worker and any second point of contact. When in contact with a hot conductor, a second point of contact with cover-up installed on it may be approached more closely than the distances specified in Table 16–1. Typically, a utility/employer allows "brush contact" or requires that an "air gap" be maintained with a covered-up conductor. No cover-up is available for transmission-line work.

A hand stop on a hot-line tool will reduce the risk of inadvertent encroachment into the minimum approach distance.

For some very special transmission-lines circumstances, the minimum approach distance for hot-line tool work is reduced when a portable protective gap (PPG) is placed at an adjacent structure.

Some live-line tool configurations, especially for transmission-line work, will have a metal fitting such as a splice or a tool-end fitting within the insulated portion of the tool. This metal will introduce electrical stresses that will require extending the minimum approach distance.

Blocking Automatic Reclosing of Protective Switchgear

16.1.5 When hot-line work is to be done on a circuit, the automatic reclosing feature of the source circuit breaker or recloser should be blocked from service and tagged.

- The nonreclose feature does not prevent an accident from occurring and does not guarantee that the circuit will trip out during an accident. When set in a nonreclose position, the breaker or recloser does not operate faster than normal. The nonreclose feature does guarantee that a circuit will not be reenergized once it does trip out.

- When the circuit is not automatically reenergized, the exposure time to the electrical hazard is reduced, which will allow a safer rescue effort if needed.

- Damage or injury may be limited by the reduced exposure to the high fault current that can occur during a fault.

- The risk of a restrike, which causes a switching surge (voltage surge), is eliminated if the circuit breaker is put into a nonreclose position.

The procedure to block the automatic reclosing of a breaker involves contacting the controlling operator, establishing continuous communication, and placing tags. On distribution lines, the reclosers are often set in a nonreclose postion and tagged by the crew doing the work.

Protecting from Voltage Surge on Transmission Lines

16.1.6 In addition to lightning, a switching surge can cause an overvoltage on a transmission line.

Options to Reduce the Magnitude of a Voltage Surge

To encourage a surge to flash over on a structure where work is not being carried out, consider the following options:

- Surge gap distance at the line terminals can be reduced temporarily for the duration of the work.

- Surge arrestors attached at the line terminals will reduce the magnitude of a voltage surge.

- A temporary portable protective gap (PPG) can be installed at an adjacent structure.

- Some insulators can be shorted out at an adjacent tower.

Reduce the Probability of a Voltage Surge

To reduce the likelihood of a voltage surge, consider the following options:

- Block the automatic reclose feature on all circuit breakers connected to the circuit. This will prevent switching surges after the line trips out.

- Ensure that no relay testing is being done on the circuit while hot-line work is in progress.

- Do not work when lightning is in the vicinity. The controlling station staff for transmission lines should have access to an information system that notifies them of impending electrical storms.

Testing Insulators for Breakdown

16.1.7 When hot-line work (especially barehand) is planned with or near existing suspension-type insulators, each insulator in the string should be tested. Transmission-line insulators can be tested while the line is in service with an insulator tester. Figure 16–1 shows how one type of insulator tester is slid up and down on a hot stick suspended parallel to an insulator string. This tester takes advantage of the fact that the electrical field surrounding a defective or shorted decreases. It works on polymeric and porcelain/glass insulator strings.

Phasing sticks can be used to test insulators on circuits up to 50 kilovolts.

If phasing sticks are used, it will be necessary to establish typical readings for the voltage system and the type of insulators being tested. For example, the

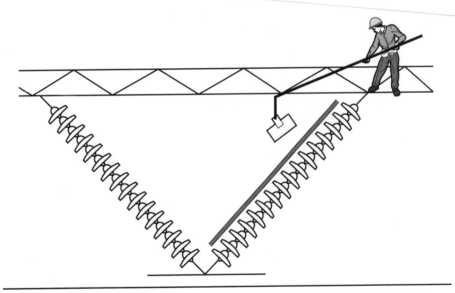

Figure 16–1 Testing insulators.

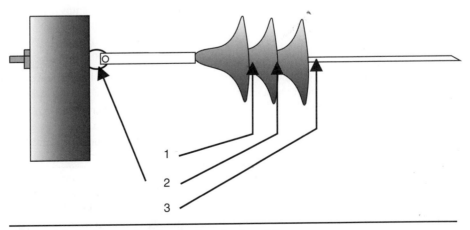

Figure 16–2 Testing insulators using phasing sticks.

following are typical readings for a 27.6-kilovolt system with three porcelain insulators:

1.5 to 2 kilovolts between ground and first insulator
3 to 4 kilovolts between ground and second insulator
14 to 16 kilovolts between ground and third insulator

Use of Temporary Jumpers

16.1.8 When work requires the replacement of any circuit component, such as taps, loops, or sleeves, the component must be bypassed with a temporary jumper. Unless the jumper is specifically designed to be installed with rubber gloves, a jumper should always be installed with hot-line tools.

Before opening or cutting a conductor, use an ammeter to check that the jumper is carrying at least one-third of the load current. A larger jumper or cleaning the terminals and conductor may be necessary to achieve the one-third load-carrying capability. Hazards and barrier to using temporary jumpers are listed in Table 16–2.

TABLE 16–2   Hazards Specific to Using Temporary Jumpers

Hazards	Barriers
Insulation failure of insulated jumpers.	Ensure that an insulated jumper has been tested as scheduled. Do a visual inspection for damaged rubber. Maintain at least a minimum approach distance from the terminations.
The current-carrying capacity of the jumper is not adequate. An arc is generated when the main conductor is cut.	Inspect the cable near the terminations for broken strands. An insulated or bare jumper should be carrying at least is 30 percent of the load current before cutting a conductor or connection. The jumper conductor size should be equal to the size of the circuit conductor. The following are the typical sizes: #2 to carry 200 amps #1/0 to carry 260 amps #2/0 to carry 300 amps #3/0 to carry 350 amps #4/0 to carry 400 amps
A worker gets between a jumper and a main conductor.	Always make and break connections with a hot-line tool. Rubber jumpers with insulated clamps can be installed and removed when wearing rubber gloves. If wearing rubber gloves, you are wholly dependent on their integrity. In case of an arc being generated, you will be within the flash.
Loss of control while installing a jumper.	Once one end of a jumper is installed, the other end is hot. Use two people with two clamp sticks, or use a jumper with a parking stud so that the other end of the jumper is secured to the same terminal.

Using Hot-Line Rope

16.1.9 Reduce the risks involved with using hot-line rope by using only rope identified as hot-line rope, electrically tested for its full length and retested on a scheduled basis. A soiled, damp rope will become conductive very quickly.

- Store and transport the rope in a special container with a desiccant to absorb any moisture.
- Test the rope in the field with a portable hot-stick tester.
- Handle the rope with clean and dry work gloves.
- Clean any snatch blocks or hand-line block that the rope will run through.
- Use a tarpaulin where the rope may touch the ground.

16.2 Working on a Hot Secondary

Specific Hazards for Working a Hot Secondary

16.2.1 Work at hot secondary voltage is not normally considered hot-line work. It does, however, require similar work procedures to working higher voltages hot (see Table 16–3).

Explosive Flash Hazard Near a Transformer

16.2.2 A step-down transformer can generate a very high current on the secondary side if the secondary wires are accidently shorted. If the secondary wires are shorted, the transformer can briefly carry a load more than ten times its rating and supply a high current to the faulted location.

The larger the transformer, the greater the capability to generate a large fault current. Depending on the impedance of the transformer, a short at the secondary

TABLE 16–3 **Hazards for Working a Hot Secondary Voltage**

Specific Hazards	Barriers
Putting oneself in series with the circuit.	Rubber gloves will give a person a second chance if an open point is accidently bridged.
Making contact while touching a second point of contact.	Work on hot secondary voltage without rubber gloves requires avoiding a second point of contact.
An uncontrolled wire makes contact with the primary or other phases of the secondary.	When the distance from the primary to the service dead end is limited, cover up the primary conductors.
Clearances between secondary bars on a pad-mount or underground transformer is close. An accidental short close to the transformer would be very explosive.	Cover up the terminals not being worked on. Work from a rubber mat. Wear rubber gloves and eye protection.

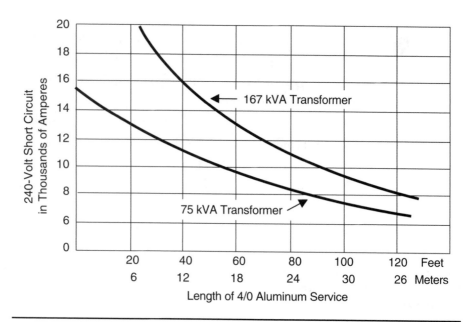

Figure 16–3 Level of fault current at various distances on service.

terminals of 100 kilovolts can be as high as 18,000 amperes. The level of fault current at a work location will depend on the distance from the transformer and the conductor size, as shown in Figure 16–3.

If an outage is not practical, use more cover-up when working secondary near the transformer. Wear eye protection when working on a hot secondary because an eye can be permanently damaged by a large flash.

The level of fault current available on a secondary conductor drops quickly with distance away from the transformer.

16.3 Rubber-Glove Work

Introduction to Rubber-Glove Work

16.3.1 The most common live-line work method on distribution voltages is hotline rubber-glove work. The voltage range for this work is from 5 to 34.5 kilovolts. Some utilities/employers do not allow rubber-glove work above 5 kilovolts, while others work with rubber gloves all the way up to and including 34.5 kilovolts.

The key to safe rubber-glove work is to isolate the worker from all second points of contact. Basically, follow the same procedure as for barehand work while using the extra protection of wearing rubber gloves (sleeves). Bucket trucks are the most common insulated platform used, but the insulated platform shown in Figure 16–4 should be mandatory if a bucket truck cannot get to the pole. Rubber gloves should not be the sole barrier between a worker and a potential fatal shock.

About Rubber Gloves

16.3.2 Rubber gloves are often used as personal protective equipment in case something goes wrong, such as when switching or just working in the vicinity of a

Figure 16–4 Insulated pole platform.

live circuit. In the situations described in this chapter, rubber gloves are used as live-line tools to perform live-line work. Rubber sleeves are used with rubber gloves to provide protection in cases of overreaching or other incident. Instead of sleeves, some rubber gloves are available that go up to the armpits.

Rubber gloves come with different voltage ratings, and it is critical, of course, that the voltage rating (class) be higher than the voltage to be worked on. Table 16–4 shows the different rubber-glove classes and ratings.

Rubber gloves are delicate and must be visually inspected before each use. The use of a portable glove inflator allows a much more thorough check for tears, rips, and punctures. Without an inflator, roll up the cuff tightly, trapping the air, then apply pressure to inflate the glove and look for damage. Most gloves come in two layers of contrasting colors, which allows any cut through one layer to be easily seen. Listening for escaping air is probably not as effective as a good visual inspection.

- Cracking and cutting damage, often from storing rubber gloves folded or pinched too tight. The rubber in a tight fold is said to be stretched equivalent to stretching the rubber to twice its length.

- Look for checking, often caused by the ultraviolet light from sunshine or fluorescent lighting.

TABLE 16–4 Rubber-Glove Ratings

Class 0	Class 1	Class 2	Class 3	Class 4
< 1,000 V	< 7.5 kV	< 17 kV	< 26.5 kV	36 kV
	∅—∅	∅—∅	∅—∅	∅—∅
Red	White	Yellow	Green	Orange
Label	Label	Label	Label	Label

- Look for embedded wood or metal splinters from climbing or embedded small wire, especially after working with extraflex copper.
- Look for unusual swelling of the rubber, often caused by exposure to petroleum products.

Between electrical tests, rubber gloves should be washed with clean water only. Add a little corn starch to make the gloves easier to put on. When not in use, store the gloves in the rubber-glove bag. *Do not* store the gloves in the truck bin with tool belts and spurs.

Rubber gloves come in different sizes. The best way to determine the size is to try them on. Measure the circumference around the palm, as shown in Figure 16–5, then add 1 inch.

Leather protectors, matched in size to the rubber gloves, are mandatory to prevent damage to the much more vulnerable rubber. Leather protectors must be inspected for splinters or other embedded objects. Ensure that the rubber glove extends past the leather protector glove. The minimum distance between the top of the protector glove and the rolled up top of the rubber glove should be as follows:

Class 1 greater than 1 inch (25 mm)
Class 2 greater than 2 inches (51 mm)
Class 3 greater than 3 inches (76 mm)
Class 4 greater than 4 inches (102 mm)

About Cover-up Equipment

16.3.3 There are two types of cover-up available: rigid (plastic) and rubber. Rubber cover-up ratings parallel the same ratings as rubber gloves. For example, the use of a class 2 rubber blanket, cover, coupler, line hose, or hood is approved for work on phase-to-phase 17,000 volts.

Measure the
Circumference
around the Palm

Figure 16–5 Where to measure for rubber-glove size (then add 1 inch).

TABLE 16–5   **Plastic Guard Equipment Ratings**

Class	Phase-to-Phase kV	Phase-to-Ground kV
2	14.6	8.4
3	26.4	15.3
4	36.6	21.1
5	48.3	27.0
6	72.5	41.8

Plastic guard equipment for electrical insulation is rated differently and provides protection differently. The voltage rating of rigid plastic cover-up is not based on the thickness of the material, as with rubber, but more on the air space between the conductor and the cover. The terms *plastic guard* and *rigid cover-up* are used interchangeably, but technically the equipment acts as a guard to keep a certain air space between the worker and the live line. This air space is less that the minimum approach distance because the human factor is removed from the minimum approach distance formula. The highest-rated plastic guards are rated higher than the highest-rated rubber cover-up. Some plastic guards are designed to couple to similarly rated rubber cover-up. The voltage or class ratings of plastic guards, unfortunately, are not the same as for rubber, as can be seen in Table 16–5.

The phase-to-phase rating for plastic guards applies only when both phases are covered. The advantage of plastic guards is the ease of installation from the end of a stick. The disadvantage is the difficulty in storing the cover-up on a truck, and they are often seen to be abused. Figure 16–6 shows some types of plastic guards.

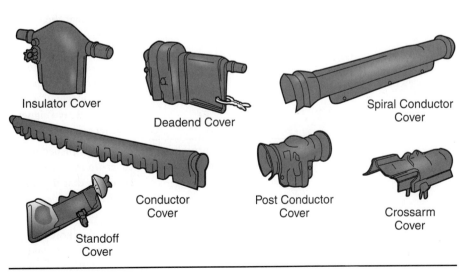

Insulator Cover

Deadend Cover

Spiral Conductor Cover

Conductor Cover

Post Conductor Cover

Crossarm Cover

Standoff Cover

Figure 16–6   Some types of cover-up.

Electrical Retesting of Rubber Goods

16.3.4 Electrical testing requirements are designed to meet various standards, and they also are mandated by law. Rubber goods should be retested according to the following schedule, at a minimum. These timelines are mandated by the U.S. Occupational Safety and Health Act (OSHA) as follows:

Rubber gloves, 6 months,
Rubber sleeves, 12 months
Rubber-insulating blankets, 12 months

These are minimum requirements, and it is quite common to retest rubber gloves as often as every 2 or 3 months.

Other rubber goods, such as rubber hose, rubber-insulator covers, and rubber-insulated jumpers require tests upon any indication that the insulating value is suspect. Many utilities have scheduled electrical retests for these rubber goods, while others have taken the position that a thorough visual inspection will pick up any defect that will cause it to fail electrically.

Rigid plastic cover-up is also used with rubber-glove work. It has the advantage of being easy to install with a hot stick. The guidelines regarding electrical testing and inspection are similar to those for rubber cover-up.

It is important to keep rubber goods clean so that they are easier to inspect, as well as to reduce the risk of electrical tracking along the surface. Cleaning requires hot water and the use of an approved chemical, followed by a thorough rinsing with clean water.

Preparation for Rubber-Glove Work

16.3.5 Table 16–6 provides guidelines for preparing to work with rubber gloves.

TABLE 16–6   **Preparing to Work with Rubber Gloves**

Step	Action	Details
1	Inspect rubber gloves.	• Ensure that the correct class of rubber glove (sleeve) is to be used. • Check to ensure that the rubber gloves (sleeves) are not due for an electrical retest. • Carry out an inspection and air test on the rubber gloves. • Do not wear a signet-type ring with a raised surface.
2	Inspect the protective cover-up to be used.	A physical inspection of rubber or plastic cover-up is very effective. In almost all cases, cover-up that has failed an electrical test also has had an obvious physical defect. Use only clean cover-up. Roll rubber hose inside and outside to look for cuts, rope burns, and corona damage. Roll rubber blankets from corner to corner, inside and outside, while looking for damage.

Step	Action	Details
		Inspect plastic cover-up, such as conductor guards, insulator guards, crossarm guards, and pole guards for cracks and cuts. The ends and lips of the covers are particularly susceptible to cracks during cold weather.
3	Inspect insulated jumpers.	In addition to inspecting the insulation on a jumper cable, check for broken strands near the terminals. The insulation can be peeled back somewhat at each terminal for a visual inspection, or you can use the type of continuity tester used to test portable protective grounds. Ensure that the insulation of the jumper is good for the voltage being worked on. Store in appropriate bags when not in use.
4	Use ground-to-ground, extended reach, or the cradle-to-cradle rubber-glove rule, as mandated by your utility/employer.	*Caution:* A conclusion in many electrical accident investigations is "The victim was not wearing rubber gloves."
5	Plan protection against any second point of contact.	Rubber-glove work should be planned and carried out so that a worker is never totally dependent on the integrity of rubber gloves. Having this second line of defense is essential when working on a circuit with rubber gloves. • Work from an insulated aerial device, or if that is not possible, • Work from pole-mounted insulated platforms, but ensure that the top and bottom bare sections are clean, dry, and on an electrical retest schedule. • Stay at a minimum approach distance from all second points of contact or cover-up or remove the neutral, secondary wires, guys, or other phases. • If two people are working at the same structure, do not work on more than one phase at a time.

Specific Rubber-Gloving Hazards

16.3.6 Table 16–7 identifies common hazards and barriers needed to carry out rubber-glove work safely.

TABLE 16–7   **Working with Rubber Gloves**

Rubber-Gloving Hazards	Barriers
Overreaching exposes an uncovered part of the body to an electrical contact.	1. Work from a position where a slip will not cause an uncovered part of the body to make contact—for example, from a position below the conductor. 2. Wear rubber sleeves to reduce the risk of contact due to overreaching.
Untying and tying-in conductor, because of the following: 1. The length of the tie wire. 2. Possible puncture of the rubber glove by the sharp end of the tie wire.	Bunch up the tie wire in the palm of your rubber glove when untying.
Installing and removing preformed dead ends or armor wrap. The preforms for larger conductors are long enough to contact other phases or objects.	For large conductor, use a dead-end clamp (shoe). If it is necessary to remove a long preform, make frequent cuts.
Temporarily removing rubber gloves for fine work or to cool off increases the probability of an inadvertent contact.	A mental lapse can occur anytime, including when rubber gloves have been removed. Tell someone working with you of your intention.
Working on more than one phase at a time. The other phase is a potential second point of contact.	Two people working on the same structure must not work on different phases at the same time. One can become a second point of contact for the other.
Working on adjacent structures at the same time.	When conductors are moved on adjacent structures at the same time, there must be communication between the two poles.
Small conductor can break while working on it.	Conductors such as #6 copper, #4 ACSR, and #8A copperweld, or smaller, should not be worked hot.
Long metallic tools can bridge or short the rubber-glove cuff.	Long-handled tools, such as a bolt cutter, press, hoist, or hammer, should have nonmetallic handles.
Improvising the temporary placement of a conductor while replacing a crossarm or other support can lead to poor clearance between conductors and to workers.	Use tools such as an auxiliary mast to support conductors while replacing a crossarm or other support items.

16.4 Hot-Line Tool Work

Introduction to Hot-Line Tool Work

16.4.1 There are procedures to do almost everything from the end of a stick. Switches can be cut into a line, solid connections can be made, armor wrap can be removed and installed, conductors on transmission lines can be unclamped and transferred into stringing blocks, and so on. Many people think that using the "tools" is the safest method of live-line work, and in some places this is backed up by regulations.

Many powerline workers consider working with live-line tools their favorite work. It takes more skill and practice to become proficient at using live-line tools than it does to untie conductors, install a wedge connector, or dead end a conductor into a dead-end clamp while working barehand or wearing rubber gloves.

Minimum Approach Distance when Working with Hot-Line Tools

16.4.2 Hot-line tools must be long enough to provide a minimum insulated working distance between any part of a worker and the energized conductor or part being worked on (see Table16–1).

Ensure that the clear insulation of conductor support tools, such as link sticks, strain carriers, and insulator cradles, are at least as long as the insulator string or the minimum distance specified in Table16–1 for the operating voltage.

Preparation for Hot-Line Tool Work

16.4.3 Table 16–8 explores the steps to take when working with hot-line tools.

TABLE 16–8   **Preparing to Work with Hot-Line Tools**

Step	Action	Details
1	Identify the weights and tensions to be lifted or pulled.	1. The weights and tensions of conductors to be lifted or pulled can be calculated as described in Chapter 15. Lifting conductor at a hilltop or at a corner can increase the weight and tension on the sticks very quickly.
		2. Check the working-load limit of the tool configuration to be used. Check the working-load limit of the components to be used, such as the saddles, tongs, link sticks, and snubbing bands.
		3. Check that the work method will allow compliance with the minimum approach distance.
		4. Check the conductor attachments at adjacent structures.
2	Inspect hot-line tools.	1. Check that the tools have had their scheduled electrical tests.
		2. Use hot-line tools that are kept clean and dry and in a protective container when not in use.
		3. A physical inspection of hot-line tools is very effective. In many cases, a stick that fails an electrical test also has an obvious visual physical defect. Physical damage to the tool, such as surface scratches or a deformed or popped rivet, can allow the moisture to enter.
		4. Hollow tools are more susceptible to contamination and may need more frequent electrical testing.
3	Wipe or clean hot-line tools.	1. Clean and dry your tools with an agent specifically made for this purpose—that is, an agent that is evaporates quickly and leaves a treatment on the surface that repels and beads water.
		2. Damp and dirty work gloves are the most probable source of surface contamination, especially if both ends of a stick have a tool on it and the worker is using both ends.

(continued)

TABLE 16–8 *(continued)*

Step	Action	Details
4	Check saddles, lever lifts, and chain tighteners.	**1.** Use saddles that are stored with the holding clamp in the closed position when not in use. **2.** Check for distortions, loose bolts, and loose rivets. **3.** When the wire-tong saddles are installed on the hot-line tool, an additional 180-degree turn on the wing nut may be applied after hand tightening. **4.** Use rope blocks to make lifts with the lifting tong. As a second barrier to the rope blocks, tie a rope sling between the saddle and the butt ring. **5.** After a lever lift is flipped into position, tie it up to prevent it from dropping during the movement of the conductor.
5	Check ropes and blocks.	**1.** Use ropes and rope blocks that are kept exclusively for hot-line tool work.
6	Protect against any second points of contact.	**1.** Work from an insulated pole-mounted platform or an insulated aerial bucket. **2.** Cover up or remove the neutral, secondary wires, guys, and other phases. **3.** Do not work on more than one phase at a time.

Typical Working-Load Limits on Hot-Line Tools

16.4.4 Check specifications from manufacturers and from your utility/employer for actual working-load limits when using hot-line tools (see Table 16–9).

Calculating the Load on Hot-Line Tools

16.4.5 Most hot-line tool work on transmission lines uses the tools in a straight tension mode, and the maximum safe working load can be determined from the ratings of the individual tools. For a configuration such as the one shown in Figure 16–7, some measuring and calculations are needed to determine the maximum safe working load.

The compression load on lifting tong B =

$$\frac{\text{Length} \times \text{Conductor Weight}}{\text{Length}} \text{ or } \frac{B \times W}{C}$$

The tension on the holding tong A =

$$\frac{\text{Length of A} \times \text{Conductor Weight}}{\text{Length of C}} \text{ or } \frac{A \times W}{C}$$

where A = length of holding tong between the conductor and the saddle
  B = length of holding tong between the conductor and the saddle
  C = distance between the saddles
  W = weight of the conductor in pounds or kilograms

Remember that the maximum height a conductor can be lifted occurs when the lowest point of sag reaches an adjacent structure. At this point the conductor weight has doubled. When planning to lift a conductor with an aerial device or with hot-line tools, multiply the weight to be lifted by a factor of 2. When the con-

TABLE 16–9   Working-Load Limits for Hot-Line Tools

Tool	Type or Size	Working-Load Limit
A wire tong (pole) is designed for compression loading. All side pulls must be balanced with an opposite side pull. Typically, for a vertical lift the minimum distance between saddles is 5 ft. (1.5 m) and the maximum unsupported length above the top saddle is 6 ft. (1.8 m).	2.5 in. (6.4 cm) 3 in. (7.6 cm)	The limiting factor for the working-load limit for a lifting pole is the saddles holding it and any horizontal strains being applied to it.
Pole saddles must hold the weight of the lifting tong, the conductor weight, and the pull exerted by the fall line on a set of blocks. For a heavy conductor, hang the set of blocks in a separate snubbing band or sling instead of the saddle.	Saddle without extension Saddle with extension	800 lbs. (360 kg) 600 lbs. (270 kg)
Lever lifts are used for the heaviest loads to be lifted.	Single-lever lift Double-lever lift	1,000 lbs. (450 kg) 1,500 lbs. (680 kg)
The allowable tension on a link stick depends on the diameter.	1.25 in. (3 cm) 1.5 in. (4 cm)	3,500 lbs. (1,580 kg) 6,500 lbs. (2,950 kg)
The working-load limits for suspension sticks and strain carrier poles used to lift or tension conductors on transmission lines vary and should be positively identified and checked out before using.	Typical heavy-duty suspension link stick Typical strain carrier pole	6,500 lbs. (3,000 kg) 7,500 lbs. (3,400 kg)
Roller link stick	1 1/4 in. (3 cm)	1,000 lbs. (450 kg)
The allowable tension on a snubbing band is shown per ring and the total for the complete unit.	—	500 lbs. (230 kg) per ring, the total load not to exceed 1,000 lbs. (454 kg)

ductor to be lifted is at a corner structure, the conteracting force of a link stick down to a temporary rope guy holding the bisect tension of the conductor must also be added to the weight to be lifted.

An Example of Hot-Line Tool Calculations

16.4.6   Figure 16–8 shows two different tool configurations. If the conductor weight is given at 200 pounds, Table 16–10 shows the compression load on the lifting tong and the tension on the holding tong for the initial position and the final position for Pole A and Pole B. Note that the distance C can be critical to the tool loading.

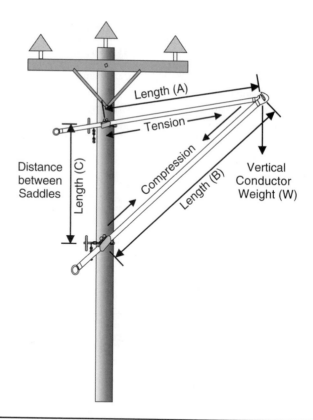

Figure 16-7 Calculating load on live-line tools.

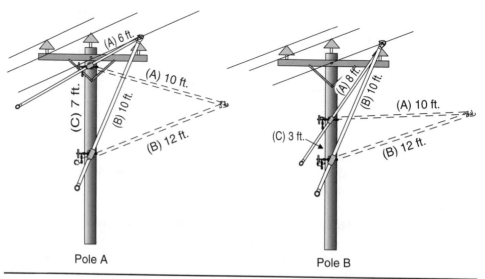

Pole A

Pole B

Figure 16-8 Example calculations.

TABLE 16–10   Example Calculations

	Pole A		Pole B	
	Initial Position	Final Position	Initial Position	Final Position
Load on Lifting Tong = $\dfrac{B \times W}{C}$	$\dfrac{10 \times 200}{7}$ = 286 lbs.	$\dfrac{12 \times 200}{7}$ = 343 lbs.	$\dfrac{10 \times 200}{3}$ = 667 lbs.	$\dfrac{12 \times 200}{3}$ = 343 lbs.
Load on Holding Tong = $\dfrac{A \times W}{C}$	$\dfrac{6 \times 200}{7}$ = 170 lbs.	$\dfrac{10 \times 200}{7}$ = 286 lbs.	$\dfrac{8 \times 200}{3}$ = 533 lbs.	$\dfrac{10 \times 200}{3}$ = 667 lbs.

Specific Hazards Involving Hot-Line Tools

16.4.7 Table 16–11 outlines barriers to specific hazards related to using hot-line tools.

TABLE 16–11   Hazards and Barriers of Working with Hot-Line Tools

Specific Hazards	Barriers
Encroaching on the minimum approach distance (Table 16–1) on the tool.	Hand stops mounted just beyond the minimum limit of approach can serve as a barrier. Some utilities require rubber gloves in addition to the hot-line tool.
Using a contaminated damp work glove on a tool can leave a conductive film.	The most likely cause of a tool failure is surface contamination. Use clean, dry work gloves.
Tools sliding through saddles after weight is applied.	Use rope blocks to make the lift. Leave the rope blocks in place to hold the weight or tie a sling between the saddle and the butt ring as a backup to saddles.
Shorting out a tie wire or preform to the structure.	When untying insulators, cut the tie wire short enough so that it cannot reach any part of the structure. Consider alternative hardware for dead-ending or clamping in.
Hot-line tools left on the circuit are susceptible to tracking and leaving a carbon trail.	Hot-line tools, especially components such as extension arms, can be left on a circuit for up to 3 weeks in a nonpolluted area. Look for visible signs of tracking before handling them.
Misuse of tools can cause a loss of control.	Never use a lifting tong in a tension mode as a link stick. Double check the attachment of the saddles and snubbing bands before securing a hot conductor to it. There is no backup when a snubbing band lets go.
At transmission-line voltages, there is some suspicion that high winds can cause a decrease in air pressure on one side of the tool and the low pressure on that side of the stick causes a flashover.	As a prudent measure, avoid hot-line tool work on transmission lines during high-wind conditions or increase the maximum approach distance on the tools.

16.5 Barehand Work

Introduction to Barehand Work

16.5.1 Like a bird on a wire, a person can make contact with a live conductor when insulated from all other conductive objects. Also, birds are not seen landing on higher-voltage conductors because the electric field around the conductor will be uncomfortable (to say the least). Above 50 kilovolts, the electric field for a human can become uncomfortable and a worker needs to be shielded.

A Faraday cage is used to shield people working barehand on high voltages. A fellow by the name of Michael Faraday introduced the concept that an electric field will not penetrate into a conducting sphere and there can, therefore, be no current flow inside a sphere. Bonding all the conductive components together, the metal bucket grid, conducting suit, hood, and boots serve as a shield. Figure 16–9 illustrates that the electric field stays outside of the shielded area of the buckets and conductive suits. The electric field is strongest next to the shield and diminishes as it approaches ground. Everything inside that shield is at the same voltage. If working from a ladder or suspended from a rope or link stick, the conductive suit worn by the worker is the Faraday cage.

When bonded on, minimum approach distances similar to those specified in Table 16–12 are kept from everything not already bonded to the conductor.

Barehand work is generally limited to a small number of specialized powerline workers. It is especially useful on transmission-line work where the use of very long hot-line tools becomes unwieldy and there is plenty of clearance to other phases and structures.

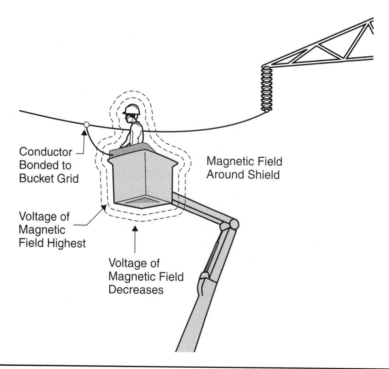

Figure 16–9   Faraday cage effect.

TABLE 16–12   **Barehand Minimum Distances**

Voltage Range Phase-to-Phase Kilovolt	Phase to Ground		Phase to Phase	
	Feet–Inches	*Meters*	*Feet–Inches*	*Meters*
30.0 to 35.0	2–4	0.7	2–4	0.7
35.1 to 46.0	2–6	0.8	2–6	0.8
46.1 to 72.5	3–0	0.9	3–0	0.9
72.6 to 121.0	3–4	1.0	4–6	1.4
138.0 to 145.0	3–6	1.1	5–0	1.5
161.0 to 169.0	3–8	1.2	5–6	1.7
230.0 to 242.0	5–0	1.5	8–4	2.5
345.0 to 362.0	7–0	2.1	13–4	4.1
500.0 to 552.0	11–0	3.4	20–0	6.1

Barehand work is done from an insulated aerial device, from an insulated ladder/platform, from a helicopter, suspended from a link stick, and suspended on a hotline rope. A few utilities allow barehand work on distribution voltages as an alternative to rubber-glove work or hot-line tool work.

This chapter provides only an overview of barehand work.

Electrical Integrity of Barehand Equipment

16.5.2 All equipment used for barehand work, such as a bucket truck boom, a live-line rope, or a live-line ladder, are a parallel path to ground and all will have some leakage current (except when using a helicopter). This leakage current on the equipment must be kept below a certain threshold before using it for barehand work. This is true for all live-line work, but with barehand work, leakage current is measured and monitored more frequently because there is no second barrier if there is a failure.

Using an Aerial Device

An aerial device used for barehand work will have a boom contamination meter circuit built where a meter can provide continuous monitoring for leakage. The empty buckets are raised so that some part of the metal grid makes contact with the line. The boom is left in contact for a minimum of 3 minutes. The leakage current is monitored and may not exceed 1 microampere per phase-to-ground kilovolt. For example, a 230-kilovolt line is about 133 kilovolts to ground. The maximum leakage current allowed is 132 amperes, but, depending on the type of meter, the alarm on the monitoring circuit may sound at 70 microamperes. The meter readings should be recorded in a log because one of the best measures is to see if there is a trend developing.

For work on a transmission line, a corona ring at the upper end of the insulated section of the boom is needed to prevent a concentration of electrical stress similar to the role of the insulation shield of an underground cable.

The inside of the buckets are lined with metal, and all metal in the upper boom area is bonded together, along with the bonding wand and clamp. The first contact on a transmission line is when a powerline worker attaches the wand to the conductor. On a 230-kilovolt line, the charging current to energize the bucket grid creates about a 1.5-foot (0.5-m) arc. After bonding on, a more secure clamp is put on the conductor by hand. A spring-loaded breakaway clamp is used in case the workers aloft become incapacitated and the boom has to be lowered with the lower controls.

Using a Ladder or Suspended from a Rope or Link Stick

An electrical test can be conducted on live-line ladders, rope, and link sticks immediately before using a portable hot-stick tester, as shown in Figure 16–10.

The conductive suit and all accessories serve as the shield for the electric field.

Conductive Clothing and Footwear

16.5.3 The conductive clothing serves as a shield around the worker, keeping the electric field effect outside of the shielding. Coveralls, work gloves, socks (not always worn), and a parka-style hood are made with conducting material. The hood is worn over the hard hat and extends forward somewhat to help shield the face from annoying sparking along the skin. Coveralls have a tail that is used to bond to the metal grid in the bucket. Conducting sole boots are worn, and conducting straps bonded to the boots are bonded to the suit with leg clips.

After the suit is put on, an ohmmeter is used to check the continuity of the suit between the tail and the leg cuffs, the gloves, the hood, and the boot soles. All the measurements should read less than 100,000 ohms.

Some Specific Hazards Involving Barehand Work

16.5.4 Table 16–13 explores the hazards of barehand work.

Figure 16–10 A hot-stick tester.

TABLE 16–13   Some Hazards of Barehand Work

Specific Hazards	Barriers
Electrical failure of equipment.	• Watch for hot-line rope that has become somewhat contaminated with use, especially when humidity is high. • Ensure that there is a check valve and a clean atmospheric vent valve in the hydraulic lines that extend over 35 ft. (10.7 m) high to prevent a conductive partial vacuum from forming. The hydraulic motor should not be shut down during barehand work. • When metal is in series with rope or link sticks (a floating electrode), a longer minimum approach is required.
Flashover of insulated tools.	• Wet, dirty work gloves can contaminate the surface of a hot-line tool, so use clean, dry work gloves. • Avoid barehand work during high winds. There is some suspicion that the slight reduction in air pressure on the lee side of a boom or tool can reduce the insulating value. • Reduce exposure to a voltage surge. Do not work barehand during electrical storms. • Reduce exposure to a voltage surge due to switching, and have the reclose function of the source breaker blocked.
Flashover of an aerial device boom while doing the contamination tests.	There are conditions, such as high humidity, when the meter readings are not acceptable. If the readings are going down while the boom is in contact it is probably leakage current that is drying out the boom. Do not use leakage current to dry the boom. This leakage current can leave conductive carbon tracking and lead to a boom flashover.
Encroaching on the minimum approach distance.	Use a dedicated observer to watch for encroachment on the minimum approach distance. The most likely encroachment has been with the heel (elbow) of an aerial device. Measure a hot-line ladder or platform to ensure it will provide a sufficient length of clear insulation for the voltage to be worked on.
Placing bonding clamps on each side of a hot joint or connector. (The typically small bonding wire may carry current and burn off.)	Install a jumper across a hot joint or connector, using hot-line tools, before moving in to bond on.
Forgetting to install a jumper or taking an ammeter reading on a jumper before cutting.	Forgetting to install a jumper can happen during a repetitive job. Considering the consequences, a crew should use a written form similar to the "Switching Order." Use an ammeter to ensure that the jumper is carrying at least 30 percent of the load before cutting or opening a conductor barehand.

(continued)

TABLE 16–13 *(continued)*

Specific Hazards	Barriers
Shorting out a portion of the insulator string with the buckets or body.	When using slings and hoists near suspension insulators, it is possible to short out some insulators in a string. If some of the insulators are already defective, the risk is compounded. Test the insulators.
	If more than 20 percent of the insulators have no insulation value, surge-limiting devices can be installed prior to barehand replacements, or insulators can be replaced by other than barehand procedures.
	For work at the energized end of an acceptable insulator string, a bucket or worker should be positioned so that no more than 10 percent of the insulator string is shorted out by the buckets, worker's body, or tools.
Conductive objects in between a hot circuit and another phase or structure that form a floating electrode (which can reduce the insulating value across an air gap).	A person in a conductive suit, a metal grid in the buckets, or two link sticks tied together form floating electrodes. A person in a conductive suit working between a tower and conductor on an insulated ladder will be a floating electrode.
	These objects can give off an electrical discharge that reduces the air-gap distance needed to prevent a flashover. Increase the maximum approach distance when a floating electrode is introduced.
Contacting an object before bonding to it.	It is probably not necessary to point this out to an experienced barehand powerline worker, but there is a need to bond or bridge to any metallic objects to be touched or brought into the work zone.

Review Questions

1. Why should doing a job "hot" not be the first option?

2. Why is the second point of contact considered a hazard when working hot?

3. What length of clear insulating section of a live-line tool should be maintained when working on a 115-kilovolt circuit?

4. What is the purpose of blocking the automatic reclosing feature of a source circuit breaker or recloser?

5. How can the probability of a voltage surge be reduced while working with live-line tools on a transmission line?

6. Why is there a higher risk when working on live secondary next to a transformer rather than a span away?

7. Name three kinds of defects to look for when doing a visual inspection of rubber gloves.

8. How can the second point of contact be eliminated when doing rubber-glove work?

9. What extra steps can be taken to prevent a wire (lifting) tong from sliding through a saddle?

10. Is it acceptable to use a 2.5-inch (6.4-cm) wire (lifting) tong as a link stick to hold conductor tension on a corner?

CHAPTER 17

Tree Work in an Electrical Utility Environment

Topics to Be Covered	**Section**
Vegetation Management in Electrical Utilities	17.1
The Hazards of Tree Work	17.2
Tree Work Near Electrical Circuits	17.3
Essential Skills for Tree Work	17.4

17.1 Vegetation Management in Electrical Utilities

Why Electrical Utilities Control Vegetation

17.1.1 A large and critical part of an electric utility maintenance program is vegetation control:

1. Next to lightning, tree contact is the most common cause of outages in an electrical system. Tree contact is the biggest cause of damage to overhead lines after a hurricane, ice storm, heavy wet snow, and so on. Restoration of power because of fallen trees, limbs, and branches is very labor intensive and time-consuming.

2. Brush growth in a right-of-way can cause line outages, especially during peak electrical demand, when the system is most vulnerable. Peak demand and/or warm temperatures can cause a long span on a transmission line to sag an additional 10 to 20 feet. Brush is also a source of fuel for a fire and the ionized air above a fire is conductive and can cause a line outage. Brush growth also restricts access to powerlines by line and tree crews.

3. The arcing associated with a tree contacting a powerline can and does start grass, brush, and forest fires. A fire can also destroy wooden transmission and distribution structures.

4. Fatalities occur every year when members of the public climb into trees, prune trees, or remove trees that are in contact or make contact with

powerlines. During storms, live conductors that are knocked down by tree damage are an extreme hazard to the public.

5. Vegetation can sustain and spread a fire in or around a substation. Vegetation at a substation can also attract animals, such as squirrels, that can climb onto the station structure and cause outages.

6. Tall-growing trees can interfere or block microwave-beam paths whose signals are used in monitoring and controlling the status of the system and operating switchgears.

7. To ensure a safe and reliable power supply, regulatory agencies require electric utilities to have a documented vegetation management program that includes the budgeting, scheduling, clearance standards, human resources, and inspections needed to maintain a right-of-way. One of the root causes of the huge Northeast blackout in August 2003 was a very preventable, poor control of vegetation.

8. An electrical utility is responsible for large tracts of land, and regulatory agencies require property owners to control noxious weeds and control erosion.

9. Regulatory and good citizenship requirements are enforced to protect the environment, especially as it pertains to water quality and wildlife habitat.

10. The source of much of the face-to-face contact and a large part of an electrical utility public relations program involves vegetation control programs. Customer relations include planning to maintain attractive right-of-ways.

Elements of a Utility Vegetation Management Program

17.1.2 A vegetation management program includes planning, scheduling resources, budgeting for tree pruning on cycle, danger tree removal, brush control, herbicide application, and tree planting.

Managing vegetation on transmission and distribution right-of-ways requires planning, scheduling, clearance standards, human resources, and inspections. An electrical utility would typically have an inventory of the number of right-of-way miles (km) within its jurisdiction broken up into geographic blocks. There would be blocks for tree pruning, and blocks for brush control work, patrol, and so on. The number of blocks would correspond with the frequency in a cycle. For example, if there were six pruning blocks, each block would be trimmed every 6 years. The workload for each block would be relatively even because the inventory for each block would also take into account factors such as types of trees (fast or slow growing), density of trees, and so on.

Quality Pruning

17.1.3 Trees are generally pruned on an established cycle. Pruning must provide for clearance to powerlines and leave trees in a healthy state. The number of blocks or cycles for pruning will depend on the speed of growth and customer sensitivity. The amount of pruning varies according to the growth rate of the tree species, as well as locations and growth conditions (soil, water, and so on).

Just cutting off the ends of branches (topping or heading) and leaving stubs used to be a common practice. When a branch was cut off at a crotch, the proper method was to make a flush cut and apply dressing to the wound. However, cut stubs were prone to decay and vigorous growth of water sprouts soon grew at the stub. The sprouts were weak and broke easily during windstorms. Flush cuts and wound dressing have been found to lead to dieback and decay.

The following are the most accepted practices for quality pruning:

- *Directional pruning* (also called *natural target pruning, drop crotch pruning,* or the *Shigo method*) has become a preferred standard for pruning near powerlines. Only the branches that head toward the powerline are pruned; those growing down or away from the line are left to grow. Depending on the location of the line of the tree, a directional pruned tree will have a V-shape, an L-shape, or removal of one side. Initially, the tree will have an unbalanced look, but it will grow to correct any lack of balance and will end up healthier than if it had been topped. (See Figure 17–1.) Directional pruning may not be appropriate for trees that have been topped many times or for trees with a dominating central trunk, such as a conifer.

- *Avoid topping and leaving no stubs.* If a branch must be shortened, it should be cut back to a lateral that is large enough so that at least one-third of the branch diameter is removed, as shown in Figure 17–2.

- *Make an undercut and a second cut from the top when removing larger branches or limbs.* Make the undercut about 18 inches (0.5 meter) from the limb's point of attachment. Make the second cut from the top, a little farther out than the undercut. This method will prevent ripping or tearing of the bark. Small branches lopped off with a pruner would, of course, be one cut.

The Final Cut

Make the final cut just outside the point where the branch meets the trunk, which is the location of the branch collar (branch bark ridge). The branch collar is part of the trunk and should not be removed. This is called the *1-2-3 method of branch removal* (Figure 17–3).

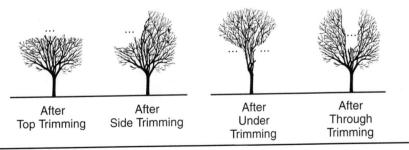

| After Top Trimming | After Side Trimming | After Under Trimming | After Through Trimming |

Figure 17–1 Directional pruning.

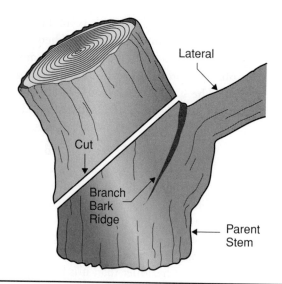

Figure 17–2 Cutting a leader.

Removing or Felling Danger Trees

17.1.4 Any tree removal program involves removing danger trees and is more difficult to plan and schedule because it is dependent on patrols and customer requests for trees to be removed. Two types of trees are referred to as danger trees.

1. *A Danger to Powerlines:* Most jurisdictions have regulations that require a utility to remove trees that are a danger to a powerline. Any diseased or unstable tree tall enough to fall within or close to striking distance of a powerline is

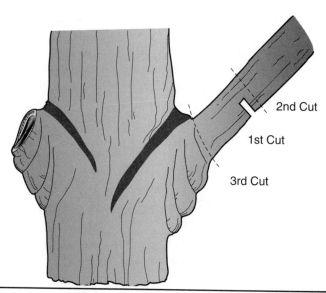

Figure 17–3 The 1-2-3 method of branch removal.

considered a danger tree (Figure 17–4). Felling a danger tree to powerlines requires an awareness of the electrical hazards and minimum working distances. To reduce the risk of a tree falling into a powerline during removal requires excellent tree felling techniques, roping, topping, and/or use of a crane.

2. *A Danger to People:* A tree can be identified as a danger tree because of the climbing or felling hazards. Unhealthy trees, rotten wood, and hangers contribute to hazards that must be identified. Indications that a tree may be suspect include signs of excavation around a tree exposing broken roots, adjacent unhealthy or dead trees, any tree with leaves that have an unusual color, and/or a tree that has been heavily pruned.

The U.S. Federal Occupational Safety and Health Act (OSHA) regulations have a rule regarding danger trees:

> Each danger tree shall be felled, removed, or avoided. Each danger tree, including lodged trees and snags, shall be felled or removed using mechanical or other techniques that minimize employee exposure before work is commenced in the area of the danger tree. . . . A danger tree includes any standing tree that presents a hazard to employees due to conditions such as, but not limited to, deterioration or damage to the tree, and direction or lean of the tree. Signs of a danger tree can be:
> 1. large, dead branches and hangers in the tree and on the ground.
> 2. cracks or splits in the trunk or where branches are attached.
> 3. cavities or rotten wood along the trunk or in major branches.

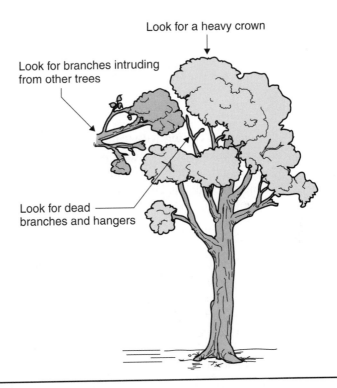

Figure 17–4 Tree inspection.

Removing a danger-to-people tree requires techniques that ensure that no one is within two tree lengths when it is felled. The techniques used can include attaching a rope or winch from an aerial lift and pulling the tree down or using a crane. Removing a tree that is leaning heavily on a powerline (during a power outage) or communications cable is a particularly unpredictable operation, and the tree should be pulled off by mechanical means.

Quality Brush Control

17.1.5 Transmission- and distribution-line owners have a vast amount of property to maintain. In addition to danger trees at the perimeter, controlling brush that has the potential to grow into a powerline is a large element of a vegetation program. Brush is woody vegetation and is defined as 4 to 6 inches (10 to 15 cm) in diameter and growing under a powerline. Brush that must be removed is any species capable of growing to conductor height. One goal of a vegetation management program is to promote compatible plant species, such as grasses and low-growing shrubs, as a ground cover on the transmission and distribution right-of-ways. Once the right-of-way brush is brought under control, maintenance is minimized and often requires only grass cutting, animal grazing, or farming.

Abiding by environmental regulations for wildlife, erosion, and noxious plants is also part of any brush control program. Selective removal of incompatible brush can be done manually, by mechanical cutting, by grubbing, and/or by spraying herbicide.

Manual Cutting

Manual cutting is effective for spot work on right-of-ways where the brush is fairly well controlled. A powered brush saw is generally used in such circumstances.

Mechanical Cutting

Mechanical cutting with a mower, such as a brushhog or flail mower and other types that are under continuous development, is commonly done where no herbicide is allowed. However, unless followed up with herbicide, cutting brush buys some time but the cut brush of some species comes back with more shoots and faster growth.

Grubbing

Brush can be removed by grubbing, which consists of using a machine such as a bulldozer to dig out the brush by its roots. To prevent erosion and reduce future maintenance, grubbing is followed up with seeding so that it can be maintained by mowing, grazing or farming. Dozer blades, such as V-shaped or toothed blades, improve the efficiency of grubbing.

Herbicide

Herbicide spraying is the most effective method for controlling brush.

Proper Use of Herbicides

17.1.6 Different types of herbicides and applications are used to control different vegetation. Herbicide use must be done only by trained and licensed personnel to ensure that the application meets safety and environmental requirements and is effective. Proper mixtures, control of drift, and accurately calibrated equipment are necessary for effective control and protection of the environment. An herbicide spraying program is usually closely aligned with a public relations program because some members of the public have negative perceptions of herbicides.

Foliage spraying is done with herbicides that kill only broadleaf plants, such as some brush, and thereby promote the growth of grasses. It is almost essential to get a right-of-way under control so that only compatible species are left to grow. Foliar herbicides may be applied either with ground equipment or aircraft. Spraying from the ground is the only way to spray individual incompatible brush, but aerial spraying is effective for dense brush, especially in rugged terrain. If brush growth is left too long and is 15 to 20 feet (4 to 6 m) tall, it probably must be cut before spraying.

Basal spraying is the application of an herbicide and diesel oil mixture to the lower portion of a trunk to control many species. The entire circumference of a trunk up to 18 inches above ground should be soaked.

Stump treatment (spraying cut stumps, stump injection) at ground level, immediately after cutting, prevents resprouting. Applying an herbicide to prevent resprouting can reduce or eliminate future regrowth and, thereby, future cutting.

Soil treatment with a pellet or granular form of an herbicide kills many brush species.

Tree growth regulators (TGR) can effectively reduce the need for frequent pruning on fast-growing trees. TGR chemical compounds shorten the amount of limb growth and are applied to the soil around a tree. The chemical stays effective for 3 to 5 years.

Soil sterilization is used to kill all vegetation and is useful in and around a substation.

Planting Trees

17.1.7 Public resistance to tree removal can be somewhat alleviated by having a tree planting program in which compatible trees are planted to replace incompatible trees that have had to be removed. Compatible trees are also planted as screening to reduce objections to substations and transmission lines being visible at road crossings.

A Knowledge of Trees

17.1.8 Arborists doing tree clearing around utility lines must know the value of trees. For example, knowing the growth rate of each species is important so that an arborist will know how far back to prune for a 6-year cycle. A knowledge of dendrology (the study of trees) helps an arborist when talking to customers and discussing the health of the trees being pruned or recommending compatible species that can be planted, and so on.

17.2 The Hazards of Tree Work

An Introduction to Tree Work Hazards

17.2.1 Table 17–1 identifies hazards and controls that arborists work with on a daily basis.

Recognize Your Skill Limits

17.2.2 Pruning and removing trees, especially near live electric circuits, is high-risk work. This work should be reserved for trained arborists. Line crews working on no-power calls and line crews in some jurisdictions are trained and expected to do some basic tree pruning and tree removal. It is wise to recognize when a tree job is beyond the skills and equipment available. In such cases, call for a qualified arborist.

TABLE 17–1   **Some Hazards and Controls of Tree Work**

Tree Work Hazards	Controls
1. Arborists have a high exposure to musculoskeletal injuries because of climbing, hauling brush, and picking up branches.	Pruning and removing trees are very physical tasks. In addition to keeping fit, every arborist should participate in a back-care program.
2. Arborists have a high exposure to repetitive strain injuries, especially from using pruners and pole saws while leaning out of buckets.	In addition to tool and bucket design, an arborist must be part of an education and exercise program that reduces repetitive strain injury.
3. Arborists have a high exposure to severe cuts when using chain saws, probably the highest-risk power tool ever invented.	Arborists use more personal protective equipment than any other electrical utility worker. In addition to a hard hat and protective footwear, when operating a chain saw an arborist also wears leg protection, eye protection, hearing protection, and protective gloves.
4. When climbing trees or working from aerial devices, arborists have a high exposure to falls from heights.	Specialized skills, equipment, and training are necessary for climbing trees safely and minimizing the risks of falling.
	The risk of tree climbing can be reduced by using a fall protection system. The one shown in Figure 17–10 later in this chapter is a belaying technique requiring very little in equipment. This method can be used when climbing and must be done to secure a rope for tree removal.
5. Arborists have a high exposure to electrical hazards. Electrical contact causes about 30 percent of all fatalities related to tree work. Direct contact with a powerline or a tree branch touching a powerline increases the risk of receiving a fatal electric burn.	Arborists must be able to recognize the components of the electrical system being worked on and must have extensive training on the proper techniques for pruning and removing trees near live circuits.

17.3 Tree Work Near Electrical Circuits

**Electrical
Awareness**

17.3.1 Work near electrical utility circuits is most commonly done by qualified, specialized *powerline clearance tree trimmers*. Powerline clearance tree trimmers are trained in the techniques and knowledge required to trim trees around powerlines. This training is accomplished through company training programs and or apprenticeship programs.

Occupational safety regulations do not allow an unqualified person to come within 10 feet (3 m) of a distribution electrical circuit and an additional 4 inches (10 cm) for every 10 kV over that, which works out to 14 feet (4.3 m) for 169 kV, 16 feet (4.9 m) for 230 kV, and 25 feet (7.6 m) for 500 kV. Working near electrical circuits is the highest-risk hazard that an arborist must control. Control starts with being able to recognize the voltage level of a line, the safe tool insulation distance, the risk of "tree shock," and step potentials.

An arborist must be able to identify the voltage levels of the power conductors, neutral, open wire bare secondary, wrapped secondary, tree wire, telephone cable, and street light circuits. Some structures will have three or four circuits, each with different voltages. While the size or length of insulation is one indicator, reading the voltage on a transformer nameplate or asking will be more accurate. It is the voltage level that determines the allowable minimum working distance.

An arborist must be able to recognize hazards such as a broken crossarm, a broken insulator, or a fallen conductor. When working under a guarantee of isolation (clearance) there should be an understanding of the lockout/tagout system and grounding that are providing safe conditions for work.

While direct contact with a conductor obviously can cause electrical burns, an arborist also must be aware of how someone can receive an electrical shock from indirect contact through touch potential, step potential, and tree shock.

**Minimum
Working
Distances for
Tree Pruning**

17.3.2 The most common and most effective barrier against electrical contact is maintenance of a space between the work zone and the electrical conductors. The U.S. Federal Occupational Safety and Health Act (OSHA) regulations specify the minimum approach distances as shown in Table 17–2. These are minimum distances for qualified arborists—not necessarily safe distances.

While the length of an insulated and regularly tested pruner is electrically safe for the distance specified, an inadvertent movement or a limb bridging across the pruner can cause electrical contact. Powerline workers should plan to stay farther away than the minimum distance recommended, possibly another 3 feet (1 m). When it is necessary to work *at or close to* the minimum distance, treat that like an exception requiring additional planning, such as the following:

1. Stop and plan your approach and movement, preferably keeping the hazard at arm's length.

2. Plan the work so that your exposure time will be minimized.

TABLE 17–2   **Minimum Working Distances for Tree Pruning**

Voltage (Phase to Phase)	Minimum Working Distance
2.1–15 kV	2 ft., 0 in. (0.6 m)
15.1–35 kV	2 ft., 4 in. (0.7 m)
35.1–46 kV	2 ft., 6 in. (7.6 m)
46.1–72.5 kV	3 ft., 0 in. (0.9 m)
72.6–121 kV	3 ft., 4 in. (1 m)
138–145 kV	3 ft., 6 in. (1.07 m)
161–169 kV	3 ft., 8 in. (1.1 m)
230–242 kV	5 ft., 0 in. (1.5 m)
345–362 kV	7 ft., 0 in. (2.1 m)
500–552 kV	11 ft., 0 in. (3.4 m)
700–765 kV	15 ft., 0 in. (4.6 m)

3. Discuss your plan with a person who will act as a dedicated observer for the duration of the work.

OSHA has specified the minimum working distances from energized conductors for qualified line-clearance tree trimmers. (See Table 17–2.)

A Human Body as an Electrical Path

17.3.3 The human body tolerates electrical current very poorly; 100 milliamperes can be fatal. Considering that a typical household circuit is fused at 15 amperes (15,000 milliamperes), the risk for a lethal electrical shock exists on all electrical circuits if the voltage is high enough to break down the resistance. A fault on a typical distribution feeder close to a substation can generate 10,000 amperes (10 million milliamperes).

It takes a certain amount of voltage to break down the initial skin resistance of a human body before a current path is established. Once a current path is established, it is the amount of current and the path the current takes through the body that does the damage. Any voltage over 750 volts has very little trouble breaking down skin resistance. A much higher voltage is required to break down the resistance for anyone wearing rubber gloves.

Keep Away from Touch Potential

17.3.4 A touch potential refers to a voltage between a person's hands and feet when the hands are touching an object that has become energized.

A tree in contact with a live circuit will have current coming down the trunk to ground. The voltage where the tree is in contact will be at full line voltage. Voltage will drop as the current travels down the tree, and the amount of voltage at ground level will depend on many factors, including the type of tree, the season, and the type of earth. A person standing beside the tree and touching it will provide another path for the current to flow to ground. The parallel path provided by the worker will carry some current, and a mere *100 milliamperes can be fatal.* Similarly, standing on the ground and touching a truck that might become energized is a touch potential hazard.

Electricity-resistant work boots are available that—when worn as personal protective equipment—can (depending on negating variables such as the voltage level and if standing in deep mud) provide increased contact resistance with the ground that may make a difference.

Keep Away from Step Potential

17.3.5 A step potential refers to a voltage between one foot and the other foot when walking on the ground in an area usually safe to walk that has become energized by electrical energy entering the earth.

The hazard is to anyone working at a location where an object in contact with earth contacts a live conductor. For example, electrical current flows into earth when a live conductor comes in contact with a tree, a truck boom makes contact, or a live conductor falls to the ground.

At the point where the current enters earth, the current breaks up and flows in many paths, depending on the makeup and resistance of the earth. The voltage at the current-entry point is higher than the voltage one or two paces away from the entry point. Therefore, a difference of potential is in the earth around the current entry point.

The voltage between the gradient rings lessens as the distance from the contact point is increased. Voltage gradients are also known as ground gradients, potential gradients, and step potentials.

Keep Away from Tree Shock

17.3.6 To receive electrical burns when working with trees, it is unnecessary for an arborist to make direct contact with a powerline; about half of all electrocution fatalities are the result of indirect contact. Because a tree is not an excellent conductor, there would be a voltage drop as the current flows through the length of the tree where the voltage is highest at the contact or entry point and lowest at the exit point, usually at ground level. A human body in a tree that is in contact with an energized line can provide another path for the current to flow toward the ground. As shown in Figure 17–5, the hands on the tree would be at a different potential than the feet because the voltage drops as it flows through the resistance of the tree.

A tree climber gets a "tree shock" when the hands are on one voltage gradient and the feet are on another, even though the climber is not yet close to the line. In other words, do not climb a tree that is in contact with a live circuit. Wearing rubber gloves does not provide adequate protection because many parts of the body are in contact with a tree when climbing.

Keep Away from the Boom of an Aerial Lift Truck

17.3.7 When an aerial lift boom is used near energized circuits, the insulated boom and insulated lower boom insert provide good protection for those working near the vehicle on the ground. However, it is not unusual for limbs and

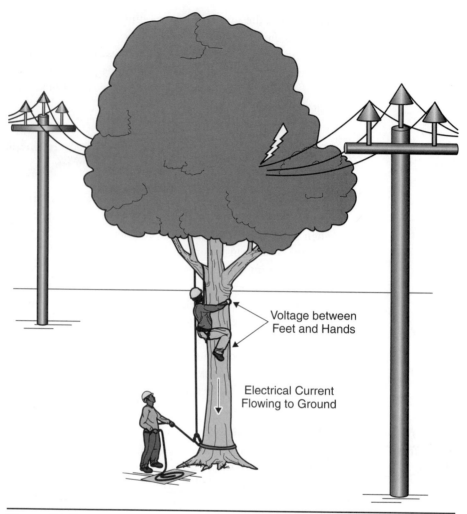

Figure 17–5   Tree shock.

branches being dropped by a tree trimmer to short-circuit the lower boom insert. While the probability is low for the lower boom insert to be short-circuited by a branch coincident with the lower boom making contact with a live circuit, the consequences for anyone touching the truck are high. If it is necessary to contact the truck, the person on the ground should ask the operator to stop all boom movement, check the position of the boom, and then do the task requiring contact with the truck.

While the boom is in the vicinity of live circuits, the worker on the ground should also keep others away from the truck and any attached equipment, notwithstanding the danger of falling limbs and branches.

TABLE 17–3   A Treetop Rescue Procedure

Step	Action	Details
1	Call loudly to the injured employee.	At the first indication of a problem, call loudly to the worker aloft, "Are you okay?" If the casualty responds but seems stunned or dazed, a rescue is probably needed, but the timing will not be as critical because the victim is breathing. Conscious victims of an electrical contact will often say they can descend on their own. Try to convince such victims to wait for a rescuer to climb up and act as a backup so that the descent will be controlled.
		If there is no response, timing is critical.
2	Call for help.	At the first indication that a rescue must be performed, call for help using a prearranged call or code words on the company radio or get help from nearby observers. The utility/contractor should have prearranged code words in place that immediately take priority over all other radio traffic.
3	Evaluate the situation.	If the casualty is still in contact, call for system control or dispatch to drop the circuit, preferably using prearranged code words to avoid a lot of discussion. If that does not work, the situation is such that the casualty is energized and the tree also may be energized. Climbing the tree presents a risk to the rescuer. Difficult as it may be to accept, from the ground it may be obvious that a rescue is not possible.
		If the casualty is in a precarious position, within the minimum approach limit, decisions regarding the need for rubber gloves, an insulated pruner or pole saw, or clean, dry rope will be needed to clear the victim.
		If the casualty is clearly not in contact, proceed with the rescue.
4	Climb up and attach a lanyard near the victim.	The rescuer climbs the tree with climbing equipment. Fall protection for the rescuer will depend on the tree, the practicality of getting a rope over a crotch quickly, the suitability of using the fall line of the casualty's climbing rope, the availability of work ropes, and the acceptability of a free climb risk.
		Climb to a position near the casualty and tie in with the lanyard. If the casualty is still in contact or too close to the line to approach safely, use an insulated pruner or pole saw to push or pull the casualty away from the line into a position that will allow the rescuer to approach the casualty.
5	Assess the casualty's condition.	If the casualty is breathing and/or conscious, the speed of the rescue is less urgent. Reassure the casualty while preparing to lower him or her to the ground. If a casualty insists on descending solo, the rescuer should insist on descending the tree with him or her.
		If the casualty is not breathing, it is urgent to get oxygenated blood to the brain as soon as possible. The best place to do that is on the ground. Before lowering a victim, some utilities/employers specify four quick mouth-to-mouth breaths to fill the lungs, some specify only lowering, and others specify starting CPR aloft.

(continued)

TABLE 17–3 *Continued*

Step	Action	Details
6	Rig for lowering the casualty.	Different methods are used. It is important to use and practice the method specified by your utility/employer.
		One method is for the rescuer to crotch in a position above the casualty. The rescuer then descends to the casualty and ties the casualty's saddle to his or her own saddles by either hooking together their carabiners, tying a rope through the two trees of both saddles and connecting them together (using the end of the casualty's fall line) as shown in Figure 17–6.

Figure 17–6 Tree rescue.

Step	Action	Details
7	Lower the casualty to the ground.	Using the rescuer's friction hitch, the rescuer and the casualty come down together. If more trained workers are present, a worker on the ground could rig up and belay the two people to the ground.
8	Apply first aid and/or CPR.	When the casualty reaches the ground, apply first aid and, if needed, CPR (Look, Listen and Feel, 2 breaths, 15 compressions, check pulse).

Conducting a Treetop Rescue

17.3.8 In most jurisdictions, occupational safety regulations require that when working in the vicinity of live circuits over 750 volts, a second person must be present within voice or visual range and trained to perform a rescue. The rescuer must also be trained in first aid and cardiopulmonary resuscitation (CPR).

A rescuer must know and have practiced how to lower a bucket using the lower controls and how to get a victim out of a bucket.

The procedure for rescuing a casualty from a tree without an aerial lift must be practiced at least annually by people who do this kind of work.

17.4 Essential Skills for Tree Work

Climbing a Tree

17.4.1 Climbing and working from a tree are very physical activities, and they are the skills that define an arborist. Tree climbing is also becoming a sport in some areas. While an aerial lift is the preferred method for productive working aloft, climbing is still necessary where even an all-terrain aerial lift cannot access the tree—for example, lines built across residential back lots, wide ditches in wet season, and island work. The climbing discussion, options, and equipment described in the following section all assume that a belaying system will be in place as fall protection.

Typically, a common climbing rope has been a three-strand 1/2-inch (12.5-mm) nylon or braided polyester rope with a Dacron exterior sheath, but it could be any other suitable rope that has at least a minimum normal breaking strength of about 5,400 pounds (24 kn) when new, a high heat tolerance, and a maximum working stretch of less than 7 percent. A knot should be tied to the end of the rope so that when descending the friction hitch will jam into it, stopping the descent in the rare situation that the climbing rope is too short.

A climbing rope should be a different color or identified by a colored internal strand to keep it distinct from working ropes. Climbing ropes designed for arborists are being manufactured. A climbing rope should not be used as a working rope to raise or lower limbs, but it is often used to safely pull up or lower hand tools or other ropes.

Historically, a bowline on a bight has been used as an arborist's saddle, but much more comfortable nylon saddles that support an arborist are available today. (See Figures 17–7 and 17–8.)

The tree-climbing procedure shown in Table 17–4 does not stand alone and must be backed up with training and verification of training.

Operating a Chain Saw

17.4.2 The bottom line for preventing serious accidents with a chain saw is to operate the saw so that no part of the body will make contact with a moving chain. Safety measures designed into the saw, such as a chain brake, chain stop when idling, and safety chains (see Figure 17–14) reduce some of the risk when they are in use and maintained. Unlike most other power tools, no guard covers a moving chain. Statistically, experienced operators have more accidents than weekend operators, probably because of high exposure.

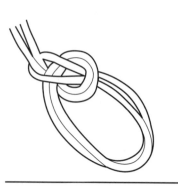

Figure 17–7 Bowline on a bight.

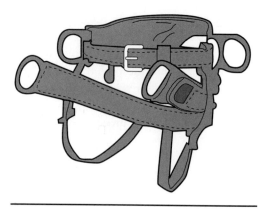

Figure 17–8 An arborist's saddle.

TABLE 17–4 A Tree-Climbing Procedure

Step	Action	Details
1	Prepare and discuss a job safety plan.	Typical job safety planning includes identifying such high-risk hazards as electrical contact, danger tree hazards, and falling hazards, then planning to control for these hazards.
2	Inspect the tree.	1. Identify the location and voltage of any nearby powerlines and places for any limb contact with the tree. 2. Choose the location for final crotching in. 3. Inspect the tree for dead and broken limbs, splits, and decay to ensure that the tree is not classified as a danger tree. 4. Check for wasp, bee, and hornet nests.
3	Choose the first and final crotch.	The crotch is the anchor point for safe climbing and for anchoring an arborist in various working positions while descending. Ideally the crotch would be directly above the work area, in a position where a slip would swing the arborist away from any powerlines. The rope is passed over a branch and around the trunk as high above the ground as possible using branches with a wide crotch. Tight V-shaped crotches should be avoided because they can bind the rope as well as feet and hands. A false crotch can be used in place of a natural crotch. A false crotch (friction saver or cambium saver) is a nylon strap with metal rings at each end, one larger than the other. The climbing rope is threaded through the two rings. A false crotch allows a rope to be placed anywhere on a trunk or branch.
4	Crotch the rope.	Climbing a tree safely requires getting the climbing rope into the tree over a suitable crotch that will serve as an anchor. A lot of devices have been developed to get the rope into the tree, especially since tree climbing has become a sport. The rope can be installed with a pruner or

Step	Action	Details
		roping tool. A common option is to install a small rope that will be used later to pull up the climbing rope. Small ropes can be installed with a throwing ball, throw bag, a special line gun, a special slingshot, a bow and arrow, or a small coil (monkey fist) of rope made by coiling the end of a rope into a bundle.
		The branches on some conifers are too dense to crotch a rope from the ground. A climber may have to carry the climbing rope up to the point to where it is to be crotched.
5	Prepare fall protection.	Belaying is a fall protection system adapted from rock climbing that is very applicable to tree climbing. The system shown in Figure 17–9 is a belaying technique; virtually no extra equipment is needed because the climbing rope is used for fall protection and, later, for work positioning. This method can be used anytime a tree must be climbed no matter which climbing method is used.
		After the climbing rope is in the tree, the climber attaches one end of the rope into both D-rings of the saddle and locks the keeper. A carabiner is attached to an anchor point (a tree) with a sling or is attached to both D-rings of a second arborist acting as an anchor. The climber should not be more than 25 pounds (11 kg) heavier than the anchoring arborist.
		The free-hanging part of the climbing rope is hitched to a carabiner with a munter hitch (see Figure 17–10) and the carabiner keeper is locked.

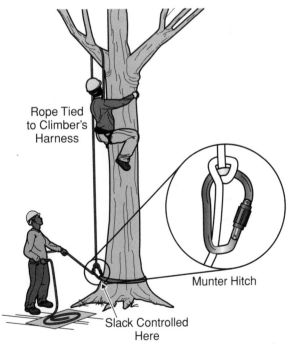

Figure 17–9 Tree-climbing fall protection.

Rope Tied to Climber's Harness

Munter Hitch

Slack Controlled Here

(continued)

TABLE 17–4 *Continued*

Step	Action	Details

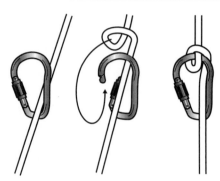

Figure 17–10 A munter hitch.

Step	Action	Details
6	Climb to first crotch.	Climb to the first crotch using any of the various climbing methods available to reach the lower branches. As the climber ascends, regardless of the climbing method, the anchoring arborist pulls the slack through the anchoring carabiner, thereby protecting the climber from falling to the ground.
		The length of the trunk and the equipment available will determine which climbing method would be most suitable. Sectional ladders are often used to get within reach of the lower branches to climb a tree.
		Tree spurs are not used very often anymore because the gaff wounds create entry points for insects and diseases. They are still used on trees that are to be cut down or on some trees that have an outer bark thick enough to withstand the gaff wounds. The gaffs on tree spurs are longer than for pole climbing, but there is always some doubt when climbing on heavy bark about the bark giving way.
		Shinning a short distance to get to the lower branches is not an uncommon practice but should be reserved for small-diameter trees and limited to less than 15 ft. (4 m). The climber should be tied in to a belay system anytime they are climbing, but it is especially necessary when climbing with spurs or shinning.
		Body thrusting up a tree using a friction hitch on the climbing rope to maintain each gain in height is a skill that must be learned and practiced. This could be called a "self-belay method."
		Some mechanical ascenders are available that are rope-gripping devices that allow a climber to move up a rope. When using limbs to climb, hands and feet should be on different limbs and dead limbs should be broken or cut off on the way up.
7	Reposition if necessary.	When the first crotch is reached and it is necessary to go higher, the climber puts the lanyard around a main stem and sits back in the arborist saddle. Two hands are available to raise the rope to the next (or final) crotch.

Step	Action	Details
8	Tie a friction hitch.	When the highest crotch is reached, the climber puts the lanyard around a main stem and then the rope for belaying can be prepared for use as the climbing rope, with a friction hitch attached to allow work while suspended by the rope and seated in the arborist saddle. Depending on the climbing method, the arborist will tie the saddle onto the climbing rope with a friction hitch before leaving the ground or after reaching the intended top position in the tree. Historically, the *taut line hitch* (Figure 17–11) has been the hitch that holds an arborist in a working position and allows a controlled descent to other working positions and to the ground. It is a rolling hitch, so it is important to tie a half hitch or a stopper knot in the tail so it will not roll out and come undone. It is easy to slide it down with minimum pressure with one hand to control the speed of descent.

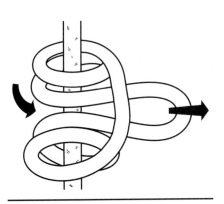

Figure 17–11 A taut-line hitch.

Two other friction hitches that can be used are the prusik and the Blakes. The prusik hitch (Figure 17–12) will not roll out but must be kept tight so it will grab. It can get too tight and will need two hands to get it to slide. The Blakes hitch (Figure 17–13) is the newest hitch and is becoming more popular. It is a little more complicated to tie and must be tied properly to hold. It can be tied with the free end of a rope and is self-adjusting. Where the tail passes through, the bottom two turns can become a hot spot that will melt if an arborist descends too quickly.

If transferring from an aerial bucket to a tree, an arborist should tie into a climbing rope with a friction hitch, anchored to a crotch in the tree before removing the lanyard attachment to the boom.

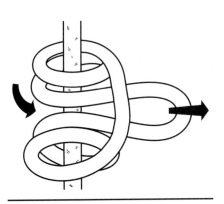

Figure 17–12 A prusik hitch.

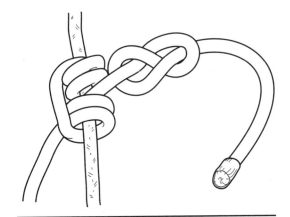

Figure 17–13 A Blakes hitch.

Step	Action	Details
9	Work and descend.	The arborist can descend and stop along the length of the rope and carry out work. The climbing rope, friction hitch, and saddle comprise a work-positioning and fall protection system. If it is necessary to re-crotch while in the tree, the arborist uses a lanyard to tie in to the tree while tying into a new crotch.

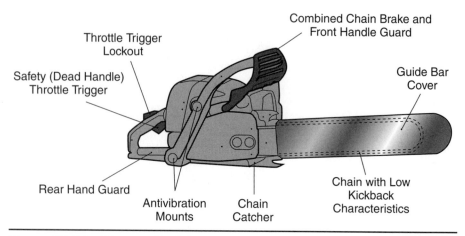

Figure 17–14   Diagram of a chain saw.

The comprehensive training and regulations regarding chain-saw use reflect the high risk of contacting a moving chain-saw blade. The risk of accidents using a power saw is reduced when the following are taken into account:

1. The power saw operator wears head, eye, hearing, hand, foot, and leg protection.

2. The saw is equipped with a chain brake and a protective device that minimizes chain-saw kickback. Kickback happens when the upper portion of the saw tip comes in contact with another object, causing the saw to jump or kick back toward the operator (see Figure 17–15).

3. The saw is well-maintained and the chain is sharp. The clutch is adjusted so that the clutch will not engage the chain drive at idling speed and is equipped with a continuous-pressure throttle-control system that will stop the chain when pressure on the throttle is released.

4. The saw engine is stopped for all cleaning, refueling, adjustments, and repairs, except for adjustments that cannot be done without the engine running.

5. The saw is started while it is held down firmly on a solid surface, such as the ground or a stump, and the chain brake is engaged.

6. Drop starting of a saw can be done safely only from outside the bucket of an aerial device.

7. When starting or operating a saw, no one is within 6 feet (2 m) of the saw operator. The saw is started at least 10 feet (3 m) away from the fueling area.

8. The saw is not operated with only one hand.

9. Loose material that may catch the saw is removed.

10. A saw weighing more than 20 pounds (9 kg) is never used above the height of an operator's shoulder, in an aerial basket, or in a tree. One reason why

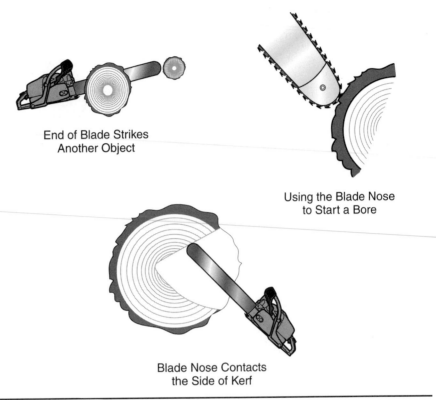

End of Blade Strikes
Another Object

Using the Blade Nose
to Start a Bore

Blade Nose Contacts
the Side of Kerf

Figure 17–15   Situations that can cause chain-saw kickback.

safety rules prevent a saw from being used above the shoulders is because a kickback is very hazardous in this position.

11. In an aerial bucket, the saw is stored in a sheath when it is not in use.

12. Wen working in a tree—except when working from an aerial bucket—a power saw weighing more than 15 pounds (6.8 kg) should be supported by a separate work rope tied in such a way that it will allow the saw to swing clear of the operator.

13. A power saw should not be raised or lowered from a tree with the motor running.

14. In addition to a chain brake, the risk of kickback is reduced when a sharp, properly tensioned "low kickback chain" is used and the saw is held firmly with two hands—and not while standing over the saw.

Personal Protective Equipment when Using a Chain Saw

The list of personal protective equipment required when using a chain saw is long. Personal protective equipment does not prevent an accident but may minimize injury. In addition to a class E hard hat and safety footwear, a chain-saw operator wears the following:

- *Safety glasses and/or face shields* are worn to protect the face from objects propelled toward the face by the saw.

- *Hearing protection* is required because a chain saw with a noise level of less than 85 decibels has not been invented. Many types of hearing protection are available, including foam plugs and ear muffs. Hearing protection with the highest NRR (Noise Reduction Rating) provides better protection.

- *Chaps or cut-resistant material,* such as ballistic nylon sewn into special chain-saw pants, will reduce the risk of cuts to the legs. *Leg protection* covers the full length of the thigh to the top of the boot on each leg.

- *Chain-saw gloves* are specially constructed to protect the back of an operator's hand should the saw kick back.

Freeing a Trapped Saw

If a saw becomes trapped while pruning, switch off the saw and, if not already attached, attach it to a separate tool line. Try lifting the branch and, with the chain-saw brake off, pull the saw from the kerf. Or use a hand saw to release the trapped saw by making a release cut outward toward the tips of the limb close enough to allow the undercut made earlier with the chain saw to be effective.

Pruning a Tree 17.4.3 Pruning a tree to provide adequate clearance to a powerline is a task that requires skill and knowledge to do a job well and safely. The directional pruning (Shigo) method has become fairly standard for pruning trees near powerlines and is defensible when discussing the results with customers.

The principles for safe pruning are similar whether pruning from a bucket or from a tree. Working from a bucket or a tree, an arborist uses an insulated pruner or pole saw (usually hydraulic from a bucket) and stays outside the minimum approach distance.

Pruning specifics

- A hanger on a conductor can be safely removed from the conductor with an insulated pruner or saw.

- A saw cut should use the 1-2-3 method of pruning. A pruner cut on limbs that could split or cause the bark to strip should be pruned using the 2-3 method, which is the same as the 1-2-3 method without the undercut. Cut 2 will remove the weight, and cut 3 allows a clean cut in the desired location.

- Many cuts may be needed to shorten branches overhanging power conductors. Each cut should leave the branch short enough that it cannot bridge phase to phase when dropped.

Roping a Limb

When a larger limb is to be removed, the limb should be roped or rigged with rope blocks. A working rope is crotched as high as practical above the limb to be removed. The end of the rope is tied near the tip of the limb. People on the ground will pull up on the limb after the arborist aloft in the tree or bucket cuts the underside about two-thirds through. When the people on the ground have the weight of the limb in hand, the limb is cut off. An optional rope on the butt of the branch can prevent the butt from swinging out toward the powerline. The branch is then lowered. A heavy branch may need to be lowered by having the fall line wrapped around an anchor point to control the descent. The rope on the butt can be used as a tag line.

In special circumstances, the limb may need to be roped so that it is pulled sideways instead of up to clear a powerline (see Figure 17–16).

Figure 17–16 Roping a branch.

17.4.4 The pruner, pole saw, and hydraulic hose (if equipped) should be scheduled regularly for an electric test and also for replacement of any parts that affect the insulated parts (see Figure 17–17). The insulated parts of the pruner and pole saw must be cleaned daily before use. Wiping down the insulated parts with methal hydrate will ensure that the tools are dry.

Unless the rope in the pole pruner is live-line rope and tested and treated as such, the insulated link in the rope should be cleaned daily.

Hanger Hazards

A hanger is a branch that has been pruned and left hanging in the tree. At the end of any pruning job, every tree should be inspected for hangers that may become hazards to the public.

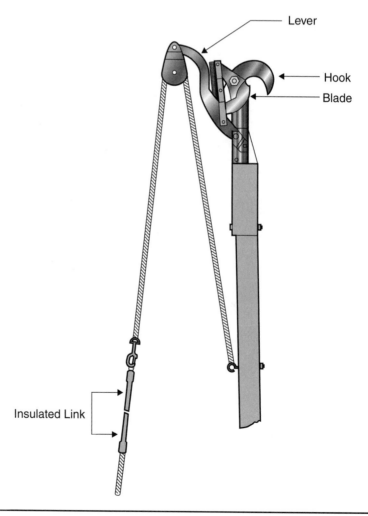

Figure 17–17 A pruner with insulated link.

TABLE 17–5   **Summary of Electrical Hazards when Pruning Trees**

Hazard	Barriers
Working around live circuits.	An electrical circuit can only be considered de-energized when protective line grounds are installed. Even conductors lying on the ground can be hot or made hot from operating errors, automatic operations, or backfeed from generators. Unless you have the protection afforded by a lockout/tagout and you can see protective line grounds on the circuit you are working on, rely on tools and procedures that prevent limbs, trees, and workers from making contact.
Inadvertently making contact with a hot conductor.	A distance of 3 ft. (1 m) should be added to the distances listed in the minimum working distances tables for routine work. Working with hands or body closer and up to the minimum limit should be considered exceptional circumstances. In such cases, keep exposure time to a minimum and have a second arborist act as a dedicated observer.
Getting a shock while in contact with an insulated conductor.	Learn to recognize the following: 1. *Tree Wire:* Some primary conductor has a polycarbonate cover that protects it from tree abrasion. It is often called "tree conductor." It can withstand a tree contact without immediately shorting out the line. It is not like underground cable with insulation and a grounded outer surface. Arborists and line crews working on this conductor must treat it as though it were bare. 2. *Weatherproof Conductor:* Some conductor is covered, but the covering is just weatherproofing and provides no insulation. It is often found on copper primary and secondary. Unless you have the protection afforded by a lockout/tagout and can see protective line grounds on the circuit you are working on, rely on tools and procedures that prevent limbs, trees, and workers from making contact.
Getting a shock from the tree.	Before going aloft, ensure that no limbs are in contact with the tree. If a limb is making contact, do not climb the tree. A limb or branch can be removed or cut using an insulated pruner or working from an insulated aerial device, while not making bodily contact with any part of the tree.

(continued)

TABLE 17–5   *Continued*

Hazard	Barriers
	A climber can put weight on a limb and cause it to make electrical contact. Climb on the side of the tree farthest from the conductor and face toward the hazard to keep it visible. Choose a crotch to tie into that would tend to swing you away from the conductor in case of a slip or fall.
	When climbing a tree that is close to the line, maintain the minimum approach distance for tree work and use a dedicated observer.
A limb making contact with a live conductor while pruning.	When working from a tree, an arborist can receive a "tree shock" when a limb makes an electrical contact, especially on higher-distribution voltages. Secure the limb with a rope so that it cannot swing into the line. Break back the limb from the conductor with an insulated tool or a rope before cutting with a saw.
	When working from a bucket, it is standard procedure to use an insulated pole pruner to remove a branch lying on a live conductor (hanger). This can be done on voltages up to 15 kV. On higher voltages, a limb contacting two conductors might short out the circuit. A short circuit, especially near a substation, will be very explosive. Use eye protection and the full length of the pruner. Ensure that no one stands under the conductor in case it burns off and falls to the ground.
A limb or branch breaking the conductor and a live wire falling to the ground.	Ensure that no one stands directly under the conductor within the span being trimmed.
Boom insulation bridged out electrically by a falling limb.	The insulated boom of the truck should be treated like personal protective equipment where it is not relied on for electrical protection but may make a difference when an inadvertent contact is made by a branch or limb bridging across.

Removing Trees   17.4.5 Table 17–6 is a typical tree felling work procedure. There can be many complications that would require a change to this procedure.

TABLE 17–6   A Typical Tree Felling Procedure

Step	Action	Details
1	Prepare and discuss a safety job plan.	The plan should identify high-risk hazards and barriers needed to protect from the hazards. High-risk hazards include nearby powerlines, climbing hazards, hangers, dead wood, a restricted escape route, and a restricted drop area for a tree. If in doubt about the tree condition, use an increment bit to help diagnose the tree.
2	Make preparations to control the direction of fall.	Acceptable use in a forest may include notching in the desired direction of the fall, varying the thickness of the hinge on one side to control the fall, and/or using a wedge in the backcut, but near powerlines and buildings a tree should be either winched, roped to a vehicle capable of pulling, or supported by a crane.
		Any tree that cannot be felled directly away from a powerline should be taken down piece by piece. Starting at the bottom, limbs are removed and work proceeds toward the crown, as in pruning. If the trunk cannot be felled, it is also removed in pieces.
		Work on problem trees may require skilled arborists and specialized equipment to carry out tasks such as climbing, working aloft, roping, piece-by-piece removal, or using a crane or winch. Problem trees are those that lean the wrong way, are hung up, have heavy tops, have broken or dead limbs (a "widowmaker" or a "chicot"), have a major fork in the trunk, have a falling path that is hard to predict (a "schoolmarm"), and/or have a restricted drop path.
		Be sure that clearance in the intended direction is adequate for the tree to fall completely to the ground. A lodged tree is very dangerous.
3	Rope the tree.	When removing a tree near a powerline, always rope it.
4	Prepare a retreat path.	Common causes of accidents include being struck by the butt, rebounding limbs, and broken tops, so it is important to clear a safe work area around the base of the tree. Remove limbs, underbrush, and other obstructions. The retreat path should be at approximately a 45-degree angle to the rear of the notch in case the tree kicks backward off the stump (see Figure 17–18). If the tree is on a slope, the retreat path should be uphill.

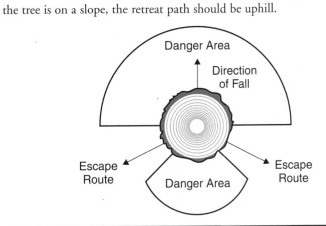

Figure 17–18   Retreat paths.

(continued)

TABLE 17–6 *Continued*

Step	Action	Details
5	Establish an "exclusion" zone.	An exclusion or danger zone is an area where everyone other than the person designated to carry out a high-risk task is kept at a safe distance. An exclusion zone should be established for everyone other than the arborist making the backcut. Because of the hazard of flying missiles, such as broken branches, etc., a typical exclusion zone should be twice the length of the tree. If rigging is used, include the bight of a winch and the area near a snatch block as the exclusion zone.
6	Cut notch.	A notch is not normally needed for trees less than 5 to 8 in. (12–20 cm) in diameter. When needed, a notch is cut on the fall side of the trunk to a depth of one-quarter to one-third of the tree diameter. The face opening of a proper notch should be equal to the depth or about 45 degrees (see Figure 17–19). Make the lower cut of the notch first to prevent the loose wedge of wood from pinching or bending the chain.

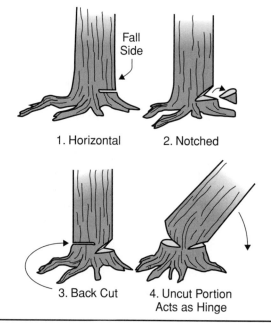

Fall Side

1. Horizontal   2. Notched

3. Back Cut   4. Uncut Portion Acts as Hinge

Figure 17–21 Cutting a T notch.

An improper notch is one where the notch closes and the tree stops falling:
1. When the notch closes, it causes the tree to be under strain. Because of the strain, the fibers separate and the tree begins to split. The tree continues to split until it breaks off, leaving a "barber chair."
2. When the tree stops, the hinge or holding wood must be cut off to drop the tree. Unless the tree is roped, there will be little control of direction of fall.

Step	Action	Details
7	Make a backcut.	Check again to ensure that everyone other than the saw operator is outside of the exclusion zone. Yelling "Timber!" is a reminder to an experienced crew.
		Make a felling cut or backcut on the opposite side of the notch, 2 in. (5 cm) above and parallel to the horizontal cut of the notch. Leave a 1-inch (2.5-cm) uncut portion (holding wood). The holding wood serves as a hinge and will help cause the tree to fall 90 degrees to the orientation of the holding wood. (See Figure 17–20.)

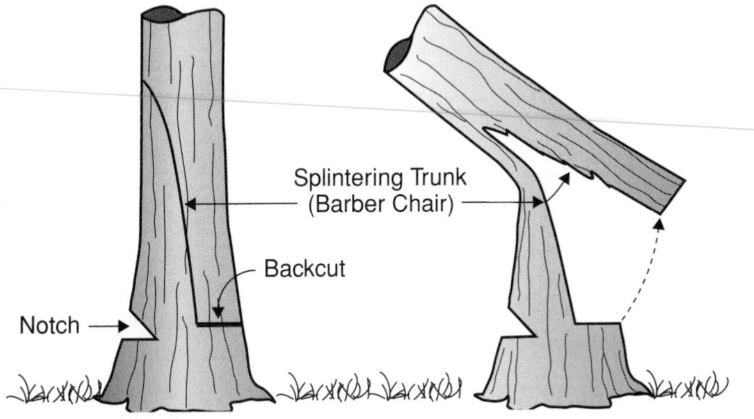

Figure 17–20   A barber chair.

Results of improper backcutting:

1. A backcut that is at the same level as the notch increases the risk of the tree butt kicking back off the stump. The saw operator should work on one side in case the tree butt bounces straight back.
2. A backcut that is made too high may prevent the tree from falling and will need to be pulled down.
3. A backcut that is below the notch may cause the tree to drop back on the stump, and the tree may need to be pulled off the stump.
4. A backcut that is too deep will cause the hinge to break and will result in little control over the direction of fall.
5. A tree leaning heavily into the direction of the notch may create a *barber chair* (Figure 17–20) as the backcut is being made. Cutting off the corners on each side of the notch before the backcut is made may help to prevent this from happening.

Note the value of having a tree roped ahead of time. If a tree must be pulled over, the saw operator must be out of the exclusion zone.

Step	Action	Details
8	Make your escape.	Saw operators escape or retreat (Figure 17–18) while not turning away and losing sight of the falling tree because misjudged circumstances (wind, heavy crown) can cause a tree to fall in a different direction than planned.
		Give the tree time to settle into its final postion before approaching it.

TABLE 17–7 Summary of Tree Removal Hazards

Hazards	Controls
Falling dead wood that can strike a worker when an overly mature tree or a mature tree such as oak, beech, or basswood is being felled. A dead top or limb that has fallen and is hung up (a widowmaker or chicot), often between two trees, can fall on workers on the ground.	Too often, falling wood is an unidentified hazard and is called a widowmaker (chicot) for good reason. Inspect the tree for dead limbs and remove it first. If there is evidence of rotten wood, inspect the whole tree. Use an increment borer or brace and bit to check for rotten wood.
Control of the falling direction of a tree can be lost. If the tree does not fall in the intended felling area, electrical contact is a possibility. Trees are electrical conductors.	Install ropes to ensure that a tree will fall in the intended drop area. The anchors for guide ropes must be secure. If a rope is used to pull the tree in a given direction, the vehicle pulling the tree should be able to keep pace with the falling tree. If a tree becomes lodged on a live circuit, stay clear of the tree. If the tree cannot be pulled clear by the ropes already attached, or by a rope installed with a hot stick and rubber gloves, call for a clearance on the line.
There is no safe path for the tree to be dropped or the planned felling area is too short for the height of the tree.	The radius of the felling area must be at least equal to the height of the tree. Everyone other than the saw operator must be outside of the "exclusion/danger zone" radius. Remove the tree piece by piece down to a level that allows it to be dropped safely. If climbing is necessary, use a secondary fall protection such as a belaying technique that requires training in the use of a carabiner and a munter hitch (Figure 17–10).
A tree hung up on conductors or in other trees is under pressure and can fall or bounce in unpredictable ways or spring back when it is cut free.	Do not work in the presence of a hung-up tree. Have hung-up trees pulled down by a rope, winch, and vehicle.
Dead stumps, the wedge cut out from the notch, or other objects in the felling area can become dangerous flying missiles when a felled tree drops on them.	Remove loose objects from the intended drop area.
The saw operator is in danger if the tree butt kicks backward.	A clear escape route must be present at an angle of approximately 45 degrees to the rear of the notch. Never escape directly away from the direction of the fall in case the tree kicks backward off the stump. On a slope, escape in an uphill direction.

Figure 17–21   Cutting branches from a felled tree.

Limbing a Tree

17.4.6 When cutting branches from a felled tree,

1. The limbs at the base and those on top of the trunk as far up toward the treetop as practical are removed first.

2. The branches resting on the ground are cut next. When cutting these branches, it is likely that the tree will sag or roll. Remove cut branches to keep the area uncluttered so that an escape area is visible.

3. When practical, the chain saw should be operated from the side opposite the limb being cut so that the trunk serves as a barrier between the operator and the saw (Figure 7–21).

4. The saw should be shut down, or the chain break applied, when moving cut limbs or branches out of the way.

Bucking a Tree Trunk

17.4.7 When bucking a tree trunk (see Figure 17–22) into, typically, 4-foot (1.2 meter) lengths, do the following:

1. Start at the top of the tree and cut sections off the trunk. If practical, raise and chock the trunk to prevent it from rolling. Work on the uphill side of the trunk.

2. If the trunk is flat on the ground, make cuts about three-quarters of the way through the tree, then roll it over and cut it through from the opposite side.

3. To lessen the weight of a tree trunk section, it may need to be cut through in a convenient location—for example where the trunk is somewhat suspended.

4. Prepare for the likelihood of the trunk rolling and/or a saw kickback by maintaining two hands on the saw and a solid footing.

Figure 17–22   Bucking a tree trunk.

Review Questions

1. What is directional pruning?

2. Where should the final cut be made when removing a branch?

3. What two types of trees are defined as danger trees?

4. To which five main hazards are arborists exposed?

5. Describe tree shock.

6. How can the munter hitch be used to protect a person climbing a tree from a fall?

7. List the personal protective equipment that must be worn when using a chain saw.

8. How can kickback of a chain saw be prevented?

9. Are pruners and pole saws used around utility lines considered live-line tools requiring the same care as any other live-line tool?

10. How do arborists protect themselves from widowmakers (chicots)?

CHAPTER 18

Working in Substations

18.1 What Is a Substation?

What Does a Substation Do?

18.1.1 A substation is a transformer station and a switching station. In substations, lines coming from different generating stations, voltage systems, and utilities are brought together, interconnected, and transformed to a needed voltage. A substation also has the equipment to provide protection for all the outgoing lines and for the transformers and switchgears inside the station yard.

The following are some of the equipment that helps make the interconnections:

- Circuit breakers that control the lines going in and out

- Regulators that adjust the voltage

- Capacitors and reactors that adjust the reactive kilovolt-amperes (VARs)

- Transformers that change the voltage of incoming lines to a different voltage for outgoing lines

- Auxiliary components such as current transformers, potential transformers, relay equipment, metering, and telecommunications that monitor the system and automatically activate switchgears during fault conditions

- Surge arrestors that shunt high-voltage lightning and other electrical surges from a system

Types of Substations

18.1.2 There is a tendency to call all stations downstream from a generating station a "substation." A substation can be a step-up transmission substation, a step-down transmission substation, an industrial substation, a distribution substation, a customer substation, or a converter station.

A step-up transmission substation is located just outside the generating station. It looks the same as all substations except that the output voltage from the transformer is stepped up to a higher transmission-line voltage. There is a practical limit to the voltage that a generator can generate, so lines (usually underground) from the generator go to the step-up transmission substation located nearby, where the voltage gets boosted to a more economical standard transmission-line voltage. The step-up substation houses the source circuit breakers for the outgoing lines.

A step-down transmission substation is usually located near a load center where the incoming transmission lines can be stepped down to a subtransmission-line voltage, which is an easier voltage line to build along streets and highways. This substation is also a switching station where lines from different parts of a grid come together and are switched to direct power to the desired locations. The input and output through the station are metered. This type of substation houses the source circuit breakers for the outgoing lines.

Large businesses often have their own step-down transmission substations that are fed directly by a transmission line. Because it costs less to supply a business that has its own substation, rates will be lowered accordingly.

Distribution substations are located near end-users. Distribution substation transformers change a subtransmission voltage to any of about a dozen standard lower-level voltages between 34.5/19.9kV and 4.16/2.4 kV. This type of substation houses the source circuit breakers for the outgoing distribution feeders.

Figure 18–1 shows a rural substation with a single radial-feed subtransmission line, a single transformer, and three low-voltage distribution feeders protected by reclosers. To keep customers on during maintenance or an emergency, a mobile substation is necessary.

An urban distribution substation has the same function and pattern but can be much more complex. It may have one or two overhead or underground incoming

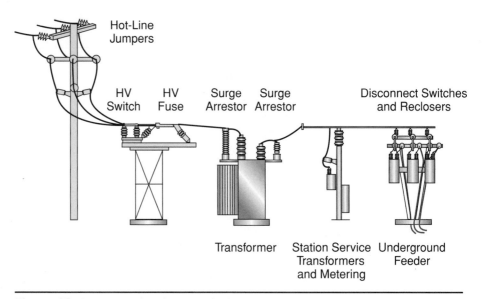

Figure 18–1 A rural distribution substation.

(230-, or 115-, or 69-kilovolt, and so on) substransmission lines, two or more transformers, and maybe eight or more outgoing overhead/underground distribution feeders. In this type of substation, one transformer can be taken out of service (depending on load); with some switching, the other transformer can pick up the load. Similarly, a distribution feeder breaker can be racked out for maintenance and the load switched to other breakers. There is a practical limit to the number of distribution feeders that can come out from one substation and distribute out along nearby streets.

Mobile Substations

If a major element in a distribution substation—such as a transformer—fails, customers can often be fed from a second bank within the substation or be back-fed from other substations. In more remote locations the economics of building double-bank substations or backfeeding from other substations are not options. Mobile substations provide the backup.

Converter Stations

Some substations are actually converter stations. These stations convert AC to DC and back again. The incoming and outgoing circuitry looks somewhat conventional, but the converters do not look like anything else. Converter stations are found at the terminals of very long overhead DC lines, a long submarine DC line, or a short DC tie line between two different systems (for example, a 50 and 60 cycle could be tied together with a DC link).

Types of Substation Construction

18.1.3 Substations can be air insulated or gas insulated. Each of these can be outdoor or indoor, totally enclosed or partially outdoor, or completely underground.

An *air-insulated substation* refers to the classic, most common substation (see Figure 18–2). Air is the insulation around the bus works and switchgear, but oil or gas is the insulating medium in the transformer, switchgear, and other equipment.

A *gas-insulated substation* can be indoors and totally enclosed or outdoors. Gas-insulated switchgears and transformers are very compact and the substation looks like just a lot of pipes. Sulfur hexafluoride (SF_6) gas is an insulating medium as well as a cooling medium for transformers and an arc-quenching medium in switchgears.

In metal-clad distribution stations, the low-voltage switchgear and bus are inside a metal cabinet. To make a substation virtually invisible to the public, the metal-clad switchgear can be in a building, the incoming and outgoing lines can be underground, and the transformers can be surrounded by a wall. Some variations of this configuration have overhead lines or transformers sitting out in the open.

Elements of a Substation

18.1.4 Substations have common elements, such as switchgears, transformers, surge arrestors, and so on, but because of voltage, insulating medium, or inside or outside differences, each element can look quite different.

Station Yard

A station yard is one large equipotential zone. There is a grounded wire-mesh network buried underneath the gravel or concrete of a substation. Each piece of equipment, the neutral of a transformer, the line neutrals, and the structure and fence are bonded to the grounding network. A lot of ground rods are driven to bring the grounding network resistance (impedance) as low as possible, at least to a level to meet standards. When there is a line-to-ground fault in the station or on a line, there will be a rise in potential on the total grounding network in the station. When everything is bonded together, there is less chance of anyone working in the yard getting between two different potentials. The grid is also extended a little beyond the fence perimeter to help protect anyone outside the fence that may be in contact during a fault.

Switchgear

The most sophisticated switchgear in an electrical system is found in a substation. Switchgears can range from large oil, air, or vacuum circuit breakers that protect extra-high-voltage lines to distribution-line reclosers to protect a distribution feeder. Circuit breakers provide automatic opening and closing under fault conditions. Oil circuit breakers have been the most common, but SF_6 gas and vacuum breakers have advantages of less size and maintenance and are more suitable for indoors (see Figure 18–2).

A substation has load break and nonload break switches that provide a visible open point to allow maintenance on the circuit breaker, transformer, and so on. Fused switchgears are also found in substations and, for example, provide protection for a station transformer in a distribution station. Figure 18–2 shows switches on each side of a circuit breaker that would provide a visible open point to allow work on the breaker.

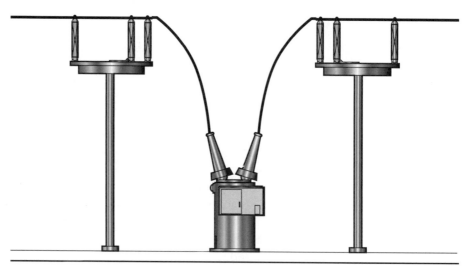

Figure 18–2 Circuit breaker between air-break switches.

High- and Low-Voltage Bus

Every circuit coming or going into a substation is connected to a bus. A bus is like a line except that it is inside the substation. It is often made of an aluminium-alloy pipe and sits on insulators or it can be an ordinary power conductor supported by suspension insulators. Depending on the bus arrangement and naming convention, a bus can be a main bus, ring bus, transfer bus, A bus, B bus, and so on. Figure 18–3 shows two 345-kilovolt transmission lines feeding the X bus and the Y bus. If one circuit feeding the bus trips out, the other circuit can be switched over to feed the other transformer.

Similarly, the low-voltage A and B buses have an arrangement so that the outgoing feeders can be switched to allow circuit breakers to be taken out of service while maintaining service by supplying customers through other circuit breakers.

Transformer

The transformer is the biggest and heaviest piece of equipment in the substation. The line voltage coming into the high side of the transformer is changed to a

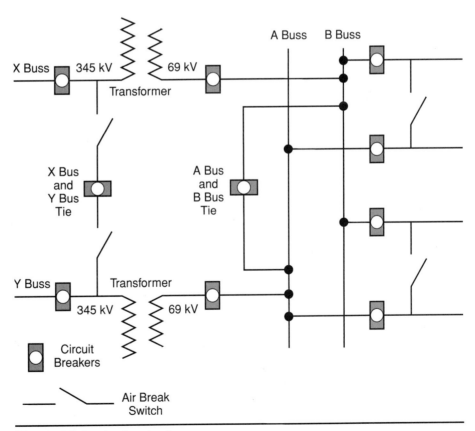

Figure 18–3 A substation bus.

standard voltage on the low side of the transformer (which is opposite the setup of a step-up transformer). Transformers are most often oil insulated and cooled, but gas insulated (SF_6) transformers are gaining popularity, especially in the city because they are noncombustible and more compact.

Voltage Regulation Equipment

The voltage being supplied from a substation must be boosted or bucked on a regular basis as demand rises and falls. Many transformers have the ability to change the transformation ratio by using tap changers. Some transformers have an off-circuit tap changer, which means that the transformer has to be taken out of service to change the taps and the tap position is stationary. Other transformers have on-load tap changers that are much like a step-voltage regulator where the taps are changed automatically under energized conditions.

Some substations will have a separate voltage regulator to boost and buck the voltage of the outgoing lines automatically under energized conditions.

Reactor

A substation reactor looks like and is about the same size as a station transformer and has large iron-core coils that generate inductive reactance. Each coil is connected phase to ground. Inductive reactance is needed in some substations to balance the capacitive reactance generated by very long extra-high-voltage transmission lines.

Capacitor

Capacitor banks in substations generate capacitive reactance to counterbalance excessive inductive reactance produced by customer load and large transformers. Capacitors banks are made up of lower-voltage capacitors that are put in series so that the series-connected capacitors can be connected to a high-voltage transmission line and neutral. Capacitors in a substation are isolated from ground by having them sit on insulators. The capacitors are surrounded with danger signs to keep people from touching the framework above the insulators.

Phase-Shifting Transformer

A phase-angle regulating transformer or phase-shifting transformer (PST) looks like a large substation transformer and is used to control the flow of power between different transmission lines and systems. It allows an operator to control the magnitude and direction of power flow by varying the phase shift between the input and the output of the phase-shifting transformer. Otherwise, when power is flowing in a grid or loop, the flow is in the easiest direction and not necessarily where it is needed.

Wave Trap

Figure 18–8 shows a set of wave traps on each phase of an incoming transmission line. The power conductors can be used as the communications line between stations by superimposing a high-frequency signal. The wave trap filters out the signal. Fiber optics will probably make the much more expensive powerline carrier redundant.

Inductor

During a fault, very high and damaging current can flow through transformers and breakers. An in-line current-limiting inductor limits the current flow by creating a very high inductive reactance.

Station Service

A substation will have a transformer to supply the power needs for the station. A substation also will have some or all of several other types of devices, such as heaters, air conditioners, lighting, and battery chargers. If you are called upon to restore a station service, remember that the fault current available in a substation is huge compared to a line and that creating a short or an arc can generate a very explosive short-circuit current.

Potential and Current Transformers

The secondaries from potential and current transformers are a low-voltage and low-current representation of the actual voltage and current on the lines. These representative voltages and current go to meters and relays. For example, if the current goes higher than the values programmed into the relay, the relay sends a signal back to the electric motor at the circuit breaker to open the circuit.

Optical devices are installed as an alternative to potential and current transformers. These optical devices take advantage of the fact that the electromagnetic field of a conductor influences the polarity of light in an optical fiber. A computer in the control room interprets the effect on the light in the fiber and signals the meters and relays accordingly.

Meter and Relay Equipment

Most substations are automated and remotely controlled. Some of the equipment needed to do this are,

- The communications links and associated terminations and hardware for powerline, telephone, fiber optics, and microwave carriers.
- The control circuits, which are low-voltage lines that open and close circuit breakers.
- The meters and relays and all the wiring from the potential and current transformers to the control building.
- The battery room and battery charger.
- The control room or building or cabinet to house much of the auxiliary equipment.

Power Flow through a Substation

18.1.5 There are many types of substations, and the power flow through a step-down substation is typically similar to the following:

- A *source* or incoming line(s) flows through . . .
- a *circuit breaker(s)* that is capable of opening the circuit under a loaded or a fault condition, and then through . . .
- a *switch* that can provide a visible open point after the breaker has opened the line . . .
- into a *high-voltage bus* to which the incoming (and outgoing) line(s) is connected . . .
- through a *transformer* that drops the voltage (other than a step-up substation) . . .
- into a *low-voltage bus* to which the outgoing lower-voltage lines are connected . . .
- through a *switch* (fused) that can provide a visible open point for the outgoing circuit . . .
- into a *circuit breaker* to provide protection and load-break capability for the outgoing circuits.

The following are complexities that can make a substation look confusing (spaghetti jungle):

- Many high-voltage circuits, and associated switchgears, feeding into two high-side buses with switchgears to tie the two buses together.
- More than one transformer.
- More than one low-voltage bus and associated switchgears to tie the buses together.
- Voltage-regulating equipment either as part of the transformer or separate.
- Capacitor banks to provide leading volt amperes reactance (VARs).
- Reactors to provide lagging volt amperes reactance (VARs).
- Phase shifters.
- Auxiliary equipment, such as potential transformers and current transformers on incoming and outgoing circuits to provide circuit condition information to relays and metering.
- Incoming and outgoing communications circuits (telephone, microwave, fiber optics, powerline carrier).

18.2 Maintaining and Operating a Substation

Entering a Substation

18.2.1 Most substations are remotely controlled. System control requires notification before anyone enters. If alarms go off in the control room, system control will know that people are there. System control will then have the option of making a call to the station before operating equipment.

Corporate safety rules and labor laws restrict entry to people who have had electrical awareness training or are under escort by a qualified worker. One reason a substation has a fence, barbed wire, and warning signs is because, unlike powerlines, the clearance from live parts to ground or to a structure is easily reached with booms, a ground rod, a ladder, and so on.

Substation Maintenance Programs

18.2.2 The ideal maintenance program is one in which work is carried out on equipment only when needed to keep it in optimal condition and where equipment that is in excellent condition is not overhauled. Reliability-centered maintenance (RCM) or predictive maintenance is preferred to maintenance based on a time schedule. There are good diagnostic tests available to reduce unnecessary maintenance and allow focus on more priority needs.

Substation maintenance personnel can do testing that will predict the need for maintenance. For example, oil samples can be taken from in-service switchgears and transformers and analyzed for levels of water, hydrogen, methane, ethane, ethylene, carbon monoxide, and carbon dioxide. A dielectric test of the oil will indicate whether contaminants such as water or particulates are present. A neutralization/ acid test will measure the level of sludge-causing acid that is present in the oil. An interfacial tension test identifies the presence of polar compounds, which indicates oxidation contaminants or deterioration of the transformer materials, such as paint, varnish, or paper. A dissolved gas analysis (DGA) checks for any gas in the oil, which would indicate that arcing, corona, or overheated connections have occurred. Ultrasonic and vibration tests can detect arcing and corona discharge and pressure or vacuum leaks. Gas chromatography can determine the condition of insulating oil and insulating papers.

SF_6 gas-insulated equipment is monitored for gas pressure, temperature, and density. A reduced gas pressure means a loss of insulation and could cause a circuit to trip out.

A thermographic (infrared) survey of a substation will point out any connections, splices, and switch components that are getting hot and need attention.

Tests are also conducted before reenergizing a transformer if there are indications that it may have been subjected to a fault current. A test for each phase-to-ground resistance and each phase-to-phase resistance and or a dissolved gas anaysis (DGA) test can be done to obtain assurance that a defective transformer is not being reenergized. Replacing all three fuses while a unit is out of service may prevent a weakened fuse from failing later.

Virtually every piece of equipment in a substation has a detailed written maintenance procedure, either the original equipment manufacturer's (OEM's) procedures or one prepared by the utility.

Detailed forms accompany each equipment maintenance procedure and are used to log all the test results and repairs.

Inspecting a Substation

18.2.3 Compared to lines, substations are inspected frequently. Transmission substations are inspected more frequently than distribution substations. A large urban distribution substation is inspected more often than a small rural distribution station. Forms are used as a thoroughness checklist and as a log. The forms for a transmission station would be different than the forms for a rural distribution station. Some inspections are more thorough and require operational checks.

A walk-through inspection would allow a look at the following:

1. *The transformer:* Depending on transformer size, available gauges, and so on, look for damaged bushings, oil leaks, and the oil level in the main tank and tap-changer compartment. Under normal operating conditions, both the oil and winding temperatures should read below 70°C. Under loaded conditions, the winding temperature might read as high as 95°C.

2. *Tap changers and voltage regulators:* The operations on the load-tap changer are read and recorded from the counter indicator. Inspection of a voltage regulator is similar to that of a transformer as far as oil leaks and so on go. More detailed inspection might have the regulator control put in the manual position and operated up or down over a small range and then returned to automatic to watch it go back to the former position. Each of the three phases of the voltage-regulator taps should be within four positions of each other.

3. *Oil, vacuum, SF_6, and air-blast circuit breakers:* Check for loose, contaminated, or damaged bushings, loose terminals, oil leaks, and proper gas pressures. Check oil level in bushings and main tank (as applicable). Check anticondensation heaters. Read and record the number of operations on the indicator.

4. *Disconnect switches:* Check for cracked, contaminated, or broken porcelain, loose connections, and corrosion to metal parts.

5. Reclosers are inspected for oil leaks. Recloser settings can be checked, where applicable, to ensure that the ground trip, reclosing, and supervisory settings are in the desired positions.

6. Check that the batteries are at about 125 volts, check that the charger is working, and check for leaks.

7. Check for broken or contaminated insulators, surge arrestors, and bushings.

8. Check capacitor tanks for leakage or damage.

9. Check current and potential transformers for damage to cases, bushings, terminals, and fuses.

10. Take any requested meter readings.

11. Check visible ground connections at equipment, structures, switching platforms, and fences. Check continuity of fence grounds.

12. Check fencing for signs, gaps under the fence, third-party metallic fencing tied into the station fencing, and security of gates.

Operating in a Substation

18.2.4 Most substations are remotely controlled, but individual components in most stations must be operated by a person. Some substations, especially rural ones, have no remote-control capability.

A powerline worker may be asked to operate switchears in a substation as an agent under the direction of system control. Using an operating drawing or a single-line diagram to follow as instructions are given by system control is essential. A single-line diagram simplifies the physical arrangement because one single line represents a circuit instead of the three phase conductors and the neutral. Figure 18–4 shows a single-line diagram for a simple rural substation. Larger stations follow the same principle, but diagrams can look very complicated because there are more transformers, buses, and tie switches.

When a switch with a handle is operated by someone standing on the ground, insulator failure can cause the frame of the switch and structure to become energized. In a substation, each of these types of switches should have a metal grid or platform that is electrically bonded to a switch handle. The grid may be buried under gravel. This equipotential arrangement ensures that an operator's feet and hands will be at the same potential when things go wrong. Rubber gloves alone are not adequate protection.

If asked to open a switch with power fuses, be aware that these devices are not designed to drop load.

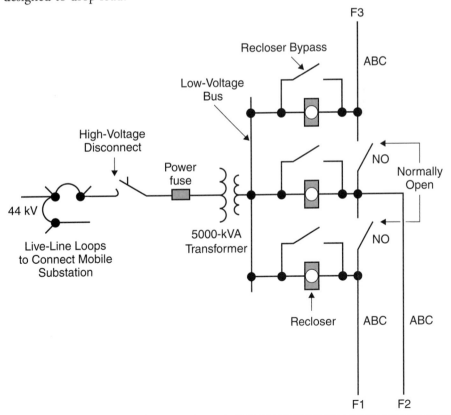

Figure 18–4   A single-line diagram for a simple rural substation.

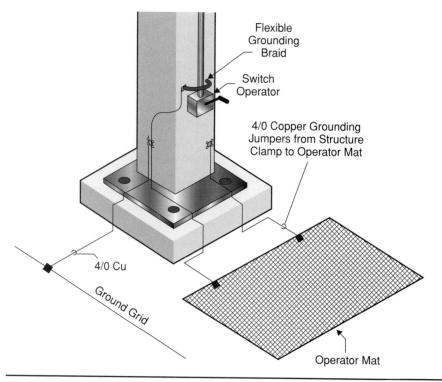

Figure 18–5   Operating mat.

If asked to open or close a recloser or breaker from a control box mounted right at the equipment, be aware that a breakdown within the recloser or breaker can cause a fault to ground and energize the grounded network. Use a portable ground-gradient mat if there is not a permanent one installed at the control box.

Hazards Working in Substations

18.2.5 Table 18–1 identifies some of the hazards that will be encountered in a substation and it identifies some of the barriers needed to provide protection from these hazards.

18.3 Constructing a Substation

Locating a Substation

18.3.1 The ideal location for a substation is close to the load center and not very visible to the public. The location must meet environmental and zoning regulations. Public meetings will probably be part of the approval process for locating a large transformer. Large transmission substations with extra-high-voltage (EHV) lines going in and out are going to be very visible, no matter where they are located.

Some substations in a city center may not be noticeable to the public. Incoming and outgoing lines may be underground, and such stations may be situated inside large buildings.

TABLE 18–1   **Hazards of Working in Substations**

Hazard	Barrier
Contact with energized overhead bus or leads going into equipment bushings and potheads.	Live apparatus is much closer than apparatus encountered in line work. Minimum approach distances for truck booms and workers are easier to bridge. Long objects, such as ladders, conduits, ground rods, and reinforcing steel, should be carried by two people, horizontally, when in the live part of the station.
Identifying the wrong equipment as having been de-energized.	Substations contain a lot of duplicate equipment. Accidents have occurred because people have climbed on the wrong breaker. Positive identification with grounds and warning tape and signs are required.
Contact with induced voltage in live substations and close to overhead conductors.	Any components sitting on insulators must be treated as hot until grounds are installed.
Contact with live underground cables when digging in a station.	In existing stations, all powerline cables must be located and nearby digging must be done by hand or a "sucker" truck.
Opening a grounding connection can interrupt a current flow, and it can create a high voltage across the open point.	Ground connections should not be removed while a substation is energized. If a connection must be replaced, a temporary jumper should be installed.
SF_6 is heavier than air, so it will displace oxygen and create an immediate suffocation hazard, as would other heavier-than-air gases.	SF_6 gas is odorless, tasteless, and nontoxic in its normal state, but an SF_6 gas leak in a basement will drift down to the lowest part of the building and displace air. To reduce the risk of a large volume of SF_6 escaping ensure that SF_6 cylinders are stored outdoors and chained so that they cannot be damaged in a fall.
Arcing inside switchgears will decompose SF_6 gas. Decomposition products are considered toxic.	The decomposed products are metal fluorides and look like white powder. They can cause a rash, skin irritation, and eye irritation. Inhaling can damage the respiratory system. Protective clothing and a full-face supplied-air respirator should be worn when entering electrical equipment. Powdered arc products should be removed with proper cleaning solvents and a vacuum cleaner equipped with a special in-line filter. Smoking, welding, or switching will cause decomposition of any escaped SF_6 into toxic material.
Damage to a control cable may prevent a critical piece of equipment from operating.	There may not be an immediate reaction to damage to a control cable. However, the damage will get worse over time and the control cable will eventually fail. This can result in equipment failing to operate at a critical time because it will not get the signal to operate. Call for repair if damaging contact is made with a cable.

The substation has to be built in a location where good grounding can be obtained. Good grounding is essential in order for relays to be activated to open switchgears for ground faults.

Construction in an Existing Station

18.3.2 Substation construction is often an addition to or a refurbishment of an existing substation where much of the existing station will stay energized. Barriers and warning signs are used to clearly mark out the energized part of the station. There can be energized underground high-voltage and distribution cables running through the construction zone that will have to be located. If digging is required around these cables, they must be hand dug or dug with a sucker truck. Typically, the first 5 feet (1.5 meters) should be dug by hand or sucker truck before digging with a machine. The station yard grounding network has to stay intact or at least ensure that no open point is bridged elsewhere. Dangerous voltage and current can appear around an open point.

Where cables have been exposed, the cables must be supported to prevent stress on the cable. Mechanical protection over exposed cable is necessary to prevent accidental contact with tools and machinery.

All metal objects, such as excavation equipment, sheds, shoring, road plates, and temporary fencing, should be grounded.

Low-voltage and communications cables can also be present in a work zone. Contact with these cables may not lead to injury but can lead to a major outage.

Civil Work for a New Substation

18.3.3 There are many different types of substation structures, and the civil work varies accordingly. The description of the civil work in this section is for the more common air-insulated substation.

A foundation plan lays out the locations for the foundations of the station structure supports, the concrete pads that support equipment, and the control building. Concrete pads may need to support weights as heavy as 700 tons and to hold circuit breakers that can shake when operating under a fault condition. Structures need footings that will resist downthrust and uplift when tension is applied.

To reduce the risk of foundations shifting, top soil and clay, which are compressible as well as affected by frost, are removed and replaced with a stabilizing backfill. The foundations are constructed with reinforced concrete. Oil retention systems are made to surround oil-filled equipment. Concrete is tested to ensure it is correct for its application.

Extensive trenching is required for powerline cables, low-voltage circuits to equipment, and relay circuits from the potential transformers and current transformers. These cables can be in conduit or raceways covered by concrete slabs.

Constructing a Grounded, Equipotential Grid

18.3.4 A substation yard is constructed to be one big, grounded, equipotential grid. The grounding grid is a mesh of wires and is bonded together at every crossing. The grid is connected and grounded so that electrical current, especially under fault conditions, will be carried into earth. The grid is equipotential, with all equipment,

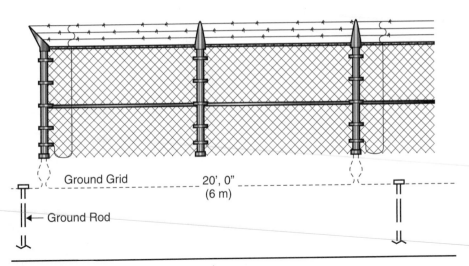

Figure 18–6   Fence connected to grid.

structures, fencing, and so on bonded together to reduce touch and step potentials to safe levels. All electrical equipment and neutrals are connected to the grid.

When a fault occurs in a substation or on one of the circuits feeding in or out of the substation, a rise in voltage occurs in the earth and on the grounded grid. Having an extensive grid that bonds structures, equipment tanks, and fencing reduces the risk of dangerous potentials between different elements.

Many ground rods are driven in a station to carry electric currents into earth under normal and fault conditions without exceeding any operating and equipment limits or adversely affecting continuity of service. The grid network is typically made up from 4/0 bare copper in a grid pattern spaced about 10 feet (3 m) apart and about 1.5 feet (0.5 m) below grade. The grid is connected together electrically at each crossing and to each ground rod, usually with exothermic connections. The grid is also connected to an operating platform and the operating handles for switches. The connections shown in Figure 18–5 must be in place to allow an operator to be in an equipotential zone to safely operate a switch.

The substation grid is connected to the fence and extended about 3 feet (1 m) outside the fence, as shown in Figure 18–6. The intent is that anyone touching the fence during a fault condition will still be on the grid bonded to the fence. Step potential from the grid outside of the fence to earth beyond the grid is kept to a minimum by the very extensive grounding inside the substation. The fence has to meet regulatory standards for height, barbed wire along the top, and warning signs.

Erecting Station Structures

18.3.5 Most new substation structures are modular. Blueprints provide assembly and erection details. Bolts must be torqued to specifications. The aluminum-alloy pipe used for buses will need some relatively exotic welding. Electrical connections that will be carrying very high fault and load current must be made to exacting standards.

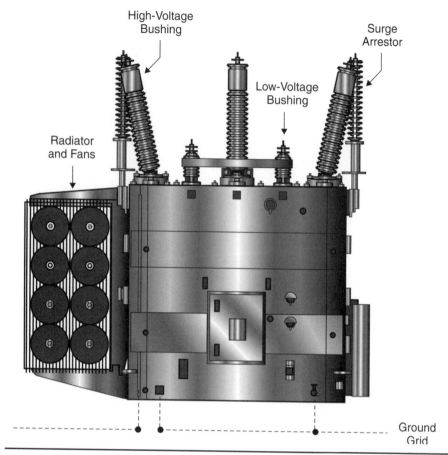

High-Voltage
Bushing

Surge
Arrestor

Low-Voltage
Bushing

Radiator
and Fans

Ground
Grid

Figure 18–7 A substation transformer.

If installing long pieces of buses or structures, the use of tag lines is essential to keep the load under control, especially in substations with live sections.

Installing Heavy Substation Equipment

18.3.6 Transformers, circuit breakers, and so on are designed with provisions for lifting, jacking, and/or rolling. Units will have to be lifted using the base frame or from the lugs/clamps at the top of a unit. An experienced rigger should be in charge to lift and move heavy, yet delicate equipment.

Wiring Auxiliary Equipment

18.3.7 There is a massive amount of low-voltage and relay-type wiring to do when constructing a substation, so it is essential to have the wiring blueprints. Each wire must be traced, color coded, and labeled. Each wire is tested to ensure that every piece of equipment and relay is connected to where it is supposed to go.

Review Questions

1. Which element in a substation will automatically open a line when there is a short circuit?

2. What is the application for a mobile distribution substation?

3. Describe the construction required to make a substation yard into an equipotential zone.

4. How are the voltage and current of an incoming high-voltage transmission line measured?

5. Why are disconnect switches in series with a circuit breaker?

6. What are the prerequisites before entering a substation?

7. List four items in a substation design that are meant to protect the public.

8. How can opening a grounding connection in a substation be a hazard?

9. Describe how SF_6 gas can be a hazard.

10. When digging in an existing substation, what kind of underground hazards must be avoided?

CHAPTER 19

Outdoor Lighting Systems

Topics to Be Covered	**Section**
Types of Outdoor Lighting	19.1
Luminaires, Lamps, and Structures	19.2
Lighting Ballasts	19.3
Lighting Circuits and Controls	19.4
Maintenance and Troubleshooting Outdoor Lighting Systems	19.5
Safety and Environmental Hazards Working with Outdoor Lights	19.6

19.1 Types of Outdoor Lighting

Applications of Outdoor Lighting

19.1.1 Outdoor lighting can be street lighting, roadway lighting, sports field lighting, airport runway lighting, and traffic lights. While electrical utilities tend to work only on streetlights, other lighting systems are discussed in this chapter because powerline contractors can be called upon to work on all kinds of outdoor lights. Similar skills and knowledge are required to install and maintain this wide variety of outdoor lighting systems. All types require a power supply, ballasts (with minor exceptions), luminaires, controls, and facilities or structure to install the luminaires.

Streetlights

Streetlights were one of the earliest loads for the original central-station type of electric system. The illumination of streets improved traffic safety, pedestrian safety, and security of people and property. A municipality normally owns and is responsible for the streetlights within its jurisdiction. Often municipalities have the local utility or a contractor look after the design, purchase, installation, and maintenance of all their streetlights. Street-lighting systems are not typically metered. The rates are fixed (flat rate), and the rate depends on many variables, such as ownership of the pole, type of pole, whether served overhead or underground, type of luminaire, size of lamp, and type of maintenance contract. Because many streelights are on poles that also carry utility lines, or fed from utility vaults that also carry high-voltage cable, a contractor must be qualified to work within 10 feet of live primary.

Streetlights and streetlight circuits are installed in the secondary position on a distribution pole, generally mandated to be at least 40 inches above any communications or television cable. A streetlight luminaire may or may not be grounded to a neutral, a downground, or both.

Roadway Lighting

Roadway lighting improves visibility at night, especially during poor weather, and reduces night accidents.

Lighting along highways and freeway intersections is owned by the road authorities, and electrical utilities are not normally involved with installation or maintenance of these lights. The utility provides a power supply to a nearby location, and the road authority or contractor installs and maintains the lights.

Sports Field and Area Lighting

Sports field and area lighting promotes business and community activities after daylight hours. Area lighting, especially for parking lots, reduces crime and adds to the general safety of the public. The electric flood lighting of sports fields is common for all outdoor field sports, including racing, football, tennis, and so on. This lighting is fed from the metered service where contractors install and maintain the lights.

Airport Runway Lights

Lighting is very critical at an airfield. An airfield has runway edge lighting, taxiway lighting, approach lighting, obstruction lighting, and beacon lighting circuits.

Traffic Lights

The first four-way electric traffic light was installed in Detroit in 1920. Traffic-signal lighting very quickly became essential at intersections, as can be confirmed when the power to the traffic lights goes off. A police officer cannot do the job as efficiently as traffic lights. The installation of traffic lights requires technical knowledge involving cable, quartz, or radio controls.

Specifications, Regulations, and Engineering

19.1.2 The design of the lighting hardware and the design of the layout for each of the many outdoor lighting systems are specialized and complex. Skilled workers who install the lights must install them exactly as specified because the specifications have to meet regulatory standards, as well as standard engineering practices.

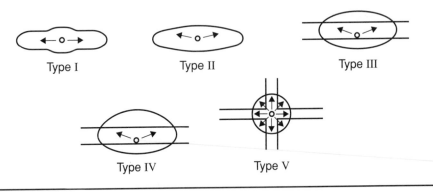

Figure 19–1 Lighting patterns.

Some of the complicating factors requiring design specialists include the following:

1. Luminaires (see Figure 19–1) are designed to produce a certain pattern of light. The reflector and lens have designs ranging from lighting a narrow laneway to a large intersection on a freeway and have five types that meet standards by the Illuminating Engineering Society of North America (IESNA) and the American National Standards Institute (ANSI). For example, the type III distribution pattern is for roadway and general parking applications and is designed to be located near the side of an area, approximately 2.75 mounting heights in width. The type V distribution pattern is for general parking and area lighting applications and is designed to be located at the center of an intersection or in a large area, and it will produce a circular distribution with the same candlepower at all angles. Replacement of a luminaire must match the existing lighting.

2. Light pollution ("artificial sky glow") is a concern of a public that wants to preserve the natural night environment by preventing outdoor lights from reflecting up into the sky. Municipalities will specify the degree that lights are to be shielded (cut off) so that the light emitted by the fixture is projected below a horizontal plane. Three types of optical systems provide different degrees of control. These include noncutoff, semicutoff and fullcutoff. The full-cutoff light is more severe in directing light to the ground in a fairly tight pattern. Higher mounting and more full-cutoff luminaires are needed to get the same lighting result as possible with semicutoff or cutoff fixtures. Figure 19–2 shows how luminaires are designed to limit the light shining into the sky.

3. There are mounting height restrictions in some municipalities because they are considered out of scale with their environment. The counterargument is that a lighting design in a community with a height restriction results in more poles needed to provide the desired light and higher energy costs. The higher mounting height also reduces glare, as can be seen when high poles are used on sports fields and at freeway intersections.

4. Lighting intensity and uniformity for the type or classification of area being illuminated must meet the standards from organizations such as ANSI and the IESNA. The light location, overhang, pattern, mounting height, type of luminaire, and lamp all contribute to meeting the required standard.

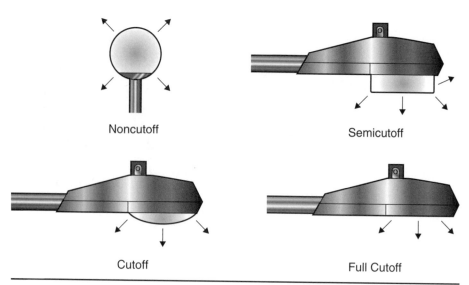

Noncutoff

Semicutoff

Cutoff

Full Cutoff

Figure 19–2   Optics for outdoor lights.

19.2 Luminaires, Lamps, and Structures

About Luminaires

19.2.1 The luminaire (fixture) shown in Figure 19–3 is a single, self-contained outdoor light. This is a common type of luminaire used as yard lights, streetlights, and area lighting. It consists of a ballast transformer, a lamp (often), and a capacitor, and it is self-contained with a control (a photocell-activated switch) that turns it on and off. Luminaires are designed to produce a certain pattern of light and are placed at a specified height.

There are also luminaires that are decorative for street lighting, clusters for sports field lighting, and clusters (halos) on high masts.

Airport runways have a wide variety of luminaires, such as those used at subsurface centerline runway lights, approach lights, centerline taxiway lights, and obstruction lights.

The luminaire for traffic lights would be the signal head. The signal head contains the lamps that are made specifically for traffic signals.

Lumens: A Measure of Light Intensity

19.2.2 Units used to measure light include the lumen, candela, foot-candle, and lux. A *candela* is a measure of luminous intensity or candlepower. A candle emits about 1 candela in all directions. The amount of light falling on a 1-square-foot

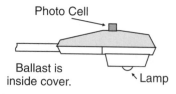

Photo Cell

Ballast is inside cover.

Lamp

Figure 19–3   A luminaire.

TABLE 19–1   **Efficiency and Lamp Life of Various Lamps**

Type of Lamp	Energy Use	Lumens per Watt	Lamp Life Hours
Incandescent	High	8 to 18	Up to 2,000
Fluorescent	Medium	55 to 79	Up to 20,000
Metal-Halide	Medium	38 to 75	Up to 20,000
High-Pressure Sodium	Low	72 to 115	Up to 24,000
Low-Pressure Sodium	Lowest	100 to 183	Up to 16,000

surface 1 foot away from a 1-candela source is defined as 1 *lumen*. In the metric system, 1 lumen per square meter is called a *lux*. One foot-candle equals 10.76 lux.

Powerline workers will probably continue to look for the watt rating when changing lamps. Lamps are designed to get as much visible light output with the least amount of energy input possible. The visible light output from a lamp is called *luminor energy,* and a lamp output is rated in lumens. The energy input of a lamp is rated in watts. In other words, the lumen is a measure of light output, not wattage. The height and the intended pattern of a streetlight determine the size of lamp. The type of lamp used determines the capital cost, the efficiency, and the lamp light.

Table 19–1 shows the efficiency (lumens per watt) and lamp life of the various types of lamps available.

Incandescent Lamps

19.2.3 An incandescent lamp generates light when current flows through a piece of wire (filament). The filament is a resistor that heats up enough to glow white hot or, in other words, is incandescent and generates light. The lamp is sealed in an oxygen-free bulb to prevent the filament from burning up. Depending on the design, an incandescent lamp can have a life of 2,500 hours.

The filament in the most common incandescent lamps is made of tungsten, which is a metal that can withstand high temperatures. By changing the length or thickness of the filament, the temperature of the filament can be changed. A cooler filament would "boil" off more slowly, and the lamp would have a longer life, but it would produce more invisible infrared and yellow light and is less efficient for producing a visible white light. At a higher filament temperature, the lamp produces a whiter visible light. The tungsten "boils" off more quickly and the lamp has a shorter life.

The design of the lamp seeks to balance efficiency and lamp life. The efficiency of an incandescent lamp is about 14 lumens per watt for a 100-watt bulb and 18 lumens per watt for a 500-watt bulb.

There are more types of incandescent lamps than any other. There are still some old streetlight systems with incandescent lamps, and replacement lamps for them should have the same color and bulb finish. Some systems will have a specific type of base that will require a screw cap of a matching size.

Incandescent lamps for street lighting are pretty well obsolete. Light-emitting diode (LED) lighting is replacing incandescent lamps in traffic lights.

Tungsten Halogen Lamps

19.2.4 Halogen lamps are incandescent bulbs that operate at very high temperatures. The life of a tungsten filament is extended because iodine (a halogen) vapor is put in the bulb. When the tungsten boils off the filament, it combines with the iodine to form a tungsten-iodide gas. When this gas touches the filament, it decomposes; the tungsten is deposited on the filament again, and the iodine is released into the bulb. This "perpetual motion" could continue forever, but the bulb eventually fails because the tungsten is not deposited evenly on the filament. To withstand the high temperatures and allow the use of smaller bulbs, halogen bulbs are made of quartz instead of glass. Halogen lamps use about 40 percent less energy than common incandescent lamps.

Gaseous-Discharge Lamps

19.2.5 Gaseous-discharge lamps have become the lamps of choice for outdoor lighting. They produce more lumens per watt than incandescent lamps. Light is produced when electric current passes through a gas. When a permanent arc is established in a gas-filled lamp, the light produced is referred to as an electric discharge or gaseous discharge.

Types of gaseous-discharge lamps include fluorescent, compact fluorescent, low-pressure sodium, and high-intensity discharge. Mercury-vapor, metal-halide, and high-pressure sodium-vapor lamps are included in the high-intensity discharge category. Fluorescent and mercury-vapor lamps are becoming obsolete for outdoor lighting.

Fluorescent Lamps

Fluorescence is a process whereby the light from the electric discharge in a gaseous-discharge lamp is made more visible and changed to a different color. For example, the color of an electric discharge through mercury-vapor gas is an invisible ultraviolet color. It is after the energy from the ultraviolet light contacts a phosphor powder that the ultraviolet light is converted to a visible white light. The phosphor powder coats the inside of the lamp. Although there are many types of fluorescent lamps, the common fluorescent lighting found in most commercial buildings is a bulb or tube filled with argon gas and a small amount of mercury vapor. The tube has a tungsten filament electrode at each end. The inside of the tube is coated with phosphor, a fluorescent material. Electric current heats the filament at each end of the tube. A cloud of electrons of opposite polarity gathers around each electrode. The electrons then form an arc that travels from one electrode to the other, alternating back and forth with the AC.

The electrons in the arc bump the atoms of argon gas and mercury vapor, which in turn produces an invisible ultraviolet light. The energy from the ultraviolet light causes the phosphor coating in the tube to emit visible white light. The makeup of the phosphor coating determines the color of the light output. Fluorescent lamps are more efficient than the common incandescent lamps and can convert more energy to a visible white light at cooler temperatures. Fluorescent lamps have a long lamp life of about 12,000 hours. However, because the electrodes decay, less energy is transferred through the mercury vapor and less and less light is emitted as the lamp gets older. Fluorescent lamps should be scheduled for replacement rather than waiting for the lamp to quit. The efficiency of a fluorescent lamp is about 50 lumens per watt.

Mercury-Vapor Lamps

A mercury-vapor lamp is a high-intensity (HI) gaseous-discharge lamp. It has an inner arc tube made of quartz that contains argon gas and a small amount of liquid mercury. When an arc is established within this inner bulb, the gas inside the lamp produces an ultraviolet light. The inside of the outer bulb is coated with phosphor, which converts the ultraviolet light into visible light.

A mercury-vapor lamp does not start immediately. First, an arc must be established across a set of starting electrodes within the inner bulb; then, the arc is transferred to the main electrodes within the bulb (Figure 19–4). To establish the arc in the bulb, between 200 and 350 volts are needed across the starting electrodes. This sets up an initial glow in the argon gas. The heat generated in the inner bulb causes the liquid mercury to vaporize. Then an arc travels between the two main electrodes, and through the argon and vaporized mercury, to produce the ultraviolet radiation. An average 400-watt mercury-vapor lamp has an output of 50 lumens per watt and a lamp life of 24,000 hours.

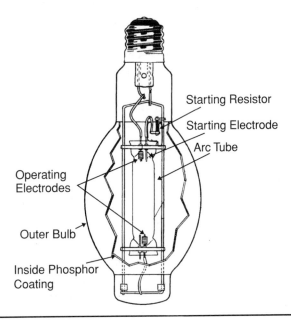

Figure 19–4   A typical mercury-vapor lamp.

Metal-Halide Lamps

A metal-halide lamp is similar to a mercury-vapor lamp, but it has other metallic elements, which results in a good-quality white light. A metal-halide lamp is about 35 percent more efficient than a mercury-vapor lamp, but it has a shorter lamp life. A 400-watt metal-halide lamp has a 75-lumens-per-watt rating with a lamp life of about 10,000 hours.

High-Pressure Sodium-Vapor Lamps

A high-pressure sodium-vapor (HPS) lamp is a small cylinder arc tube. Because of its small size, there is no room for installing starting electrodes. Instead, the ballast supplies a high voltage of approximately 2,500 volts to start the arc in the lamp. After the lamp is started, the voltage supply drops to a lower operating level.

High-pressure sodium-vapor lamps are commonly used for streetlights because they are very efficient. A 400-watt high-pressure sodium-vapor lamp has about a 100-lumens-per-watt rating and a 24,000-hour lamp life.

Low-Pressure Sodium-Vapor Lamps

Low-pressure sodium-vapor lights are even more efficient than high-pressure sodium-vapor lights, but they were not well accepted as streetlights because of the very yellow color of the light emitted. High-pressure sodium-vapor lights have a more acceptable color, although the light is still quite yellow.

Light-Emitting Diodes

19.2.6 It may be difficult to consider light-emitting diodes (LEDs) as lamps, but they are used more and more to replace lamps. They are replacing incandescent lamps in traffic lights and are especially effective for colored warning lights, such as those at airports. They use about 15 percent of the power an incandescent lamp would use and have a life of about 100,000 hours.

LEDs are very small "chips" made from thin layers of semiconducting material that emit light when a voltage is applied across them. These small chips are put together as a package that makes up a light. The lighting package is recognizable by the dot-like appearance (see Figure 19–5).

A traffic light using an LED concentrates the light in a very tight angle and is very visible from a long distance, even when in direct sunlight. Eventually all traffic lights will be converted to LED lights. There are LED modules designed to fit into the existing lamp socket of Vehicle Traffic Control Signal Heads (VTCSH).

Lighting Structures

19.2.7 Street-lighting structures can be poles in an existing line or poles specifically made for street lighting. They range from a very ordinary utility pole to those made especially for a given application. One type of streetlight pole that requires someone familiar with the hazards of live-front transformers is the type of pole where the transformer sits in the base of the pole (pole trans). This type of transformer is a substitute

Figure 19–5 LED traffic lamps.

to a pad-mount transformer and feeds customers in the subdivision as well. Streetlight poles are very accessible using ordinary utility equipment such as a bucket truck.

The very tall highway lighting standards found at multilane highway intersections and at sports fields would require equipment and skills similar to those used to install transmission-line structures. For maintenance, a typical 150-foot (46-m) mast (see Figure 19–6) may have a pulley arrangement inside its structure to lower its luminaire to the ground. Sports field lighting structures often include climbing hardware to allow climbing for maintenance.

Traffic-signal heads are mounted on all kinds of different poles, as well as being hung from strand-wire between poles. When installed on poles, whether on top, on a mast arm, or to the side of a pole, hardware is supplied to level the signal head

Figure 19–6 A tall mast pole.

and to aim the lights in the correct direction. Traffic control is certainly always an issue when working on traffic lights.

The facilities for installing luminaires at airport runways will range from subsurface fixtures to relatively high poles.

19.3 Lighting Ballasts

The Function of a Ballast

19.3.1 Just as ballast is needed in a ship to stabilize it from the waves on the ocean, a ballast is needed to stabilize the voltage and current in a gas-discharge lamp. In an incandescent lamp, the filament is a fairly constant resistor and, therefore, the voltage and current are constant. In a gaseous-discharge lamp, there is no fixed resistance and the lamp needs a variable voltage supply. It needs a very high voltage to strike an arc between the two electrodes within the vacuum tube. After the arc is struck, the resistance decreases and the normal 120-, 240-, 277-, or 480-volt rating will maintain the arc. Because an arc is like a short circuit, the ballast limits the current and prevents the current from continuing to increase and eventually burn out the lamp. The ballast automatically adjusts to supply the proper voltage over the lamp's life. As the lamp gets older, the ballast will supply the needed higher voltage to maintain an arc.

A ballast is a large inductor or reactor. It takes the place of a resistor and limits current flow while it lowers the voltage as the lamp tube begins to conduct. A ballast consists of a wire coil, an iron core, and sometimes a capacitor. A high-pressure sodium lamp may show a voltage rating of 120 volts or 240 volts, but it cannot operate without a ballast. A ballast is needed to provide a high voltage to start the lamp. A ballast is also needed to act as a current-limiting device because once this type of lamp is ignited, the arc within the lamp creates a short circuit.

Reactor Ballasts

19.3.2 A common fluorescent light that can be started without needing a voltage boost still needs a ballast to control the current. A reactor ballast consisting of a coil of wire connected in series with the lamp acts as a choke coil and controls the current (Figure 19–7). As the current increases, more inductive reactance is generated. The inductive reactance of the coil acts as a self-

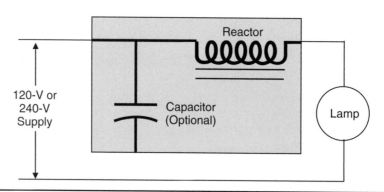

Figure 19–7 A reactor ballast.

limiting load that increases as the current increases. A capacitor is not necessary, but when it is connected in parallel, it will improve the power factor of the load without canceling the effect of the inductive reactance of the coil connected in series.

Autotransformer Ballasts

19.3.3 An autotransformer ballast (Figure 19–8) is used with high-intensity gaseous-discharge lamps to provide the voltage boost needed to get the initial arc to strike in the lamp. The secondary coil of the autotransformer is connected in series and thus acts as a choke coil to control the current. A capacitor is not necessary but can be added to improve the power factor of the load.

Regulator Ballasts

19.3.4 The regulator ballast (Figure 19–9) is a transformer with the primary and secondary isolated from one another. The secondary magnetic circuit is operated in saturation, which keeps the secondary voltage at a constant level. A capacitor in series with the lamp sets up a capacitive reactance, which limits the current. The lamp, therefore, is almost at a constant wattage.

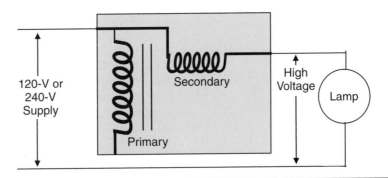

Figure 19–8 An autotransformer ballast.

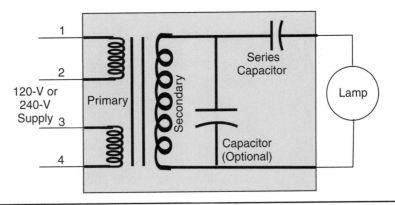

Figure 19–9 A regulator ballast.

Testing a Ballast

19.3.5 Testing a Ballast

TABLE 19–2 **Testing a Ballast**

Test	Details
Test the insulation of the ballast for short circuits.	To test for a short-to-ground, connect together all the primary and secondary leads and, using a 500 V insulation tester (megger or ohmmeter), test between the leads and ballast case or ground. The insulation reading should be better than 0.5 megohms.
Test for proper output voltage using an open-circuit voltage test.	To check for proper voltage output, disconnect the secondary leads or remove the lamp to provide an open circuit. With the primary connected, the secondary voltage should be as stated on the ballast nameplate. Gaseous discharge lamps need a high voltage to start the initial electric arc. A ballast will step up a 120 V supply voltage to provide a 750 V to 4,000 V output. For example, a high-pressure sodium lamp needs a high starting voltage of about 4,000 V. After the lamp starts, the operating voltage of the lamp will vary depending on the type of lamp and wattage rating. Wait until the lamp is at normal brilliance, or approximately 30 seconds, before doing a voltage check on a gaseous-discharge luminaire. The voltage should settle to its normal operating voltage when the light is at normal brilliance.
Determine whether the ballast can limit the current as it is designed to do using a short-circuit test.	Remove the lamp and connect together the secondary leads to form a dead short. Apply a normal supply voltage to the primary and take a current reading on the shorted secondary leads. The purpose of a ballast is to limit the current, so there should be very little current between the secondary leads. Typically, the current for a mercury lamp should be 2 to 2.7 A for a 175 W lamp and 4.2 to 5.3 A for a 400 W lamp.
Check the primary coil for shorted turns or damage with a no-load current test.	Remove the lamp or open the secondary leads so that no load is on the secondary of the ballast. Apply a normal supply voltage to the primary and take a current reading on the primary leads. A reading of more than 50 percent of the rated primary current indicates a damaged ballast.

19.4 Lighting Circuits and Controls

Power Supply to Outdoor Lights

19.4.1 Each luminaire must be supplied with the proper voltage and current. The power supply can come from any of the following:

1. Existing secondary bus or service with the lights connected in parallel, which is very common for streelights and yard lights.

2. A separate secondary with each light connected in parallel is a dedicated streetlight supply wire metered at one location. A photoelectric control can control all the lights on the circuit, or each light can still have individual photocell control. This is common for an underground supply where no other secondary circuits are nearby.

3. Use a high voltage with the lights connected in series. This was common for streetlights but is now common for lighting such long distances as airport runways.

4. Use a feed from a transformer in the base of the light standard, which is useful for the very large and high lights far apart from each at freeway intersections and for feeding a subdivision, as well as for lights.

5. Streetlights fed from underground systems could have a source pad-mounted controller cabinet that receives power from a nearby underground transformer. It is typically a 100-amp, single-phase, three-wire, 240-volt dedicated service. From there, a streetlight circuit runs to a given number of lights.

Some power-supply systems will have a fuse between the circuit and each light fixture on that circuit. On lights fed from underground, the fusing is done with in-line fuse holders and is accessible at a hand hole in the pole. Some luminaires will have fuses inside the fixture, but many do not have any.

Control (Switching) Outdoor Lights

19.4.2 Outdoor lights are switched on an off with a photo cell, a manual switch, or remote-control switching. Traffic lights are, of course, always on.

A photocell is ideal for initiating the switching for streetlight, roadway lighting, and area-lighting control. One control combined with relays can switch on entire streets at once; however, it is also common to have a photoelectric control in each individual light. When light strikes a photocell, a current is generated. The current from the photocell travels through a relay coil that keeps an armature from closing the relay contacts. When there is not enough light to generate current, the relay armature is released and the contacts close. A time-delay feature prevents the photocell from opening the contacts because of exposure to temporary lights, such as lightning or car headlights. Photoelectric controllers are made "fail safe" so that a component failure or dirt on the photocell will keep the contact closed and the light will stay on all day (day burner). If the eye is pointed toward the sunset, it will be quite late turning on the light. Typically, the eye is pointed north so that all

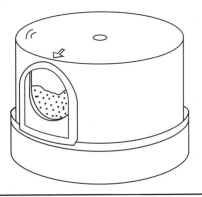

Figure 19–10 Typical photocell.

lights in a set of individually controlled lights will be switched on and off at approximately the same time.

Manual switching, which includes remote control, is best for intermittent-use facilities such as a sports field. At airports, the lighting conditions dictate the lighting needs, and the many different lighting circuits are generally switched in and out remotely from a control room.

Street-Lighting Controls

Streetlights are turned on and off individually or in groups using a control switch and a control circuit. They can be any of the following:

1. Individual lamp controls

2. Control switch with a pilot wire

3. Cascading relay system

Streetlight control switches that turn lights on and off can be photoelectric, a time-clock control, or manually switched. Photoelectric controls have taken over from manual switching or, in most cases, time-clock controls.

Controlling Individual Lights

19.4.3 Many streetlights and all yard lights are independently fed from any nearby and available 120/240-volt source controlled by an individual in-head photocell. This works well in residential areas where there are transformers and secondary bus. Because there is no interconnection with any other lights on a street, these lights are the easiest to troubleshoot because when this light is not working, the source of the trouble will be at that light or supply.

Pilot-Wire Control System

19.4.4 A pilot-wire streetlight system is a system that uses a pilot wire (a separate wire strung to all the streetlights) to control many lights from one spot so that they all go on and off at the same time. Each individual light does not have to be supplied from the same source. It can be fed from any available and nearby 120/240-volt source. This works well in residential areas where there are transformers and secondary bus. The pilot wire is strictly a wire to turn the lights on and off. It is energized from a 120/240-volt supply through a photocell and will activate a relay when it gets dark.

One photoelectric control switch energizes the pilot wire when it becomes dark. When the pilot wire is energized, the normally open relay contact connected to the pilot wire closes. Each relay in the system energizes a number of lights. A relay is just a switch activated remotely by the pilot wire. It is also possible to have a photoelectric control de-energize the pilot wire when it becomes dark. This releases the contacts of the normally closed relays and the lights are energized. The normally closed relay system allows the lights to become day burners when the control switch or pilot wire becomes defective. Figure 19–11 shows normally open relays that are closed when the pilot wire is energized.

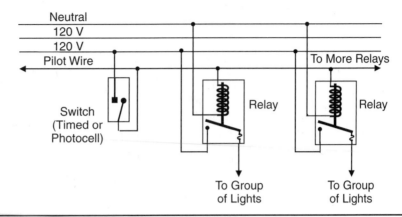

Figure 19–11 A pilot-wire control system.

Normally open relay systems

1. One control switch, photoelectric or timed, energizes the pilot wire when it becomes dark.

2. The normally open relay contacts close when the pilot wire energizes the relay coil.

3. Each relay energizes a number of lights.

Normally closed relay systems

1. One control switch, photoelectric or timed, de-energizes the pilot wire when it becomes dark.

2. When the pilot wire de-energizes the coil in the normally closed relay, the armature is released and the contacts close.

3. Each relay energizes a number of lights.

The normally closed relay system allows the lights to come on when the control switch or pilot wire becomes defective.

Cascading Lighting-Control System

19.4.5 A cascading relay system energizes and controls all the streetlights from one transformer and one control. This works well in areas where there are few or no existing transformers or secondary bus and works well on underground supply to lights. A streetlight wire is strung with relays installed along its length. To prevent having a very large relay (switch) to energize all the lights, each section of the lighting circuit activates the relay that energizes the next lighting circuit. Figure 19–12 shows that when a relay is energized it will energize a pilot wire to energize the next relay.

The length of the feed will be limited by the voltage drop that will occur when the feed becomes too long for the size of wire.

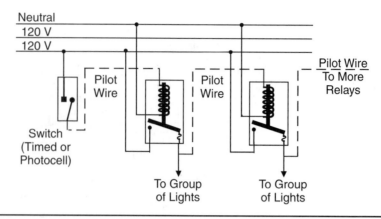

Figure 19–12 A cascading control system.

Series Outdoor Lighting Systems

19.4.6 At one time, almost all streetlights were installed in a series circuit, but, because they are most suited to the more inefficient incandescent lamps, they have generally been replaced. Runway lighting at airports is a most common application of series lighting.

In a series circuit, many lights can be fed with one relatively small and continuous wire that starts at the source transformer, forms a loop through the streets being illuminated, and goes back to the transformer.

In a series lighting circuit, a relatively small constant current flows through one relatively small continuous wire. The wire starts at the source transformer, forms a loop through the streets being illuminated, and goes back to the transformer. The circuit is insulated for a primary-level voltage.

The series circuit wire is fed at a primary voltage and is insulated and placed in a primary position on overhead distribution poles. For an underground installation, the cable would be a primary voltage cable. A high voltage is needed because in a series circuit the sum of the voltage drop across each individual light is equal to the source voltage. The number of lights in the circuit determines the amount of source voltage needed to feed the lights. It would be impractical to build a transformer with the exact voltage and current output needed for each series lighting circuit. A special constant current transformer, also called a "regulating transformer," is used to raise and lower the voltage automatically, depending on the number of streetlights in the circuit. A constant current has to be maintained because if one lamp burns out the total resistance of the lighting circuit becomes smaller and the current would tend to increase. The voltage will go as high as needed (up to several thousand volts) to supply a constant current through the circuit. As light units are added, the primary voltage will go up to continue to provide a constant current (typically 6.6, 7.5, or 20 amperes) through the special series circuit lamps.

A hazard to powerline workers is that the voltage across any break in a series circuit will be equal to the output voltage of the transformer. Maintenance should be

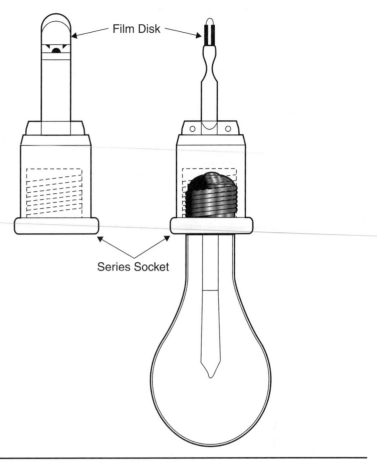

Figure 19–13 A special series circuit lamp.

done with the circuit isolated and grounded to ensure that a circuit is not opened, cut, or joined unless a break is "jumpered" to avoid an open-circuit condition.

Because there would be a primary voltage across any open point in the circuit, the lamp and socket are designed not to break the continuity when the light element ruptures or a lamp is removed from the socket. The lamp is designed to automatically bypass the current. Figure 19–13 shows the special series circuit lamp with the thin film of insulation between two points on the lamp that is punctured by the high voltage across the break restoring the lighting circuit. A lamp used in a series circuit has a heavier filament because it has to carry a relatively high current compared to lamps connected in parallel. The socket in most series light fixtures is designed so that removing a bulb will not open the circuit.

Airport Runway Lighting

19.4.7 Series circuit lighting is ideal for an airport runway because of the many lights and long-distance feeds needed to get to all the lights. The utility supplies power to one location, and airport authorities or contractors look after the installation and maintenance of the vast lighting network.

A single primary cable fed from a constant current regulator (CCR) can, for example, run out and feed all the lights for 2 miles (3 km) along the edge of one runway and then come back to the source in the same trench or cableway to form a circuit. There would be quite a few individual circuits because each circuit can be controlled separately, providing a lot of switching flexibility. Figure 19–14 is a schematic drawing of what the runway-lighting circuits can look like. Because of the relatively high voltage and a low constant 6.6- or 20-ampere current, the conductor in the cable can be quite small. A typical cable might be #6 copper and rated at 5,000 volts. The skills involved in installing, terminating, and splicing primary cable are similar to those required for work on primary distribution systems.

The control room (tower) has very flexible control over the lighting system, and some systems use a powerline carrier to send the switching and data information

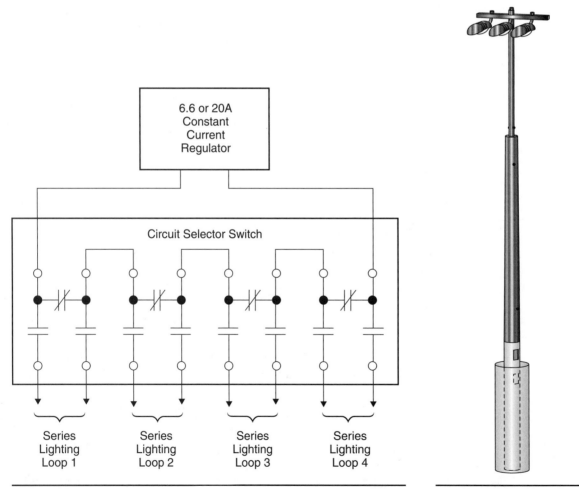

Figure 19–14   Runway-lighting circuits control.

Figure 19–15   A typical sports field lighting pole.

through the cable itself. Control of the lighting can also be by telephone lines, fiber optics, or wireless radio. The operating flexibility includes monitoring the status of each lamp and the ability to adjust the light brilliance in each circuit by increasing or decreasing the current flow out of the constant current regulator. In some cases, a pilot can adjust the lighting through the aircraft radio.

Outdoor Area Lighting

19.4.8 Outdoor area lighting refers to lighting parking lots, highways, and sports fields. While a huge variety of different luminaires, poles, and so on are available, the trend is to use a high mast for area lighting of parking lots and multilane highway intersections. A typical 150-foot (46-meter) light pole can be topped by a 14-foot circumference fixture (halo) that can, for example, hold twelve 400- to 1,000-watt high-pressure sodium bulbs. The halo on these structures can be lowered to ground level for maintenance. Some computerized systems will send a message to the responsible road authority when there is electrical trouble or burned out bulbs.

Figure 19–15 shows a typtical sports field lighting pole. The lighting for sports like car racing and football must be very high to reduce nighttime shadows for television broadcasting.

Traffic-light Control Systems

19.4.9 Installing traffic lights involves structures, signal heads, a controller, and vehicle detectors. The structure shown in Figure 19–16 is one example of the many ways that a signal head can be installed. It also shows the complicating factors of streetlights and street names on the same structure. From installation on a decorative structure, mast arm to suspension on a strand between two poles, the purpose is to install a signal head in a precise location, at the correct level, and aimed in the correct direction. Specifications must meet standards such as those of the International Municipal Signal Association (IMSA).

Power cables that feed a traffic-signal controller will be energized from any nearby overhead or underground secondary. They can be direct burial, in poly-pipe conduit, and overhead.

Cables used to energize and control the signal head and pedestrian head (also called the "ped head") are referred to as IMSA cables and come with various numbers of color-coded wires. The following is a standard color-coding scheme:

Red = Northbound
Green = Southbound
Blue = Westbound
Orange = Eastbound
Yellow = Pedestrian movement
White = Left-turn movement
Brown = Spare

The timing and cycle settings in a controller will be predetermined by traffic engineering and are based on traffic studies that will include coordination with other traffic lights, traffic volume, traffic speed, priority traffic, and so on. Ideally, traffic-signal coordination means that the signals turn green for approaching traffic.

Figure 19–16   A signal head installed on a streetlight pole.

The traffic-signal controller is the signal's brain and is programmable to take in all the fixed information and variable information, such as a car entering the intersection and activating the vehicle detector signal or by an emergency vehicle triggering a priority.

A vehicle detector signals the controller that a vehicle is present at an intersection. Inductive loops that cut into the pavement in each traffic lane have been the most common type. Where video detection is used, a video camera sends its image into a controller that then processes the information. There are also wireless magnetic detectors, self-powered vehicle detectors (SPVDs), that are buried below the surface. They use batteries that need replacement every 4 to 5 years.

19.5 Maintenance and Troubleshooting Outdoor Lighting Systems

Lighting Maintenance Programs

19.5.1 Troubleshooting "dark" lights one at a time as calls come in is not efficient and is bad public relations because this type of maintenance is always the result of a customer complaint. Some lighting systems, such as those at airports and high-mast highway lighting, have built-in monitoring systems that will notify the maintenance authority of the need for repair. The most common maintenance program adopted by lighting-system owners is the scheduling of lamp replacement and cleaning in geographic blocks.

Regularly scheduled cleaning is necessary because dirt that accumulates on or in luminaires can reduce light output and reduce the life of luminaire components. With the long operating life of high-density discharge lamps (HID) and LED packages, cleaning of luminaires may be necessary before group lamp replacement is carried out. As lamps age, the number of failures rise, and when a block of lights reaches the average rated life in hours for that type of lamp, group lamp replacement is scheduled.

To manage a light maintenance program, the complete lighting system is kept on maps and, in some cases, electrical schematic drawings. The maps show location number, controller locations (relays), conduit locations, junction box locations, transformer locations, type of luminaire light, type and size of replacement lamp, and so on. Structures are numbered on the maps and in the field to aid in locating trouble. A worker can determine the type of light involved for maintenance work before leaving the work center.

To keep records and maps up to date and accurate, it is important to fill out the required forms that the utility has for that purpose when any work is done on a streetlight.

Locating the Cause of a No-Light Problem

19.5.2 Table 19–3 is a troubleshooting procedure that is applicable for some types of streetlight systems.

Resolving Some Specific Lighting Problems

19.5.3 Table 19–4 lists some typical more mysterious lighting problems and some possible causes.

19.6 Safety and Environmental Hazards Working with Outdoor Lights

Outdoor Lighting Safety Hazards

19.6.1 Working with outdoor lights has its own special hazards. In addition to the usual environmental hazard of working in the vicinity of live circuits, there are also chemical, ultraviolet-radiation, and high-voltage hazards.

Ultraviolet-Radiation Hazard

The inner tubes of mercury-vapor and high-pressure sodium-vapor lamps put out an intense ultraviolet radiation. The outer phosphor-coated bulb protects people from exposure to the ultraviolet radiation. If exposed, the eyes will develop the same "sand-in-the-eye" symptoms as those from exposure to an electric arc or welding arc.

Even though the outer bulb is broken, it is possible for the inner bulb to continue to emit an unseen ultraviolet radiation without the outer bulb acting as a

TABLE 19–3   Resolving a No-Light Problem

Step	If	Then
1	There is no light.	Replace the lamp. Check for an arc-damaged socket or center contact.
2	There is still no light.	Check for power at the socket.
3	There is no power at the socket.	Check for power at the source leads of the ballast.
4	There is power at the source leads of the ballast.	If only one lamp is out, the lamp is not defective and the source is alive, so the ballast is most likely defective. There may be an odor of burned insulation coming from the ballast. Test or replace the ballast. Ballasts cannot be repaired in the field.
5	There is *no* power on the source leads of the ballast.	Check the luminaire fuse (if equipped) and check the relay fuse or breaker in the source circuit.
6	The luminaire fuse (if equipped) is open.	Check for a short in the luminaire. Remove the lamp and do an insulation test at the source leads to the light using a 500 V insulation tester (megger or ohmmeter).
7	The source side fuse of the relay feeding the streetlight bus is found open.	The relay is probably defective and must be replaced.
8	The load-side fuse of the relay is found open.	There is a problem downstream, on the streetlight bus or in a luminaire. Patrol the bus and/or do an insulation test at the luminaires. On a pilot-wire system, only the lights controlled by that relay will be out. On a cascading system, all the lights downstream will be out.
9	No faults have been found.	Check the photoelectric controller. Typically, defective and unfused photo controllers should keep the streetlight bus energized 24 hours a day. If the fuse on the source side of a fused controller is open, change out the controller. If the fuse on the load side is blown, patrol the streetlight bus and/or check for defective relays on the load side.

filter. The outer bulb can break while replacing a lamp and expose the worker to ultraviolet burns from the inner bulb. Disconnecting the power source will prevent a person from receiving ultraviolet-radiation burns.

High-Voltage Hazard

Gaseous-discharge lamps need a high voltage to start the initial electric arc. A ballast will step up the 120-volt supply voltage to provide a 750 to 4,000-volt output. For example, a high-pressure sodium-vapor lamp needs a high starting voltage of about 4,000 volts. After the lamp starts, the operating voltage of the lamp will vary depending on the type of lamp and its wattage rating. Wait until

TABLE 19–4   Causes of Some Lighting Problems

Problem	Possible Causes
1. Lamp replacement is very frequent in some locations.	Incandescent lamps can fail prematurely if exposed to vibration or voltage surges. The capacitors may be shorted out. If so, replace the capacitors.
	A ballast with a higher wattage than the lamp will cause premature burnout of gaseous-discharge lamps. The nameplate on the ballast will show which type of lamp is matched to the ballast. A defective or incorrect ballast may be the cause, so be sure that a multitapped ballast is connected to the correct voltage.
	Typically, incandescent lamps and series incandescent lamps should be replaced as a group yearly. Mercury-vapor, high-pressure sodium, and fluorescent lamps should be replaced as a group every 5 years.
2. The light stays on 24 hours a day.	Change out any photoelectric controller that is not fused because it is designed to stay closed when it becomes defective.
3. Lamp does not start.	*Lamp:* The lamp may be at the end of its life. Replace it. There could be a poor socket contact, so check for lamp tightness.
	Photocell: Check for a defective photocell by installing a replacement.
	Low Voltage: A low-voltage supply could be the cause, so check the voltage.
	Ballast: Make sure the multitapped ballast is connected to the correct voltage. Try a new ballast. For cold temperatures, install a ballast rated for a low-temperature start.
4. The lamp is on for a while, goes out, and comes on again in a continuing cycle.	The lamp is near the end of its life and must be replaced.
	There could be a ballast-to-lamp mismatch. For example, a 175 W lamp might be supplied by a 250 W ballast.
	A low-voltage supply is unable to keep the arc in the lamp going. Check the supply voltage.
	Headlights from traffic are causing the photoelectric cell to turn off the light. Turn the cell to another direction.
	Make sure the proper lamp has been installed.
5. The light is out, even though it is good and the source circuit is alive.	Change out the probably defective ballast or test the ballast.
6. The lamp is flickering continuously.	The lamp is probably approaching the end of its life. Replace the lamp.
7. The ballast is very hot.	The ballast temperature is higher under no-load conditions than under a loaded condition. The lamp is probably burned out. A thermal protector on the ballast should protect the ballast from being damaged.
8. The light does not appear as bright as it should be.	Regular maintenance during group replacement of lamps should include cleaning the globe, as well as polishing the reflector and refractor. Check the output voltage of the ballast or replace lamp.

TABLE 19–5   **Typical Operating Voltage for Gaseous-Discharge Lamps**

Lamp	125 W	150 W	250 W	400 W	700 W	1000 W
Metal-Halide			100 V	120 V		250 V
Mercury-Vapor	125 V		130 V	135 V	140 V	145 V
High-Pressure Sodium-Vapor		100 V	100 V	105 V		110 V

the lamp is at normal brilliance (or approximately 30 seconds) before doing a voltage check on a gaseous-discharge luminaire. The voltage should settle to its normal operating voltage when the light is at normal brilliance. Some typical operating voltages are found in Table 19–5.

High-Voltage Hazard Working with Series Lighting Circuits

Series lighting circuits are not secondary circuits. The source-constant current transformer can supply several thousand volts, depending on the number of lights in the circuit. The voltage across a break in the circuit will be equal to the full-line voltage.

If the series loop is to be opened or repaired, the risk of electrical shock is reduced by opening the source transformer and grounding at the point of work.

Toxic-Chemical Hazard

Mercury, sodium, and phosphor are toxic chemicals. These chemicals can be found inside the outer bulbs of gaseous-discharge lamps and are released when the outer bulbs are broken. Staying outdoors and upwind when working with these lights reduces the risk of exposure. *Mercury* is hazardous to the human body. Mercury is usually in a gaseous state because it vaporizes at 14°F (10°C). In the gaseous state, it can easily enter the body through the lungs. *Sodium* is a highly active poisonous chemical that oxidizes very quickly in air. Sodium in contact with water produces a chemical reaction that creates sodium hydroxide (caustic soda), which can damage the lungs when inhaled. *Phosphors* are poisonous and must not be inhaled.

Outdoor Lighting Environmental Hazards

19.6.2 The capacitors used in older luminaires (before 1979) are impregnated with polychlorinated biphenyls (PCBs). PCBs are not biodegradable and will stay in the environment and end up in the food chain. PCB waste must be disposed of properly according to regulatory requirements.

The mercury and lead found in lamps are toxic substances. Some companies will separate and recycle lamp components such as glass, metal, mercury, and phosphor powder.

Review Questions

1. Using watts and lumens as units, how is the efficiency of a lamp defined?

2. Which of the following lamps are high-intensity discharge lamps?
   - ( ) Fluorescent
   - ( ) High-pressure sodium
   - ( ) Halogen
   - ( ) Mercury-vapor
   - ( ) Incandescent

3. What is the purpose of a ballast in a gaseous-discharge lamp?

4. Why can a break in a series lighting circuit be a hazard to a powerline worker?

5. If a streetlight stays on in daylight, what could be the cause?

6. If a gaseous-discharge lamp replacement is very frequent at a specific location, what are some possible causes?

7. If the outer bulb of a mercury-vapor lamp breaks while replacing the lamp, to what hazard is the worker exposed?

8. Why should a worker wait until the lamp is at normal brilliance or approximately 30 seconds before doing a voltage check on a gaseous-discharge luminaire?

9. What can be done to reduce exposure to toxic chemicals such as mercury, sodium, and phosphor found in the bulbs of gaseous-discharge lamps?

10. What type of lighting system is common at airport runways, and why?

CHAPTER 20

Revenue Metering

Topics to Be Covered   **Section**

Introduction   20.1
Determining Cost to the Customer   20.2
Types of Revenue Metering   20.3
The Workings of a Meter   20.4
Single-Phase Metering   20.5
Polyphase Metering   20.6
Transformer-Rated Metering   20.7

20.1 Introduction

Metering an Electrical System

20.1.1 Every part of an electrical system is metered. Meters are found in transmission and distribution substations to record voltage, current, power, reactive power, and other data needed to operate and monitor the system. Much of the metering is telemetering used to monitor remote generating stations and substations. This chapter, however, deals with the "cash registers" for an electrical utility—namely, revenue metering at the customer.

20.2 Determining Cost to the Customer

Three Main Types of Charges to Customers

20.2.1 Typically, a customer can be asked to pay three types of charges:

1. An *energy charge,* which is the actual kilowatt-hours (kWh) used.

2. A *capacity* (or *demand*) *charge,* which can be the kilowatt (kW) demand or the peak kilovolt-ampere (kVA) demand.

3. A *customer charge* that is not a function of either energy used or peak demand but is a charge to cover the cost of the facilities to supply power.

Utilities can have dozens of different rates that are variations on these basic charges.

Variables That Affect Cost

20.2.2 Customers supplied by an electrical utility can be residential, industrial, commercial, or another utility. The rates charged to these customers depend on the type of service, type of load, quantity of load, and when the load is used. Some of these variables are measured through metering, and some costs are fixed when the service contract is negotiated.

Fixed charges

- Minimum charge
- Supply voltage
- Location
- Interruptible power

Metered charges

- Energy consumption in kilowatt-hours (kWh)
- Peak demand
- Power factor
- Load factor

Minimum Charge for Service

There is a fixed cost to a utility when it supplies power to a customer. A minimum charge relates to the wire and transformer needed to supply the energy a customer *may* require. The minimum charge is to cover the fixed cost of providing *voltage* regardless of the amount of current used. For a residential customer, the minimum charge saves a utility the extra expense of installing demand meters to track actual demand.

Energy Consumption

Energy consumption is the volts × amperes used by a customer. The voltage supplied is relatively constant; therefore, the amount of *current* used by the customer is the largest variable measured by a kWh revenue meter.

The largest portion of energy consumed by a customer is real or true power. A standard kilowatt-hour meter measures real power, which is equal to volts × amperes × hours × 1,000. Some reactive power is also used by a customer, but it is not normally metered for a residential customer.

Peak Demand

The peak demand is the maximum rate of consumption by a customer during a billing period. The demand for power can be very intermittent. Meanwhile, the utility has to generate, transmit, and transform the energy to supply the peak load when required.

Most utilities measure the peak demand for larger customers and not for residential customers. The reason most residential rates do not include demand charges is because the metering and tracking of residential demand add to a cost many utilities do not consider worthwhile. Residential consumers have very similar usage patterns so that a minimum charge can cover the fixed costs without much error.

Commercial and industrial customers have a more varied usage pattern. Their peak demand is measured so that a utility can recover the extra cost of supplying the capability to meet the demand. Measurement of peak demand encourages customers to spread out their need for energy.

1. *Demand* is a measurement of the instantaneous power used by a customer. For example, when ten 100-watt lights are on at the same time, they are using 1 kW of demand at that moment.

2. *Peak demand* is the highest amount of instantaneous power used by a customer during a billing period. Peak demand for power is measured as peak kWs or peak kVAs. For example, if the ten 100-watt lights are the largest load drawn during the billing period, the peak demand registered on a demand meter will be 1 kW. The load would have to be on for a given minimum time to register on the demand meter; for example, 15, 30, or 60 minutes are commonly specified demand intervals.

3. *Energy* is the amount of power used over time measured in kWhs. For example, the energy used by ten 100-watt lights after 1 hour will be 1 kWh.

Power Factor

Industrial or commercial customers frequently have large inductive loads that the utility must supply. A low power factor means that the utility must generate, transmit, transform, and distribute extra power to supply the inductive load.

A normal kilowatt-hour meter measures only the resistive load. For customers with a possible low power factor, a meter is installed to measure the kVA peak as well as the kW peak. The ratio of the kW peak to the kVA peak is the power factor.

One method of billing is to charge for the highest of either 100 percent of the kW peak or 90 percent of the kVA peak. Usually, a customer with a low power factor takes corrective action to keep the power factor above the level at which there would be extra billing.

Load Factor

An electrical utility needs an equal amount of equipment to supply a customer that consumes a relatively constant supply of power 24 hours a day and a customer that uses a similar amount of power for relatively short periods each day. The customer who uses the power 24 hours a day has a higher load factor and is billed at a lower rate.

The load factor is a percentage indicated by the ratio of the power consumed to the power that could have been consumed if the power had been used continuously.

$$\frac{(I_1 \times V_1) + (I_2 \times V_2)}{1,000} = total\ kVA\ load$$

Supply Voltage

Residential, small industrial, and commercial customers are supplied with their utilization voltage. Large customers are usually supplied by a line at subtransmission or transmission voltage feeding into a substation owned by the customer. There is less cost to the utility to only supply the circuit feeding the customer without supplying transformation. The customer is, therefore, billed at a lower rate.

Customer Location

It is reasonable for a utility to charge a higher rate to a remote cabin than to a home on a residential street. The cost to get power to the customer is reflected in rates. The rate structure takes into account the customer density at a location. Rural rates are higher than city rates.

Interruptible Power

A large industrial customer can get a better rate if its contract includes an agreement to reduce its demand for power during times when the utility is in short supply. During a utility's peak-load periods or in storm conditions, customers with an interruptible-power contract are asked to cut back their demand for power to previously negotiated levels.

Time of Use

Valley-hour rates or off-peak discounts can be attractive to some industries or residential customers. When load is shifted to off-peak hours, the electric utility benefits because the utility delays the need to build more generation and energy is being sold at times when generators would otherwise be underutilized. One variable to time-of-use metering is to have a lower-peak-demand penalty if the peak demand is during off-peak hours.

20.3 Types of Revenue Metering

Three Kinds of Power Are Measured

20.3.1 There are three kinds of electrical power:

1. Real power
2. Apparent power
3. Reactive power

Revenue metering involves the measurement of one or more of the three kinds of power and/or energy used by a customer (see Table 20–1).

TABLE 20–1   **Units of Measure for Billing Purposes**

Kinds of Power	Power	Energy
Real Power	Peak kW	kWh
Apparent Power	Peak kVA	kVAh
Reactive Power	Peak kVAR	kVARh

Power is a measurement of energy use at a given instant; for example, real power is the voltage $\times$ amperage used by a customer at a given instant. Energy is the amount of power used over a given period of time:

$$energy = power \times time$$

Meters are available to measure a variety of combinations involving the three types of power/energy.

Self-Contained Meters

20.3.2 A *self-contained meter* is a meter that can be installed without the use of current or potential transformers. The meter can carry the actual load current through its current coil and can use the actual service voltage in the meter potential coil.

Most customers take power at a secondary voltage. At this voltage, a self-contained meter can measure the actual voltage at the customer entrance. The voltage rating of a self-contained meter is normally 240 volts or less, but 600-volt meters are available. Self-contained meters are generally 200 amperes or less, although some higher-rated meters are on the market.

Transformer-Rated Meters

20.3.3 When current or voltage is too high to be carried by a self-contained meter, instrument transformers are used to send a representative current and voltage to the meter. A *transformer-rated meter* is used to measure a representative current from the current transformer and a representative voltage from the potential transformer.

The outward appearance of a transformer-rated meter is similar to a self-contained meter. The transformer-rated meter, however, has a lower voltage and current rating than the self-contained meter. For example, a transformer-rated meter used for a primary service could be rated at 120 volts and 5 amperes. The values measured by a transformer-rated meter are multiplied by the ratio of the current and potential transformers.

Primary or Secondary Metering

20.3.4 Some customers buy power at a primary voltage and use their own transformers to step it down to a utilization voltage. A transformer-rated meter and its associated potential and current transformers are used to send a representative voltage and current from the primary to the meter.

Metering Demand

20.3.5 Demand meters measure the maximum rate at which electricity was used and can be measured as kilowatts (kW), kilovolt-amperes (kVA), or kilovolt-amperes reactive (kVAR). The meter is generally a combination energy and demand meter.

The electromechanical demand meter illustrated in Figure 20–1 shows that a pointer attached to a bimetal strip is heated by a heating element within the meter. A bimetal strip has two metals bonded together. When heated, the metals expand at different rates, which forces the strip to bend. The bimetal strip bends, and it moves a pointer across the meter dial. The pointer attached to the bimetal strip is called a *pusher pointer* and, in turn, pushes a *maximum-demand pointer*. The maximum-demand pointer stays in the farthest position it was pushed. The position of the pointer is the maximum demand for power used by the customer between meter readings.

A peak demand that lasts only a short time is not recorded on the demand meter. The heater element has a time-response feature so that the element takes time to reach its maximum heat. Two common elements are a 10-minute element and a 16-minute element.

Metering Power Factor

20.3.6 A customer's power factor can be measured as the power factor during peak demand or as the power factor of the total energy used.

1. One way to measure the power factor during peak demand is through the use of a kW demand meter and a kVA demand meter. When the peak demand for real power and the peak demand for apparent power are known, then the power factor during the peak can be calculated.

2. One way to ensure that a customer will pay for all the energy used is to meter the apparent energy. A VAR-hour meter is used when a customer is being billed for apparent energy. A VAR-hour meter is often identified by a large R on the meter face.

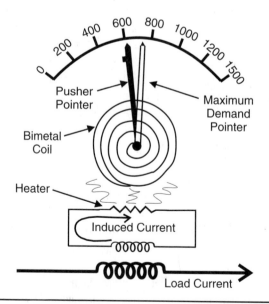

Figure 20–1 Demand meter.

Time-of-Use Metering

20.3.7 Time-of-use (TOU) metering offers a customer a lower price for energy used during nonpeak hours. The meter has the ability to record the time when the power was used. Many residential customers have not been offered this service because of the expense of the needed metering change. Offering TOU metering to large industrial and commercial customers increases the demand on the utility valley hours. Electronic revenue meters are easily programmed for the various TOU options a utility may offer to customers.

Prepayment Metering

20.3.8 Prepayment metering is like using a vending machine. A token or a magnetic card is inserted in the slot of the meter to make payment before the energy is used. The meter switches off the power when the payment runs out.

Automatic Meter Reading

20.3.9 Automatic meter reading (AMR) is the remote collection of meter data by way of some kind of communications link from a central location. Each meter has an individual identification and is modified to receive and send signals. The communications link can be a telephone line, a powerline carrier, a radio frequency, a coaxial cable, or a satellite. Each system competes for establishment in electrical utilities.

A powerline carrier system, for example, modulates the AC voltage wave to send a signal to the meter, and the AC wave is modulated to send the signal back to the central computer. In addition to reading the meter, an AMR system can be programmed to monitor customers for over- and under-voltage, momentary outages, meter tampering, peak demand, and time of use. Outages can be mapped, and system loads can be monitored and controlled. When a communications system is set up, it can be expanded to include the reading of other meters, monitoring burglar alarms, monitoring fire alarms, and operating equipment at remote sites.

20.4 The Workings of a Meter

Two Types of Meter Construction

20.4.1 There are two main types of meter construction: the electromechanical and the electronic meter. An *electromechanical* meter relies on a disk being turned in the same way that an electric motor turns an armature. The more voltage or current, the faster the disk rotates. The disk is connected by way of gears to a clock that registers the amount of power used.

An *electronic* meter measures the current and potential going through it without any moving parts. Features such as time of use and peak-demand measurements can be programmed more readily in an electronic meter. An electronic meter is very adaptable to AMR systems.

The Current Coil in a Meter

20.4.2 The current to be measured flows through a current coil in the meter. The coil is made up of a small number of turns of large wire. In a self-contained meter, all the load current flows through the current coil. The few turns in the current coil indicate that very little inductive reactance is created; therefore, the magnetic flux induced on the meter disk is in phase with the load current and the line voltage.

The nameplate on a meter shows the range of load for which the meter is designed. For example, a meter commonly referred to as a "100-amp" meter shows a range of 0.75 to 100 amperes on the nameplate.

The Potential Coil in a Meter

20.4.3 A potential coil inside the meter measures the voltage in a service. The coil is made up of many turns of fine wire. The voltage in the coil induces a magnetic field onto the meter disk. The strength of the magnetic field is dependent on the magnitude of the voltage. The potential coil is an inductive load, and the magnetic field it induces on the meter disk lags the field produced by the current coil by 90 degrees.

The voltage-coil ratings match the various standard voltages to be measured. Typical voltage ratings are 120, 240, 480, and 600 volts. These voltages can come directly from the secondary service being measured or from a potential transformer that steps down the voltage of a subtransmission or a primary circuit.

Why the Disk Turns

20.4.4 The magnetic field from the potential coil induces an electromotive force (emf) on the metal meter disk. The induced emf on the disk has nowhere to go because the disk is not part of a circuit. The emf, therefore, causes current to flow in the form of circular (eddy) currents on the disk.

The north and south poles on the potential coil are 90 degrees out of phase with the north and south poles of the current coil. As seen in Figure 20–2, the interaction of the eddy currents being attracted and repelled between the poles of the potential and current coils causes the disk to turn.

The permanent magnet in the meter provides a magnetic brake on the aluminum disk. Without the damping effect of the "breaking" magnet, the interaction of the electrical fluxes would tend to cause a continuous acceleration of the disk. Although a magnet would not normally affect an aluminum disk, the magnetic field of a permanent magnet will affect the eddy currents that rotate the disk. The retarding torque or drag applied to the disk is proportional to the speed.

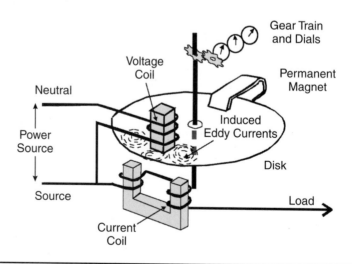

Figure 20–2 Turning the meter disk.

Moving the magnet outward or inward on the disk, or installing a shunt that bypasses part of the flux of the magnet field, can make adjustments to the braking effect. Changing the braking effect is known as the "full-load" meter adjustment.

Elements of a Meter

20.4.5 One current coil and one potential coil working together to turn one disk define one element in an electromechanical meter (Figure 20–3). One element can measure the current and voltage of a two-wire service. Three- and four-wire services require more meter elements. The general rule of thumb is that there is a need for one less element than the number of wires in the service to be measured.

In an electronic meter, the measuring element produces an output pulse. When the energy flowing through the meter increases, the number of pulses increases.

Kh Constant

20.4.6 A meter is designed to have a disk rotate within a certain optimum speed to save wear and tear on the meter. A meter is rated for a certain range of expected load, and the gearing between the disk and the register is set up to control the disk speed.

The *Kh constant,* also known as the *test constant,* is a constant that relates the number of disk rotations to the load being registered. The value of the Kh constant is the watt-hours per turn of the disk. For example, when a meter nameplate shows a Kh of 7.2, it means that 7.2 watt-hours have been used with one rotation of a disk, or 1,000 revolutions of the disk = 7.2 kilowatt-hours. In an electronic meter the Kh constant is a given value in watt-hours of one pulse issued by the meter.

Kr Constant

20.4.7 While the Kh constant regulates the speed of the disk rotation, the *Kr constant* regulates the speed of the register. A meter is designed to have the register show the amount of energy used over a certain period of time. A meter is rated for a certain range of expected load, and the register should show the amount of energy used without repeating between-meter-reading intervals.

The Kr constant, also known as the *meter multiplier,* is a number that represents the ratio between the register gear train and the value registered on the meter dial. A Kr or multiplier of 10 would mean that the amount of energy consumed by the customer is ten times the amount shown on the register.

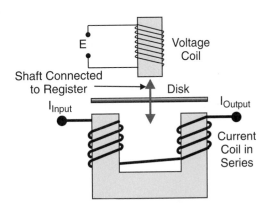

Figure 20–3 One element of a meter.

A-Base Meter

20.4.8 A revenue meter must be connected into a service so that the current coils are in series and the voltage coil is in parallel. A bottom-connected or a front-connected meter or an *A-base meter* must have the input and output leads wired into the meter (Figure 20–4). When connecting an A-base meter under live conditions, it is critical to connect the current in series. A parallel connection would put a voltage across the low-resistance current coil and result in an explosive dead short. An A-base meter is readily removable. Most A-base meters are used with instrument transformers.

S-Base Meter

20.4.9 A *socket-connected meter—S-base—*is plugged into a meter base that has been prewired to match the lugs of the meter to be installed (Figure 20–5). Most self-contained meters are S-base.

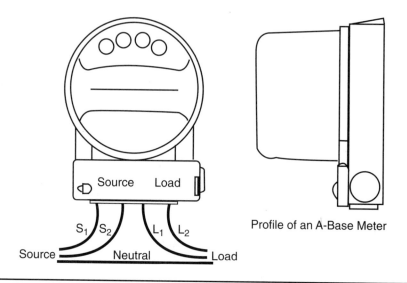

Figure 20–4 A-base meter.

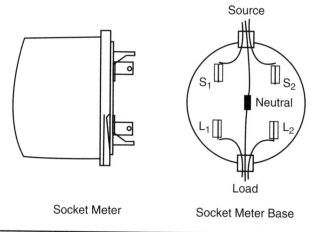

Figure 20–5 Socket-base meter.

The meter is often installed with the top incoming lugs alive. If the meter base is not wired correctly or if there is a short circuit in the customer's wiring, the installation of the meter will energize the short circuit. The integrity of the customer wiring should be tested to avoid having the meter explode during the installation.

20.5 Single-Phase Metering

Single-Phase Meter

20.5.1 Most residential and smaller businesses are supplied with a single-phase service.

There are a lot of different revenue meters and a lot of data that must be recorded when one is being installed. Single-phase meters can be self-contained, transformer-type, demand, A-base (bottom connected), S-base, two-wire, three-wire, 100-amp, 200-amp, various multipliers, and so on.

Figure 20–6 shows the typical workings of a single-phase, two-wire, A-base meter.

Two-Wire or Three-Wire Service

20.5.2 On a standard North American single-phase service, the service and the meter are either two-wire or three-wire.

A two-wire service, as metered in Figure 20–7, consists of a 120-volt leg and a neutral. There is no 240-volt supply on a two-wire service. The voltage coil in the meter is energized at 120 volts. Only one current coil is needed.

A three-wire service is a 120/240-volt service. The voltage coil in the meter is connected across 240 volts. The load on the two legs of the service will not normally be equal and, therefore, two current coils are needed, one for each leg of the service.

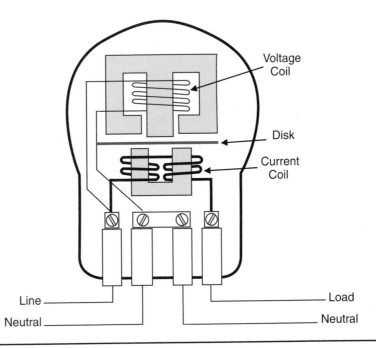

Figure 20–6   A single-phase, two-wire, A-base meter.

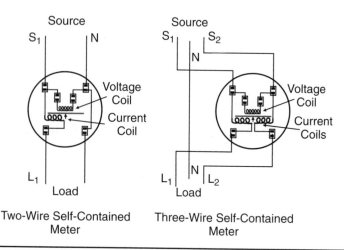

Figure 20–7 Two-wire and three-wire meters.

Checking Load on a Meter to Allow Safe Removal

20.5.3 An uncontrollable electrical flash can occur when a socket-based meter is removed under load. Some utilities allow a meter to be removed if the load is 10 kilowatts or less.

Table 20–2 can be used to determine whether a load is more or less than 10 kilowatts. Count the number of disk revolutions in 30 seconds and, with reference to the meter (Kh), a higher number of disk revolutions than shown on the chart means that the load is more than 10 kilowatts.

For example, the disk of a meter with a Kh of 7.2 will rotate 11 times in 30 seconds to register a load of 10 kilowatts.

When the load is more than 10 kilowatts, the customer's main disconnect should be opened before removing the meter.

TABLE 20–2 Ten-Kilowatt Load

Kh	Time in Seconds	Disk Revolutions
0.36	30	231
0.6	30	138
0.66	30	126
0.72	30	115
2.0	30	41
3.0	30	27
3.33	30	25
3.6	30	23
6.0	30	14
7.2	30	11

Calculating Load, Using the Meter Spin Test

20.5.4 On occasion, it can be beneficial to know the actual instantaneous power demand used by a customer.

The instantaneous kW demand being registered by a self-contained meter can be determined by the following formula:

$$kW = \frac{3.6 \times Kh \times Rev.}{Sec.}$$

where
3.6 = the number of seconds per hour ÷ 1,000
Kh = the meter constant found on the meter nameplate
Rev. = the number of disk revolutions (choose 10 for easier calculations)
Sec. = time in seconds for the total number of revolutions counted

The meter multiplier (Kr constant) on a self-contained meter does not affect the spinning of the disk and is, therefore, not applicable to this formula.

To determine the load registered by a transformer-rated meter, multiply the answer in the preceding formula by the product of the current transformer (CT) ratio, voltage transformer (VT) ratio, and meter multiplier.

Tests before Installing a Meter

20.5.5 A socket-connected meter (S-base) is plugged into a meter base which has been prewired to match the lugs of the meter to be installed. The meter is often installed with the top incoming lugs alive. Many S-base meters are self-contained, which means that the installation or removal of the meter is like closing or opening a switch. There is a greater risk that a fault will be explosive if the service is fed from a large transformer over a short distance on large service conductors.

If the meter installation is protected on the source side by the customer's main switch, open the switch before installing or removing the meter. On installations where the utility transformer is the source and it is impractical or seemingly unnecessary to open the transformer, test the integrity of the customer wiring to reduce the risk of accidentally installing the meter on a short circuit or picking up an excessive load. Before energizing a service with a socket-base meter, test at the meter base to ensure that there is no short circuit or backfeed in the customer's wiring. The insulation tester method and the voltmeter method described here apply to the 120/240-volt meter base shown in Figure 20–8 and the 120/208-volt meter base fed from a 208-volt network shown in Figure 20–9.

Insulation Tester Method

A 500-volt insulation tester, which is like an ohmmeter, can be used at the meter base (Figures 20–8 and 20–9) to test for a short circuit. If the customer's main disconnect is open, there should be an infinity reading between L_1 and L_2, as well as between L_1 and neutral and L_2 and neutral.

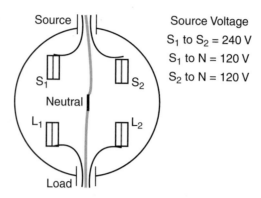

Figure 20–8 A 120/240-volt single-phase three-wire meter base.

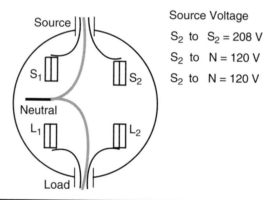

Figure 20–9 A self-contained 120/208-volt single-phase three-wire meter base.

Voltmeter Method

1. A voltage check between L_1 and L_2 and the neutral will confirm that the service is not fed back from another source.

2. With the source side alive, and the customer's disconnect open, there should be no voltage present between the source terminals, S_1 or S_2, and the load terminals, L_1 and L_2. A voltage reading other than 0 means that there is a connected load or a load wire is shorted to the neutral or ground.

3. To check for a short between the two load wires, install a temporary jumper (some utilities use a special fused jumper) between L_1 and the neutral. The voltage between S_1 and L_2 should read 0 volts. A voltage reading other than 0 will mean that there is a connected load or a phase-to-phase short.

4. To check for a short between the two load wires, install a temporary jumper (some utilities use a special fused jumper) between L_1 and the neutral. The voltage between S_1 and L_2 should read zero volts. A voltage reading other than zero will mean that there is a connected load or a phase-to-phase short.

Checking a 120/240-Volt Service with Super Beast

20.5.6 The Super Beast is an instrument that can be used to check out a service at the meter base (Figure 20–10 in Table 20–3). It imposes an artificial unbalanced load on the service at the meter base. This will test the customer wiring from the meter base to an open main breaker and will test the source-side service wires. A voltage drop of 5 to 7 volts is an indication of trouble. The Super Beast is also a useful tool when investigating a trouble call with bright lights in part of a house and dim lights in the other part.

Test for Three-Phase Wye Service Using the Super Beast

20.5.7 The Super Beast can be used on 120/208 wye systems. A portable meter-base adapter is used between the Super Beast and the three-phase meter base (Figure 20–11 in Table 20–3). Connect the meter-base adapter to the back of the Super Beast. Install the green neutral clip of the Super Beast to the neutral bolt of the meter-base adapter. The Super Beast is not designed for use on a three-phase delta circuit.

1. Connect the clips of the meter-base adapter to the neutral and line 1 and line 2 in the meter base.

2. Take readings on line 1 and line 2. The meter-reading interpretation is the same as for the preceding 120/240-volt single-phase procedure.

3. Move one clip lead from either line 1 or line 2 to line 3 and again interpret the meter readings as for the 120/240-volt single-phase procedure.

20.6 Polyphase Metering

Three-Phase Metering

20.6.1 *Polyphase metering* refers to energy metering on more than a one-phase service. A powerline worker normally refers to it as three-phase metering.

Three-phase energy could be measured by metering each phase separately and calculating the resultant total amount of energy used. Three-phase power, however, is normally measured with one unit, which saves space, connections, and calculating the total energy from three separate readings.

The principle of a three-phase meter is similar to a single-phase meter. The meter will have three current coils, one for each phase, connected in series with the load. It will have at least one voltage coil connected between two of the phases.

Three-phase meters, like single-phase meters, can be self-contained, transformer rated, demand, primary, or secondary, A-base or S-base.

Elements in a Three-Phase Meter

20.6.2 One current coil and one potential coil working together to turn one disk are defined as one element in a meter. Two-, three-, and four-wire services require more meter elements. The general rule of thumb is that energy can be metered with one less element than the number of wires in the service.

A four-wire, three-phase service can be measured with a three-element meter, which will have three current coils, three potential coils, and three disks.

Another variation for metering a four-wire, three-phase service is a 2 1/2-element meter, as shown in Figure 20–12. This meter measures the current in all three phases, but the voltage is measured from two phases. The voltage must be reasonably balanced in all three phases for this metering to be accurate.

TABLE 20–3 How to Use the Super Beast

Job Steps	Additional Information

1. Remove the kilowatt-hour meter and inspect the meter base. Connect the green clip to the neutral and insert the Super Beast into the meter base.

Figure 20–10 Super Beast instrumentation.

2. Push the switch to the left and read the meters.

If the left meter reads 120 volts, *then* the left conductor is okay.

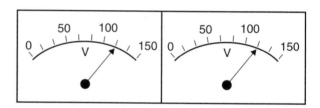

If only the left meter drops, *then* the left conductor is open.

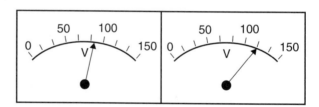

If the left meter drops and the right meter increases, *then* the neutral is open.

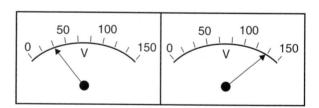

3. Push the switch to the right and read the meters.

If the right meter reads 120 volts, *then* the right conductor is okay.

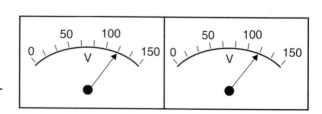

Figure 20–11 Meter readings on Super Beast.

Job Steps	Additional Information
If only the right meter drops, *then* the right conductor is open.	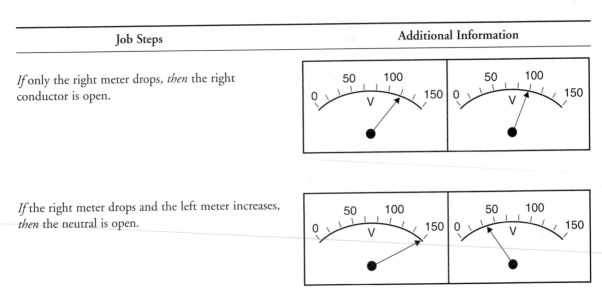
If the right meter drops and the left meter increases, *then* the neutral is open.	

Element Arrangement

20.6.3 The elements in a meter can be vertically arranged (as seen in Figure 20–12) or horizontally arranged (as seen in Figure 20–13). The arrangement can also be set up to turn one, two, or three disks.

Figure 20–13 shows a horizontal, three-element meter that can register the energy of a three-phase, four-wire service with a single disk.

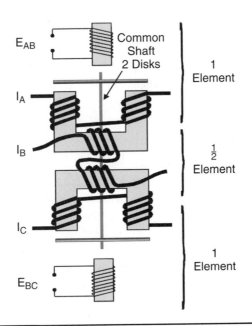

Figure 20–12 A four-wire, 2 1/2-element meter.

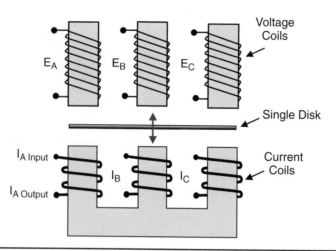

Figure 20–13 A single-disk, three-element horizontal meter.

Making Metering Connections

20.6.4 The connections to a meter follow certain principles. Variations depend on the manufacturer and regulatory agencies. Drawings should be consulted when making connections to a three-phase meter because a mistake can lead to awkward circumstances for a utility.

- For each phase, the source wires to the current coil and the voltage coil must be the same polarity.

- The load wires from the potential coil must have a polarity opposite the polarity of the current coil. In other words, depending on the type of service and meter, the load side of the potential coil must be connected to another phase or to the neutral.

- Each current coil must be connected in series with the load.

- Each potential coil must be connected in parallel, like a voltmeter.

- The color coding of the wiring must be followed.

- The three phases must be in a proper phase rotation.

Electronic Metering

20.6.5 The electronic (static or solid state) revenue meter will eventually take over from the electromagnetic meter. A multitude of measurements can be programmed into an electronic meter. It is also more suitable for automatic meter-reading systems.

In an electronic meter, the current and voltage act on solid-state (electronic) metering elements to produce an output pulse. A pulse initiator produces contact closures (pulses) proportional to the watt-hours being measured.

The electronic meter illustrated in Figure 20–14 is a three-element, four-wire, transformer-rated meter. A typical electronic meter can be programmed to carry out many functions:

- It can be a multirate meter with more than one readout, each becoming operative at a specified time corresponding to a different tariff rate.

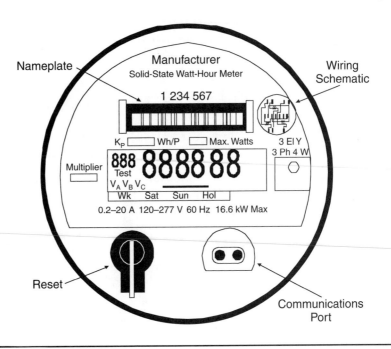

Figure 20–14   A three-phase, four-wire, transformer-rated electronic meter.

- It can be used to check the voltage and current in each phase, the power factor on each phase, and instantaneous kilowatt and kilovolt-ampere for each phase.

- The meter can check itself for proper function, much like a computer checks itself out. It also can check itself for proper installation, such as phase rotation.

- It can register the time of use, along with taking into account holidays and weekends.

- It can register kilowatt demand and kilovolt-ampere demand.

- It is easily adapted to all the benefits associated with automatic meter reading by access through the communications port.

Installing a Three-Phase Self-Contained Meter

20.6.6 Installing a self-contained meter is like closing a switch and making sure you are not closing in on a fault. Carry out the insulation tester method or the voltmeter method to ensure that no short circuit is present in the customer's wiring.

The live installation of a self-contained meter on services more than 240 volts should be avoided. If a meter is accidently installed where a customer's wiring is faulted, a very explosive fault could occur because of the potentially high fault current available.

The meter base shown in Figure 20–15 is for a 120/208-volt, three-phase service. This type of service, especially at higher voltages, often has a main switch on the source side of the meter. The first option should be to isolate the service at the switch instead of energizing the service with the meter.

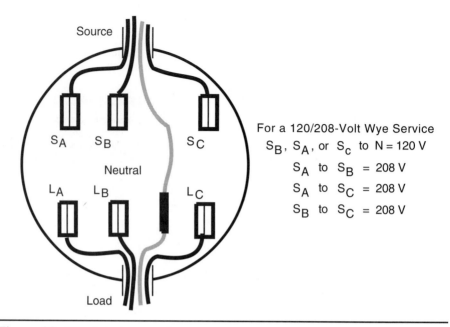

For a 120/208-Volt Wye Service

S_B, S_A, or S_C to N = 120 V

S_A to S_B = 208 V

S_A to S_C = 208 V

S_B to S_C = 208 V

Figure 20–15   A 4 wire meter base

Insulation Tester Method

To test the meter base shown in Figure 20–15, a 500-volt insulation tester can be used to test for a short circuit. If the customer's main disconnect is open, there should be an infinity reading between L_A and L_B, L_A and L_C, L_B and L_C, as well as between the neutral and each of L_A, L_B, and L_C.

Voltmeter Method

1. A voltage check between L_A, L_B, and L_C and the neutral will confirm that the service is not fed back from another source.

2. When testing the meter base in Figure 20–15, with the source side alive and the customer's disconnect open, there should be no voltage between any source terminal—for example, S_A and each of the load terminals L_A, L_B, and L_C. A voltage reading other than 0 means that there is a connected load, the service is alive from another source, or a load wire is shorted to the neutral or ground.

3. To check for a short between any of the three load wires, install a temporary jumper between L_A and the neutral. The voltage between S_A and L_B or L_C should read 0 volts. Similarly, install a jumper between L_C and the neutral, and the voltage between S_A and L_A or L_B should read 0 volts. A voltage reading other than 0 means that there is a connected load or a phase-to-phase short.

Testing the integrity of the customer's service as shown for the meter base in Figure 20–15 can be adapted to other types of meter bases. Variations of these meter bases will be found in the field but, in each three-phase meter base, the A phase will be the left element, the C phase will be the right element, and the B phase will be the middle element.

Testing the integrity of the customer's service as shown for the meter base in Figure 20–15 can be adapted to other types of meter bases. Variations of these meter bases will be found in the field but, in each three-phase meter base, "A" phase will be the left element, "C" phase the right element, and "B" phase will be the middle element.

20.7 Transformer-Rated Metering

Transformer-Rated Meter Use

20.7.1 A transformer-rated revenue meter is used where the voltage and/or current is too high or impractical for a self-contained meter. A transformer-rated meter measures a current and voltage that have been stepped down by instrument transformers. The secondary of a voltage transformer (VT or PT) and a current transformer (CT) is an accurate representation of the primary voltage and primary current being measured.

The installation shown in Figure 20–16 has a current transformer in series with each phase. It has two voltage transformers that measure the phase-to-neutral voltage on two phases. There is a test block that provides access to do metering tests and to provide fuse protection. Figure 20–17 shows a three-phase, 120/208-volt, transformer-rated metering installation with current transformers.

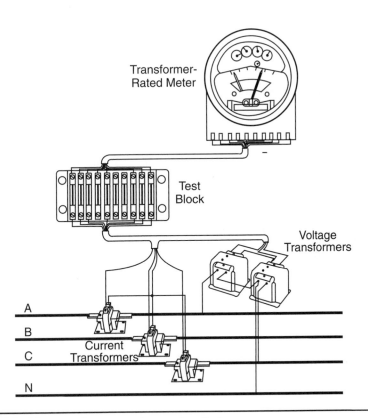

Figure 20–16 Transformer-rated meter installation.

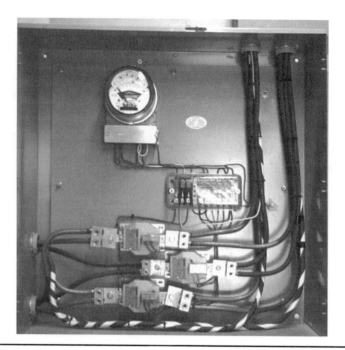

Figure 20–17 Three-phase metering cabinet.

Voltage Transformer

20.7.2 A voltage transformer (VT) is used when the energy to be measured is supplied at a high voltage, such as subtransmission, primary, or high secondary voltage. A voltage-transformer output supplies a voltage at a manageable level to a revenue meter, typically rated at 240 or 120 volts.

A multiplier equal to the turns ratio of the transformer calculates the actual voltage of the circuit being measured. For example, a 4,800/120-volt VT has a multiplier of 40:1.

Figure 20–18 shows how a voltage transformer and a current transformer are shown in technical drawings.

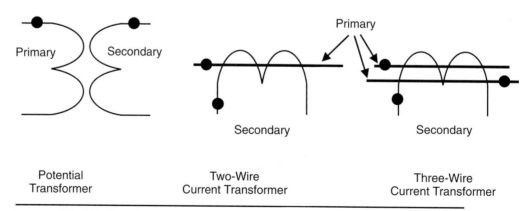

Figure 20–18 Drawings representing instrument transformers.

Current Transformer

20.7.3 A current transformer reduces the current to a transformer-rated meter. A transformer-rated meter is typically designed to operate at a maximum of 5 amperes. A low current allows the use of small wires with minimal losses in the metering circuit. Current transformers for metering are two-wire or three-wire, bar-type, donut-type, or bushing designs.

The two-wire current transformers (CTs) shown in Figure 20–19 have one primary and one secondary winding. The conductor running through the donut-type CT is considered the primary winding. This type of CT is installed in each leg of a 120/240-volt service or on each phase of a three-phase service.

Three-Wire Current Transformer

One CT can be used with a three-wire, 120/240-volt service. Both 120-volt conductors go through one CT. To have the *current* in the two opposite-polarity 120-volt legs go through the CT in the same direction, the two wires go through the CT from opposite directions. The current from the two legs are added together to double the secondary current. For example, a 200/5 CT becomes a 200/10 CT with this setup.

A three-wire CT used on a 120/240-volt service has two primary windings and one secondary winding. In Figure 20–20, the three-wire CT is actually a two-wire

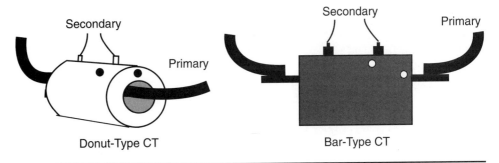

Donut-Type CT

Bar-Type CT

Figure 20–19 Two types of two-wire current transformers.

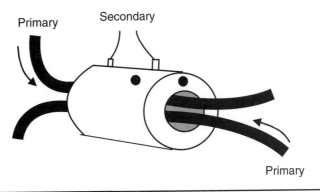

Figure 20–20 A three-wire current transformer.

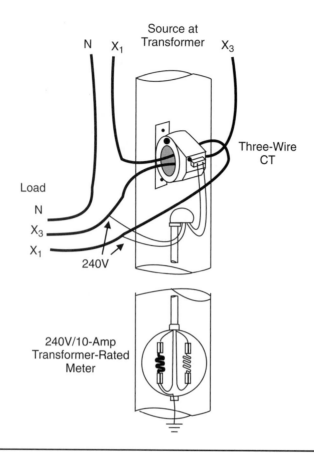

Figure 20–21   A three-wire CT on a 120/240-volt service.

CT with two wires going through it acting as two primary windings. The secondary current from the CT represents the sum of the two 120-volt legs of the service.

The type of service shown in Figure 20–21 is a 120/240-volt service metered at a customer transformer pole. This central metering installation measures the energy at one location and then allows for services to go from this pole to a house, a barn, and other buildings owned by the customer. With this type of service, a customer can install a smaller service entrance panel in each building instead of installing one large-capacity service entrance to feed all the buildings.

Polarity Markings

As with all transformers, the polarity of an instrument transformer must be known and marked on the transformer. For example, when the current enters at the marked primary terminal, the marked secondary terminal is in phase with the primary. The polarity of the primary and secondary terminals of instrument transformers is normally marked with a large dot.

High-Voltage Hazard with Current Transformers

A current transformer is like other transformers:

The input V × I = The output V × I

When the current is stepped down, the voltage is stepped up at the same ratio. The voltage would be expected to be high at the terminals, but when there is a load, such as a meter or relay, a voltage drop brings the voltage to a safe level. When the load is removed, the voltage at the secondary terminals and at terminals where relays are installed will be very high. This high voltage can puncture the insulation of the current transformer, and it is a dangerous shock hazard to any person in contact with the secondary circuit.

Therefore, before a load is removed from an energized current transformer, the secondary terminals must be shorted out. Typically, a shorting device at the secondary terminals is part of the current transformer design and can be closed safely while the load is still on the secondary. There are many different types of current transformer designs. If you are uncertain about how to short out the secondary, get help.

The meter base for a socket-mounted, transformer-rated meter often has an automatic shorting device that will close the metering circuit when the meter is removed.

A Multiplier on a Current Transformer

When an instrument transformer is used, the meter is reading and registering a representative voltage and/or current, and, therefore, the reading must be multiplied by a meter multiplier to obtain the actual status of the energy used.

The ratio of the current transformer (CT) and voltage transformer (VT) must also be calculated into the total. The VT multiplier is always equal to the transformer ratio. The CT multiplier depends on how the CT is wired. A bar-type CT multiplier is always equal to the transformer ratio. When one wire goes straight through a donut CT, the multiplier is the same as the transformer ratio. For example, a CT with a ratio of 400:5 (80:1) will have a multiplier of 80.

A CT multiplier can be reduced by looping the primary through the CT more than once. For example, when the primary is looped through the CT twice (as shown in Figure 20–22), the secondary current is doubled. A 400:5 CT will

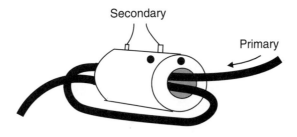

Looped Primary Conductor

Figure 20–22 A double-looped primary.

become a 400:10 CT (200:5 or 40:1), which changes the multiplier to 40. The secondary of a 400:5 CT is rated to 5 amperes. Therefore, a double-looped primary should be used only where the primary is 200 amperes or less to limit the secondary to 5 amperes.

Table 20–4   Specific Hazards of Installing and Removing Meters

Specific Hazards	Barriers
Striking or pounding on the glass cover can break the glass and cause severe cuts.	Use a meter installer and removal tool (Figure 20–23) on S-base meters to reduce the risk of injury from breaking glass.
A high explosive fault current can be available at a meter installation, especially at an installation fed from a large transformer and a short run of large service conductors. Any accidental arc can be explosive.	Using an insulation tester or the voltmeter method, conduct tests to ensure there is no fault in the service. Use a meter installer and removal tool (Figure 20–23) on S-base meters to reduce the risk of injury from explosive faults. Wear eye protection and flame-resistant clothing.
Unknown potential shorting hazards, such as a broken meter lug or dropping an excessive load, can cause an explosive fault while removing a socket-based meter.	Check the load on the meter, as per Section 20.5.3. If facilities are available, open a source switch, bypass the load, or have the load reduced. Use a meter installer and removal tool (Figure 20–23) on S-base meters to reduce the risk of injury from explosive faults. Wear eye protection and flame-resistant clothing.
Picking up or dropping a load with a 480/277- or 600/348-volt, self-contained meter can cause an explosive arc because the available fault current can be very high at these voltages.	Avoid picking up or dropping load with a 480/277- or 600/348-volt, self-contained meter. Avoid picking up or dropping load with any bypass facility at these voltages. Use a meter installer and removal tool (Figure 20–23) on a 480/277- or 600/348-volt, self-contained meter if it is necessary to install it alive. Wear eye protection and flame-resistant clothing.
There is a high voltage in the meter base when a transformer meter is removed.	Unless there is an automatic shorting device in the meter base, short out the CTs before removing the transformer-rated meter.
A third party makes contact with an unprotected meter base.	If the meter base (socket) is to be left energized, install a meter or cover and seal before leaving the site to protect the public.

Figure 20–23   A meter installer and removal tool.

Review Questions

1. Energy consumption is the volts × amperes used by a customer. What is the largest variable measured by a kWh revenue meter?

2. What is meant by peak demand?

3. Why would a utility charge extra for peak demand?

4. Revenue metering involves the measurement of one or more of the three kinds of power and/or energy used by a customer. What are they?

5. Why is a transformer-rated meter used for some services?

6. How many elements are in a meter that is normally used in a three-wire service?

7. The disk of a meter with a Kh constant of 3.6 rotates 100 times. How much energy was used?

8. How much power is being used by a customer when a meter with a Kh of 7.2 has 10 rotations of its disk in 40 seconds?

9. How can one CT be used to meter a 120/240-volt, three-wire service?

10. Why is there a high-voltage hazard when there is current flowing through the primary of a current transformer while the secondary is open circuited?

Appendix

TABLE A-1 Calculations Involving Power

To Find	Direct Current	Single-Phase AC	Three-Phase Wye AC
Kilowatts	$\dfrac{I \times E}{1{,}000}$	$\dfrac{I \times E \times pf}{1{,}000}$	$\dfrac{I \times E \times 1.73 \times pf}{1{,}000}$
Kilovolt-Amperes (kVA)		$\dfrac{I \times E}{1{,}000}$	$\dfrac{I \times E \times 1.73}{1{,}000}$
Amperes (when kW are known)	$kW \times \dfrac{1{,}000}{E}$	$kW \times \dfrac{1{,}000}{E \times pf}$	$\dfrac{kW \times 1{,}000}{1.73 \times E \times pf}$
Amperes (when kVA is known)		$\dfrac{kVA \times 1{,}000}{E}$	$\dfrac{kVA \times 1{,}000}{1.73 \times E}$

The preceeding table gives formulas used to calculate power in three-phase and single-phase circuits. Calculations for field applications use the kilovolt-ampere formulas.

Calculations involving three-phase power use line-to-line (phase-to-phase) voltage.

The square root of 3 is normally used at the value of 1.73.

A.1.1 Calculations with "Handy Numbers"

To be able to do the preceeding calculations quickly in the field a "Handy Number" can be used for approximations.

Approximate kVA = Amperes × "Handy Number"
Approximate amperes per phase = kVA ÷ "Handy Number"

TABLE A–2 **Examples of "Handy Numbers" for Some Voltage Systems**

	Calculating Approximate Loads with "Handy Numbers"			
	3-Phase kV	"Handy Number"	1-Phase kV	"Handy Number"
kVA = Amps × "Handy Number" *or* Amps per Phase = kVA ÷ "Handy Number"	230	400		
	115	200		
	69	120		
	46	80		
kVA = Amps × "Handy Number" *or* Amps per Phase = kVA ÷ "Handy Number"	25	40	14.4	14
	12.5	22	7.2	7
	8.32	14	4.8	5
	0.208	0.36	0.12	0.12

To calculate the "Handy Number" for other voltage systems:

- For three-phase lines, the "Handy Number" = Ø-to-Ø voltage × 1.73 ÷ 1,000
- For single-phase lines, the "Handy Number" = Ø-to-neutral voltage ÷ 1,000

A.1.2 Examples Using "Handy Numbers"

Question: One phase of an 8.3/4.8 kV-feeder has 80 amperes more load than the other two phases. To balance the feeder, how many kVA should be transferred to the other two phases?

Answer: Using a "Handy Number," which is 5 for a 4.8-kV single-phase line, × 80 amperes = 400 kVA. Therefore, 200 kVA should be transferred to each of the other two phases.

Question: Load on each of the three phases of a 120/208, 50 kVA pad-mount transformer bank are 150 A, 170 A, and 140 A. Is the transformer overloaded?

Answer: The average load on the three phases is 150 + 170 + 140 ÷ 3 = 153 Amperes. Using the "Handy Number," which is 0.36 for 120/208 volt service × 153 = 55 kilovolt-amperes. The transformer is only slightly above its rating, but the load should be balanced more between the three phases to prevent one transformer winding from being overloaded.

TABLE A–3 Metric Conversion: Linear

To Convert	Multiply By	To Obtain
inches	25.4	millimeters
inches	2.5	centimeters
feet	0.3	meters
yards	0.9	meters
miles	1.6	kilometers

TABLE A–4 Metric Conversion: Weight

To Convert	Multiply By	To Obtain
fluid ounces (U.S.)	28.4	grams
pounds	0.45	kilograms
ton	0.9	tonne

Table A–5 Metric Conversion: Volume

To Convert	Multiply By	To Obtain
fluid ounces (U.S.)	29.6	milliliters
1 gallon (U.S.) (8.3 lbs.)	3.8	liters
1 gallon (Imperial) (10 lbs.)	4.5	liters
1 quart (U.S.)	0.95	liters
1 quart (Imperial)	1.1	liters
cubic yard	0.8	cubic meters
cord (128 cu. ft.)	3.6	cubic meters

TABLE A–6 Metric Conversions: Miscellaneous

To Convert	Multiply By	To Obtain
BTU/hr	0.2931	watts
horsepower (hp)	746	watts
pounds per sq. in.	6.9	kilopascal (kPa)
acre	0.4	hectare

TABLE A–7 Speeds

Speed of Light	Speed of Sound
300,000 km/sec. 186,000 mi/sec.	1,256 ft/sec. = 382.8 m/sec. = 856.3 mi/hr. = 1,378.1 km/hr.

TABLE A–8 Temperature Conversions

From Fahrenheit to Celsius	From Celsius to Fahrenheit
To convert from degrees Fahrenheit to degrees Celsius, subtract 32 degrees from the temperature and multiply by 1.8.	To convert from degrees Celsius to degrees Fahrenheit, multiply the temperature by 1.8 and add 32 degrees.

TABLE A–9 Metric System Prefixes

Tera	1,000,000,000,000 (10^{12})	Deci	0.1 (10^{-1})
Giga	1,000,000,000 (10^{9})	Centi	0.01 (10^{-2})
Mega	1,000,000 (10^{6})	Milli	0.001 (10^{-3})
Kilo	1,000 (10^{3})	Micro	0.000 001 (10^{-6})
Hecto	100 (10^{2})	Nano	0.000 000 001 (10^{-9})
Deca	10 (10^{1})	Pico	0.000 000 000 001 (10^{-12})

TABLE A–10 Geometric Figures

Area of a Circle	Circumference of a Circle	Area of a Triangle	Area of of a Sphere	Volume of a Sphere
πr^2 ($\pi = 3.14$)	πD or $2\pi r$	Base $\times \frac{1}{2}$ Height	πD^2 or $4\pi r^2$	$D^3 \times 0.5236$

Index

A

A-base meter, 640
AC transmission, 99
Active power, 97
Adaptive VAR compensators (AVC), 426
Additive or subtractive polarity, 380–381
Aerial devices, 489–493, 551–552, 565–566
Air-blast circuit breakers, 284
Air-break switches, 590
Air-insulated substation, 589
Airbrake inspection, 468, 470
Airport runway lighting, 621–623
Alternating current (AC)
  advantages of, 85
  amperage lagging voltage, 92, 93
  apparent power, 97
  average value, 89
  capacitance (C), 93–94, 97
  capacitive load, 91
  capacitive reactance (X_c), 91, 95
  capacitive resistance, 94
  capacitors, 94, 95
  characteristics of, 85–86
  circuits in phase with each other, 90
  current and voltage, rise and fall of, 87, 88
  effect of AC frequency on electrical transmission, 100
  effective value, 89, 90
  frequency, 86
  frequency on reactance, effect of, 96
  generation of, 86–87
  impedance, 91
  induction, 91, 92, 96
  inductive load, 90
  inductive reactance (X_L), 91, 92, 93
  instantaneous value, 89
  loads, 90–91
  out of phase, 90
  peak value, 89
  in phase with each other, voltage and current in, 90
  power factor, 98
  power factor correction, 99
  power triangle, 98
  reactance, 90, 91
  reactive power, 97–98
  resistance, 91, 96
  resistive loads, 90
  sine wave, use of a, 88–89
  values and voltage of AC, 89
  wave, AC represented by a, 87
American National Standards Institute (ANSI), 71
Ammeter, 72, 445–446
Amorphous, 386
Amperage lagging voltage, 92, 93
Amperes, 69, 113
Anchor pulling eye, using an, 512, 513
Angular displacements
  delta secondary, 408
  delta-wye transformer banks, 407
  substation transformers, 407–408
  wye-delta transformer banks, 407
  wye secondary, 407
Anodic, 343
Apparent power, 97, 634
Arc hazards, 265–266, 267
Arc-strangler switch, 297–298
Arrestors, lightning, 334
Asbestos, cables wrapped with, 14
Automatic meter reading, 637
Autotransformer, 433
Autotransformer ballasts, 615
Average value, 89

B

Backfeed, 379
Ball-and-socket studs, 352
Bandwidth setting, 432
Banked secondaries, 395–396
Barber chair, 583

Barehand work, 121, 550–554

Basal spraying, 561

Basic-impulse level (BIL), 335

Biological hazards, identification and protection from, 29

Biomass, burning of, 57

Bisect tension, calculating, 524–526

Blackout of 2003, 306–307

Blackouts, 61, 62

Blakes hitch, 573

Blocks, working, 510–511

Body belts, sizing, 36–37

Bonding principle, 348, 353–358, 373

Boom contact, 136–137, 138, 139

Boom contamination meter, 121

Boom-equipped vehicle
contamination, monitoring boom, 483–484
electrical protection for insulated booms, 482–485
electrical protection for noninsulated booms, 478–480, 482
grounding procedures, 480
stabilization procedures, 475–478

Bowline, 499

Bowline bend, 500, 501

Bowline on a bight, 500, 501, 570

Bracket grounds, working and grounding between, 360

Braid-on-braid rope, 497

Braided rope, 496

Briefing, job, 14–15

Brownouts, 61

Brush control, 560

Bucket, working up in a, 38–39

Bucket rescue, 43–44

Bucking a tree trunk, 585–586

Bus, 58

C

Cable-separable connectors (elbows), 295–296

Candela, 608

Capacitance (C), 93–94, 97

Capacitive load, 91

Capacitive reactance in series, 456

Capacitive reactance (X_c), 91, 94, 95

Capacitive test point, 297, 372

Capacitors, 94, 95, 431, 440–444, 592

Capacity charge, 631

Capstan hoist, using a, 516

Cascading lighting-control system, 619–620

Cathodic, 343, 344

Cavitation, 472

Cellular antenna or microwave dish, working near, 145

Central processing unit (CPU), 268

Chain saw operation, 569, 574–576

Chain saw resistance footwear, 12

Chains, using, 508–510

Chemical effect, 52

Chemical energy, 51

Chemical hazards, protection from, 13–14

Choker hitch, using a, 519

Circuit breakers, 284

Circuit identification, 276–277

Circuit protection
circuit breaker operation, 305–306
corrosion, protection from, 342–344
distribution feeder, specifying protection for a, 313–323
distribution protection, 307–313
downstream fuses, specifying, 320, 322
downstream recloser, specifying, 318–319
feeder study, interpreting a, 316
fuse-saving philosophy, 315
fuse size and speed, specifying, 319–320
high-voltage distribution conversion, 322–323
hydraulic-recloser frame size, specifying a, 316–317
over-current trouble calls, 322, 323
over-voltage protection, 323–337
planning a protection scheme, 313
protection scheme philosophy, 315–316
protection zones, 306

protective relaying, 304–305
purpose of, 303
recloser protection zone, 317–318
recloser speed and operating sequence, specifying, 318
recloser-to-fuse coordination table, 321
relays controlling circuit-breaker operation, 305
sectionalizers, specifying, 322
system grounding for protection, 337–341
time current characteristic (TCC) curve, 318, 321
time-delayed-instant philosophy, 315
transmission system protection, 304–307
trip coil size, specifying, 317

Clamp-on tester, 341, 342

Class C (conductive) hard hats, 11

Class E (electrical) hard hats, 11

Class G (general) hard hats, 11

Clearance, 17

Climbing methods, 569, 570–573

Clip-on meter, 73

Clove hitch, 500, 501

Cogeneration, 55–56

Cold, working in the, 24–25

Cold load pickup, 74–75

Collapsible bull wheel, using a, 512, 514

Combined-cycle generation, 55

Common mode, 424

Communications cables, working near, 29

Compensation settings, 436

Compensator starter, 376

Conduct, general, 7

Conductance, 77–78

Conductive harmonic interference, 452

Conductor length, calculating, 522

Conductor loss, 386–387

Conductor resistance, 78

Conductor size and length, 427

Confined spaces, working in, 18–21, 23, 24

Connecting different polarities, 381–382

Constant-current transformer, 376

Contamination, monitoring boom, 483–484

Contamination meter readings, 485

Continuity testing, 382

Control switch, 437

Convection thunderstorm, 324–325

Converter stations, 589

Copper loss, 387

Copper-to-aluminum connections, 344

Core loss, 386

Corona discharge, 465

Corona ring, 551

Coupling capacitive voltage transformer (CCVT), 60

Cover bushing transformer, 393

Cover-up equipment, 540–542

CPR summary, 42

Cradle to cradle rule, 9

Culture of line work, 7–8

Current and voltage, rise and fall of, 87, 88

Current coil, 637, 638

Current flow, direction of, 86

Current limiting fuse, 291–292, 299

Current-limiting fuse protection, 390

Current-limiting reactor, 93

Custom power, supplying, 425

Customer charges, 631

Customer connections, 64

Customer location, 634

Customer service staff, 67

Cutting or joining a grounded connector, 368

Cycles per second, 86

D

DC transmission
advantages of, 100–101
description of transmission lines, 101
disadvantages of, 101
resistance to current flow on DC, 101

submarine transmission lines, 101, 102
underground lines, 101
uses of, 100
working on DC circuits, 102

Dead-front arrestor, 332, 333

Dead-front transformer, grounding a, 371–372, 373

Defective insulators, 465

Defective pedestal-type insulators supporting switchgear, 268

Delta secondary, 408

Delta systems
connections to, 393, 401–402, 403–404
current in a delta system, 108
ground fault protection in a delta circuit, 109
return flow in a delta circuit, 108–109
voltage in a delta system, 108

Delta-wye transformer banks, 405, 407

Derrick operations, 474, 480–481, 485–489

Design engineers and technicians, 67

Design factor, 495

Dielectric overshoe footwear (Electrical Hazard (EH) Footwear), 12

Differential mode, 424

Digger derrick. *See* Derrick operations

Dip pole, 370

Direct-bury system, 66

Directional pruning, 557

Discharge resistors, 444

Dissimilar metals in circuit, 342–343

Dissolved gas analysis (DGA), 595

Distribution bracket grounding procedure, 361–362, 364–365

Distribution-class arrestor, 332–333

Distribution cutout, operating a, 289–290

Distribution equipotential grounding/bonding procedure, 361

Distribution feeder voltage, 430–431

Distribution protection, 307–313

Distribution static compensator (DSTATCOM), 425

Distribution substation, 63, 64, 307, 308, 429, 587

Distribution system, 51, 62, 63, 64

Distribution system workers, 67

Distribution transformers, 63, 64

Distribution voltages (kV), 72

Diversity, 75

Dose, 144

Double braid rope, 497

Down-pull, vertical load applied by a, 524

Downstream fuses, 313, 320, 322

Downstream multishot protection, 312

Downstream recloser, specifying, 318–319

Downstream sectionalizers, 312–313

Driving hazards, 471

Drop crotch pruning, 557

Drowning, protection from, 25–26

Dry-well canister fuses, 298–299

Duct and maintenance hole (manhole) system, 66

E

E (electromotive force), 76, 77, 81, 91

Earth resistance testers, 76

Earth return system neutral, 110

Eddy current, 386

Effective value, 89, 90

Efficiency, transformer, 387

Electric field, 358

Electric-field (capacitive) induction, 123, 124

Electric field induction, reducing voltage from, 359

Electric fields *versus* magnetic fields, 141

Electric shock, seeking medical attention for, 42–43

Electrical circuits
  connecting a load in series with a
    circuit, 116
  contact, making, 115
  working on or near circuits, 115
Electrical conductive footwear, 12
Electrical current, 69, 72–75
Electrical energy
  alternative sources, 56
  distribution, electrical, 62–67
  generation of, 52–57
  power, electrical, 80–83
  transmission of, 57–62
Electrical-factor distance, 147
Electrical generator, 70
Electrical potential, safety with, 70
Electrical power pools, 61, 62
Electrical power systems
  distribution system, 51
  generation system, 51
  transmission system, 51
Electrical shock resistance footwear
    (ESR), 12
Electrical system emergencies, 49
Electrical units
  ampere, 69
  distribution voltages (kV), 72
  electrical current, 69, 72–75
  electrical potential, safety
    with, 70
  electricity, defined, 69
  electromotive force (emf), 70
  extreme high voltage, 71
  extreme low voltage, 71
  ion, 69
  kilowatt-hour, 70
  nominal voltage, 71
  normal high voltage, 71
  normal low voltage, 71
  ohms, 70
  pressure, 70
  resistance, electrical, 75–80
  subtransmission line voltages
    (kV), 72
  transmission line voltages (kV), 72
  utility operating diagrams, 71
  utility voltages, 72
  utilization voltages (V), 72

voltage, 70, 71
voltage drop, 71
volts, 70
watt, 70
Electrical utility enclosed space
    entry permit, 20
Electromagentic induction, 123
Electromagnetic fields (EMFs)
  cellular antenna or microwave
    dish, working near, 145
  definition of, 139–140
  dose, 144
  electric fields *versus* magnetic
    fields, 141
  electromagnetic spectrum, 140
  health risks, 144
  interest in, 139
  limits of exposure, 133
  measurement of, 142–143
  natural levels, 144
  reducing the strength of EMF, 142
  RF/MW transmitter, induced
    current from a, 145
  sources of power, 141
  ultraviolet radiation (UV), 146
Electromagnetic induction, 347,
    358–360
Electromagnetic microwaves
    (MW), 145
Electromagnetic spectrum, 140
Electromechanical meter, 637
Electromotive force (emf), 70
Electronic meter, 637
Electronic sectionalizer, 289
Electrostatic induction, 347
Elements, 639
Emergencies, managing
  bucket rescue, 43–44
  CPR summary, 42
  electric shock, seeking medical
    attention for, 42–43
  first aid summary, 40–42
  managing and communicating
    emergencies, 40
  pole top, rescue from, 44–47
  substation structure, rescue
    from, 44
  tower top, rescue from, 44

Employee safety responsibilities and
    rights, 3
Employers responsibilities, 2
Enclosed space, working in, 18–21,
    23, 24
Energy charge, 631
Energy consumption, 632
Equipment voltage-time curves,
    335–336
Equipotential bonding, 353–355
Equipotential grounding, 356–357
Equipotential zone, 348
Ergonomic distance, 147
European-style climbers, 33
Expulsion-cutout fuse links, 291
Extended reach rule, 9
Extra high voltage (EHV) lines, 58
Extreme high voltage, 71
Extreme low voltage, 71
Eye protection, 11

F
Fall arrest systems, 31
Fall of potential test, 341
Fall protection systems, 30
Farad, 94
Faraday cage, 125, 550
Fault, protective grounds whipping
    during a, 369
Fault current (short-circuit current),
    75, 311–312
Feed-through, 371
Feeder data, gathering, 313
Feeder information, calculating,
    314–315
Feeder protection, 312
Feeder study, interpreting a, 316
Feeder voltage regulators, 429,
    431–440
Ferroresonance, 454–458
Ferrule, 351
Fiber rope, using, 496–499
Field calculations, 112
Final sag, 527
Fire in the electrical environment
    fighting, 47–48
    fire extinguishers, types of, 48
    water and electricity, 48–49

First aid summary, 40–42

Fission, 54

Fixed charges, 632

Flame-retardant clothing (FR), 12–13

Flash-bang method, 325

Flashover, 328

Fluorescent lamps, 610–612

Foliage spraying, 561

Footwear, wearing safety, 11–12

Forestry crews, 67

Frequency, 86, 96

Friction, effects of, 511–512

Frontal thunderstorm, 324–325

Frostbite, first aid for, 25

Fuel cells, 57

Full-range current-limiting fuse, 292

Fuse-saving philosophy, 315

Fuse size and speed, specifying, 319–320

Fuses, 291–293, 313

G

G (conductance), 77, 78

Gaff gauge, 36

Galvanic corrosion, 343

Galvanic series of metals used in line hardware, 343

Gas-insulated substation, 589

Gas pipelines, working near, 29

Gas turbines, 55

Gaseous-discharge lamps, 610–612

Gauss (Gs), 142

General-purpose current-limiting fuse, 292–293

Generation system, 51

Generator, simple, 53

Geographic based maps, 279, 280

Geomagnetically induced current (GIC), 305

Gigawatt (GW), 82

Gradients when one phase had protective ground installed, 369

Granny knot, 502

Ground cable and clamps, 351

Ground clamp attachment, 371

Ground electrodes, choice of, 136–137

Ground fault interrupter (GFI), 73, 309–310

Ground faults, 127, 128

Ground-gradient effect, 326

Ground gradients, 128–129

Ground-rod resistance, measuring, 341, 342

Ground to ground rule, 8

Ground trip toggle, 288

Ground *versus* neutral connections, 338

Ground wire, 338

Grounding a live circuit, 365

Grounding differences of Wye and Delta, 350

Grounding elbow, 371

Grounding hardware, protective, 350

Grounding principle, 347–348, 370

Grounding sets, inspecting and testing, 348–349

Grounding transformers, 376

Guy tension, calculating, 523

H

Hand line, using a, 514–515

"Handy number" calculations, 112, 113

Harmonic interference, 449, 452–453

Head protection, 11

Hearing protection, wearing, 13

Heat, working in the, 24

Heights, working at

    body belts, sizing, 36–37

    bucket, working up in a, 38–39

    European-style climbers, 33

    fall arrest systems, 31

    fall protection systems, 30

    gaff gauge, 36

    "hitchhiking," 32

    Jelco pole choker, 31

    ladder hazards, 30, 32, 33

    locking snap hook, 38

    pole-climbing fall arrest system, 31

    pole cut-out test, 36

    pole hazards, 30, 34, 38, 39, 40

    pole strap, using a, 32, 37–38

    retractable lanyard, using a, 31

    safety belts, using, 31

    safety concerns, 30

    spur gaff, 34–35

    spurs, climbing with, 30, 34

    suspension system, 31

    tower hazards, 39, 41

    travel restraint system, 31

    work positioning system, 31

Helicopters, safety precautions when working around, 26–28

Henry, 92

Herbicides, use of, 561

Hertz (Hz), 86

High-and low-voltage bus, 591

High-intensity (HI), 611

High leg, 412

High-pressure sodium-vapor (HPS) lamps, 612

High resistance, 78, 79

High-voltage, troubleshooting, 449, 451

High-voltage direct current (HVDC), 100

High-voltage distribution conversion, 322–323

High-voltage environment, electric-field effect in, 124, 125

High-voltage hazard, 626, 628

"Hitchhiking," 32

Horsepower (HP), 82

Hot-line clamp, operating a, 282–283

Hot-line rope, using, 537

Hot-line work

    barehand work, 550–554

    blocking automatic reclosing of protective switchgear, 534

    cover-up equipment, 540–542

    definition of, 531

    hazards, 549

    insulators for breakdown, testing, 535, 536

    load limits, working, 546–547, 546–548

Hot-line work, *Continued*
  minimum approach distance
    (MAD), 532–533, 545
  procedures, 531–532, 545–546
  rope, using hot-line, 537
  rubber-glove work, 538–540,
    542–544
  second point of contact, protec-
    tion from, 532
  secondary, working on a hot,
    537–538
  temporary jumpers, use of, 536
  tool calculations, 547–548, 549
  voltage surge, protection
    from, 534
Hot-stick tester, 552
Human-factor distance, 147
Human-factor minimum approach
    distance, 148
Hydraulic generator, 53
Hydraulic-recloser frame size, speci-
    fying a, 316–317
Hydraulic sectionalizer, 289
Hydraulic system, monitoring a,
    471–475
Hypothermia, first aid for, 25

I

I (electrical current), 72, 76, 77, 80,
    81, 91
Ice, protections while working on,
    25–26
Identification, circuit, 276–277
Impedance, 78, 91, 340, 387
In series, 116
Incandescent lamps, 609–610
Inching method, 282
Incidents and accidents,
    reporting, 7
Independent nature of the work,
    2, 28
Induction, 91, 92, 96, 356
Inductive harmonic interfer-
    ence, 452
Inductive load, 90
Inductive reactance, 78, 455–456
Inductive reactance (X_L), 91, 92, 93
Inductor, 593

Installation tests, 643
Instantaneous value, 89
Instrument transformers, 376
Insulation coordination, 335
Insulation resistance testers, 76
Insulation testers, 76
Insulation testing, 382, 383
Intermediate-class arrestor, 332
Interruptible power, 634
Inverters, 100
Ion, 69
Ionization of air, 266
I^2R loss, 387
Iron loss, 386
Isolating switchgear, 265
Isolating switchgears, 281–283
Isolation guarantee, 17, 274–275

J

J (Joule's law), 80
Jelco pole choker, 31
Jib capacity, 491
Job briefing, 14–15
Job planning, 14–15
Job sequence, 15
Joule's law, 80
Jump-starting procedures, 470
Jumper ground, 351

K

Keilling knot, 46
Kh constant, 639
Kilovolt-ampere (KVA), 81, 113
Kilovolts per meter (kV/M), 142
Kilowatt-hours (kWh), 70, 83
Kilowatts (kW), 81, 82, 83, 97, 113
Knots, types of, 499–504
Kr constant, 639

L

Ladder hazards, 30, 32, 33
Lateral taps, 65
Lead cables, working with, 14
Leakage current, 121
Left-handed sheet bend, 503
Light-emitting diodes (LEDs), 612
Light pollution, 607
Lighting ballasts, 614–616

Lighting systems, outdoor
  airport runway lighting,
    621–623
  candela, 608
  cascading lighting-control
    system, 619–620
  circuits and controls, 616–624
  fluorescent lamps, 610–612
  gaseous-discharge lamps,
    610–612
  high-pressure sodium-vapor
    (HPS) lamps, 612
  incandescent lamps, 609–610
  light-emitting diodes
    (LEDs), 612
  light pollution, 607
  lighting ballasts, 614–616
  lighting structures, 612–614
  low-pressure sodium-vapor
    lamps, 612
  lumens, 608–609, 609
  luminaires, 607, 608
  luminor energy, 609
  maintenance, 624–625
  mercury-vapor lamps, 611–612
  metal-halide lamps, 612
  optics, 608
  outdoor-area lighting, 623
  photocell, 617
  pilot-wire control system, 618–619
  safety hazards, 625–628
  series outdoor lighting systems,
    620–621
  specifications, regulations, and
    engineering, 606–607
  sports field lighting, 621–623
  traffic-light control systems,
    623–624
  troubleshooting, 624–625
  Tungsten halogen lamps, 610
  types of, 605–608
Lighting transformer, 406
Lightning
  arrestors, lightning, 334
  circuits, effect on, 327–328
  effects of, 324–326
  safety tips, 326–327
  tracking storms, 327

Limbing, 585
Line crews, 67
Line-drop compensation, 436–437
Line loss (I^2R), 99
Live distribution line, 129–130
Live-front transformer, grounding a, 372
Load, calculating, 643
Load, checking the, 642
Load, lifting a, 514–520
Load-break disconnect, 282
Load-break elbows, 296
Load current, 73, 74, 383–385
Load factor, 633–634
Load loss, 387
Loading, transformer, 388–389
Loads placed in series, 117
Lock to lock rule, 9
Locking snap hook, 38
Lockout/tagout procedure, 17, 18, 274–275
Loop primary, 65
Losses, transformer, 386–387
Low-pressure sodium-vapor lamps, 612
Low-voltage, troubleshooting, 449, 450
Lumens, 608–609, 609
Luminaires, 607, 608
Luminor energy, 609
Luminous effect, 52

M

Magnetic effect, 52
Magnetic field, 358
Magnetic field induction, 359–360
Magnetic-field induction, 123, 125–126
Main feeder, 63
Maps to locate switchgears, using, 276–281
Marline, 504
Material data safety sheets (MSDS), 13
Maximum-demand pointer, 636
Maximum permissible exposure (MPE), 145
Maximum sag, 527

Mechanical protective footwear, 12
Megavolt-ampere (MVA), 81
Megawatts (MW), 81, 82
Meggers, 76
Mercury-vapor lamps, 611–612
Metal-clad circuit breakers, 284–285
Metal-halide lamps, 612
Metal-oxide varistors (MOV), 332
Meter and relay equipment, 593
Meter multiplier, 639
Metered charges, 632
Metering. *See* Revenue metering
Metering an electrical system, 631
Metering demand, 635
Methyl hydrate (methanol), 14
Mho, 77
Microwave communication, 60–61
Microwave systems, 60
Milliamperes (mA), 73
Milliwatts per squared centimeter (mW/cm^2), 145
Minimum approach distance (MAD), 15, 17, 146–148, 532–533, 545
Minimum charge for service, 632
Minimum working distances, 563–564
Mobile substations, 589
Molded dry-well canister, 299
Mounter hitch, 572
Multimeter, 72, 73
Multipoint junctions, 299–300

N

National Manual on Uniform Traffic Control Devices (MUTCD), 18
Natural levels, 144
Natural target pruning, 557
Nature of line work, 1–2
Neutral indicator, 437
Neutral potential, 339
Neutral separation at transformer, 462–463
Neutralizing transformer, 376
Neutrals
    neutral connections and ground connections, 391

open neutral, 133
    as part of the grounded system, 338
    safety precautions, 133
    sources of neutral current, 132
    sources of neutral voltage, 133
    voltage and current on a, 132
Neutrons, 54
No-load loss, 386
No-power, 415
Noisy ground, 424
Nomenclature, switchgear, 277–278
Nominal voltage, 71
Nonexpulsion (NX) current-limiting fuses, 291
Nonexpulsion switchgear, 297–298
Nonload-break disconnect, operating a, 281–282
Nonload-break elbows, 296
Nonreclose feature on breakers and reclosers, 293–294
Normal high voltage, 71
Normal low voltage, 71
Normal mode, 424
Nuclear generation, 54–55
Nx switches, 297–298

O

Occupational Safety and Health Administration (OSHA), 3
Ohmmeter, 76
Ohms, 70, 76
Ohm's law, 76, 77, 78, 81, 82, 339
Oil circuit breakers, 284
Omnibus, 58
One-line distribution drawings, 279
One-person tasks, 28
Open-delta transformer banks, 405–406
Open neutral, 133
Operating a disconnect switch with an operating handle at ground level, 269–270
Operating electronic reclosers, 287–289
Operating hydraulic reclosers, 286–287

Optics, 608
Orientation to powerline work, 1
Out of phase, 90
Outdoor-area lighting, 623
Outdoor environment, working in an, 1–2
Outdoor lighting systems. *See* lighting systems, outdoor
Over-current, causes of, 311
Over-current protection, 310, 339–340
Over-current trouble calls, 322, 323
Over-voltage, 323–324, 323–337, 330
Overhead conductors, 57, 58
Overhead distribution, 446, 447
Overhead system, 65, 66
Overhead transformer fuse protection, 389, 420
Overheating, 388

P
Pad-mount design, 66
Pad-mount transformer fusing, 390
Pad-mounted switching cabinet, 300
Parallel, connection in, 395
Parallel circuit
    accident examples, 122
    application, 119
    barehand, leakage current working, 121
    boom contamination meter, 121
    characteristics, 119
    human body in parallel circuit, 121, 122
    leakage current, 121
    loads connected in parallel, 121
    making parallel contact, 118
    protection from contact, 122
    total resistance, calculating, 120
Parallel path to control current, providing a, 349–350
Parallel shunt, 348
Partial power, 415
Partial-range current-limiting fuse, 292
Peak demand, 632, 633

Peak load current, 74
Peak value, 89
Penstock, 53
Permanent faults, 311
Permit Required Confined Space, 18
Personal communication services (PCS), 145
Personal protective grounds
    applying protective grounds, 361–365
    applying the grounding principle to control current, 348–349
    basis for installation, 347–348
    bonding principle to control voltage, using the, 353–358
    bracket grounds, working and grounding between, 360
    cutting or joining a grounded connector, 368
    distribution bracket grounding procedure, 361–362, 364–365
    distribution equipotential grounding/bonding procedure, 361
    electric field induction, reducing voltage from, 359
    electromagnetic induction, 358–360
    fault, protective grounds whipping during a, 369
    gradients when one phase had protective ground installed, 369
    grounding a live circuit, 365
    grounding principle, 347–348
    hazards to ground workers, 368
    magnetic field induction, controlling current from, 359–360
    portable generator, protective grounding for backfeed from, 369–370
    single-point grounding, 361, 362–363
    transformer pole or lateral tap pole, working from, 370
    transmission bracket grounding procedure, 365, 366–367

    transmission equipotential grounding/bonding procedure, 363
    underground cable, 370–374
Personal safety risk, managing
    approved equipment, using only, 8
    chemical hazards, protection from, 13–14
    eye protection, 11
    flame-retardant clothing (FR), 12–13
    footwear, wearing safety, 11–12
    head protection, 11
    hearing protection, wearing, 13
    rubber gloves as personal protective equipment, 8–11
Phase designations, 106
Phase rotation, 106
Phase-shifting transformer, 592
Phases 120 degrees apart, 105–106
Phasing between two sources, confirming, 270
Phasing sticks, 272, 535
Phasing tester, using a, 271, 272, 273
Phasor, 400
Photocell, 617
Piggyback clamp, 352
Pilot-wire control system, 618–619
Pipeline-cathodic protection hazard, 344
Planning, job, 14–15
Planning engineers and technicians, 67
Planning maps, 280–281
Planting trees, 561
Plastic guard, 540–542
Point-of-work grounds, 356
Polarity, 85, 86, 380, 381
Pole band, 358
Pole-climbing fall arrest system, 31
Pole cut-out test, 36
Pole hazards, 30, 34, 38, 39, 40
Pole strap, using a, 32, 37–38
Pole top, rescue from, 44–47
Polychlorinated biphenyls (PCBs), 13–14, 48, 628

Portable generator, protective grounding for backfeed from, 369–370

Portable protective gap (PPG) device, 336

Potential and current transformers, 593

Potential coil, 638

Potential energy, 51

Potential gradients, 128–129

Potential test, 70

Potential tester, 70

Potential transformer (PT), 432

Power factor, 98, 99, 633, 636

Power flow, 594

Power-follow current, 331

Power leg, 412

Power quality
  capacitors, 440–444
  corrective measures, 424–425
  custom power, supplying, 425
  definition of, 424
  distribution feeder voltage, 430–431
  distribution substation voltage, 429
  feeder voltage regulators, 431–440
  ferroresonance, 454–458
  grounding considerations, 425
  harmonic interference, 449, 452–453
  radio and television interference (TVI) complaints, 463–465
  sensitivity to power quality, 423
  supply disturbances, 424
  tingle voltage, 458–463
  transmission-line voltage, 428–429
  troubleshooting, 444–449
  voltage as a measure of quality, 426–428
  voltage flicker, 453–454

Power quality, effect on, 431

Power triangle, 98

Powerline carrier systems, 60

Powerline clearance tree trimmers, 563

Prepayment metering, 637

Pressure, 70

Primary feeder, 63, 64

Primary network, 65, 66

Primary or secondary metering, 635

Primary step-down transformer installations, 419–420

Protection scheme philosophy, 315–316

Protection zones, 306

Protective relaying, 304–305

Protective switchgear, 265, 284–293

Pruning, 556–558, 576–580

Prusik hitch, 573

Public electrical contact, reducing the risk of, 29

Puncture-resistant sole (PR), 12, 328

Pusher-pointer, 636

R

R (resistance), 76, 77, 80

Radial feeders, 63

Radial system, 62

Radio and television interference (TVI) complaints, 463–465

Radio frequency (RF), 145

Rain on insulators, effect of, 79

Ratchet chain hoist, 509

Reactance, 78, 90, 91

Reactive power, 97–98, 634

Reactor, 592

Reactor ballasts, 614–615

Real power, 634

Recloser protection zone, 317–318

Recloser speed and operating sequence, specifying, 318

Recloser-to-fuse coordination table, 321

Reclosers, 285–286

Rectifiers, 100

Reef knot, 501

Reenergization, 356

Regulator ballasts, 615–616

Reliability-centered maintenance (RCM), 595

Remote terminal units (RTUs), 268

Remotely controlled switchgear, 267

Removing or felling trees, 558–560, 580–585

Reporting incidents and accidents, 7

Rescue procedures, 567–569

Residential wiring protection, 307–309

Resistance, 91, 96

Resistance, electrical, 75–80

Resistive loads, 90

Retractable lanyard, using a, 31

Retreat paths, 581

Revenue metering
  A-base meter, 640
  apparent power, 634
  automatic meter reading, 637
  capacity charge, 631
  current coil, 637, 638
  customer charges, 631
  customer location, 634
  electromechanical meter, 637
  electronic meter, 637
  elements, 639
  energy charge, 631
  energy consumption, 632
  fixed charges, 632
  installation tests, 643
  interruptible power, 634
  Kh constant, 639
  Kr constant, 639
  load, calculating, 643
  load, checking the, 642
  load factor, 633–634
  meter multiplier, 639
  metered charges, 632
  metering an electrical system, 631
  metering demand, 635
  minimum charge for service, 632
  peak demand, 632, 633
  potential coil, 638
  power factor, 633, 636
  prepayment metering, 637
  primary or secondary metering, 635
  reactive power, 634

Revenue metering, *Continued*
real power, 634
S-base meter, 640
self-contained meters, 635
single-phase metering, 641–642
socket-connected meter, 640
supply voltage, 634
test constant, 639
time of use, 634
time-of-use metering
(TOU), 637
transformer-rated meters, 635
types of, 634–635
variable affecting cost, 632–634
Reverse feed through a voltage
regulator, 440
RF/MW transmitter, induced
current from a, 145
Rigging
anchor pulling eye, using an,
512, 513
application, 495
blocks, working, 510–511
capstan hoist, using a, 516
chains, using, 508–510
choker hitch, using a, 519
collapsible bull wheel, using a,
512, 514
design factor, 495
equipment, 96
fiber rope, using, 496–499
friction, effects of, 511–512
hand line, using a, 514–515
knots, types of, 499–504
load, lifting a, 514–520
rope block, using a, 516–518
sling, connecting a load with a,
518–520
splicing fiber rope, 504–505
tensioned conductors, working
with, 520–528
transformer gin, using a, 515
web slings, using, 512, 513
wire rope, using, 505–508
working-load-limit rating, 495
working load limits (WLL),
495–496
Rigid cover-up, 540–542

Riser pole, 295
Risks in line work, 8
Rod gap, 331
Rolling blackouts, 62
Rope block, using a, 516–518
Rubber-glove work, 538–540,
542–544
Rubber gloves as personal protective
equipment, 8–11
Rugged nature of the work, 2
Running bowline, 500
Rural distribution substation, 588

S
S-base meter, 640
Saddle, arborist, 570
Safe work model, 4
Safety belts, using, 31
Safety committee, 3
Safety hazards, 625–628
Safety management system, 3–4
Safety responsibilities and
expectations
briefing, characteristics of a good
job, 7
characteristics of a good safety
meeting, 6–7
employee safety responsibilities
and rights, 3
employers responsibilities, 2
management culture, establishing
the, 5–6
new employee orientation, 6
safe work model, 4
safety committee, 3
safety management system, 3–4
specialist culture, impact on, 5–6
worker culture, impact on, 4–5
Satellites, 60
SCADA systems (supervisory
control and data
acquisition), 278
Schematic drawings, using electrical, 278–279
Scott connections, 406
Screw anchor, 489
Second harmonic, 449
Second point of contact, 80, 532

Secondary, working on a hot,
537–538
Secondary-class arrestor, 333
Secondary fault current, 385
Secondary network, 395–396
Secondary system, 63, 64
Sectionalizers, 289, 322
Sectionalizers, downstream,
312–313
Self-contained meters, 635
Self-inductance, 92
Sensitivity to power quality, 423
Sequence, job, 15
Series and parallel secondary
connections, 409
Series capacitors, 442
Series circuit, 116–118
Series outdoor lighting systems,
620–621
Sheet bend, 503
Shield wire, 333
Shock, protection from, 134
Shock-resistant footwear, 479
Short-circuit fault, 120
Shot stones, 24
Shunt capacitors, 442, 444
Shunt reactors, 93
Simple generator, 53
Sine wave, use of a, 88–89
Single-line drawing, 278
Single-phase hydraulic recloser, 286
Single-phase in-span disconnect
switch, 282
Single-phase metering, 641–642
Single-phase service, 391, 394
Single-phase tap, 63
Single-phase transformer connec-
tions, 391–396
Single-phase voltage regulator, 438
Single-point grounding, 361,
362–363
Single-unit, three-phrase, pad-
mount transformer, 398
Slack adjusters, 469
Slack string operation, 19
Sling, connecting a load with a,
518–520
Slip-resistant footwear, 12

Socket-connected meter, 640
Soil resistance, 341
Soil sterilization, 561
Soil treatment, 561
Solar energy, 51
Solenoid coil, 287
Solid braid rope, 497
Solid-material-filled power fuses, 291
Solid-state breakers (SSB), 425
Sorting insulators for live-line work, 336
Spark gap, 331
Spark gap surge protection, 331
Sparkover, 328
Specialist culture, impact on, 5–6
Spiking tool, 374
Splicing fiber rope, 504–505
Sports field lighting, 621–623
Spur gaff, 34–35
Spurs, climbing with, 30, 34
Square knot, 501, 502
Static electricity, 123
Station-class arrestor, 332
Station service, 593
Station yard, 590
Stations, communication between, 59
Steam turbine, 54
Steel core configurations, 377
Step-down transmission substation, 588
Step potentials, 128–129, 130–131, 131, 132, 326, 565
Step-up transmission substation, 587–588
Step-voltage regulator, 432, 433, 434
Step-voltage transformer, 432
Stray-current corrosion, 344
Stray voltage, 458
Stringing sag, 527
Structure numbers, 202, 276–277
Stump treatment, 561
Submarine transmission lines, 101, 102
Substation structure, rescue from, 44

Substation transformers, 407–408
Substations
    air-break switches, 590
    air-insulated substation, 589
    capacitor, 592
    construction of, 589, 598, 600–602
    converter stations, 589
    definition of, 587
    distribution substations, 587
    elements of, 589–594
    feeder protection, 312
    gas-insulated substation, 589
    hazards, 598, 599
    high-and low-voltage bus, 591
    inductor, 593
    maintenance and operation, 594–598
    meter and relay equipment, 593
    mobile substations, 589
    phase-shifting transformer, 592
    potential and current transformers, 593
    power flow, 594
    reactor, 592
    rural distribution substation, 588
    station service, 593
    station yard, 590
    step-down transmission substation, 588
    step-up transmission substation, 587–588
    switchgear, 590
    transformer, 591–592
    types of, 587–588
    voltage regulation equipment, 592
    wave trap, 592–593
Subtransmission circuit, 63, 64
Subtransmission gang-operated disconnect switch, 281–282
Subtransmission line voltage, 429
Subtransmission line voltages (kV), 72
Sulfur-hexafluoride (SF6) circuit breakers, 284
Supervisory Control and Data Acquisition (SCADA), 64, 286

Supply disturbances, 424
Supply voltage, 634
Surge arrestors
    classes of, 332–333
    dead-front arrestor, 332, 333
    distribution-class arrestor, 332–333
    intermediate-class arrestor, 332
    metal-oxide varistors (MOV), 332
    rod gap, 331
    secondary-class arrestor, 333
    spark gap, 331
    station-class arrestor, 332
    types of, 330–331
    use of, 330
    valve-type arrestor, 331
Surge protection, 340
Surgeon's knot, 502, 503
Suspension system, 31
Switched capacitors, 442–443
Switchgear, 63, 293–294, 294–300, 590
    arc hazards, 265–266, 267
    defective pedestal-type insulators supporting switchgear, 268
    designs to extinguish arcs, 267
    geographic based maps, 279, 280
    hot-line clamp, operating a, 282–283
    isolating switchgears, operating, 281–283
    isolation guarantee, 274–275
    load-break disconnect, 282
    lockout/tagout procedure, 274–275
    maps to locate switchgears, using, 276–281
    nomenclature, switchgear, 277–278
    nonload-break disconnect, operating a, 281–282
    one-line distribution drawings, 279
    operating a disconnect switch with an operating handle at ground level, 269–270
    operating three-pole switches, 267–268

Switchgear, *Continued*
phasing between two sources, confirming, 270
phasing tester, using a, 271, 272, 273
planning maps, 280–281
protective switchgears, operating, 284–293
remotely controlled switchgear, 267
SCADA systems (supervisory control and data acquisition), 278
schematic drawings, using electrical, 278–279
single-phase in-span disconnect switch, 282
subtransmission gang-operated disconnect switch, 281–282
switching order, using a, 275–276
telescopic switch stick, switching from the ground using a, 270
three-phase load interrupter and power fuses, 283
transmission-line map, 279
types of, 265
zero-awaiting interrupter, 267
zero-forcing interrupter, 267
Switching and connection arrangement, 300
Switching order, using a, 275–276
Switching surges, 328
Switchyards, 58

T
T notch, 582
T (time of current flow), 80
Tailboard Conference Plan, 16
Taps, 379–380
Taut-line hitch, 503, 573
Telescopic switch stick, 270, 271
Temperature-dependent transformer rating, 388
Temporary jumpers, use of, 536
Tension stringing operation, 19
Tensioned conductors, working with, 520–528

Terminals, cable between, 372
Teslas (T), 142
Test constant, 639
Test for turns ratio, 378–379
Thermal effect, 52
Thermal energy, 51
Third harmonic, 449
Three-phase
120/208-volt service, 410
120/240-volt service, 411
240/416-volt service, 411, 412, 413
240/480-volt service, 412
277/480-volt service, 413–414
347/600-volt service, 414
240-volt service, 411, 412, 413
277-volt service, 413–414
347-volt service, 413–414
480-volt service, 412
600-volt service, 414
120-volt transformer bank, 412
secondary-voltage arrangements, 409–415
wye-wye transformer, 398
Three-phase capacitor bank, 443
Three-phase connections, 106, 397–409
Three-phase load interrupter and power fuses, 283
Three-phase power, 111
Three-phase transformer banks in parallel, 406
Three-phase transformer with single-phase transformers, 400
Three-phrase circuit
application of, 103
calculations involving power, 112
characteristics of, 103–104
Delta-connected systems, 107, 108
field calculations, 112
generation of three-phase power, 104–105
"handy number" calculations, 112, 113
phase designations, 106
phase rotation, 106
phases 120 degrees apart, 105–106

three-phase connections, 106
three-phase power, 111
Wye and Delta systems, 106–107, 108, 109–111, See also Delta systems (*See also* Wye systems)
Three-phrase lateral, 63
Timber hitch, 504
Time current characteristic (TCC) curve, 318, 321
Time-delay setting, 436
Time-delay switch, 436
Time-delayed-instant philosophy, 315
Time of use, 634
Time-of-use metering (TOU), 637
Tingle voltage, 458–463
Total resistance, calculating, 120
Touch potential, 130–131, 564–565
Tower hazards, 39, 41
Tower top, rescue from, 44
Toxic-chemical hazard, 328
Traffic, protection from, 18, 19
Traffic-light control systems, 623–624
Transformer, 591–592
Transformer gin, using a, 515
Transformer pole or lateral tap pole, working from, 370
Transformer-rated meters, 635
Transformers
additive or subtractive polarity, 380–381
angular displacements (*See* Angular displacements)
applications, 376
backfeed, 379
banked secondaries, 395–396
choosing transformers, 399
compensator starter, 376
components of, 376–377
conductor loss, 386–387
connecting different polarities, 381–382
constant-current transformer, 376
continuity testing, 382

core loss, 386
cover bushing transformer, 393
current-limiting fuse protection, 390
delta systems, connections to, 393, 401–402, 403–404
delta-wye transformer banks, 405
efficiency, transformer, 387
grounding transformers, 376
hazards, 420
impedance, 387
installations, 418–419
instrument transformers, 376
insulation testing, 382, 383
load current, 383–385
loading, transformer, 388–389
losses, transformer, 386–387
nameplate for a single-phase transformer, 392–393
nameplate for three-phase unit, 399–400
neutral connections and ground connections, 391
neutralizing transformer, 376
open-delta transformer banks, 405–406
overhead transformer fuse protection, 389, 420
overheating, 388
parallel, connection in, 395
polarity, 380
polarity testing, 381
power quality, effect on, 431
primary step-down transformer installations, 419–420
protection, 388–391
purpose of, 375
scott connections, 406
secondary fault current, 385
secondary network, 395–396
series and parallel secondary connections, 409
single-phase service, 391, 394
single-phase transformer connections, 391–396
single-unit, three-phrase, pad-mount transformer, 398
steel core configurations, 377

taps, 379–380
temperature-dependent transformer rating, 388
test for turns ratio, 378–379
three-phase, secondary-voltage arrangements, 409–415
three-phase, wye-wye transformer, 398
three-phase connections, 397–409
three-phase transformer banks in parallel, 406
three-phase transformer with single-phase transformers, 400
troubleshooting, 415–416, 417
turns ratio, 378
underground installations, 419
underground transformer fuse protection, 389–390, 420
vectors, using, 400–401, 401
voltage conversion, working on a, 416–419
voltage imbalance, 408–409
voltage regulator, 376
voltage standards, 383
voltage surge protection, 390–391
voltage-survey accuracy, 387–388
wye-delta transformer banks, 404–405
wye systems, connections to, 393, 401, 402–403
Transient faults, 311
Transition pole, 370
Transmission bracket grounding procedure, 365, 366–367
Transmission equipotential grounding/bonding procedure, 363
Transmission-line map, 279
Transmission line voltage, 58
Transmission-line voltage, 428–429
Transmission line voltages, 72
Transmission system, 51, 62
Transmission system protection, 304–307
Transmission system substations, 58, 59–61

Transposition, 126, 127
Travel restraint system, 31
Tree-growth regulators (TGR), 561
Tree shock, 565
Tree work
   aerial devices, and, 565–566
   basal spraying, 561
   brush control, 560
   bucking a tree trunk, 585–586
   chain saw operation, 569, 574–576
   climbing methods, 569, 570–573
   directional pruning, 557
   drop crotch pruning, 557
   electrical awareness, 563
   foliage spraying, 561
   hazards, 562, 564, 565, 579–580, 584–585
   herbicides, use of, 561
   inspection methods, 559
   limbing, 585
   minimum working distances, 563–564
   natural target pruning, 557
   planting trees, 561
   powerline clearance tree trimmers, 563
   pruning, 556–558, 576–580
   removing or felling trees, 558–560, 580–585
   rescue procedures, 567–569
   retreat paths, 581
   soil sterilization, 561
   soil treatment, 561
   step potential, 565
   stump treatment, 561
   touch potential, 564–565
   tree-growth regulators (TGR), 561
   tree shock, 565
   vegetation management programs, 555–556
Trenching, 22–23
Trip coil size, specifying, 317
Truck inspection, daily, 467–468
Tungsten halogen lamps, 610
Turns ratio, 378

Twisted rope, 496
Two half hitches, 500, 501

U
Ultraviolet-radiation (UV), 146,
    625–626
Under-oil backup current-limiting
    fuses, 291
Under-oil bayonet-style fuses, 298
Under-oil expulsion fuses (bayonet
    style), 291
Underground cable, 370–374
Underground distribution
    switchgears, 294–300
Underground lines, 101
Underground system, 66, 65,
    446, 448
Underground transformer fuse
    protection, 389–390, 420
Underground utilities, working in,
    22–23
Uninterruptible power supply
    (UPS), 425
Upstream documentation, 15
Uranium, 54
Utility-owned fiber-optic cable, 60
Utility voltages, 72
Utilization voltages (V), 72

V
Vacuum circuit breakers, 284
Valve element, 331
Valve-type arrestor, 331
VAR compensators (SVC), 426
Vaults, working in, 21–22

Vector drawing method, 523
Vectors, using, 400–401, 401
Vegetation management programs,
    555–556
Vehicle grounding, 133–134, 135,
    137–138
Voltage, 70, 71, 426–428
Voltage-changing stations, 58
Voltage control, 426
Voltage conversion, working on a,
    416–419
Voltage detector, 368
Voltage drop, 71, 427, 430
Voltage flicker, 453–454
Voltage gradients, 127,
    128–129, 132
Voltage imbalance, 408–409
Voltage-level setting, 432
Voltage rating, 10
Voltage regulation, 426, 427
Voltage regulation equipment, 592
Voltage regulator, 376
Voltage standards, 383
Voltage surge, 328, 329,
    390–391, 534
Voltage-survey accuracy, 387–388
Voltage transformers (VT) 70
Voltmeter, 70, 445–446
Volts, 70
Volts per meter (V/m), 142

W
W (watts), 81
Water bowline, 500
Water hammer, 472

Water surge, 329
Watt-second, 81
Watts, 70, 81, 97
Watts power, 97
Wave trap, 60, 592–593
Web hoist, 509–510
Web slings, using, 512, 513
Wild phase, 411
Winching procedures, 487–488
Wire rope, using, 505–508
Wood pole work in poor soil, 369
Work positioning system, 31
Worker culture, impact on, 4–5
Working-load-limit rating, 495
Working load limits (WLL),
    495–496
Wye and Delta systems, 106–107,
    108, 109–111
Wye-delta transformer banks,
    404–405, 407
Wye systems
    application, 109
    configurations, 110
    connections to, 393, 401,
        402–403
    converting from delta to
        wye, 111
    earth return system neutral, 110
    neutral, 110
    voltage and current, 109

Z
Z (impedance in ohms), 91
Zero-awaiting interrupter, 267
Zero-forcing interrupter, 267